D1546305

Chemiosmotic Proton Circuits in Biological Membranes

In Honor of **PETER MITCHELL**

Peter Mitchell

Chemiosmotic Proton Circuits in Biological Membranes

In Honor of **PETER MITCHELL**

Edited by

V. P. Skulachev
Moscow State University

Peter C. Hinkle
Cornell University

1981

ADDISON-WESLEY PUBLISHING COMPANY, INC.
Advanced Book Program/World Science Division
Reading, Massachusetts

London · Amsterdam · Don Mills, Ontario · Sydney · Tokyo

The cover illustration, taken from Peter Mitchell's "first grey book" with some lettering removed, was entitled "Coupling through Proton Circuits." It shows the translocation of protons through an oxido-reduction system (top) driving ATP synthesis, antiport and symport systems. The "first grey book" entitled "Chemiosmotic Coupling in Oxidative and Photosynthetic Phosphorylation," published by Glynn Research, Ltd. in 1966 was an enlarged version of Peter Mitchell's first review of chemiosmotic coupling published in *Biological Reviews* **41**, 445–502 (1966).

Library of Congress Cataloging in Publication Data
Main entry under title:

Chemiosmotic proton circuits in biological membranes.

"In honor of Peter Mitchell."
Bibliography: p.
1. Membranes (Biology)--Addresses, essays, lectures.
2. Biological transport--Addresses, essays, lectures.
3. Bioenergetics--Addresses, essays, lectures.
4. Mitchell, Peter Dennis. I. Skulachev, V. P.(Vladimir Petrovich) II. Hinkle, Peter C. III. Mitchell, Peter Dennis.
QH601.C475   1982   574.19'121   81-17642
ISBN 0-201-07398-6   AAACR2

Reproduced by Addison-Wesley Publishing Company, Inc., Advanced Book Program/World Science Division, Reading, Massachusetts, from camera-ready copy prepared by the authors and the offices of the editors.

Printed in the United States of America

ABCDEFGHIJ-HA-8987654321

CONTENTS

This book is dedicated to Peter Mitchell, on the occasion of his 60th birthday. We thought that this was a suitable time to document the extensive field of proton transport reactions which has grown from his early studies.

Peter Mitchell was born in Mitcham, Surrey, England, on September 29, 1920. He attended Jesus College, Cambridge, and received the degree of Ph.D. in 1951 from the Department of Biochemistry, Cambridge for work on the mechanism of action of penicillin with J.F. Danielli. At Cambridge he also had contact with David Keilin, who greatly influenced his view of the function of cytochromes. From 1950 to 1955 he held the post of Demonstrator at the Department of Biochemistry, Cambridge. From 1955 to 1963 he directed the Chemical Biology Unit in the Department of Zoology, Edinburgh University.

In 1961 Peter Mitchell proposed his "chemiosmotic hypothesis" of energy conservation in oxidative and photosynthetic phosphorylation (Nature 191, 144-148). This hypothesis was first regarded as bizarre and impossible by the bioenergetics establishment, largely because biochemists were poorly educated about electrochemical gradients across membranes and transport phenomena. The brilliance of the proposal was demonstrated, in retrospect, by the fact that all basic aspects of coupling by electrochemical proton gradients that are being considered today were included, in principle, in the original paper.

In 1963 he had an acute gastric ulcer, retired from his position at Edinburgh, and together with Jennifer Moyle, established a small laboratory in Glynn House in Cornwall called Glynn Research Laboratories. There he has remained, doing theoretical and experimental work on proton transport with a small group, including - over the years - only a few postdoctoral fellows. Since 1973 he has been the recipient of numerous awards and prizes, including the Nobel Prize for Chemistry in 1978.

We organized this book to honor Peter Mitchell and to show the biochemical and biophysical communities the breadth of this new field of research. The Chemiosmotic Theory explains a broad range of phenomena in transport and coupling of biochemical reactions, so that the electrochemical proton gradient across membranes, $\Delta \bar{\mu}_H{}^+$, is now regarded as a central energy currency equal in importance to ATP. The details of the exact mechanisms by which the proton gradient is generated and utilized are still controversial, as illustrated by many of the articles in this book, but the central role of protons in the processes covered is generally agreed upon. We have chosen to cover mostly studies of proton transport by isolated enzymes and to de-emphasize general controversies about whether the coupling protons equilibrate completely with the bulk aqueous phases on each side of the membrane or recent arguments about coupling stoichiometries. The authors were asked to review their subject and encouraged to speculate about mechanisms or functions.

Peter Mitchell agreed to contribute to this book in the spirit of a reply to a toast. In his article he generalizes his ideas about mechanisms of proton transport to other ions, so perhaps researchers in other fields of transport should be alerted Mitchell is coming!

   We wish to thank Dr. Maija Hinkle for important editorial
assistance and Mrs. Joyce Broadhead for excellent secretarial
work. Their help partly made up for our chronic communication
problems.

   Finally, we all wish our friend Peter a Happy Birthday
and many more productive and exciting years.

                              Vladimir P. Skulachev
                              Peter C. Hinkle

CONTRIBUTORS

Roberto Bogomolni, Department of Biochemistry and Cardio-
    vascular Research Institute, University of
    California, San Francisco, California 94143, USA.
                                        (pp. 283-309)

John R. Bowyer, Department of Biochemistry, Dartmouth
    Medical School, Hanover, New Hampshire 03755, USA.
                                        (pp. 105-122)

Paul D. Boyer, Department of Chemistry and Molecular
    Biology Institute, University of California, Los
    Angeles, California 90024, USA.   (pp. 395-406)

Britton Chance, Johnson Research Foundation, University of
    Pennsylvania, Philadelphia, Pennsylvania 19104, USA.
                                        (pp. 161-169)

David Crowther, Biology Department, Brookhaven National
    Laboratory, Upton, New York 11973, USA. (pp. 245-257)

Stanley D. Dunn, Section of Biochemistry, Molecular and
    Cell Biology, Cornell University, Ithaca, New York
    14853, USA.   (pp. 435-448)

P. Leslie Dutton, Department of Biochemistry and Biophysics,
    University of Pennsylvania, Philadelphia,
    Pennsylvania 19104, USA.   (pp. 259-270)

Fergus G. P. Earley, Department of Biochemistry, University
    of Southampton, Southampton SO9 3TU, England
                                        (pp. 59-68)

Lars Ernster, Department of Biochemistry, Arrhenius
    Laboratory, University of Stockholm, S-106 91
    Stockholm, Sweden.   (pp. 483-508)

Peter B. Garland, Department of Biochemistry, Medical
    Sciences Institute, University of Dundee, Dundee
    DD1 4HN, Scotland, U.K.   (pp. 211-220)

Alexei N. Glagolev, A. N. Belozersky Laboratory of
    Molecular Biology and Bioorganic Chemistry, Moscow
    State University, Moscow 117234, U.S.S.R.
                                        (pp. 577-600)

xiii

L. Grinius, Department of Biochemistry and Biophysics,
    Vilnius University, Vilnius 232031, U.S.S.R.
                                        (pp. 551–565)

Ferruccio Guerrieri, Institute of Biological Chemistry,
    Faculty of Medicine, University of Bari, Bari,
    Italy.   (pp. 459–470)

Franklin M. Harold, Department of Biochemistry, Biophysics
    and Genetics, University of Colorado Medical
    School, Denver, Colorado 80262, USA.   (pp. 537–550)

Donald L. Heefner, Department of Molecular and Cellular
    Biology, National Jewish Hospital and Research
    Center/National Asthma Center, Denver, Colorado
    80206, USA.   (pp. 537–550)

Leon A. Heppel, Section of Biochemistry, Molecular and
    Cell Biology, Cornell University, Ithaca, New York
    14853, USA.   (pp. 435–448)

Geoffrey Hind, Biology Department, Brookhaven National
    Laboratory, Upton, New York 11973, USA.
                                        (pp. 245–257)

Peter C. Hinkle, Section of Biochemistry, Molecular and
    Cell Biology, Cornell University, Ithaca, New York
    14853, USA.   (pp. 49–58)

Jürgen Hoppe, Gesellschaft für Biotechnologische Forschung
    mbH.. Mascheroder Weg 1, D-3300 Braunschweig-
    Stöckheim, Federal Republik of Germany
                                        (pp. 449–458)

H. R. Kaback, Laboratory of Membrane Biochemistry, Roche
    Institute of Molecular Biology, Nutley, New Jersey
    07110, USA.   (pp. 525–536)

Yasuo Kagawa, Department of Biochemistry, Jichi Medical
    School, Minamikawachi-machi, Tochigi-ken, Japan
    329-04.   (pp. 421–433)

Yuriy A. Kamensky, A. N. Belozersky Laboratory of Molecular
    Biology and Bioorganic Chemistry, Moscow State
    University, Moscow 117234, U.S.S.R.   (pp. 123–146)

Tsoo E. King, Department of Chemistry and Laboratory of
    Bioenergetics, State University of New York at
    Albany, Albany, New York 12222, USA.   (pp. 147–159)

Jane Knoth, Department of Biological Sciences, Wayne State
    University, Detroit, Michigan 48202, USA.
                                            (pp. 365–374)

Alexander Konstantinov, A. N. Belozersky Laboratory of
    Molecular Biology and Bioorganic Chemistry, Moscow
    State University, Moscow 117234, U.S.S.R.
                                            (pp. 123–146)

Igor A. Kozlov, Isotope Department, A. N. Belozersky
    Laboratory of Molecular Biology and Bioorganic
    Chemistry, Moscow State University, Moscow 117234,
    U.S.S.R.   (pp. 407–420)

Wolfram S. Kunz, A. N. Belozersky Laboratory of Molecular
    Biology and Bioorganic Chemistry, Moscow State
    University, Moscow 117234, U.S.S.R.   (pp. 123–146)

C. P. Lee, Department of Biochemistry, Wayne State
    University, School of Medicine, Detroit, Michigan
    48201, USA.   (pp. 483–508)

Rebecca Locke, Neurochemistry Laboratory, Department of
    Psychiatry, Dundee University, Dundee, Scotland,
    U.K.   (pp. 567–576)

Richard H. Lozier, Department of Biochemistry and Cardio-
    vascular Research Institute, University of
    California, San Francisco, California 94143, USA.
                                            (pp. 283–309)

Richard E. McCarty, Section of Biochemistry, Molecular
    and Cell Biology, Division of Biological Sciences,
    Cornell University, Ithaca, New York 14853, USA.
                                            (pp. 271–281)

Russell E. MacDonald, Department of Biochemistry, Molecular
    and Cell Biology, Cornell University, Ithaca, New
    York 14853, USA.   (pp. 321–335)

Stuart McLaughlin, Department of Physiology and Biophysics, Health Sciences Center, SUNY, Stony Brook, New York 11794, USA.   (pp. 601-609)

Katsumi Matsuura, Department of Biochemistry and Biophysics, University of Pennsylvania, Philadelphia, Pennsylvania 19104, USA.   (pp. 259-270)

Peter Mitchell, Glynn Research Institute, Bodmin, Cornwall, PL30 4AU, U.K.   (pp. 611-633)

Nathan Nelson, Department of Biology, Technion-Israel, Institute of Technology, Haifa, Israel.(pp. 471-482)

David Nicholls, Neurochemistry Laboratory, Department of Psychiatry, Dundee University, Dundee, Scotland, U.K.   (pp. 567-576)

David Njus, Department of Biological Sciences, Wayne State University, Detroit, Michigan 48202, USA.
                                                   (pp. 365-374)

Yuri A. Ovchinnikov, Shemyakin Institute of Bioorganic Chemistry, USSR Academy of Sciences, Moscow, U.S.S.R.   (pp. 311-320)

Sergio Papa, Institute of Biological Chemistry, Faculty of Medicine, University of Bari, Bari, Italy.
                                                   (pp. 459-470)

Veronica M. Poore, Department of Biochemistry, University of Southampton, Southampton SO9 3TU, England.
                                                   (pp. 59-68)

Efraim Racker, Section of Biochemistry, Molecular and Cell Biology, Division of Biological Sciences, Cornell University, Ithaca, New York 14853, USA.
                                                   (pp. 377-394)

C. Ian Ragan, Department of Biochemistry, University of Southampton, Southampton SO9 3TU, England
                                                   (pp. 59-68)

Jan Rydström, Department of Biochemistry, Arrhenius Laboratory, University of Stockholm, S-106 91 Stockholm, Sweden.   (pp. 483-508)

G. Sachs, Laboratory of Membrane Biology, University of
    Alabama in Birmingham, University Station,
    Birmingham, Alabama 35294, USA   (pp. 347-364)

Gottfried Schatz, Biocenter, University of Basel, CH-4056
    Basel, Switzerland.   (pp. 181-196)

Walter Sebald, Gesellschaft für Biotechnologische Forschung
    mbH.. Mascheroder Weg 1, D-3300 Braunschweig-
    Stöckheim, Federal Republik of Germany (pp. 449-458)

Vladimir P. Skulachev, Department of Bioenergetics, A. N.
    Belozersky Laboratory of Molecular Biology and
    Bioorganic Chemistry, Moscow State University,
    Moscow 117234, U.S.S.R.   (pp. 3-46)

E. C. Slater, Laboratory of Biochemistry, B.C.P. Jansen
    Institute, University of Amsterdam, The Netherlands.
                                            (pp. 69-104)

Carolyn W. Slayman, Departments of Physiology and Human
    Genetics, Yale School of Medicine, New Haven,
    Connecticut 06510, USA.   (pp. 337-345)

Clifford L. Slayman, Departments of Physiology and Human
    Genetics, Yale School of Medicine, New Haven,
    Connecticut 06510, USA.   (pp. 337-345)

Stuart Smith, Department of Biochemistry, University of
    Southampton, Southampton SO9 3TU, England
                                            (pp. 59-68)

Nobuhito Sone, Department of Biochemistry, Jichi Medical
    School, Minamikawachi-machi, Tochigi, Japan 329-04.
    329-04.   (pp. 197-210)

Walther Stoeckenius, Department of Biochemistry and Cardio-
    vascular Research Institute, University of
    California, San Francisco, California 94143, USA.
                                            (pp. 283-309)

Bernard L. Trumpower, Department of Biochemistry, Dartmouth
    Medical School, Hanover, New Hampshire 03755, USA.
                                            (pp. 105-122)

Ian C. West, Department of Biochemistry, University of
    Newcastle upon Tyne, NE1 7RU, U.K.   (pp. 509–523)

Mårten Wikström, Department of Medical Chemistry, University
    of Helsinki, SF–00170 Helsinki 17, Finland.
                                            (pp. 171–180)

H. T. Witt, Max–Volmer–Institut für Biophysikalische und
    Physikalische Chemie, Technische Universität, Berlin,
    Strasse des 17. Juni 135, 1000 Berlin 12, Federal
    Republic of Germany   (pp. 221–244)

Michael Zallakian, Department of Biological Sciences,
    Wayne State University, Detroit, Michigan 48202,
    USA.   (pp. 365–374)

Introduction

THE PROTON CYCLE: HISTORY AND PROBLEMS OF THE MEMBRANE-LINKED ENERGY TRANSDUCTION, TRANSMISSION, AND BUFFERING

Vladimir P. Skulachev

Department of Bioenergetics, A.N. Belozersky Laboratory
of Molecular Biology and Bioorganic Chemistry
Moscow State University, Moscow 117234, USSR

THE PROTON CYCLE CONCEPT. The discovery of the principle of energy transduction in oxidative and photosynthetic phosphorylation has been an event of major importance in the last two decades. These two processes constituted the main biological mechanism of conserving external energy as ATP. The fact that redox reactions of the respiratory and photosynthetic systems are coupled to ATP synthesis via transmembrane circulation of protons can be regarded as a fundamental law of bioenergetics. In all fairness, it should be called the Mitchellian law.

The simplest and the most general scheme illustrating the principle is shown in Fig. 1. An energy source (light or a respiratory substrate) is used to transport H^+ ions uphill across the hydrophobic barrier of a membrane. As a result, the light or chemical energy is transduced to an electrochemical potential difference of hydrogen ions (protonic potential, $\Delta\bar{\mu}H$) composed of differences in electric ($\Delta\psi$) and chemical (ΔpH) potentials. The energy accumulated in the relatively stable form of $\Delta\bar{\mu}H$ is utilized for ATP

V. P. Skulachev and Peter C. Hinkle (eds.), Chemiosmotic Proton Circuits in Biological Membranes
in honor of Peter Mitchell   ISBN 0-201-07398-6

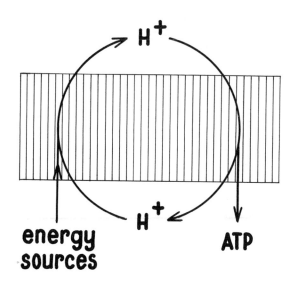

Figure 1. The Proton Cycle.

synthesis coupled to downhill H^+ movement.

The scheme in Fig. 1 does not specify the mechanisms of $\Delta\bar{\mu}H$ formation and utilization. There might be translocation of H^+ as such or a more complicated process, such as an antiport of hydrogen atoms and electrons (redox loop). The scheme also does not show how far H^+ ions penetrate the water phase after crossing the membrane. They could enter the bulk water phase, or, under certain conditions, $\Delta\bar{\mu}H$ generators and consumers might operate so fast and could be localized so close to each other, that protons do not leave the membrane/water interface. In an intermediate situation the movement of H^+ ions in the water phase could be limited by non-stirred water localized between membranes. In mito-chondria this might occur in narrow cavaties of intermembrane (or intercristal) and intracristal spaces. In any case, utilization of an energy source gives rise to an electric

and/or pH asymmetry across the insulating structure of a
membrane, and ATP-synthetase uses this asymmetry to form
ATP.

A SHORT HISTORY.

First ideas and observations. The idea that circulation of
protons crossing a hydrophobic membrane barrier underlies
the coupling between the redox reactions and ATP synthesis
was first formulated in 1961 by Mitchell, who called it the
chemiosmotic hypothesis of oxidative phosphorylation (1).
In fact, Mitchell's paper contained all the major postulates
of the protonic cycle scheme. Mitchell suggested that there
is a $\Delta\bar{\mu}H$ ($\Delta\psi$ and ΔpH) across a coupling membrane which is
formed by a redox chain or by H^+-ATPase enzymes plugged
through the hydrophobic layer of this membrane. If the $\Delta\bar{\mu}H$
formed by the redox chain is sufficiently high to reverse
the H^+-ATPase reaction, the latter forms ATP. Thus, $\Delta\bar{\mu}H$ is
the factor coupling oxidation with phosphorylation.

The origin of this idea, probably began with Lundegard
who suggested in 1945 that an electron transfer chain
organized across a membrane could produce H^+ on one side and
consume H^+ on the other (2). This suggestion was used by
Conway and Brady (3) to explain H^+ secretion in the gastric
mucosa. In the early fifties, Davies, Ogston and Krebs
(4,5) first considered the possible role of charge separation in oxidative phosphorylation. However, in their complicated scheme including two hypothetical redox chains,
protons served to couple one oxidoreduction with another,
while ATP formation per se did not require charge separation.
In 1960 Robertson (6) postulated a scheme based on the

assumption that charge separation occupies a position between the redox reactions and ATP synthesis. However, this
idea was not developed further by the author. In 1968
Robertson noted: "I did not have enough insight to suggest
that the breakdown of ATP might bring about a charge separation and hence an ion movement - a possibility which Mitchell
must have seen clearly at about this time" (7).

Introducing the concept of a reversible H^+-ATPase,
Mitchell completed the protonic cycle so that it became a
new working hypothesis, in contrast to the so-called chemical
scheme which assumed direct chemical interaction of the
redox and phosphorylation enzyme.

At that time, there were several reasons to look for an
alternative to the chemical hypothesis.

(i) Many laboratories tried to find a high-energy
intermediate composed of a respiratory chain enzyme or coenzyme and a component of th ATP-synthetase mechanism. Although this intermediate held a central position in the
chemical scheme, nobody had either observed or isolated it.

(ii) The chemical scheme failed to explain the fact
that both respiratory and photosynthetic phosphorylations
require topologically closed membranous structures.

(iii) A group of compounds of very different chemical
structures was found to induce the same characteristic
change in mitochondrial energetics, known as uncoupling.
These "uncouplers" caused an inhibition of phosphorylation
and a stimulation of both respiration and ATP hydrolysis.

Uncouplers. The effect of the first uncoupler, 2,4-dinitro-
phenol, on oxidative phosphorylation was demonstrated in
1948 by Loomis and Lipmann (8). Pentachlorophenol, dicou-

marol, salicilate, derivatives of benzimidazole and phenylhydrazone were later shown to be uncouplers as well. According to the chemical scheme, uncouplers should substitute
either for phosphate or for another compound involved in the
formation of an intermediate of oxidative phosphorylation.
However, it was difficult to imagine how this specific
function could be carried out by such a variety of chemical
substances. Mitchell was the first to point out that all
uncouplers are weak acids of rather high solubility in
lipids. He suggested that they are proton carriers, dis-
charging $\Delta\bar{\mu}H$ (1). This postulate of the chemiosmotic hypothesis was the first to be experimentally verified.

In 1967 Chappell and Haarhoff (9) found that liposome
membranes became permeable to H^+ ions in the presence of an
uncoupler. Mitchell (10) demonstrated that this was also
the case with mitochondrial membranes.

The protonophore activity of uncouplers was further
shown to correlate with the ability of these compounds to
stimulate respiration and to inhibit phosphorylation, demonstrating that it is not a side-effect. In 1966 Bielawski,
Thompson and Lehninger (11) and independently Babakov,
Ermishkin and Liberman (12) described a decrease in the
electric resistance of a planar bilayer phospholipid membrane
(BLM) induced by 2,4-dinitrophenol and oleate, respectively.
Both compounds were known to be uncouplers. The latter has
been studied in our group as a possible mediator of heat
production in muscle mitochondria of cold-exposed animals
(13). We then compared a range of compounds which differed
widely in uncoupling activity, using natural (mitochondria)
and model (BLM) systems (14,15). The compounds had the same
activity sequence as uncouplers and as proton conductors.

The rule was formulated that any substance decreasing BLM resistance should possess uncoupling activity. Using this rule, we predicted uncoupling activity for several compounds that had never been studied in energy coupling systems.

$\Delta\bar{\mu}H$ across natural membranes. In 1965-1969, Mitchell and Moyle carried out a systematic study of several natural coupling membranes, mitochondria and bacteria, to detect generation of $\Delta\psi$ and ΔpH under conditions of membrane energization (10,16-20). Uncoupler-sensitive changes were found in the outside concentrations of H^+ and K^+ $[H^+]_o$ and $[K^+]_o$ when respiration or ATP hydrolysis was initiated in the presence of the K^+ ionophore, valinomycin. The increase in $[H^+]_o$ and decrease in $[K^+]_o$ were interpreted as evidence for the formation of ΔpH and $\Delta\psi$, respectively (the interior of mitochondria or bacteria becoming more negative and alkaline).

Valinomycin was first used in bioenergetics in 1964 by Moore and Pressman (21), who described a valinomycin mediated, energy-linked K^+ accumulation by mitochondria. The authors speculated that a protein receptor was responsible for the valinomycin-induced increase in K^+ conductance of mitochondrial membranes. Later several groups showed that valinomycin increases the K^+ conductance of purely lipid model membrane systems, BLM's and liposomes (9,22,23). This observation supported Mitchell and Moyle's use of valinomycin to measure $\Delta\psi$. Nevertheless, the advocates of the chemical scheme suggested that valinomycin removed an intramembrane lipid barrier preventing a hypothetical K^+-ATPase from interaction with K^+.

To exclude such a possibility, Liberman's and my groups

undertook a study in which K^+ was replaced by a set of
synthetic ionized compounds (24,25). Many ionized synthetic
acids and bases were tried with the BLM system. We chose
the ones that easily penetrated BLM's made of mitochondrial
phospholipids. These permeant artificial ions were equilibrated with non-energized mitochondria. Energization resulted
in the uptake of cations and extrusion of anions. This
activity correlated with hydrophobicity and the charge of
the molecule but not with other details of the chemical
structure. Compounds extremely different in structure
demonstrated the same behaviour if their permeabilities
across BLM were similar. The sign of the charge was critical
for the direction of the energy-linked ion flow. For example,
tetraphenyl phosphonium was transported into mitochondria,
whereas its negatively charged analog, tetraphenyl borate,
differing in one atom only (B instead of P) was extruded
from mitochondria in an energy-dependent fashion. Opposite
relationships were found in inside-out submitochondrial
particles (24-26).

Later the methods of synthetic penetration ions was
used to measure $\Delta\psi$ across bacterial membranes (for reviews,
see refs. 25,27). Electrochromic shift of the pigments of
photosynthetic membrane was used by Witt and associates to
monitor $\Delta\psi$ in chloroplasts and certain bacteria (28). Later
fluorescent probes for $\Delta\psi$ were developed, confirming the
data obtained by our and Witt's methods.

In our group, submitochondrial particles as well as
bacterial chromatophores were incorporated into a phospholipid-
impregnated membrane filter. In this system, respiration,
light or ATP-dependent $\Delta\psi$ generation was measured directly
by a voltmeter (29-31). Recently, Felle et al. directly

measured $\Delta\psi$ in a single E. coli cell, using microelectrodes
(32). The $\Delta\psi$ values were in excellent agreement with those
obtained with tetraphenyl phosphonium. They do not agree
with the data by Tedeschi who failed to obtain energy-linked
$\Delta\psi$ formation in mitochondria with the microelectrode method
(33). The failure may be due to a greater fragility of the
mitochondrial membrane resulting in shunting near the microelectrode.

To measure ΔpH, several methods were developed, using
the same approach as with $\Delta\psi$ measurements by permeant synthetic ions. The only difference was the use of permeant
weak acids and bases, instead of strong one. Both the direction and the size of ΔpH were found to be in agreement with
Mitchell's prediction (alkalization of the negatively charged
compartment, a ΔpH increase accompanied by a $\Delta\psi$ decrease in
the presence of a penetrating ion, the total $\Delta\bar{\mu}H$ being maintained at a level of about 200-250 mV) (27,34).

$\Delta\bar{\mu}H$ across reconstituted membranes. The main difficulty with
interpreting the $\Delta\bar{\mu}H$ measurements on natural membranes is due
to their complicated enzymatic and ion carrier patterns. For
instance, one could not exclude that, instead of being an
intermediate common to the respiratory and the ATPase system,
$\Delta\bar{\mu}H$ was a by-product of one of them.

The way to simplify the situation was to reconstitute a
model membrane containing only one type of $\Delta\bar{\mu}H$ generator.
This was first done by Kagawa and Racker (35,36) who reconstituted vesicles from phospholipids and mitochondrial H^+-
ATP-synthetase. An indication of th ATP-dependent $\Delta\bar{\mu}H$
formation was obtained with uncoupler and valinomycin probes.

A similar approach was applied by Hinkle et al. (37) in Racker's group and by Jasaitis et al. (38) in our group to reconstitute cytochrome oxidase $\Delta\bar{\mu}H$ generator. Supplementing the reconstitution medium with both cytochrome oxidase and H^+-ATP-synthetase, Racker and Kandrach (39) obtained vesicles which carried out ATP formation coupled to electron transport by cytochrome oxidase. The indispensable condition for re-constituting respiratory phosphorylation was to use intra-vesicular reduced cytochrome $\underline{c}$ as the electron donor. If electrons were supplied by both internal and external cyto-chromes $\underline{c}$, respiration proved to be non-phosphorylating.

In terms of the Mitchellian theory, the inhibitory effect of oxidation of the external cytochrome $\underline{c}$ on ATP synthesis coupled with internal cytochrome $\underline{c}$ oxidation could be predicted assuming that these two oppositely arranged oxidative processes had to generate oppositely directed protonic potentials, so that the resulting $\Delta\bar{\mu}H$ proved negli-gible. On the other hand, this effect could not have been explained in a satisfying fashion by any other concept but the chemiosomotic one.

To verify the above assumption about the oppositely directed potentials, we applied the method of synthetic permeant ions to reconstituted cytochrome oxidase and H^+-ATP-synthetase vesicles (I called these vesicles proteolipo-somes). Oxidation of external cytochrome $\underline{c}$ did generate a membrane potential (the proteoliposomal interior negative) opposite to both the internal cytochrome $\underline{c}$ oxidation and the ATP hydrolysis (the interior positive) (38). These data were confirmed later in other laboratories for the same as well as for other energy-transducing enzyme complexes by means of dif-ferent $\Delta\psi$ and ΔpH probes (for reviews, see 27,36,40) and, in our

group, by means of direct voltmetric measurements in a proteoliposome-membrane filter system (26,29,41-44).

The above set of studies clearly showed that (i) $\Delta\bar{\mu}H$ is
necessary for oxidative phosphorylation and (ii) both respiration and ATP hydrolysis are competent in generating $\Delta\bar{\mu}H$
of one and the same direction.

ATP formation supported by an artificially-imposed $\Delta\bar{\mu}H$. Is
protonic potential not only necessary but also sufficient for
supporting membrane-linked ATP synthesis? This question
should be answered to complete the logical verification of the
Mitchellian concept. If the answer is "yes", artifically
imposed $\Delta\psi$ or ΔpH can drive ADP phosphorylation in the absence
of respiratory or photosynthetic electron transfer.

The first observation of this kind was made in 1966 by
Jagendorf and Uribe (45) who described dark ATP formation
after transfer of chloroplasts from an acidic to an alkaline
solution. The following investigations confirmed and extended
this work, showing that $\Delta\psi$, as well as ΔpH, can support phosphorylation in mitochondria, bacteria, their particles and
proteoliposomes (for review, see ref. 46).

The last straw. Logically speaking, the above pieces of
evidence were sufficient for considering the chemiosmotic
hypothesis as being experimentally proved. However, intellectual inertia prevented Mitchell's concept from being generally
accepted. People wanted to see more and more "miracles"
predicted by the founder of the new bioenergetics. His
opponents systematically attacked each argument of his suppor-
ters, trying to explain the data in terms of the so-called
conformational or of the local proton transfer (Williams')

concepts. They said that intact membrane systems were too
complicated, and reconstituted ones too artifical. Experiments with artifically imposed $\Delta\bar{\mu}H$ were criticized because of
small absolute values of synthesized ATP, which were limited
by the small internal volume of the studied vesicles.

The last straw, however, was experiments with bacteriorhodopsin. In 1971, Oesterhelt, Blaurock and Stoeckenius
(47,48) described a new type of bacterial pigment, bacteriorhodopsin, which proved to be responsible for light energy
utilization by halophilic bacteria. In 1973, Oesterhelt and
Stoeckenius demonstrated light-dependent, bacteriorhodopsin-
mediated H^+ extrusion from intact bacteria which was sensitive to uncouplers (49).

In 1974-1975 Oesterhelt and Stoeckenius, and independently our group, discovered photophosphorylation in halobacteria (50,51). At about the same time, we reconstituted
bacteriorhodopsin proteoliposomes and described $\Delta\psi$ and ΔpH
formation in the light (52). Thus it was proved that bacteriorhodopsin is a light-driven H^+ pump producing $\Delta\bar{\mu}H$ to
support ATP formation. This system of photophosphorylation
was dramatically different from the usual one (containing
chlorophyll) in all essential features with a single exception - both mechanisms used $\Delta\bar{\mu}H$ as the coupling intermediate.

In 1974, Racker and Stoeckenius (53) reconstituted
proteoliposomes from a mixture of bacteriorhodopsin, beef-
heart H^+-ATP-synthetase and soy-bean phospholipids. The
vesicles composed of constituents from all three kingdoms of
living organisms (bacteria, animals and plants) were shown to
be competent in ADP photophosphorylation. In this system
mitochondrial H^+-ATP-synthetase utilized a $\Delta\bar{\mu}H$ that was
produced in a manner quite different from the natural one

(bacteriorhodopsin instead of respiratory chain enzymes).
So, the system resembled that with artificially-imposed $\Delta\bar{\mu}H$
as the energy source. However, bacteriorhodopsin - H^+-ATP-
synthetase proteoliposomes had an important advantage. In
this chimerical system, ATP synthesis could proceed as long
as light was available since it was not limited by a small
intravesicular volume, which limited long-term phosphorylation when supported by an artifically imposed $\Delta\bar{\mu}H$ in other
systems.

The results with bacteriorhodopsin so obviously con-
tradicted "anti-Mitchellian" concepts that a fundamental
change in public opinion occurred, and the proton cycle
scheme was accepted by the bioenergetical community as an
experimentally proven theory. In 1978, Mitchell received the
last piece of evidence for the triumph of his concept from
the hands of the King of Sweden - the Nobel prize in chemistry.

THE PRESENT STATE OF THE PROTONIC CYCLE CONCEPT

Principles of organization of $\Delta\bar{\mu}H$ generators. There are at
least 10 different enzymes or enzyme complexes competent in
$\Delta\bar{\mu}H$ formation, namely (i) NADH dehydrogenase, (ii) cytochrome
b-c_1 complex, (iii) cytochrome oxidase, and (iv) transhydrogenase which comprise the respiratory chain of mitochondria
and bacteria, (v,vi) photosystems I and II of chloroplasts,
(vii) bacteriorhodopsin, (ix) H^+-ATP-synthetase of mitochondria, chloroplasts, and bacteria, and (x) H^+-PPase of
certain photosynthetic bacteria. An ATPase localized in the
outer membrane of fungal and, probably, plant cells may well
prove to be the 11th $\Delta\bar{\mu}H$ generator (for discussion, see ref.
54).

Unfortunately, none of these enzymes has as yet been studied to a degree allowing the mechanism of the energy transduction to be elucidated. In particular, it is not known which charged species cross the hydrophobic barrier of the membrane when the protonic potential is generated.

This is even true of bacteriorhodopsin, the simplest and best-known $\Delta\bar{\mu}H$ generator. Its primary structure was published by Ovchinnikov et al. (55) in 1978 (see also 56), and by Khorana et al. in 1979 (57). Henderson and Unwin (58-60) have elucidated the three-dimensional structure of bacterio-rhodopsin at a 8 Å resolution, and a very reasonable hypothesis about the relation of the primary to the three-dimensional structure has been put forward (61).

Until recently, it was assumed that bacteriorhodopsin translocates one H^+ ion per each photon inducing isomerization of the retinal chromophore. The mechanism was suggested to involve four main states: (i) a light-induced isomerization of retinal; (ii) deprotonation of the Schiff base connecting the retinal residue to a lysine residue of the polypeptide, resulting in the release of H^+, previously bound to the Schiff base nitrogen, into extracellular solution (an H^+ transfer along an outward H^+-conducting pathway is involved); (iii) reverse isomerization of retinal; (iv) reprotonation of the Schiff base nitrogen with an intra-cellular H^+ ion transferred along an inward H^+ pathway.

Such a rather simple version of the bacteriorhodopsin $\Delta\bar{\mu}H$ generator was shaken by some indirect evidence that more than one H^+ is translocated per each effective photon absorbed (for review, see ref. 62), and indications that halobacteria possess another retinal-dependent, light-driven pump transporting Na^+ instead of H^+ (63-66). Both observations

should be a warning to those who wish to follow the simplest
version of the bacteriorhodopsin mechanism.

For further progress in bacteriorhodopsin studies, the
groups involved in transmembrane charge transfer should be
eluciated. One could do this by modifying certain amino acid
residues and measuring partial reactions of charge displacements in bacteriorhodopsin molecules. The latter can be
monitored with novel techniques developed in our group to
measure such displacements with a 50 ns resolution. This
technique used a phospholipid-impregnated collodion film,
treated on one side with bacteriorhodopsin-containing fragments of H. halobium membrane. These fragments attached to
the film. Illumination of this system with a 51 ns laser
flash, inducing a single turnover of bacteriorhodopsin, was
found to generate an electric potential which was measured by
electrodes on each side of the collodion film. Three main
electrogenic phases were resolved, greatly differing in their
time constants: $\tau_1 < 50$ ns, $\tau_2 = 50$ μs, $\tau_3 = 10$ ms, which
roughly corresponded to a retinal isomerization-connected
charge displacement, Schiff base deprotonation and reprotonation, respectively (67,68).

Bacterial photosynthetic reaction center complexes are more
complicated than bacteriorhodopsin, including two or even
three polypeptides and several prostetic groups (bacterio-
chlorophylls, bacteriophenophytines and Fe-CoQ). Complete
information is not available about the primary structure or
the three-dimensional arrangement of the chromoproteins.
Three light-induced unidirectoral electrogenic phases were
resolved on the way from cytochrome c to "free" (secondary)
CoQ, the shortest one ($\tau < 50$ ns) being the largest. The

shortest phase is connected, most probably, with electron transfer from chlorophyll to Fe-CoQ, directed from the internal to external surface of the chromatophore membrane (30,69).

The small µs stages of electrogenesis might be due to (i) CoQ^- movement from an intramembrane place to the outer surface of chromatophore membrane (where Fe-CoQ is located) or, more probably, to H^+ movement in the opposite direction (from water to the intramembrane CoQ^-), and (ii) electron transfer from cytochrome c localized on the inner membrane surface to oxidized bacteriochlorophyll inside the membrane (69).

There are some indications that the electrogenesis by photosystems I and II may also involve stages of electron transfer directed across the membrane (for review, see ref. 28).

Electron transfer directed perpendicularly to the membrane plane was supposed to explain charge separation by cytochrome oxidase (10,70,71). Surprisingly, however, later experiments indicated that H^+ ions were released into the extramitochondrial space when cytochrome c or ferrocyanide was oxidized by mitochondria (for review, see ref. 72). This qualitative result, if it is not a side-effect, indicates that cytochrome oxidase is a proton pump organized in a more complicated manner than a transmembrane electron carrier. As to side-effects, they are minimized in cytochrome oxidase proteoliposomes. The only difficulty here is that acidification coupled to cytochrome c oxidation is rather small, being limited, apparently, by a small intraproteoliposomal volume. For the final solution to this problem, experiments with large proteoliposomes are desirable.

Bacterial cytochrome oxidase proteoliposomes, oxidizing external cytochrome $\underline{c}$, did not acidify the medium (73). Two alternative explanations can be considered. (i) Bacterial cytochrome oxidase is a simple electron carrier and proton pumping is an additional function inherent only in the mito-chondrial enzyme. (ii) Proton pump machinery can be readily detached from the bacterial cytochrome oxidase complex when the enzyme is purified. An indication in favour of the latter alternative was obtained by Van Verseveld et al. (cit. after Wikström, ref. 72) who observed some acidification of the medium when cytochrome oxidase was activated in the bacterial membrane.

The sequence of redox events in <u>the cytochrome b-c</u>$_1$ <u>complex</u> can be described in terms of Mitchell's Q-cycle scheme (74-76) which is now supported by many independent lines of evidence (for reviews, see refs. 77,78). For this energy coupling site, which is most probably present not only in the respiratory but also in the photosynthetic redox chain, the following two mechanism of $\Delta\bar{\mu}H$ generation may be considered. (i) Electron transfer between two $\underline{b}$-type cyto-chromes is directed across the membrane. In this case, the charged species transported through the hydrophobic barrier is an electron. (ii) Electron transfer is directed along the membrane being coupled with a transmembrane H^+ transport via H^+-permeable channels or protonic pathways. Similar possi-bilities may be considered for <u>NADH</u> <u>dehydrogenase</u> with the only difference that flavin and non-heme iron proteins, instead of cytochromes, are involved.

The attractive feature of the original chemiosmotic hypothesis is that it not only explained the principle of coupling of two entirely different processes, i.e. redox reactions and ATP synthesis, but also rationalized the mechanism of redox energy transduction. Alternation of hydrogen atom and electron carriers in redox chains, proposed by Mitchell (1,10), looked like an explicit $\Delta\bar{\mu}H$-forming system. Indeed, if there is a series of three redox components, the first and the third being H atom carriers, and the second an electron carrier, oxidation of the first carrier by the second should result in H^+ release, whereas that of the second by the third, in H^+ uptake. If the electron carrier can cross the hydrophobic barrier while the H atom carriers cannot, the overall redox process automatically produces a $\Delta\bar{\mu}H$. It is this mechanism that Mitchell suggested for NADH dehydrogenase, b-c_1 complex, cytochrome oxidase and photosynthetic redox systems (10). In none of the above mentioned cases was this mechanism directly proved or disproved. However, this simple principle applied to cytochrome oxidase can account for the separation of only one of two charges if we assume Wikström's proton pump model for this energy coupling site (72).

In any case, there is a coupling site that should be organized in an entirely different manner and this fact was clear to Mitchell as early as 1966. I mean the transhydrogenase reaction. In mitochondria, this process is energy-linked as was first shown by Ernster and associates (79-81). Mitchell suggested that it represents an additional $\Delta\bar{\mu}H$ generator of the respiratory chain (10). Indeed, in our group it was shown that mitochondrial and chromatophore transhydrogenase generated a $\Delta\psi$. The direction of this $\Delta\psi$ depended on the [NADPH] x NAD$^+$]/[NADP$^+$] x [NADH] ratio (43,82,93). A peculiar feature of the transhydrogenase reaction is that the transfer of reducing equivalents, in this case H^-, between NADPH and NADH occurs without exchange of H^+ with water. Thus, $\Delta\bar{\mu}H$ generation cannot be described as a sequence of alternating H atom and electron carriers. Therefore transhydrogenase is a precedent for a redox $\Delta\bar{\mu}H$ generator organized in a fashion other than a redox loop. The mechanism of transhydrogenase-linked $\Delta\bar{\mu}H$ formation remains obscure. A promising hypothesis concerning this coupling site was recently put forward in our group by Kozlov (84,85).

Very many studies have been made on the mechanism of H^+-ATP-synthetase, the key enzyme of oxidative and photosynthetic phosphorylation. However, no final solution has been reached in spite of the large body of interesting information obtained. From the experiments of Boyer's group (86) and Kozlov's calculation of ATPase and ATP-synthetase kinetics (85; see also 87), one can conclude that the $\Delta\bar{\mu}H$-consuming reaction is ATP released from the F_1 catalytic site, rather than the synthesis of ATP in this site. This conclusion is supported now by several independent lines of evidence, including the energy-dependent release of the AMPPNP inhibition of ATPase in submitochondrial particles described by Kozlov's group (87,88).

A good working hypothesis is that two processes contribute to the membrane potential formation by this enzyme complex: (i) H^+ movement along a protonic pathway from the outer surface of the mitochondrial membrane to the membrane core where the ATPase catalytic site of the factor F_1 β-subunit is located and (ii) $ATP^{4-}/ADP^{3-} + P_i^{3-}$ antiport between the catalytic site and the inner surface of the membrane (88-91). The latter process, as was postulated by

Kozlov (92,93), involves translocation of the adenine nucleotides via a non-catalytic nucleotide binding site localized
on the F_1 α-subunit.

Practically no systematic studies on H^+-pyrophosphatase
have been published, although membrane potential formation
by this enzyme was revealed with the permeant ion method in
1970 (83). Recently this process was measured directly in a
proteoliposome-membrane filter system (44).

Protonic potential as a convertible energy currency for
the cell. Postulating the existence of a protonic potential,
Mitchell assumed that it operates as a transient between
oxidation and phosphorylation (1,10). Later, it turned out
that the functions of the protonic potential are multiple
and not confined to the role of a coupling component in the
membrane-linked ATP synthesis. Among functions alternative
to ATP synthesis, we should first mention osmotic work. Very
many processes of the uphill transport of substances across
coupling membranes are supported by the $\Delta\bar{\mu}H$ energy. This is
true of all the known energy-dependent transport in mitochondria
and of many transport pathways in bacteria. Similar systems
are found in outer membranes of fungal and plant cells, as
well as in chloroplasts (for reviews, see refs. 27,34, 94,95).

It is remarkable that $\Delta\bar{\mu}H$-dependent transport systems
are involved in the very process of ATP formation by mitochondria when they export ATP to cytosol. In fact, both the
ADP and P_i influxes and the ATP efflux occur in a $\Delta\bar{\mu}H$-con-
suming manner, so that the ADP + P_i/ATP antiport is coupled
with translocation of one H^+ ion from cytosol to the mitochondrial matrix. Assuming that formation of the one intramitochondrial ATP by H^+-ATP-synthetase is coupled to downhill

transport of two H^+ ions, one third of the $\Delta\bar{\mu}H$ energy required to form the exported ATP is spent not on ATP formation per se but on the osmotic work of uphill transport of ADP, P_i and ATP. Apparently, this value is even higher than one third since the transport of respiratory substrates from the cytosol to matrix is, as a rule, also $\Delta\bar{\mu}H$-consuming (34).

Catecholamine-storing chromaffin granules of adrenal medulla are an example of a structure specialized in $\Delta\bar{\mu}H$-dependent osmotic work. These membrane vesicles possess an H^+-ATPase similar, but not identical, to the mitochondrial $F_o \cdot F_1$ complex. $\Delta\bar{\mu}H$ formed at the expense of ATP hydrolysis is used to accumulate huge amounts of catecholamines and ATP inside the vesicles. The same system is used to store catecholamines and acetylcholine in some other types of cells and tissues (for review, see ref. 96).

The chemical work of $\Delta\bar{\mu}H$ includes, besides ATP synthesis, such processes as inorganic pyrophosphate formation in some bacteria and reverse transfers of reducing equivalents in redox chains. An example of the latter case is transhydrogenase which usually operates in the $\Delta\bar{\mu}H$-consuming direction. In bacteria such as Thiobacillus ferrooxidans, reverse electron transfer is the only mechanism to reduce NAD(P) and flavins (for review, see ref. 34). This means that a large portion of the protonic potential energy must be consumed to support these processes of $\Delta\bar{\mu}H$-linked chemical work.

Regulatory heat production can also be $\Delta\bar{\mu}H$-dependent. In our group, fast uncoupling was discovered in muscles of pigeons exposed for 15 mim to cold (13, 97-99). This work published in 1960-1963 was recently confirmed by Grav and Blix who found uncoupling in the muscles of the north seal under cold conditions (100). The observation on cold uncoup-

ling in muscles was followed by a series of interesting
studies on brown fat tissue which specializes in cold-induced
$\Delta \bar{\mu} H$-to-heat energy transduction. This process is mediated by
an OH^--translocating protein localized in the inner mitochondrial membrane (for reviews, see refs. 101,102).

Recently studies of bacterial motility have indicated
that it is and example of $\Delta \bar{\mu} H$-supported mechanical work. In
1956, Mitchell noted that it is theoretically possible to
drive locomotion of a bacterial cell by ionic gradients
(103). It was proposed that a bacterial flagellum plays the
role of a giant ionophore (103,104). This assumption was
later ruled out, again theoretically, as ineffective (105).
Nevertheless, the more general idea of an ion-driven locomotion was later experimentally proven.

In 1974, Adler and his colleagues observed, apparently
without being influenced by Mitchell's ideas, that an E. coli
mutant deficient in oxidative phosphorylation, requires
respiration to be motile, although the ATP level was not
affected by oxygen. Moreover, lowering of ATP levels did not
stop respiration-supported motility while the addition of an
uncoupler did (106).

In 1975, we confirmed Adler's observation using Rh.
rubrum (107). We showed that in this case too, bacterial
motility did not correlate with ATP levels. Moreover, there
was a good correlation between the motility rate and the
level of membrane potential produced by the photosynthetic
redox chain. From these observations we suggested that
motility of bacteria is supported by $\Delta \bar{\mu} H$, rather than by ATP
hydrolysis (107-110). Later our group (109-110) and two
other laboratories, (111,112), found that Rh. rubrum, a
Streptococcus and Bacillus subtilis were paralyzed by ex-

haustion of endogenous sources for $\Delta\bar{\mu}H$ generation but became
motile for several minutes when artifical $\Delta\psi$ or ΔpH was
imposed. Now the concept of $\Delta\bar{\mu}H$-driven bacterial motility is
generally accepted. We defined this wonderful biological
device as a protonic motor and suggested a tentative scheme
of its organization (110,113,114).

The fact that the flagellum can rotate both clockwise
and counter-clockwise indicates that there is an "adjusting
gear" for switching over the direction of rotation in spite
of the fact that the direction of $\Delta\bar{\mu}H$ remains constant (113).
In addition, an important observation was made by Berg et al.
(115), who found that Streptococcus motility could be supported by an oppositely directed $\Delta\bar{\mu}H$. Such an effect, if not
a consequence of some complicated interplay of porter systems
of the bacterial cells, may help exclude certain versions of
the protonic motor mechanism. Moreover, it may be considered
as direct evidence in favor of the concept regarding $\Delta\bar{\mu}H$ as
the immediate energy source for rotation of bacterial flagellum. Indeed, if there were any intermediate between $\Delta\bar{\mu}H$
and rotation, such as a gradient of ions other than H^+ or a
chemical high-energy compound, the oppositely directed $\Delta\bar{\mu}H$
would hardly be effective.

Usually, if Nature invents something that is really
good, it keeps applying the invention over and over again
whenever this can help solve its problems. So, the question
arises where else $\Delta\bar{\mu}H$-consuming rotors are used in the living
organisms. Analyzing this question, we first turned to non-
flagellar motile procayrotes. Experiments carried out in our
group by Glagoleva et al. (116) showed that the gliding
motiliy of trichomes of multicellular filamentous cyanobacteria Phormidium uncinatum is driven by a naturally-

generated or artificially-imposed protonic potential, rather
than by ATP. These cyanobacteria do not possess flagella.
Their motility is assumed to be induced by fibrils localized
under the other membrane of the trichome (117,118). Apparently, the fibrils are in some way connected with the $\Delta\bar{\mu}H$-
bearing cytoplasmic membrane of the trichome-forming bacterial cells. There is an indication that the gliding of
Flexibacter is also supported by $\Delta\bar{\mu}H$ (119). According to
our data, even the rotatory movement of chloroplasts of
Nitella utilizes the $\Delta\bar{\mu}H$ produced by the photosynthetic
redox chain, rather than ATP (54).

It is in principle possible that a protonic motor may
be a part of certain mechanisms other than the motility
systems of cells or organelles. In fact, a rotating M-disc
may be convenient for transducing $\Delta\bar{\mu}H$ into various kinds of
mechanical work, such as translocation of large molecules or
supramolecular aggregates across the bacterial membrane.
This phenomenon, as was discovered recently by one of my
former co-workers, Dr. L. Grinius, is $\Delta\bar{\mu}H$-dependent (for
review, see ref. 120). The rate of DNA transport is very
high if calculated per nucleotide residue of the polynucleo-
tide chain. One of the tentative schemes explaining this
effect can be based on the assumption that a $\Delta\bar{\mu}H$-linked
rotatory movement of a M-disc-like component is coupled with
a linear translocational movement of the DNA molecule across
the bacterial membrane.

The data summarized above seem to be sufficient to
conclude that $\Delta\bar{\mu}H$, like ATP, is a convertible form of energy
for the cell. This concept that has been developed in our
group since 1975 (54,107,109,114) has been very productive
and has provoked such novel observations as $\Delta\bar{\mu}H$-linked moti-

lity of flagellar bacteria and cyanobacteria, $\Delta\bar{\mu}H$-supported
DNA transport, as well as lateral long-distance power transmission and the $\Delta\bar{\mu}H$-buffering role of the Na^+/K^+ gradient (see
below). In fact, examples of all the major types of work of
the living cell were found to be $\Delta\bar{\mu}H$-driven. There is (i)
Chemical work of the ATP and PP_i syntheses and reverse electron transfer against a redox gradient; (ii) osmotic work of
uphill transport of a great variety of compounds; (iii)
mechanical work of bacterial motility; (iv) heat production
upon cooling of warm-blooded animals. Besides, one should
keep in mind that the electric form of energy ($\Delta\psi$) is a
constituent of $\Delta\bar{\mu}H$. These relationships are shown in Fig. 2.

An obligatory feature of convertible energy currency is
transportability. This is necessary first for making possible
energy exchange between different energy producers and consumers. For ATP, this is acheived simply by means of ATP
diffusion in the cytoplasm. For $\Delta\bar{\mu}H$, this may be done by
transmission of a membrane potential along the membrane.
Calculation of energy dissipation accompanying lateral power
transmission along coupling membranes showed that such a
transmission should be effective even over mm distances which
is quite sufficient to organize intracellular energy transport
(121,122). Giant mitochondria discovered in many types of
eucaryotic cells (for review, see ref. 121) can be considered
as structures responsible for $\Delta\bar{\mu}H$ transmission. Such a
suggestion was put forward in 1969-1971 (123,124,125).
Unfortunately, some technical difficulties have prevented
direct measurement of $\Delta\psi$ transmission along giant mitochondria,
which are organized as networks of very thin mitochondrial
tubules. Therefore, we turned to another type of coupling
membrane for studying long distance power transmission in

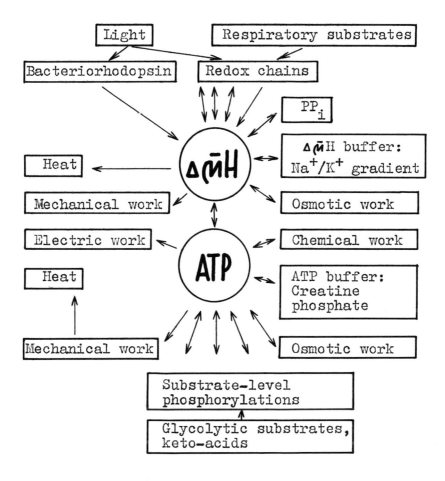

Figure 2. General scheme of energetics of the living cell.

the form of $\Delta\bar{\mu}H$. This was trichomes of cyanobacteria.

A trichome can be several mm long. It represents a linear sequence of many hundreds of cyanobacterial cells. There is an indication that these cells can be connected with "Microplasmadesmata" (126). If there is an electric conductance between trichome-composing cells, one may hope that the electric potential difference generated across the cytoplasmic membrane near one end of the trichome can be transmitted along the trichome and utilized in its distal end to carry out work.

To verify this suggestion, we used light as a source of $\Delta\bar{\mu}H$ generation and motility as $\Delta\bar{\mu}H$-dependent work. Illumination of about 5% of the trichome length with a small light beam initiated motility of the trichome under conditions when other energy sources were unavailable (122,127).

In the next series of experiments, $\Delta\psi$ transmission along trichomes was monitored with a classical electrophysiology technique. The above-mentioned partial illumination resulted in $\Delta\psi$ transmission all over the trichome length (122,127). Computer simulation of these data revealed a good agreement between (i) the measured amplitudes and the kinetics of $\Delta\psi$ and (ii) those calculated if one assumed that electric cable properties are inherent in cyanobacterial trichome.

Thus the data on filamentous cyanobacteria can be considered as a precedent of intercellular power transmission in the form of membrane potential. It seems to be reasonable to speculate that some coupling membranes, other than those of cyanobacteria, can also play the role of electric cables to transmit power. The inner membrane of giant mitochondria is a good candidate for such a function (121).

Na^+/K^+ gradient as a reserve of membrane-linked energy. It is obvious that the level of $\Delta\bar{\mu}H$ as a convertible form of energy must be stabilized to prevent undesirable fluctuations of all the $\Delta\bar{\mu}H$-dependent processes. In 1978, I suggested that the unknown function of Na^+/K^+ gradient across the cytoplasmic membrane of procaryotic cells is $\Delta\bar{\mu}H$ buffering

(128). The following system of energy conversion has been
postulated:

$$\text{Energy sources} \xleftrightarrow{\quad \Delta\bar{\mu}\text{H-generators} \quad} \Delta\psi \qquad (1)$$

$$\Delta\psi \xleftrightarrow{\quad K^+\text{-uniporter} \quad} \Delta pK, \Delta pH \qquad (2)$$

$$\Delta pH \xleftrightarrow{\quad Na^+/H^+\text{-antiporter} \quad} \Delta pNa \qquad (3)$$

It is assumed that under an excess of external energy
sources all the above energy conversions proceed from left to
right. As a result, a portion of these sources is spent to
accumulate K^+ in the cell interior and to extrude Na^+ from the
cell to the outer medium.

The hypothesis was based on observations indicating the
existence of a Na^+/H^+ antiporter in the cytoplasmic membrane
of different species of microorganisms and on certain pieces
of indirect evidence that K^+ is transported electrophoretically
from the medium to cytoplasm (for review, see ref. 128). The
latter process was considered by Mitchell as an objectionable
but inevitable side-effect of $\Delta\psi$ formation (10,19). As to
Na^+/H^+ antiport, Mitchell regarded it as favorable for increasing the pH-buffer capacitance of the cytosol (19).

A study carried out in this group during the last three
years (54,129-131) confirmed the $\Delta\bar{\mu}$H-stabililizing role of the
Na^+/K^+-gradient in bacteria. The following results were
obtained.

(i) Na^+/K^+ gradient supports the motility of H. halobium,
E. coli and Phormidium uncinatum under conditions when other
energy sources are absent.

(ii) Under the same conditions, Na^+/K^+ gradient stabilizes the ATP level as well as membrane energization measured

with ANS^- and dis-C_3(5) probes.

(iii) Only ΔpK is responsible for $\Delta\psi$ stabilization in E. coli. On the other hand, both ΔpK and ΔpNa contribute to motility rate stabilization.

(iv) The capacitance of the Na^+/K^+ energy buffer decreases in the range: halophilic H. halobium > E. coli > freshwater Ph. uncinatum.

The results on H. halobium proved to be especially revealing. The motility of this bacterium could be supported by the Na^+/K^+ gradient for more than 9 h. This means that halobacteria can invest a very large portion of energy into a Na^+/K^+ gradient during light hours when solar energy is available - to regain it during the night.

It is interesting that the cell spends its Na^+/K^+ gradient energy with great parsimony to prevent the bankruptcy of cellular energetics when this last energy source is exhausted. Addition of the K^+ ionophore, valinomycin, resulting in an immediate efflux of all the intracellular K^+ pool, was found to induce a fast increase of the ATP level which, however, proved unstable and decreased sharply immediately after maximum was reached (131).

Apparently, a K^+ uniporter (or channel) and a Na^+/H^+ antiporter are regulated to optimize ion fluxes and intracellular concentrations of the ions. In particular, the K^+ influx under energized conditions must not be too fast to avoid significant inhibition of other $\Delta\psi$-linked functions. If external energy sources are exhausted, the K^+ efflux must be sufficiently fast to substitute, at least partially, for $\Delta\bar{\mu}H$-generating enzyme systems. If, however, it were as fast as in the presence of valinomycin, long-term $\Delta\bar{\mu}H$ buffering would be impossible. Some evidence of this type of regulation

was obtained for $\underline{E}$. $\underline{coli}$, $\underline{Streptococcus}$ $\underline{faecalis}$ (for review,
see ref. 128) and quite recently for a marine bacterium,
$\underline{Alteromonas}$ $\underline{haloplanktis}$ (132).

When $\Delta\psi$ under energized conditions is too small to
create a sufficient $[K^+]_{in}$, additional mechanisms for impor-
ting K^+ may be mobilized. In $\underline{E}$. $\underline{coli}$, this can be exemplified
by a situation when the synthesis of a K^+-ATPase is induced
by greatly decreasing $[K^+]_{out}$ (133). Additional systems of
Na^+ export are also necessary if ΔpH is low. There are some
indications (134) that alkalization of the medium promotes an
increase in the H^+/Na^+ stoichiometry of the antiporter. If
it becomes > 1, the Na^+ efflux is electrogenic and, hence,
driven by both ΔpH and $\Delta\psi$. Besides, a special Na^+-ATPase may
be activated as shown for $\underline{Streptococcus}$ $\underline{faecalis}$ at pH > 7.4
(135).

In halobacteria, besides the Na^+/H^+ antiporter responsible for the major portion of Na^+ extrusion, an additional
mechanism, a light-driven Na^+ pump (Na^+-bacteriorhodopsin)
has been described (63-66).

In citrate-fermenting $\underline{Klebsiella}$ $\underline{aerogenes}$ decarboxylation of oxaloacetate to pyruvate was coupled to Na^+ extrusion.
The process, according to the recent observation by Dimroth
(136), is catalyzed by a membrane-linked biotin enzyme. The
splitting of the enzyme-biotin-COO^- complex resulting in CO_2
release required Na^+. Inverted sub-bacterial particles
accumulated Na^+ coupled with oxaloacetate decarboxylation.
Both decarboxylation and Na^+ influx were inhibited by avidin.
Conversion of oxaloacetate to pyruvate and CO_2 liberates 7
kcal/mol. This value is smaller than that required for the
formation of $\Delta\bar{\mu}H$ sufficient to reverse the ATPase reaction
under physiological conditions. On the other hand, ΔpNa is

usually equilibrated with ΔpH which is lower than total $\Delta\bar{\mu}$H.
So, decarboxylation can, in principle, be an auxiliary ΔpNa-
forming mechanism, and this is the case in K. aerogenes.

Possible non-energetic functions of protonic potential. An
interesting perspective of the future studies on protonic
potential is elucidation of its possible non-energetic functions. Some of them were reviewed by Harold (137). His
group has obtained intriguing preliminary data concerning the
role of $\Delta\bar{\mu}$H as a factor governing morphogenesis of a multicellular organism.

In this context, I would like to illustrate how old
unsolved biological problems may be attacked from a new angle
if protonic potential is introduced into the field of vision.
The problem in question is the obscure function of animal
rhodopsin.

This chromoprotein was discovered almost a century
earlier than its bacterial analog functioning as a $\Delta\bar{\mu}$H
generator. An indication of some electrogenic activity of
animal rhodopsin was obtained in 1964 when the so-called
early receptor potential (ERP) of retina was described (138).
It was a very rapid small biphasic photoelectric response
preceding the late receptor potential, i.e. excitation of the
visual cell. ERP kinetics was too fast to be asociated with
post-rhodopsin steps of the visual process. The EPR amplitude was not more than several mV even under saturating
illumination. Such a small value made one regard ERP as an
epiphenomenon without any functional significance (for review,
see ref. 139).

In recent years, interest in rhodopsin-linked photoelectric activity was stimulated by the discovery of such

activity in bacteriorhodopsin. Trissl et al. (140-142)
illuminating a solid Teflon film covered on one side with
rhodopsin, recorded a small but measureable photoeffect (0.5-
3 mV). In Ostrovsky's group, our method, previously developed to measure bacteriorhodopsin-mediated generation of
electric potentials (143-145), was recently applied to visual
rhodopsin (146). Illumination of cattle photoreceptor discs
associated with the surface of a phospholipid-impregnated
millipore filter induced a significant electric potential
(20-25 mV). The action spectrum of the photoeffect coincided
with the absorption spectrum of rhodopsin. Independently,
the same technique was used by Chapron (147,148) who obtained
a qualitatively similar photoeffect, but of lower amplitude
(less than 1 mV). Small photopotentials were also observed
by Bamberg et al. (149) who studied rhodopsin proteoliposomes
attached to a planar phospholipid membrane. Previously,
Ostrovsky and co-workers revealed a photopotential of the
same direction (disc interior positive) using a penetrating
synthetic anion, phenyldicarbaundecaborane (150). Later
Cafiso and Hubbell (151) and Benett et al. (152) confirmed
this observation with other membrane potential probes.

A systematic comparative study of the photoelectric
activitiy of animal and bacterial rhodopsins was recently
carried out in this group together with Ostrovsky's laboratory (153-155). Photoreceptor discs or bacteriorhodopsin
membrane sheets were incorporated into a collodion film
impregnated with a decane solution of phospholipids. Under
continuous illumination, both animal and bacterial rhodopsins
were found to generate a potential difference across the
film, the rhodopsin-free side being positive. Bacterio-
rhodopsin-supported $\Delta\psi$ persisted throughout the illumination

period.   However, the $\Delta\psi$ formed by animal rhodopsin reached
about 0.5 V and then rapidly fell to zero.

The study of 15 ns laser flash-induced single turnover
of the two rhodopsins revealed their striking similarity.
(i) A single turnover resulted in the formation of a significant $\Delta\psi$ (35-60 mV).   (ii) This photoresponse was composed
of three main electrogenic phases, the 1st phase being
directed oppositely to the 2nd and 3rd.   (iii) The contributions of these phases to the overall photoeffect increased
in the order of 1st < 2nd < and 3rd.   (iv) The 1st phase τ
was faster than 50 ns, that of the 3rd phase was several ms.
The 2nd phase developed in a μs time scale (τ was about 50 μs
and 500 μs for bacterial and animal pigments, respectively).
(v) The photopotential produced by the 1st flash discharged
in a sec time scale.   (vi) If we take into account that the
N- and C-ends of the polypeptide chain of both animal and
bacterial rhodopsins are located on the opposite sides of the
membrane, we can conclude that both chromoproteins generate
photopotentials of the same direction (the N-side positive).
(vii) A blue flash added after a green one produced an oppositely directed photopotential.

It should be stressed that the majority of these features
proved to be quite different in a "non-rhodopsin" photoelectric
generator, the bacteriochlorophyll system of Rhodospirillum
rubrum chromatophores, studied with the same technique (69).
In this system, all the phases of electrogenesis were of the
same direction, the first phase was the largest one, in the
photopotential decay there was a fast phase (τ = 30 ms), etc.

All these data indicate that the essential photoelectric
parameters of animal rhodopsin are similar to those of
bacteriorhodopsin.   So, the minimal hypothesis about the

function of animal rhodopsin is that it generates a light-
driven membrane potential, since only this role is performed
by bacterial rhodopsin. Alternatively, the ability of animal
rhodopsin to transduce light into electric energy may be an
atavism preserved during the long process of evolution from
bacteria to higher animals.

What may be the consequence of $\Delta\psi$ generation by animal
rhodopsin? In terms of the popular Hagins' hypothesis of
vision (156), absorption of a photon by rhodopsin results in
the release of accumulated Ca^{2+} ions from the discs into the
cytoplasm of the rod cell. This means that a rhodopsin-
generated photopotential should increase the Ca^{2+} permeability
of the disc membrane.

There are several indications of a light-induced increase
in the disc membrane permeability (for review, see ref. 142).
In particular, a non-specific ion conductivity rise in discs
after illumination has been reported. Unfortunately, this
effect was measured with slow techniques so it was impossible
to judge whether it was sufficiently fast to take part in the
cascade of events resulting in the excitation of a visual
cell.

To answer this question, we used our collodion film
model in the following modification. Now discs were adsorbed
on both sides of the film and the electric resistance across
the film was measured. The first flash induced a measurable
decrease in the resistance (155). This decrease was a steady
effect if measured in the sec time scale. Only after several
minutes of dark incubation, the resistance spontaneously
returned to a level that was close to the initial. Each
succeeding flash was less effective than the preceding one.
The resistance of the film without discs was not influenced

by the flashes. If this effect is due to the lowering of the
disc membrane resistance, one expects that the discharge of
the photopotential would depend upon the number of flashes,
being the slowest in the first flash. Experiments confirmed
this prediction. Using this approach, we succeeded in dis-
criminating between (i) a transient increase in the conductivity due to the charge translocation by rhodopsin and (ii)
a steady conductivity increase caused by changes in the
insulating properties of the disc membrane. The latter
process was found to need less than 25 ms to start. This
value is sufficiently low that the disc conductivity increase
could be involved in the chain of processes of photoreceptor
cell excitation (155).

As a possible mechanism for the light-dependent conductivity increase, we postulated that a local electric field
produced by a rhodopsin molecule that has absorbed a photon
induces an electric break-down of the hydrophobic barrier of
the disc membrane (155). According to Benz and Zimmerman
(157,158) a 1 V potential difference across a planar phospholipid membrane induces an increase in the membrane conductivity that develops within < 10 ns the essential characteristics of this effect proved to be similar to those in the
disc membrane after illumination. A potential difference as
high as 1 V across the disc membrane is hardly probable even
for a local electric field. However, there are several
reasons to suggest that the electric break-down voltage for
the disc membrane is much lower than that for the model
membrane. (i) The disc membrane contains not only phospholipids but also proteins. (ii) The disc membrane phospholipids contain a high percentage of extremely unsaturated
fatty acids (up to six double bonds). (iii) There is a Ca^{2+}

asymmetry across the disc membrane with a much higher Ca^{2+} concentration inside the disc, (i.e. the side that charges positively under illumination). All these factors favor the electric break-down of membranes (159,160).

Taking into account all these data, we postulated the following mechanism for the primary events of the visual process in retina:

(i) Absorption of photon by rhodopsin.

(ii) Rhodopsin-mediated transmembrane H^+ translocation or another charge displacement resulting in the local electric field formation.

(iii) Local electric breakdown of the photoreceptor disc membrane.

(iv) Ca^{2+} release from the disc interior into the cytoplasm of the rod (155).

Quite recently, an indication was found that such a mechanism may be applied in a photoreceptor system other than rhodopsin. Walker et al. (161) found that the Stentor photoreceptor pigment, stentorin, composed of a protein and a specific, covalently bound chromophore, hypericin, is competent in light-dependent transmembrane H^+ pumping. This activity was demonstrated in both live Sentor and reconstituted sentorin proteoliposomes. This observation explains the formation of a photoelectric potential difference across the outer membrane of the Sentor, previously measured with microelectrodes (162). It was also found that formation of a protonic potential scross the Sentor membrane is a necessary step of the photoreception process rather than a side-effect. Addition of a protonophore in amounts too small to accelerate respiration in mitochondria inside the Sentor cell abolished both the phototaxis and the protonic photopotential across the outer cell membrane. An indication was also obtained that the light-driven H^+ translocation across the outer membrane of the <u>Sentor</u> induced a Ca^{2+} influx into the cell (161).

SUMMARY. The development of membrane bioenergetics during the last two decades has confirmed Mitchell's idea that a protonic potential is responsible for the coupling between the redox reactions and ATP formation. Following Mitchell's concept, bioenergeticists have made several discoveries indicating that the protonic potential has a wider role in cellular function than simply that of the coupling inter-mediate in oxidative phosphorylation.

It was found that such a non-oxidative mechanism of external energy source utilization as bacteriorhodopsin produces $\Delta\bar{\mu}H$. Non-phosphorylating systems of $\Delta\bar{\mu}H$ utilization were described. They are: mechanism for uphill transport of ions and metabolites; protonic motors used in the motility apparatus of procaryotes; enzymes competent in transfer of reducing equivalents against the redox gradient, such as transhydrogenase; uncoupling system converting $\Delta\bar{\mu}H$ to heat to maintain body temperature. The conclusion was made that $\Delta\bar{\mu}H$, like ATP, is a convertible energy currency for the cell.

A system specialized in $\Delta\bar{\mu}H$ buffering was postulated. The Na/K gradient was shown to play this role in the bacterial cell. In multicellular procaryotes, such as filamentous cyanobacteria, $\Delta\bar{\mu}H$ can play the role of a transportable form of energy which can be transmitted from cell to cell via intercellular contacts.

Indications of some non-energetic functions of protonic potential were also obtained, among them the electrogenic activity of animal rhodopsin.

REFERENCES

1. Mitchell, P. (1961) Nature 191, 144-148.
2. Lundegard, H. (1945) Arkiv. Bot. 32A, 1-139.
3. Conway, E.J. and Brady, T.G. (1948) Nature 162, 456-457.
4. Davies, R.E. and Ogston, A.G. (1950) Biochem. J. 46, 324-333.
5. Davies, R.E. and Krebs, H.A. (1952) Symp. Biochem. Soc. 8, 77-92.
6. Robertson, R.N. (1960) Biol. Rev. 35, 231-264.
7. Robertson, R.N. (1968) Protons, Electrons, Phosphorylation and Active Transport. Cambridge University Press, Cambridge.
8. Loomis, W.F. and Lipmann, F. (1948) J. Biol. Chem. 173, 807-808.
9. Chappell, J.B. and Haarhoff, K.N. (1967) in Biochemistry of Mitochondria (E.C. Slater, Z. Kaniuga and L. Wojtczak, eds.) pp. 75-91, Academic Press, London.
10. Mitchell, P. (1966) Chemiosmotic Coupling in Oxidative and Photosynthetic Phosphorylation, Glynn Research, Bodmin.
11. Bielawski, J., Thompson, T.E. and Lehninger, A.L. (1966) Biochem. Biophys. Res. Commun. 24, 943.
12. Babakov, A.V., Ermishkin, L.N. and Liberman, E.A. (1966) Molek. biofizika Conf. Abstr.
13. Levachev, M.M., Mishukova, E.A., Sivkova, V.G. and Skulachev, V.P. (1965) Biokhimiya 30, 864-874.
14. Skulachev, V.P., Sharaf, A.A. and Liberman, E.A. (1967) Nature 216, 718-719.
15. Skulachev, V.P., Sharaff, A.A., Yagujinsky, L.S., Jasaitis, A.A., Liberman, E.A. and Topali, V.P. (1968) Curr. Modern Biol. 2, 98-105.
16. Mitchell, P. and Moyle, J. (1965) Nature 208, 147-151.
17. Mitchell, P. and Moyle, J. (1967) Biochem. J. 104, 588-600.
18. Mitchell, P. and Moyle, J. (1967) Biochem. J. 105, 1147-1162.
19. Mitchell, P. (1968) Chemiosmotic Coupling and Energy Transduction. Glynn Researhc, Bodmin.
20. Mitchell, P. and Moyle, J. (1969) Eur. J. Biochem. 7, 471-484.

21. Moore, C. and Pressman, B.C. (1964) Biochem. Biophys. Res. Commun. 15, 562–567.
22. Lev, A.A. and Buzhinsky, E.P. (1967) Citologiya 9, 102–106.
23. Mueller, P. and Rudin, D.O. (1967) Biochem. Biophys. Res. Commun. 26, 398–410.
24. Liberman, E.A., Topali, V.P., Tsofina, L.M., Jasaitis, A.A. and Skulachev, V.P. (1969) Nature 222, 1076–1078.
25. Liberman, E.A. and Skulachev, V.P. (1970) Biochim. Biophys. Acta 216, 30–42.
26. Drachev, L.A., Jasaitis, A.A., Kaulen, A.D., Kondrashin, A.A., La Van Chu, Seminov, A.Yu., Sevrina, I.I. and Skulachev, V.P. (1976) J. Biol. Chem. 251, 7072–7076.
27. Harold, F.M. (1977) Curr. Top. Bioenerg. 6, 83–149.
28. Witt, H.T. (1981) in this book.
29. Barsky, E.L., Dancshazy, Z., Drachev, L.A., Il'ina, M.D., Jasaitis, A.A., Kondrashin, A.A., Samuilov, V.D. and Skulachev, V.P. (1976) J. Biol. Chem. 251, 7066–7071.
30. Skulachev, V.P. (1979) in Photosynthesis in Relation to Model Systems (J. Barber, ed.) pp. 175–188, Elsevier/North Holland Biomedical Press, Amsterdam-New York-Oxford.
31. Konstantinov, A., Skulachev, V.P. and Smirnova, I.A. (1980) FEBS Lett. 114, 302–306.
32. Felle, H., Porter, J.S., Slayman, C.L. and Kaback, H.R. (1980) Biochemistry 19, 3585–3590.
33. Tedeschi, H. (1980) Biol. Rev. 55, 171–206.
34. Skulachev, V.P. (1972) Energy Transduction in Bio-membranes, Nauka, Moscow.
35. Kagawa, Y. and Racker, E. (1971) J. Biol. Chem. 246, 5477–5487.
36. Racker, E. (1981) in this book.
37. Hinkle, P.C., Kim, J. and Racker, E. (1972) J. Biol. Chem. 247, 1338–1339.
38. Jasaitis, A.A., Nemeček, I.B., Severina, I.I., Skulachev, V.P. and Smirnova, S.M. (1972) Biochim. Biophys. Acta 275, 485–490.
39. Racker, E. and Kandrach, A. (1973) J. Biol. Chem. 248, 5841–5847.
40. Racker, E. (1979) in Membrane Bioenergetics (C.P. Lee et al, eds.) pp. 569–591, Addison-Wesley Publ. Co., London-Amsterdam-Don Mills-Sydney-Tokyo.

41. Drachev, L.A., Frolov, V.N., Kaulen, A.D., Liberman,
     E.A., Ostroumov, S.A., Plakunova, V.G., Semenov, A.Yu.
     and Skulachev, V.P. (1976) J. Biol. Chem. 251, 7059-
     7065.
42. Drachev, L.A., Jasaitis, A.A., Mikelsaar, H., Nemecek,
     I.B., Semenov, A.Yu., Semenova, E.G., Severina, I.I.
     and Skulachev, V.P. (1976) J. Biol. Chem. 251, 7077-
     7082.
43. Drachev, L.A., Kondrashin, A.A., Semenov, A.Yu. and
     Skulachev, V.P. (1980) Eur. J. Biochem. 113, 213-217.
44. Kondrashin, A.A., Remennikov, V.G., Samuilov, V.D.
     and Skulachev, V.P. (1980) Eur. J. Biochem. 113,
     219-222.
45. Jagendorf, A.T. and Uribe, E. (1966) Proc. Natl.
     Acad. Sci. USA 55, 170-177.
46. Skulachev, V.P. (1975) in Energy Transducing Mechanisms
     (E. Racker, ed.), pp. 31-73, MTP, Butterworths, London.
47. Oesterheldt, D. and Stoeckenius, W. (1971) Nature New
     Biol. 233, 149-152.
48. Blaurock, A.E. and Stoeckenius, W. (1971) Nature New
     Biol. 233, 152-155.
49. Oesterhelt, D. and Stoeckenius, W. (1973) Proc. Natl.
     Acad. Sci. USA 70, 2853-2857.
50. Danon, A. and Stoeckenius, W. (1974) Proc. Natl. Acad.
     Sci. USA 71, 1234-1238.
51. Belyakova, T.N., Kadzyauskas, Yu.P., Skulachev, V.P.,
     Smirnova, I.A., Chekulaeva, L.N. and Jasaitis, A.A.
     (1975) Dokl. AN SSSR, 223, 483-486.
52. Kayushin, L.P. and Skulachev, V.P. (1974) FEBS Lett.
     39, 39-42.
53. Racker, E. and Stoeckenius, W. (1974) J. Biol. Chem.
     249, 662-663.
54. Skulachev, V.P. (1980) Can. J. Biochem. 58, 161-175.
55. Ovchinnikov, Yu.A., Abdulaev, N.G., Feigina, M.Yu.,
     Lobanov, N.A., Kiselev, A.V. and Nazimov, I.A. (1978)
     Bioorg. Khimiya 4, 1573-1574.
56. Ovchinnikov, Yu.A., Abdulaev, N.G., Feigina, M.Yu.,
     Kiselev, A.V. and Lobanov, N.A. (1979) FEBS Lett. 100,
     219-224.
57. Gerber, G.A., Anderegg, R.J., Helihy, W.C., Gray, C.P.,
     Bieman, K. and Khorana, H.G. (1979) Proc. Natl. Acad.
     Sci. USA 76, 227-231.
58. Unwin, P.N.T. and Henderson, R. (1975) J. Mol. Biol.
     94, 425-440.
59. Henderson, R. and Unwin, P.N.T. (1975) Nature 257,
     29-32.

60. Henderson, R. (1977) Ann. Rev. Biophys. Bioeng. 6, 87-109.
61. Ovchinnikov, Yu.A. (1979) Eur. J. Biochem. 94, 321-336.
62. Stoeckenius, W., Lozier, R.H. and Bogomolni, R. (1981) in this book.
63. Matsuno-Yagi, A. and Mukohata, Y. (1977) Biochem. Biophys. Res. Commun. 78, 237-243.
64. Lindley, E.V. and MacDonald, R.E. (1979) Biochem. Biophys. Res. Commun. 88, 491-499.
65. MacDonald, R.E., Greene, R.V., Clark, R.D. and Lindley, E.V. (1979) J. Biol. Chem. 254, 11831-11838.
66. Greene, R.V. and Lanyi, J.K. (1979) J. Biol. Chem. 254, 10986-10994.
67. Drachev, L.A., Kaulen, A.D. and Skulachev, V.P. (1978) FEBS Lett. 87, 161-167.
68. Drachev, L.A., Kaulen, A.D., Khitrina, L.V. and Skulachev, V.P. (1981) Eur. J. Biochem., in press.
69. Drachev, L.A., Semenov, A.Yu., Skulachev, V.P., Smirnova, I.A., Chamorovsky, S.K., Kononenko, A.A., Rubin, A.B. and Uspenskaya, N.Ya. (1981) Eur. J. Biochem., in press.
70. Mitchell, P. (1979) Eur. J. Biochem. 95, 1-20.
71. Mitchell, P. and Moyle, J. (1979) in Cytochrome Oxidase (T.E. King et al., eds.) pp. 361-372, Elsevier/ North Holland Biomedical Press, Amsterdam.
72. Wikström, M. (1981) in this book.
73. Ludwig, B. (1980) Biochim. Biophys. Acta 594, 177-189.
74. Mitchell, P. (1975) FEBS Lett. 56, 1-6.
75. Mitchell, P. (1975) FEBS Lett. 59, 137-139.
76. Mitchell, P. (1976) J. Theor. Biol. 62, 327-367.
77. Konstantinov, A. (1981) in this book.
78. Trumpower, B.L. (1981) in this book.
79. Danielson, L. and Ernster, L. (1963) Biochem. Biophys. Res. Commun. 10, 91-96.
80. Danielson, L. and Ernster, L. (1963) Biochem. Z. 338, 188-205.
81. Ernster, L. and Lee, C.P. (1964) Intern. Biochem. Congr. Abstr. 10, 729-730.
82. Grinius, L.L., Jasaitis, A.A., Kadziauskas, J.P., Liberman, E.A., Skulachev, V.P., Topali, V.P., Tsofina, L.M. and Valdimirova, M.A. (1970) Biochim. Biophys. Acta 216, 1-12.
83. Isaev, P.I., Liberman, E.A., Samuilov, V.D., Skulachev, V.P. and Tsofina, L.M. (1970) Biochim. Biophys. Acta 216, 22-29.
84. Kozlov, I.A. (1980) Biokhimiya 44, 1731-1737.

85. Kozlov, I.A. (1981) in Current Topics in Membranes
     and Transport (C. Slayman, ed.), v. 16, Academic Press,
     New York - London, in press.
86. Choate, G.H., Hutton, R.H., Boyer, P.D. (1979) J. Biol.
     Chem. 254, 286-290.
87. Kozlov, I.A. (1980) First Eur. Bioenerg. Conf. Abstr.,
     pp. 157-158.
88. Chernyak, B.V., Chernyak, V.Ya., Gladysheva, T.B.,
     Kozhanova, Z.E. and Kozlov, I.A. (1981) Biochim. Biophys.
     Acta 635, 552-570.
89. Kozlov, I.A. (1981) in this book.
90. Mitchell, P. (1973) FEBS Lett. 33, 267-274.
91. Mitchell, P. and Moyle, J. (1974) Biochem. Soc. Spec.
     Publ. 4, 91-111.
92. Kozlov, I.A. (1975) Bioorg. Khimiya 1, 1545-1569.
93. Kozlov, I.A. and Skulachev, V.P. (1977) Biochim.
     Biophys. Acta 463, 29-89.
94. West, I. (1980) Biochim. Biophys. Acta 604, 91-126.
95. West, I. (1981) in this book.
96. Njus, D., Zallakian, M. and Knoth, J. (1981) in this
     book.
97. Skulachev, V.P. and Maslov, S.P. (1960) Biokhimiya 25,
     1058-1064.
98. Severin, S.E., Skulachev, V.P., Maslov, S.P., Benediktov,
     I.I. and Shestakov, V.G. (1960) Dokl. AN SSSR 131,
     1447-1450.
99. Skulachev, V.P. (1963) Proc. 5th Intern. Congr. Biochem.
     (1961, Moscow), 5, 365-375.
100. Grav, H.J. and Blix, A.S. (1979) Science 204, 87-89.
101. Smith, R.E. and Horwtiz, B.A. (1969) Physiol. Rev.
     49, 330-425.
102. Nicholls, D.G. (1981) in this book.
103. Mitchell, P. (1956) Proc. R. Soc. Edinb. Sect. 25,
     32-34.
104. Mitchell, P. (1972) FEBS Lett. 28, 1-5.
105. Pastushenko, V.F. (1975) Bioelectrochem. Bioenerg.
     2, 52-60.
106. Larsen, S.H., Adler, J., Gargus, J.J. and Hogg, R.W.
     (1974) Proc. Natl. Acad. Sci. USA 71, 1239-1243.
107. Skulachev, V.P. (1975) Proc. FEBS Meet. 10, 225-238.
108. Belyakova, T.N., Glagolev, A.N. and Skulachev, V.P.
     (1976) Biokhimiya 41, 1478-1483.
109. Skulachev, V.P. (1977) FEBS Lett. 74, 1-9.
110. Glagolev, A.N. and Skulachev, V.P. (1978) Nature 272,
     280-282.

111. Manson, M.D., Tedesco, P., Berg, H.C., Harold, F.M. and Van der Drift, C. (1977) Proc. Natl. Acad. Sci. USA, 74, 3060-3064.
112. Matsuura, S., Shioi, J. and Imae, Y. (1977) FEBS Lett. 82, 187-190.
113. Glagolev, A.N. (1980) J. Theoret. Biol. 82, 171-185.
114. Skulachev, V.P. (1980) in Sovjet. Sci. Rev., Ser. Biol. (V.P. Skulachev, ed.), pp. 83-155, Harwood Academic, New York.
115. Manson, M.D., Tedesco, P.M. and Berg, H.C. (1980) J. Mol. Biol. 138, 541-561.
116. Glagoleva, T.N., Glagolev, A.N., Gusev, M.V. and Nikitina, K.A. (1980) FEBS Lett. 117, 49-53.
117. Halfen, L.N. and Castenholz, R.W. (1970) Nature 225, 1163-1165.
118. Halfen, L.N. and Castenholz, R.W. (1971) J. Physiol. 7, 133-145.
119. Ridgway, H.F. (1977) J. Bacteriol. 131, 544-556.
120. Grinius, L. (1981) in this book.
121. Skulachev, V.P. (1980) Biochim. Biophys. Acta 604, 297-320.
122. Chailakhian, L.M., Drachev, L.A., Glagolev, A.N., Glagoleva, T.N., Murvanidze, G.A., Potapova, T.V. and Skulachev, V.P., Biochim. Biophys. Acta (submitted).
123. Skulachev, V.P. (1969) Energy Accumulation in the Cell, Nauka, Moscow.
124. Skulachev, V.P. (1971) Curr. Top. Bioenerg. 4, 127-190.
125. Davidson, M.T. and Garland, P.B. (1977) J. Gen. Microbiol. 98, 147-153.
126. Giddings, T.H., Jr. and Stachelin, A. (1978) Cytobiologia, 16, 235-249.
127. Glagolev, A.N., Glagoleva, T.N., Levin, S.A., Potapova, T.V. Skulachev, V.P. and Chailakhian, L.M. (1980) Dokl. AN SSSR, 255, 1490-1493.
128. Skulachev, V.P. (1978) FEBS Lett. 87, 171-179.
129. Broun, I.I., Glagolev, A.N., Grinius, L.L., Skulachev, V.P. and Chetkauskayte, A.V. (1979) Dokl. AN SSSR, 247, 971-974.
130. Skulachev, V.P. (1979) in Cation Flux across Biomembranes (Y. Mukohata and L. Packer, eds.) pp. 303-319, Academic Press, New York - San Francisco - London.
131. Arshavsky, V.Yu., Baryshev, B.A., Broun, I.I., Glagolev, A.N., Skulachev, V.P. FEBS Lett (submitted).
132. Sedgwick, E.G. and MacLeod, R.A. (1980) Can. J. Biochem. 58, 1206-1214.

133. Rhoads, D.B. and Epstein, W. (1977) J. Biol. Chem. 252, 1394-1401.
134. Schuldiner, S. and Fishkes, H. (1978) Biochemistry 17, 706-710.
135. Harold, F.M. and Heefner, D.L. (1981) in this book.
136. Dimroth, P. (1980) FEBS Lett. 122, 234-236.
137. Harold, F.M. (1977) Ann. Rev. Microbiol. 31, 181-203.
138. Brown, K.T. and Murakami, M. (1964) Nature 201, 626-628.
139. Cone, R.A. and Pack, W.L. (1972) in Handbook of Sensory Physiology (W.R. Loewenstein, ed.) vol. 1, pp. 345-367, Springer, Heidelberg.
140. Trissl, H.W., Darszon, A. and Montal, M. (1977) Proc. Natl. Acad. Sci. USA 74, 207-210.
141. Trissl, H.W. (1979) Photochem. Photobiol. 29, 579-588.
142. Montal, M. (1979) Biochim. Biophys. Acta 559, 231-257.
143. Skulachev, V.P. (1976) FEBS Lett. 64, 23-25.
144. Drachev, L.A., Kaulen, A.D., Semenov, A.Yu., Severina, I.I. and Skulachev, V.P. (1979) Anal. Biochem. 96, 250-262.
145. Skulachev, V.P. (1979) Methods Enzymol. 55, 586-603, 751-776.
146. Bolshakov, V.I., Kalamkarov, G.R. and Ostrovsky, M.A. (1972) Dokl. AN SSSR 248, 1485-1488.
147. Chapron, Y. (1979) C.R. Hebd. Seances acad Sci. Paris, 288, 155-158.
148. Chapron, Y. (1980) Photobiochem. Photobiophys. 1, 297-304.
149. Bamberg, E., Bauer, P.J. and Fahr, A. (1980) Annu. German Biophys. Soc. Meet., Abstr. B(7).
150. Bolshakov, V.I., Kalamkarov, G.R. and Ostrovsky, M.A. (1978) Dokl. AN SSSR 240, 1241-1244.
151. Cafiso, D.S. and Hubbell, W.L. (1980) Biophys. J. 30, 243-264.
152. Bennett, N., Michel-Villaz, M. and Dupont, Y. (1980) Eur. J. Biochem. 111, 105-110.
153. Bolshakov, V.I., Drachev, A.L., Drachev, L.A., Kalamkarov, G.R., Kaulen, A.D., Ostrovsky, M.A. and Skulachev, V.P. (1979) Dokl. AN SSSR 248, 1462-1466.
154. Drachev, L.A., Kalamkarov, G.R., Kaulen, H.D., Ostrovsky, M.A. and Skulachev, V.P. (1980) FEBS Lett. 119, 125-131.
155. Drachev, L.A., Kalamkarov, G.R., Kaulen, A.D., Ostrovsky, M.A. and Skulachev, V.P. (1981) Eur. J. Biochem., in press.

156. Hagins, W.A. (1972) Ann. Rev. Biophys. Bioeng. 1, 131–158.
157. Benz, R. and Zimmermann, U. (1980) Biochim. Biophys. Acta 597, 637–642.
158. Benz, R. and Zimmermann, U. (1981) Biochem. Biophys. Acta 640, 169–178.
159. Pilwat, G., Hampp, R. and Zimmermann, U. (1980) Planta (Berl.), 147, 396–404.
160. Chernomordik, L.V. (1979) Electric break-down of bilayer phospholipid membrane. Thesis. Electrochem. Inst. of USSR Acad. Sci., Moscow.
161. Walker, E.B., Yoon, M. and Song, P.-S. (1981) Biochim. Biophys. Acta 634, 289–308.
162. Song, P.-S., Häder, D.P. and Poff, K.L. (1980) Arch. Microbiol. 126, 181–186.
163. Glagolev, A.N. (1981) in this book.

$\Delta\bar{\mu}H^+$ Generators

COUPLING RATIOS OF PROTON TRANSPORT BY MITOCHONDRIA

Peter C. Hinkle

Section of Biochemistry, Molecular and Cell Biology
Cornell University, Ithaca, New York   14853

One of the most basic facts about proton transport in mitochondria that should be established before detailed mechanisms can be contemplated is the stoichiometry of protons transported for each equivalent of chemical reaction (electron transfer, ATPase, transhydrogenase, etc.). Determination of transport stoichiometries is far from routine, however, and the results of different laboratories currently differ by as much as a factor of three (1-5).

A summary of some schemes for coupling ratios in mitochondria being considered today is shown in Table I.   I will briefly review this controversy, describe some recent work which indicates that the coupling ratios are probably higher than I thought previously, and propose a direct type of coupling mechanism with higher proton stoichiometry.

DIRECT MEASUREMENT OF PROTON STOICHIOMETRY. The pulse technique, first used by Mitchell and Moyle (1), consists of small additions of oxygen or ATP to anaerobic mitochondria producing a small burst of proton transport which can be monitored with a recording pH meter. This method is the most direct but can underestimate the amount of proton transport because of back

V. P. Skulachev and Peter C. Hinkle (eds.), Chemiosmotic Proton Circuits in Biological Membranes
in honor of Peter Mitchell   ISBN 0-201-07398-6

TABLE I

Proposed Coupling Ratios of Mitochondria

	A	B	C	D	E
H/O (succinate)	4	8	6	4	6
H/O (NADH)	6	12	–	6	10
H/ATP (F_1-F_o)	2	3	2	2	3
H/ATP (transport)	0	1	1	1	1
P/O (succinate)	2	2	2	1.3	1.5
P/O (NADH)	3	3	–	2	2.5

A: Mitchell (1,8), B: Lehninger (2,10), Azzone (3,4), C:
Wikström (5), D,E.: Hinkle (6).

diffusion of transported protons across the membrane. The H/O
values observed by Mitchell and Moyle are shown in Column A of
Table I. Mitchell later showed that treatment of mitochondria
with N-ethylmaleimide increased the amount of proton transport
measured (7), an effect he attributed to the participation of
transhydrogenase in the respiratory chain. Later Lehninger's
group reported the same effect of N-ethylmaleimide, but attributed it to inhibition of endogenous phosphate transport (2),
a well supported interpretation. Lehninger's group also used
an initial rate method for measuring coupling ratios (2).
This method consists of initiating respiration by addition of
succinate and measuring the initial rates of respiration and
proton transport using an oxygen electrode and a pH electrode.
The results of this method are shown in Column B of Table I.
Neither electrode, however, is capable of measuring the true
initial rates of respiration or proton transport and non-
linear rates of both are expected because of respiratory
control. Actually, the rate of oxygen uptake is usually

obtained after the burst of proton transport is over. Thus this method probably overestimates H^+/O ratios, although the error could be in either direction, depending on the response times of the electrodes.

The determination of the H^+/ATP ratio of F_1F_o ATPase in mitochondria has also been done by pulse methods. Mitchell and Moyle found a value close to 2 (8) by giving ATP pulses and measuring the resulting proton efflux with a pH meter. The method is not as good as oxygen pulses, however, because the K_m for ATP is much higher than for O_2 and because the hydrolysis of ATP forms net acid, requiring complex corrections. We found the H^+/ATP ratio of inverted submitochondrial particles to be close to 2 by similar methods (9). Under the same conditions the measured H^+/O ratio with succinate as substrate was very close to 4 (9), however. These values were pH dependent and we could only say that they were minimum estimates. It is entirely possible that a cation-proton exchange system could have caused proton back-diffusion causing underestimates of the true ratios. Lehninger's group has reported a ratio of 3 H^+/ATP by pulse methods in mito-chondria (10). However, the coupling of proton and charge movement with P_i and ATP transport across the mitochondrial membrane has made interpretation of ATP pulse experiments in mitochondria difficult.

INDIRECT MEASUREMENT OF PROTON STOICHIOMETRY. Because of the problems of back-diffusion in direct measurements of proton transport stoichiometry I have come to rely more on indirect methods, although each of these methods has possible errors as well. One indirect method is to measure the electrochemical proton gradient, $\Delta\bar{\mu}_{H}+$, under conditions where the H^+-ATPase of

mitochondria or submitochondrial particles is close to equilibrium. The ratio of the free energy of ATP synthesis, ΔG_{ATP},
to the free energy of the proton gradient, $\Delta \bar{\mu}_H+$, should give
the stoichiometry of proton transport per ATP synthesized.
Mitchell and Moyle first calculated $\Delta \bar{\mu}_H+$ in mitochondria from
measurements with ion-specific electrodes (11). They found a
$\Delta \bar{\mu}_H+$ of 227 mV during β-hydroxybutyrate oxidation. There have
been many determinations since which range between 160 and 230
mV (12-16). Most methods use labeled ^{86}Rb and acetate or
other permeant acids to measure $\Delta \psi$ and ΔpH, separating the
mitochondria from the medium by centrifugation or filtration.
One potential source of error is underestimation of the gradients due to leakage of probes out of the mitochondria when
the pellet is being formed and the mitochondria became anaerobic. Two other possible errors are use of the wrong value
for the internal volume when calculating the internal probe
concentration and possible binding of ions to membranes and
proteins inside. Each of these possible errors probably
caused an overestimation of $\Delta \bar{\mu}_H+$ since early workers used low
values of internal volume (0.4 µl/mg (11,13)) compared with
recent measurements (approx. 0.6 to 1 µl/mg (16)). It should
also be remembered that a two-fold error in internal volume
causes a 36 mV error in $\Delta \bar{\mu}_H+$ because two probe gradients are
added. Thus the lower values for $\Delta \bar{\mu}_H+$ in mitochondria of
180 - 190 mV are likely to be right. Such values indicate a
coupling stoichiometry of 3 to 4 H^+/ATP (12-16) under most
conditions.

    We have measured $\Delta \bar{\mu}_H+$ and ΔG_{ATP} in submitochondrial
particles, using ^{36}ClO$_4$ and ethylamine as probes and filtration without washing to separate the particles from the medium
(E.A. Berry and P.C. Hinkle, in preparation). We originally

reported that the measured $\Delta\bar{\mu}_{H^+}$ was 260 mV (17) and H^+/ATP was
near 2. We have since realized, however, that because of the
low ionic strength inside the vesicles there is significant
binding of the probes. This binding decreases at higher salt
concentrations and is largely electrostatic. It is quite
complex and can be both cation and anion binding, presumably
due to localized charge clusters on proteins and lipids of the
membrane surface. We have measured this binding and when
corrections are made for it the value of $\Delta\bar{\mu}_{H^+}$ formed by respiration is about 190 mV, and the H^+/ATP ratio is about 3. The
binding effect is undoubtedly the explanation for the observation by Sorgato and Ferguson (18) that measurements of $\Delta\psi$ and
ΔpH in submitochondrial particles in a Tris chloride medium
were lower than in a low salt medium. The Tris Cl was probably
permeant enough to have raised the salt concentration inside
the vesicles.

Another indirect measure of proton coupling ratios is the
stoichiometry of calcium ion uptake by mitochondria. Early
work (19) led to the conclusion that there were two calcium
ions taken up per "site", and it was assumed that all three
"coupling sites" were equal. The numbers are actually close to
5 with NADH-linked substrates, and 3 with succinate (20, and
unpublished observations), consistent with column E of Table I
if calcium permeates with two charges. Mitchell has proposed
more complex reactions for Ca^{++} uptake, however (21).

P/O RATIOS. The P/O ratio of oxidative phosphorylation should
ideally be the ratio of H^+/O to H^+/ATP. In mitochondria it is
well established that one proton is used in the transport of
ADP and P_i into the matrix (22) so the H^+/ATP ratio used should
be the overall stoichiometry of synthesis and transport. The

P/O measurement involves conventional chemical methods, although measurement of oxygen uptake may have errors, which
usually cause underestimations. We have found that measured
P/O ratios are close to 1.4 with succinate and 2.2 with β-
hydroxybutyrate as substrates (6). We originally suggested
that the actual ratios might be 1.33 and 2.0 (Column D, Table
1) but now suggest that 1.5 and 2.5 are better estimates of
the theoretically maximal ratios (Column E, Table I). These
ratios are based on total oxygen uptake. Some people use only
the change in oxygen uptake which occurs when ADP + P_i are
added to mitochondria to calculate the P/O (or ADP/O) ratio,
but this can lead to an overestimation of the true ratio.
When respiration is partially inhibited with malonate, respiratory control is lost but phosphorylation continues. This
is because respiratory control is a measure of the extent to
which the high value of $\Delta\bar{\mu}_{H^+}$ formed by respiration in the
absence of ADP (State 4) can inhibit the respiratory chain.
When ADP is being phosphorylated (State 3), $\Delta\bar{\mu}_{H^+}$ is lower and
a "leak" pathway for proton influx is largely turned off (13).
When the total oxygen uptake is used to calculate the ADP/O
ratio, as suggested by Chance and Williams (23), the ratio
remains about the same at 1.4. When the change in oxygen
uptake, ΔO, is used the ratio increases to very high values
with increasing malonate presumably because the "leak" is a
longer fraction of the proton influx and the overcorrection is
larger.

Beavis (24) has reported corrected P/O measurements which
gave the old theoretical values. Such a procedure cannot give
values higher than ADP/ΔO, however. Probably the major systematic error in P/O measurements is the calibration of the
oxygen electrode. We routinely use submitochondrial particles
and carefully determined NADH additions to calibrate the

electrode every day.

Another way to measure the maximum P/O ratio is to measure
the equilibrium position of a coupling site. This was done for
the first site recently in submitochondrial particles (25). It
was found that the value of ΔG_{ATP} in equilibrium with reverse
electron transfer from the succinate–fumarate couple to the
NADH–NAD couple was significantly higher than the value of ΔE
between the two redox couples. It was claimed that the values
indicated a P/O ratio of 1.33 consistent with 4 protons transported by Site I and 3 protons per ATP by the ATPase. It was
also close to 1.5, however, with 3 protons at Site I and 2
protons per ATP.

We have used similar methods to measure the equilibrium of
reverse electron transfer from the cytochome c couple to the
succinate–fumarate couple (T. Scholes and P.C. Hinkle, in
preparation). The ratio $\Delta G_{ATP}/\Delta E$ depends on the fraction of
$\Delta\bar{\mu}_H+$ which is ΔpH. This is because, as all agree, 4 protons
are released inside submitochondrial particles but only two
charges cross the membrane per electron pair traversing from
succinate to cytochrome c. Thus if $\Delta\bar{\mu}_H+$ were all ΔpH then four
protons would enter into the driving force of $\Delta\bar{\mu}_H+$ whereas if
$\Delta\bar{\mu}_H+$ were all $\Delta\psi$ then there would be only two protons per
electron pair. Under conditions where $\Delta\bar{\mu}_H+$ is about equally
divided between $\Delta\psi$ and ΔpH we observed that at a ΔG_{ATP} of 230
mV the ΔE from succinate to cytochrome c was 238 mV, consistent
with P/O = 1 and $H^+/ATP = 3$. The variation of coupling stoichiometry with the composition of $\Delta\bar{\mu}_H+$ is not expected during
steady phosphorylation because the imbalance of charge and
proton transport across the membrane cannot be maintained
except during static equilibrium measurements.

In mitochondria the equilibrium between ΔG_{ATP} and ΔE (succinate–cyt. c) is not dependent on the fraction of $\Delta \bar{\mu}_{H^+}$ which is ΔpH because the two net protons are formed in the external medium and do not contribute significantly to ΔpH.

WORKING HYPOTHESIS.   The scheme shown in fig. 1 is our current working hypothesis of the stoichiometries.   The cytochrome

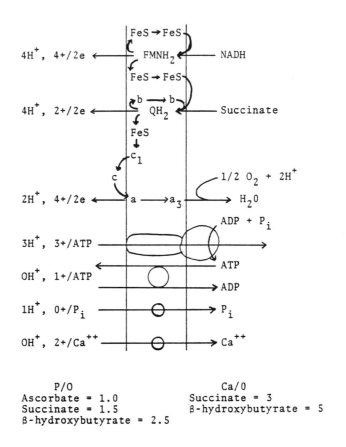

	P/O		Ca/0
Ascorbate = 1.0		Succinate = 3	
Succinate = 1.5		β-hydroxybutyrate = 5	
β-hydroxybutyrate = 2.5			

Figure 1.   Scheme for stoichiometry of proton transport by the mitochondrial inner membrane.   The numbers at the left refer to protons and charges transported per electron pair, ATP, P_i or Ca^{++}.

oxidase region transports 2 protons and 4 charges per electron pair, as proposed by Wikström (5). This is lower than that possible based on the ΔE and $\Delta\bar{\mu}_H+$, but since the reaction is essentially irreversible (to O_2) there must be energy lost. The cyt. b-c$_1$ region transports 2 protons and 2 charges per electron pair with two additional protons formed (net) outside mitochondria, which all agree upon. The first coupling region is proposed to transport 4 protons and 4 charges, which is just possible from comparison of ΔE and $\Delta\bar{\mu}_H+$ if $\Delta\bar{\mu}_H+$ is as low as 190 mV and the point where electrons leave site I is a little more positive than usually assumed. The exact redox potential at the gap between site I and II is not well known and depends on the mechanism of electron transport in the b-c$_1$ region.

To account for a stoichiometry of 4 protons per electron pair it is interesting to consider pathways of electron transfer in the FeS-flavin region which are analogous to the Q-cycle proposed by Mitchell for the cyt. b-c$_1$ region (26), or recent variations on the Q-cycle (28). There are probably 6 FeS centers with midpoint potentials ranging from -370 mV to -80 mV (27). Such a scheme is shown at the top of fig. 1. The flavin at the active site can be reduced from one side with one electron coming from NADH and one from a FeS center. Reduced flavin can then be oxidized from the other side by two FeS centers, the first at a higher potential than the second. This allows reduction of FeS centers more negative than the average midpoint of the flavin. The electrons on both FeS centers would then cross the membrane inward, generating $\Delta\psi$. Such a mechanism suggests that oxidant-induced reduction of some FeS centers should occur, which we plan to investigate.

REFERENCES

1. Mitchell, P. and Moyle, J. (1967) Biochem. J. 105, 1147-1162.
2. Reynafarje, B., Brand, M.D. and Lehninger, A.L. (1976) J. Biol. Chem. 251, 7442-7451.
3. Pozzan, T., Miconi, V., DiVirgilio, F. and Azzone, G.F. (1979) J. Biol. Chem. 254, 10200-10205.
4. Azzone, G.F., Pozzan, T. and DiVirgilio, F. (1979) J. Biol. Chem. 254, 10206-10212.
5. Wikström, M.K.F. and Krab, K. (1979) Biochim. Biophys. Acta 549, 177-222.
6. Hinkle, P.C. and Yu, M.L. (1979) J. Biol. Chem. 254, 2450.
7. Mitchell, P. (1972) FEBS Symp. 28, 353-370.
8. Mitchell, P. and Moyle, J. (1968) Eur. J. Biochem. 4, 530-539.
9. Thayer, W.S. and Hinkle, P.C. (1973) J. Biol. Chem. 248, 5395-5402.
10. Alexandre, A., Reynafarje, B. and Lehninger, A.L. (1978) Proc. Natl. Acad. Sci. USA 75, 5296-5300.
11. Mitchell, P. and Moyle, J. (1969) Eur. J. Biochem. 7, 471.
12. Padan, E. and Rottenberg, H. (1973) Eur. J. Biochem. 40, 431-437.
13. Nicholls, D.G. (1974) Eur. J. Biochem. 50, 305-315.
14. Azzone, G.F., Pozzan, T. and Massari, S. (1978) Biochim. Biophys. Acta 501, 307-316.
15. Van Dam, K., Wiechmann, A.H.C.A., Hellingwert, K.J., Arents, J.C. and Westerhoff, H.V. (1978) FEBS Symp. 45, 121-132.
16. Holian, A. and Wilson, D.F. (1980) Biochem. 19, 4213-4221.
17. Berry, E.A. and Hinkle, P.C. (1978) Fed. Proc. 37, 776.
18. Sorgato, M.C. and Ferguson, J.J. (1978) FEBS Lett. 90, 183.
19. Rossi, C.S. and Lehninger A.L. (1964) J. Biol. Chem. 239, 3971-3980.
20. Nicholls, D.G. (1977) Biochem. Soc. Trans. 5, 200-203.
21. Moyle, J. and Mitchell, P. (1977) FEBS Lett. 84, 135-140.
22. Klingenberg, M. and Rottenberg, H. (1977) Eur. J. Biochem. 73, 125-130.
23. Chance, B. and Williams, G.R. (1956) Adv. Enzymol. 17, 65.
24. Beavis, A. (1980) Fed. Proc. 39, 2056.
25. Rottenberg, H. and Gutman, M. (1977) Biochem. 16, 3220.
26. Mitchell, P. (1976) J. Theoret. Biol. 62, 327.
27. Ingledew, W.J. and Ohnishi, T. (1980) Biochem. J. 186, 111.
28. Wikstrom, M., Krab, K., and Saraste, M. (1981) Ann. Rev. Biochem., 50, 623-655.

NADH DEHYDROGENASE

C. Ian Ragan, Stuart Smith, Fergus G.P. Earley,
and Veronica M. Poore

Department of Biochemistry, University of
Southampton, Southampton SO9 3TU, England.

INTRODUCTION. Schatz and Racker (1) showed that the rotenone-sensitive reduction of ubiquinone analogues (e.g. UQ-1) by NADH in submitochondrial particles was coupled to ATP synthesis. Later, Lawford and Garland (2) showed that this same redox reaction caused proton-translocation and a stoichiometry of one proton per electron was found. From this they suggested that electron transport was arranged in a Mitchell loop (3) with FMN as the H-carrying arm and one or more Fe/S centres as the electron-carrying arm.

Of the numerous purified preparations of NADH dehydrogenase, only Complex I (4) retains the capacity for rotenone-sensitive reduction of ubiquinone analogues. Complex I incorporated into liposomes acts as a redox-linked proton pump (5) and, in the presence of the ATP synthetase complex, drives ATP synthesis coupled to NADH-UQ-1 oxidoreductase (6).

V. P. Skulachev and Peter C. Hinkle (eds.), Chemiosmotic Proton Circuits in Biological Membranes
in honor of Peter Mitchell   ISBN 0-201-07398-6

Despite this promising start, progress on the mechanism of the enzyme has been slow because of the extraordinary complexity of both the redox reactions and the protein structure. In this chapter I will try and bring together the information so far derived from EPR spectroscopy (e.g. 7) and chemical modification and fractionation of the enzyme (e.g. 8).

COMPONENTS OF NADH DEHYDROGENASE. Purified NADH dehydrogenases contain FMN, iron and acid-labile sulphide. Several different Fe/S centres have been identified in the enzyme by low temperature EPR spectroscopy (9-12) and some relevant information is summarized in Table 1. There are some uncer-

Table 1. Properties of Iron-Sulphur Centres of NADH Dehydrogenase

Centre[1]	Midpoint[2] potential (mV)	pH[3] dependence	Cluster[4] structure	Concentra-[5] tion
N1a	-370	60 mV/pH	Binuclear	1?
N1b	-220	none	Binuclear	1
N2	-80	60 mV/pH	Tetranuclear	1
N3	-240	none	Tetranuclear	1
N4	-240	none	Tetranuclear	1
N5	-275	none	Tetranuclear	0.25

[1]Terminology of Ohnishi (e.g. 7). [2]Values are for beef heart submitochondrial particles and were determined potentiometrically (7). [3]From (13). [4]From (14) and (15). [5]These are highest values as explained in the text and are expressed as the number of unpaired electrons/FMN.

tainties about the number of EPR visible centres. The mid-point potentials of the N1 type centres have a tendency to become up to 100 mV more negative in some (16) but not all (12) purified Complex I preparations. The extremely low E_m which centre N1a can attain may account for the failure of Albracht et al. (17) to find this particular species in Complex I. However, they also fail to see centre N1a in sub-mitochondrial particles using conditions of reduction apparently similar to those of Ohnishi. The stoichiometry is also uncertain as the quantitation performed by Ohnishi (7) was probably of centre N1b rather than N1a (16). Centre N1b has been found to be present at a spin concentration close to the FMN content (16) although Albracht et al. (17) using different methodology find only 0.5 spins per FMN. Moreover, in their bovine heart preparations, but not in Ohnishi's (16), the N1b spectrum is better simulated as two centres (unfortunately termed 1a and 1b) each present at a concentration of 0.25 spins per FMN. These differences may arise from variations in both the preparations and in the techniques used for reduction of the centres (16).

Centre N2 has a considerably higher E_m than the other centres but it too becomes more electronegative in Complex I (12). The spectra of centres N3 and N4 were properly resolved by simulation (17) but unfortunately there is some confusion of terminology, Ohnishi's N3 being Albracht's centre 4 and vice versa. Centre N5 may not be a true constituent of the enzyme because of its low concentration and its absence from C. utilis (17) or plant mitochondria (18).

Possible associations of these centres with polypeptides of NADH dehydrogenase are shown in Fig. 1, which is a highly speculative summary of current information on the structure of the enzyme. The polypeptide composition of Complex I is

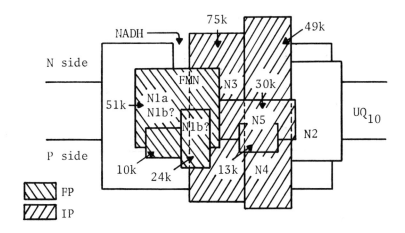

Fig. 1   Structure of NADH dehydrogenase

very involved and some 26 polypeptides have been identified
(19,20). However, the enzyme may be resolved into smaller
subfragments and into individual subunits which retain the
original redox groups. The basis of such resolution is the
use of chaotropic reagents, in particular $NaClO_4$ (21), which
selectively solubilizes polypeptides which comprise 30% of
Complex I protein and contain all of the FMN and 80% of the
Fe/S centres (22). The soluble material may be separated
(21) into two soluble fractions of relatively simple polypeptide composition which I have called the flavoprotein (FP)
fraction and the iron-protein (IP) fraction. The organization
of the polypeptides shown in Fig. 1 is based on this chaotropic resolution.

THE STRUCTURE OF NADH DEHYDROGENASE. The FP fragment of Complex I is a water-soluble iron-flavoprotein accounting for

all of the FMN of Complex I (21). It consists of three polypeptides in equimolar ratio with molecular weights of 51, 24
and 10 kdaltons (23). It catalyzes the oxidation of NADH by
a variety of electron acceptors and photolabelling studies
have identified the 51 kdalton subunit as the NADH binding
site (24). Further fractionation has shown that both the 51
and 24 kdalton subunits contain Fe/S centres (25). EPR
studies suggest that there may be two binuclear centres or
one tetranuclear centre in the 51 kdalton subunit and a further binuclear centre in the 24 kdalton subunit (25). One
of these centres has a spectrum very similar to that of N1b
(16). In Fig. 1, I have placed FMN in the 51 kdalton subunit,
close to the NADH binding site. This is to allow it to act
as a "transformer" for distribution of electrons from the $2e^-$
donating NADH to the $1e^-$ accepting Fe/S centres (13). Centre
N1a, with its low mid-point potential, should also be placed
close to the site of reduction by NADH. Labelling studies of
isolated or membrane-bound Complex I show that the FP fragment
is inaccessible to hydrophilic surface probes (26). Access
for NADH may therefore be provided by a specific channel in
the surrounding structure (8).

The IP fragment accounts for at least nine Fe atoms per
Complex I FMN (22) implying the presence of at least three
Fe/S centres, two of which have been detected by EPR (27).
Polypeptides of molecular weights 75, 49, 30, 18, 15 and 13
kdaltons are present in this fragment (20) and further resolution (22) has shown that Fe/S centres are associated with
the 75 and 49 kdalton subunits and with a fraction containing
the 30 kdalton subunit and a 13 kdalton subunit in equimolar
ratio. Since only the N-1 type centres are binuclear I
suggest that the three centres of the IP fragment are tetra-

nuclear in the native state even though they have a tendency
to become iron-deficient during the course of purification.
Thus, a fully native IP fragment would contain twelve iron
atoms per Complex I FMN. From the properties of centre N2
described later, I have located the other centres N3, N4 and
N5 in the IP fragment. The polypeptide assignments are quite
speculative. Centre N3 is close enough to the FMN to show
dipole-dipole interaction (13) and the 75 kdalton subunit is
photolabelled by arylazido NAD$^+$ (24) and must be close to the
51 kdalton subunit. Centres N4 and N5 are arbitrarily
assigned to the other iron-containing polypeptides.

The 75 and 49 kdalton subunits of IP are the only polypeptides of this fragment which are exposed to the aqueous
phase when the enzyme is in the membrane. Moreover, they are
transmembranous (26). The 30 kdalton subunit has been implicated in binding the FP fragment into the overall structure
(28) and is also tightly associated with the 49 and 13 kdalton
subunits (22). The IP and FP subunits are inaccessible to
lipid-soluble photoactivatable probes such as iodonaphthyla-
zide (29) and an arylazidophosphatidylcholine (20) while the
subunits of the insoluble residue from chaotropic resolution
are heavily labelled and must surround the IP and FP fragments. The insoluble residue accounts for four iron atoms per
Complex I FMN (22) and most likely contains the remaining
centre, N2, since this centre is probably the reductant for
ubiquinone (12) and its mid-point potential is dependent on
the phospholipid associated with Complex I (12). Thus it is
reasonable to place this centre in a polypeptide which is in
contact with the phospholipid phase of the membrane. Some
contact with the aqueous phase is also suggested by the pH-
dependence of the E_m of centre N2 (13).

The model of Fig. 1 proposes at least seven Fe/S centres in Complex I, three binuclear and four tetranuclear. The iron to flavin ratio would then come to 22 to one which is certainly within the range found.

MECHANISM OF NADH DEHYDROGENASE. The sequence of electron transfer within the enzyme is unknown although the mid-point potential measurements suggest that centre N1a is close to NADH and centre N2 is the donor to ubiquinone. Attempts have been made to provide evidence for looping of electron transport across the membrane by measuring changes in E_m induced by ATP in mitochondria or submitochondrial particles. Most of these have been carefully reviewed by Ohnishi (7) and Devault (30). In pigeon heart mitochondria, centre N1a exhibits an ATP-induced E_m decrease in the presence of mediators, which may be a response to a pH decrease on the N-side of the membrane since N1a has a pH dependent E_m (13). Gutman et al. (33) reported an ATP-dependent reduction of an N-1 type centre (N1b?) using $NADH/NAD^+$ to poise the potential while others (13) found little or no response of centre N1b whether the substrate couple or mediators were used for poising. As Ohnishi (7) points out, ATP-dependent reduction is difficult to reconcile with any centre which is an acceptor of reducing equivalents from NADH. There is good agreement on the responses of centre N2 (34, 31, 32) which shows ATP-dependent reduction or oxidation depending on whether poising is by succinate/fumarate or $NADH/NAD^+$. This is consistent with centre N-2 located more to the P-side of the membrane or shuttling from one side to the other (30). Centre N4 shows an ATP-dependent decrease in E_m (like N2) using $NAD^+/NADH$ for redox poising, but no response using mediators. Since the E_m of centre N-4 is not pH dependent, this suggests a location on the P side of the membrane.

These results do not lend themselves very readily to a loop-like organization. The potential H-carriers (FMN or possibly centre N1a) should donate electrons with the release of H^+ on the P-side. Centre N1a could fulfill this function since its precise location is not clear. Centre N2 reduction may occur with uptake of a proton which would have to come from the N-side of the membrane. Centre N2 could then reduce ubiquinone. Of course, if there are some iron-sulphur centres which are not detectable by EPR, then any mechanism based only on centres N1, 2, 3, 4 and 5 is going to be incomplete.

CONCLUSION. The rather unsatisfactory evidence for H-conduction by the known carriers of NADH dehydrogenase is rather reminiscent of the state of affairs in the b-c_1 complex before the Q-cycle was introduced (35). Indeed, Mitchell (36) has proposed that a bound $QH\cdot/Q$ couple might act as the link between the low-potential centres and high-potential centre N2. A radical signal in Complex I attributed to ubisemiquinone has been reported (37). Its low potential (38) would make it an attractive candidate for an H-carrier in the enzyme but it is absent from some Complex I preparations (38) and its position relative to the rotenone-site, for example, is unknown.

It is always possible to put forward less direct schemes for proton translocation which do not involve loops and can accommodate H^+/electron stoichiometries greater than one. Such proposals are very hard to test and there seems to be no good reason to abandon the loop idea on current evidence even if it may need to be supplemented by a separate proton pump when the stoichiometry question is finally answered to everyone's satisfaction.

REFERENCES

1. Schatz, G. and Racker, E. (1966) J. Biol. Chem. 241, 1429-1437.
2. Lawford, H.G. and Garland, P.B. (1971) Biochem. J. 130, 1029-1044.
3. Mitchell, P. (1968) Chemiosmotic Coupling and Energy Transduction, Glynn Research, Bodmin.
4. Hatefi, Y., Haavik, A.G. and Griffiths, D.E. (1962) J. Biol. Chem. 237, 1676-1680.
5. Ragan, C.I. and Hinkle, P.C. (1975) J. Biol. Chem. 250, 8472-8476.
6. Ragan, C.I. and Racker, E. (1973) J. Biol. Chem. 248, 2563-2569.
7. Ohnishi, T. (1979) in Membrane Proteins in Energy Transductions (R.A. Capaldi ed.) pp. 1-87, Marcel Dekker, New York and Basel.
8. Ragan, C.I. (1980) in Subcellular Biochemistry Vol. 7, (D.B. Roodyn, ed.) pp. 267-307, Plenum, New York and London.
9. Orme-Johnson, N.R., Orme-Johnson, W.H., Hansen, R.E., Beinert, H. and Hatefi, Y. (1971) Biochem. Biophys. Res. Commun. 44, 446-452.
10. Albracht, S.P.J. and Slater, E.C. (1971) Biochim. Biophys. Acta 245, 503-507.
11. Orme-Johnson, N.R., Hansen, R.E. and Beinert, H. (1974) J. Biol. Chem. 249, 1922-1927.
12. Ohnishi, T., Leigh, J.S., Ragan, C.I. and Racker, E. (1974) Biochem. Biophys. Res. Commun. 56, 775-781.
13. Ingledew, W.J. and Ohnishi, T. (1980) Biochem. J. 186, 111-117.
14. Albracht, S.P.J. and Subramanian, J. (1977) Biochim. Biophys. Acta 462, 36-48.
15. Salerno, J.C., Ohnishi, T., Blum, H. and Leigh, J.S. (1977) Biochim. Biophys. Acta 494, 191-197.
16. Ohnishi, T., Blum, H., Galante, Y.M. and Hatefi, Y. Submitted for publication.
17. Albracht, S.P.J., Dooijewaard, G., Leeuwerik, F.J. and van Swol, B. (1977) Biochim. Biophys. Acta 459, 300-317.

18. Rich, P. and Bonner, W.D. (1978) in Functions of Alternative Respiratory Oxidases (D. Lloyd, H. Degn and G.C. Hill, eds.) pp. 61-68, Pergamon, New York.

19. Heron, C., Smith, S. and Ragan, C.I. (1979) Biochem. J. 181, 435-443.

20. Earley, F.G.P. and Ragan, C.I. (1981) FEBS Lett. In the press.

21. Hatefi, Y. and Stempel, K.E. (1969) J. Biol. Chem. 244, 2350-2357.

22. Ragan, C.I., Galante, Y.M. and Hatefi, Y. Unpublished observations.

23. Galante, Y.M. and Hatefi, Y. (1979) Arch. Biochem. Biophys. 192, 559-568.

24. Chen, S. and Guillory, R.J. (1980) Fedn. Prc. 39, 2057.

25. Ragan, C.I., Galante, Y.M., Hatefi, Y. and Ohnishi, T. Submitted for publication.

26. Smith, S. and Ragan, C.I. (1980) Biochem. J. 185, 315-326.

27. Ragan, C.I., Galante, Y.M., Hatefi, Y. and Ohnishi, T. Unpublished observations.

28. Crowder, S.E. and Ragan, C.I. (1977) Biochem. J. 165, 295-301.

29. Earley, F.G.P. and Ragan, C.I. (1980) Biochem. J. 191, 429-436.

30. Devault, D. (1976) J. Theor. Biol. 62, 115-139.

31. Ohnishi, T. (1973) Biochim. Biophys. Acta 301, 105-128.

32. Ohnishi, T. (1976) Eur. J. Biochem. 64, 91-103.

33. Gutman, M., Beinert, H. and Singer, T.P. (1975) in Electron Transfer Chains and Oxidative Phosphorylation (E. Quagliariello, S. Papa, F. Palmieri, E. Slater and N. Siliprandi, eds.) pp. 55-62, North Holland, New York.

34. Gutman, M., Singer, T.P. and Beinert, H. (1972) Biochemistry, 11, 556-562.

35. Mitchell, P. (1976) J. Theor. Biol. 62, 327-367.

36. Mitchell, P. (1979) Nobel Lecture.

37. King, T.E., Yu, L., Nagaoka, S., Widger, W.R. and Yu, C.A. (1978) in Frontiers of Biological Energetics (P.L. Dutton, J.S. Leigh and A. Scarpa, eds.) pp. 174-182, Academic Press, New York.

38. Ohnishi, T., Blum, H., King, T.E. and Widger, W.R. Unpublished observations.

THE CYTOCHROME b PARADOX, THE BAL-LABILE FACTOR AND THE Q CYCLE

E.C. Slater

Laboratory of Biochemistry, B.C.P. Jansen Institute,
University of Amsterdam, The Netherlands

IDENTIFICATION AND STRUCTURE OF CYTOCHROME b

Cytochrome b was one of the components of cytochrome described in David Keilin's remarkable paper "On cytochrome, a respiratory pigment, common to animals, yeast, and higher plants", published in 1925 (1), that established the essential role of these haemoproteins in intracellular respiration. Using the microspectroscope, Keilin observed that the characteristic band of this cytochrome at 564.5 and 565.7 nm, respectively, appeared and disappeared at the same time as those of cytochromes a and c when the oxygen supply was withdrawn from or restored to a suspension of yeast cells or the wing muscle of the living wax-moth. Addition of cyanide had the same effect as withdrawal of oxygen. In 1938, Eric Ball (2) showed that cytochrome b is unique among the three cytochromes with respect to its midpoint potential (-40 mV at pH 7.4, compared with 270 mV and 290 mV for cytochromes c and a, respectively).

V. P. Skulachev and Peter C. Hinkle (eds.), Chemiosmotic Proton Circuits in Biological Membranes
in honor of Peter Mitchell   ISBN 0-201-07398-6

Keilin and Hartree (3) showed that cytochrome b is reduced together with the other cytochromes when succinate is
added to a suspension of (submitochondrial) particles isolated
from heart muscle, a preparation that became known as the
Keilin and Hartree heart-muscle preparation. Already in 1925,
however, Keilin (1) had shown that after addition of urethane
in the presence of air, cytochrome b remains reduced whereas
cytochromes c and a are oxidized. By the 1940's, it was generally accepted that cytochrome b is involved in the succinate
oxidase system and that it is the first electron acceptor in
the cytochrome system. Indeed, as late as 1949, the minimum
hypothesis was to assume that succinate dehydrogenase and
cytochrome b are identical (4). However, it is now known that
two distinct multi-subunit enzymes are required for the reduction of cytochrome c by succinate, namely succinate:Q oxidoreductase and QH_2:ferricytochrome c oxidoreductase (5), that
succinate dehydrogenase is part of the former and that the
succinate-reducible cytochrome b observed by Keilin (1) is
part of the latter. It is of interest to add that Hatefi (6)
has shown that succinate:Q oxidoreductase also contains a low-
potential cytochrome b, that is scarcely reducible by succinate.

In the last 5 years or so, several groups have identified
cytochrome b as one of the subunits revealed by dodecyl sulphate polyacrylamide gel electrophoresis of QH_2:ferricyto-
chrome c oxidoreductase. Its apparent molecular weight calculated from its relative electrophoretic mobility in dodecyl
sulphate is about 30 000, but is was pointed out (7) that the
hydrodynamic properties of the polypeptide are so abnormal
that neither this method nor others based on hydrodynamic behaviour would give reliable results. The solution has come
from the nucleotide sequence of the mitochondrial gene for

cytochrome b which has been determined for man (8) and ox
(personal communication) by Sanger and his colleagues, and
for yeast by Tzagaloff (9). The amino acid sequence may be
read off the nucleotide sequence. From this, the molecular
weight of haem-free ox cytochrome b may be calculated to be
42 505.

Von Jagow (10) has isolated cytochrome b from ox QH_2:
ferricytochrome c oxidoreductase with the amino acid composition shown in Table I. Two conclusions may be drawn from these
data: (1) non-coding sequences are absent from the mitochondrial gene for this polypeptide and there is no subsequent
processing of the primarily translated apoprotein; (2) the
preparation isolated by von Jagow (10) is pure. (A third
comment is in order, namely admiration for the accuracy of
the amino acid analyses.)

It is known that QH_2:cytochrome c oxidoreductase contains
2 mol protohaem per monomer enzyme (11). Since von Jagow's
purified cytochrome b contains 1 mol protohaem per 33 000 g
and the molecular weight appeared to be about 60 000, it was
assumed that it is a dimer of the 30 kD subunits revealed by
SDS polyacrylamide gel electrophoresis (10). However, this
conclusion must be abandoned now that it is known that the
molecular weight of the monomer is 42 505 (haem-free). Since
about 1.3 mol protohaem is present per 42 505 g of von Jagow's
preparation, it seems much more likely that cytochrome b is a
monomer containing 2 protohaem prosthetic groups and that some
of the haem, which is non-covalently bound, is lost during
isolation in the presence of detergents.

These two protohaems correspond to the two distinct succinate-reducible cytochromes b that are usually referred to as
b-562 and b-566, respectively (see e.g. (12)). However, since
the intact QH_2:ferricytochrome c oxidoreductase is a dimer,

Table I. Amino Acid Composition of Ox-heart Cytochrome b

| Amino acid | From DNA sequence [*] | | Amino acid analysis (10) |
	number per molecule	mol %	mol %
Gly	25	6.6	6.6
Ala	27	7.1	7.2
Val	18	4.7	4.7
Leu	60	15.8	15.7
Ile	37	9.8	9.4
Phe	23	6.1	6.2
Trp	12	3.2	3.0
Tyr	16	4.2	4.0
Met	15	4.0	3.8
Pro	22	5.8	5.9
Cys	4	1.1	1.0
Ser	23	6.1	5.9
Thr	26	6.9	7.6
Asp	11	2.9	} 7.5
Asn	18	4.7	
Glu	6	1.6	} 3.5
Gln	6	1.6	
His	12	3.2	3.1
Lys	10	2.6	2.7
Arg	8	2.1	2.2
	379	100.1	100.0

[*] F. Sanger, personal communication.

4 molecules of protohaem are present per dimer. Indeed, it has been proposed (13) that the minimum unit of the enzyme contains

4 b species, listed in Table II. The differences between high-
and low-potential b-562, and between b-566 and b-558, may
reflect slight differences in conformation between the two
monomers containing subunits of identical primary structure.
It is known that the redox potential, and optical and EPR
spectra of cytochrome b are very susceptible to changes in
protein conformation.

Table II.   Cytochromes b present in dimer of QH_2:ferricyto-
chrome c oxidoreductase

Designation	mol/dimer	$E_{m,7}$ (mV) (12)	g_z in EPR spectrum (13,14)	Shift by antimy-cin in optical (reduced) and EPR (oxidized) spec-trum
b-562	1	40	3.457	+
b-562 (high potential)	1	150	3.441	+
b-566	1	-30	3.713 or 3.785	−
b-558	1	-30	3.785 or 3.713	−

In what follows I shall restrict myself to considering one
of the two protomers in the dimeric enzyme and refer to the two
protohaems in the single cytochrome b molecule as b-562 and
b-566, respectively. The possible differences between the two
protomers must not, however, be forgotten.

The conserved amino acid sequences in the three cytochromes b whose mitochondrial gene has been sequenced is shown in
Fig. 1. Long sequences are completely conserved and even longer
ones if account is taken of homologous replacements. Possible

Amino acid

1- 20	M - - R K - - - - - - - - N - - - - D -
21- 40	P - P S - I S S W W N - G S L L G - C L
41- 60	- - Q I - T G - F - A M H Y - - - - - -
61- 80	A F S S - - H I - R D V - - G - I - R Y
81-100	- H A N G A S - F F - - - - - H - - - G
101-120	L Y Y G S - - - - - - T - W N - G - I -
121-140	- - - - - A T A F - G Y - - - - G Q M S
141-160	- W G A T V I T N L - S A I P - - G - -
161-180	- V - W - W G G - S V - - - T - - R F F
181-200	- - H - - - P F I I - A - - - - H L - -
201-220	L H - - G S - N P - G I - - - - D - - -
221-240	- H - Y - - - K D - - - - - L - - L - L
241-260	- - - - - - - P - - L G - P D N Y - - -
261-280	N P L - T P - - I - P E W Y - L - - Y A
281-300	I L R S - P - K L - G V - - - - - - I L
301-320	- L - - - P - - - - S - - - - - - F - -
321-340	L S - - - - - - - - - - - - - L - - I G
341-360	- - - V - - P - - - - G Q - A - - - Y F
361-380	- - - L - - - P - - - I E N - - - - - -
381-385	- - - - -

Fig. 1 Conserved amino acids in mitochondrial (QH$_2$: ferricytochrome c oxidoreductase) cytochrome b from human (8), ox (personal communication) and yeast (9). The numbering corresponds to the yeast cytochrome. The mammalian cytochrome contains an additional amino acid between nos. 4 and 5 and lacks nos. 109, 113, 381 (ox only) and 382-385.

haem-binding ligands are 8 histidines, 3 lysines, 4 arginines and 2 methionines. The sequence 26-55 containing one histidi-

ne and one methione is almost completely conserved except for
homologous replacements. The same applies to sequence 75-106,
that contains one histidine. There is also a long sequence
142-158 that does not contain any conserved haem-binding group.
The large number of conserved prolines (14), particularly in
the carboxyl half of the molecule, is striking.

The first 143 amino acids in cytochrome b fused to an intron form a maturase required for the proper splicing of pre-
cursor-RNAs transcribed from the cytochrome b gene in yeast
(but not in mammals where no introns are present in this gene)
(15). As pointed out by Slonimski (16), it should be possible
to find mutants that overproduce wild-type maturase. It would
be interesting to determine if it contains the haem-binding
groups. Four invariant histidines, one lysine, three arginines
and one methionine are present in this portion of the molecule.

The structure of QH_2:ferricytochrome c oxidoreductase has
been determined to 15-20 Å resolution by electron diffraction
of two-dimension crystals (17). The cytochrome b is very
likely largely within the membrane in direct contact with the
phospholipid bilayer. As indicated in Table I it is strongly
hydrophobic.

THE CYTOCHROME b PARADOX

A cytochrome has been defined by the Enzyme Commission of
the International Union of Biochemistry (18) as "a haemopro-
tein whose characteristic mode of action involves transfer of
reducing equivalents associated with a reversible change in
oxidation state of the prosthetic group". The cytochrome b
paradox is that it does not always seem to undergo this reversible change in oxidation state under conditions in which one

expects it to be acting as an electron carrier.

The first hint of the paradox was published by Keilin in 1929 (19). He reported that when succinate is added to a heart-muscle suspension in the presence of cyanide, cytochromes a and c are reduced almost instantaneously and later cytochrome b is reduced. On shaking the suspension with air, cytochrome b is oxidized, whereas cytochromes a and c remain reduced. Since cyanide virtually completely stops respiration catalysed by the Keilin and Hartree heart-muscle preparation, I could not understand this observation when I first read it shortly after joining Keilin in 1946.

The paradoxical behaviour of cytochrome b was shown next by the observation that NADH only slowly and incompletely reduces cytochrome b in the presence of cyanide or absence of oxygen (20) under conditions in which it is reduced by succinate. In fact, I did not at that time regard this as paradoxical. Since BAL + oxygen (see below) inactivates both the succinate and the NADH oxidase systems, I concluded that a BAL-labile factor is the common link between both systems and that cytochrome b is slowly reduced by NADH by a side path.

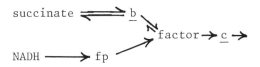

The real shocker, however, was provided by Britton Chance, who in 1952 (21) reported that the reduction of cytochrome b in the presence of cyanide is too slow to be compatible with a role for this cytochrome in the succinate oxidase system, as present in the Keilin and Hartree preparation. Some time later, he found that cytochrome b is sufficiently rapidly reduced in intact yeast (22) and intact rat-liver mitochondria,

but, also in opposition to my findings, that it is also readily reducible by NAD-linked substrates (23).

To confuse the situation still further, Jackson and
Lightdown, although confirming my results with the concentration of NADH that I used (24), found that, in higher concentrations, NADH can rapidly reduce cytochrome b in Keilin and
Hartree particles. Jo Colpa-Boonstra (25) confirmed this.
Since, however, I had used an amount of NADH that is saturating for NADH oxidation, there was (and still is) no simple
explanation for the discrepancy.

The next chapter in this story was also opened by Britton
Chance (26), who showed in 1952 that cytochrome b, reduced by
substrate in the presence of antimycin, is reoxidized when the
suspension becomes anaerobic (26). However, perhaps because
this paper, the abstract of which was printed, was not presented by Brit, who was otherwise engaged winning a gold medal in
the Helsinki Olympic Games, it became forgotten, seemingly also
by Brit, because in 1958 he showed that the amount of cytochrome b reducible by succinate added to submitochondrial
particles is increased by antimycin, even when the latter is
added after the suspension is anaerobic (27). Moreover, the
absorption peak of the "extra cytochrome b" is at a higher
wavelength than that of normal cytochrome b. When it was found
(28-30) that a high phosphorylation potential favours reduction
of the "extra cytochrome b", it seemed to both Brit and myself
(and others) that we had found one of the long-sought "high-
energy intermediates of oxidative phosphorylation". Mårten
Wikström and Jan Berden (31) and others, however, showed con-
vincingly that it was not antimycin that was bringing about
the extra reduction but the O_2 that was added together with the
antimycin. Ferricyanide had already been shown to have the same
effect (32). That an oxidant is required to reduce cytochrome b

is paradoxical. So, also, is the reverse side of the coin, namely that reduction of b is impaired by addition of reductant (33).

In 1962, yet another paradoxical behaviour of cytochrome b was described. In 1948, I had found that after treatment of heart particles with BAL (2,3-dimercaptopropanol) and oxygen, succinate oxidation is irreversible inactivated and I was able to show that the electron-transfer chain is cut between cytochromes b and c. I concluded that this treatment irreversibly destroys a factor necessary for reduction of cytochrome c by cytochrome b (34). Although I did not accept at that time Yukushiji and Okunuki's (35) evidence for cytochrome c_1, I showed that the band that what they (correctly) ascribed to cytochrome c_1 was not affected by BAL (+ O_2) treatment (36). In 1950, Pother and Reif (37) showed that antimycin also cuts the chain between cytochromes b and c and concluded that it acts on my factor. In 1955, Keilin and Hartree (38) restored cytochrome c_1 to its rightful place in the chain and confirmed that BAL + O_2 has no effect on it. Thus, we could then write

$$\rightarrow b \rightarrow \text{factor} \rightarrow c_1 \rightarrow c \rightarrow$$

where the factor is the site of action of both BAL (+ O_2) and antimycin. In 1962, however, Deul and Thorn (39) showed that when antimycin is added to a BAL-treated preparation, the reduction of cytochrome b is strongly inhibited, not its oxidation as would be expected if both act on a factor required for the oxidation of cytochrome b. Except for showing us that BAL and antimycin do not have the same site of action, we did not understand this result, although we did realise that it was difficult to reconcile with the conventional linear electron transfer chain.

IDENTIFICATION OF THE BAL-LABILE FACTOR

The clue to the identification of the BAL-labile factor
came from Bernie Trumpower's studies on a soluble protein factor (OxF) found by Racker and co-workers (40) to be required
for electron transfer. In 1976, Trumpower (41) showed that in
preparations of succinate:cytochrome c oxidoreductase from
which OxF had been extracted, the reduction of cytochrome b
is inhibited by addition of antimycin. In 1979, he showed (42)
that OxF is identical with an iron-sulphur protein identified
by Rieske in 1964 (43). Since this has a well characterized
EPR spectrum, it was easy to test if this is the site of BAL
action. Simon de Vries and I (44) found that this is the case
(see, also, below).

THE SOLUTION OF THE CYTOCHROME b PARADOX - THE Q CYCLE

The cytochrome b paradox was early recognised as such and
many schemes were put forward in an attempt to resolve it and
at the same time to provide a chemical explanation of what was
generally believed, namely that the passage of two electrons
from the single-electron donor cytochrome b to the single-electron acceptor cytochrome c is required for the synthesis of
one molecule of ATP. In 1955, I suggested that the BAL-labile
factor might play a role (45) and at the Spallanzani symposium
in 1959 I proposed (46) a two-pronged respiratory chain

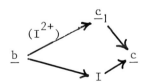

in which component I acts as an electron carrier in the lower
limb and reduced I modulates the rate of the upper limb. This
was later further elaborated (25) to the extent that it became
unbelievable and was deservedly ignored and almost forgotten
even by myself, although parts were incorporated into the b
dimer hypothesis (47), the last kick of the chemical hypothesis of oxidative phosphorylation.

In 1972, Wikström and Berden (31) broke new ground in offering
a mechanism for the oxidant-induced reduction of cytochrome
b that is quite different from the type favoured by most of us
at that time. They suggested that QH_2 formed by reduction of
succinate or NADH is oxidized in two steps, first an oxidation
by cytochrome b to the semiquinone and secondly the oxidation
of the semiquinone by cytochrome c, which is also, according
to this scheme, the oxidant of cytochrome b via cytochrome c_1.

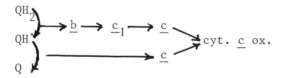

The upper limb (between b and c_1) was thought to be the site
of action of antimycin and the lower limb that of BAL. The
oxidant-induced reduction of cytochrome b was explained by
proposing that oxidant (ferricyanide or O_2), by oxidizing
cytochrome c, promotes the oxidation of the semiquinone,
thereby pulling the thermodynamically unfavourable reduction
of b by QH_2.

Although, in the light of later studies, this mechanism
is now no longer tenable, it was important because it showed
that the apparently paradoxical behaviour of cytochrome b
could have a simple kinetic explanation and it paved the way

for the Q cycle. Indeed, the modification (48) of the Wikström-
Berden mechanism in which the two arms are interchanged, so
that the semiquinone becomes the reductant of cytochrome $\underline{b}$,
contains features that are incorporated in the variant of the
Q cycle that we favour (see below).

One of the problems that I had with Peter Mitchell's
chemiosmotic hypothesis was a difficulty in relating his redox
loops to my understanding of the respiratory chain. Indeed, in
his first paper (49) on the Q cycle in August, 1975, Peter
acknowledges that two major interrelated difficulties had
hampered understanding of the $\underline{b}$-$\underline{c}_1$ region of the respiratory
chain. "One difficulty is, as pointed out by Slater, the appa-
rent lack of a hydrogen carrier for Loop 3. The other difficulty is the peculiar kinetic and thermodynamic behaviour of the
$\underline{b}$ cytochromes, which has received much attention, but not yet
a completely satisfactory explanation." The Q cycle was proposed to remove this difficulty.

I must say that I did not much like it, since it required
that the acceptor of succinate dehydrogenase (with its associated Fe-S clusters) be ubisemiquinone rather than the quinone
itself, and that the semiquinone be formed by reduction by
ferrocytochrome $\underline{b}$. Kröger pointed out another serious objection,
namely the postulate that cytochrome $\underline{b}$ be reduced by the $QH_2/Q^{\cdot}$
couple, which is, in fact, a strong oxidant. Very soon after-
wards, however, Peter published in November, 1975, a more
general scheme in which the sequence of electron and proton
transfers was left open, as was also the electron acceptor for
succinate dehydrogenase (50). Perhaps because I was primarily
interested just in this sequence of electron transfer, I rather
lost interest in the Q cycle. My interest was revived by the
recent work of Bernie Trumpower and particularly by the exhaustive review of the possible variants of the Q cycle in-

cluded in his thesis by my student Gerrit van Ark (51).

The one common feature of all the variants of Q cycle is that one Q species acts as reductant and a second species as oxidant of cytochrome b, and that the two species do not come into contact. Cox and Gibson (52) were, in fact, the first to place ubiquinone on both sides of cytochrome b. Earlier, Martius (52a) had suggested that reduced phylloquinone delivers electrons to cytochrome b and tocopherolquinone accepts the electrons. Neither of these authors, however, suggested a Q cycle.

The only variant of the Q cycle that, in my opinion, accommodates the experimental findings is the model of the QH_2:ferricytochrome c oxidoreductase given in Fig. 2. The various features of this reaction scheme and the experimental evidence will be treated in turn.

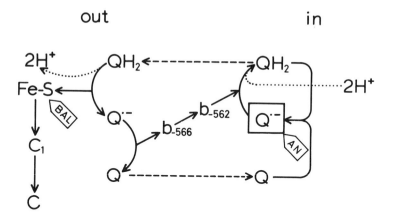

Fig. 2.   Q cycle. Curved arrows represent chemical equations, straight full arrows the pathway of electron transfer and dotted arrows diffusion. BAL is British Anti Lewisite (2,3-dimercaptopropanol) and AN antimycin. $Q^{\cdot-}$ placed in a box is the antimycin-sensitive EPR detectable ubisemiquinone. $Q^{\cdot-}$ not placed in a box is, at the time of writing, hypothetical.

1. Kröger and Klingenberg's view (53) is accepted that the Q/QH_2 couple is the mobile carrier between the dehydrogenases (succinate, NADH, glycerol 1-phosphate and others) and that most of the ubiquinone in the membrane has a "pool" function. In heart mitochondria there are present about 0.4 mol succinate:Q oxidoreductase and 0.2 mol NADH:Q oxidoreductase per QH_2:ferricytochrome c oxidoreductase monomer (54). By "pool" function is meant that, in principle, all molecules of Q reduced by a Q reductase are accessible to all molecules of the cytochrome c reductase. Since, as Kröger (55) has pointed out, only very small amounts of the free semiquinone can exist in equilibrium with Q and QH_2, the dismutation is very rapid, and reduction of Q by succinate is first order with respect to Q (53), it is inconceivable to me that the semiquinone formed by the Q cycle in QH_2:ferricytochrome c oxidoreductase could act as acceptor for the succinate:Q oxidoreductase, as envisaged by Mitchell (49) in his first paper on the Q cycle and by Trumpower (56).

Assuming a pool function for Q, it can be calculated, from the hyperbolic relation between the rate of oxidation of succinate and the degree of occupancy of the common antimycin- and HQNO-binding site in cytochrome c reductase, that in heart submitochondrial particles the intrinsic rate of oxidation of QH_2 (i.e. when all the ubiquinone is in the form of QH_2) is much higher than the intrinsic rate of reduction of Q by succinate (i.e. when all the ubiquinone is in the form of Q) (57). 2. As first suggested by Trumpower (56), the QH_2 is oxidized to the semiquinone by OxF (now identified with the Rieske Fe-S protein (44)) which is located on the side of the mitochondrial inner membrane facing the inter-membrane phase. The semiquinone in turn reduces cytochrome b (first the lower-potential b-566, then the higher-potential b-562). The evidence for

these statements is: (a) in the presence of antimycin, destruction of the BAL-sensitive factor (now identified with the Fe-S
cluster of the Rieske protein (44) and with OxF) greatly inhibits the reduction of cytochrome $\underline{b}$ (39)[*]. The same is true when
OxF is extracted from the particles (42). The amount of residual Fe-S cluster after treatment with different concentrations
of BAL is directly correlated with the fraction of cytochrome
$\underline{b}$ that is rapidly reduced in the presence of antimycin (Table
III). Thus the Fe-S cluster is necessary for the reduction of
cytochrome $\underline{b}$ by QH_2. Since the reduced cluster is insufficient-
ly strongly reducing ($E_{m,7}$ = 280 mV) to reduce cytochrome $\underline{b}$-
566 ($E_{m,7}$ = -30 mV), the reductant must be the other product
of the reaction, namely the semiquinone. The semiquinone/Q
couple is probably sufficiently reducing, but the QH_2/semi-
quinone couple would not be (see below). (b) Trumpower has
shown by extraction and reconstitution that the Rieske Fe-S
protein is required for the oxidation of QH_2 by cytochrome $\underline{c}$
(42). Destruction of x% of the Fe-S cluster by treatment with
BAL + O_2 causes x% inhibition of the intrinsic rate (see below)
of oxidation of QH_2 (57). Since the semiquinone that is the
presumed reductant of cytochrome $\underline{b}$ has not been observed by EPR,
its redox potential has not been determined. Since, however,
the $E_{m,7}$ of free $Q^{\cdot-}/Q$ dissolved in a lipid environment has
been calculated to be -235 mV (51) and that of $Q_c^{\cdot-}/Q_{total}$ (see
below) is -65 mV, it is very likely sufficiently reducing.
Also it is not known whether it is the semiquinone anion $Q^{\cdot-}$

---

[*]Malviya et al. (58) have stated that the reduction of $\underline{b}$-566
only, not of $\underline{b}$-562, is inhibited by antimycin after BAL treatment. However, Ksenzeko and Konstantinov (59) and we (Zhu,
Q.-S. and Berden, J.A., unpublished) have confirmed Deul and
Thorn's (39) original observation with the microspectroscope
that the reduction of both cytochromes $\underline{b}$ is inhibited.

or QH$^{\cdot}$ that is the reductant. Q$^{\cdot-}$ has been written into the
scheme, purely on analogy with Q$_c^{\cdot-}$. (c) Bowyer and Trumpower
(60) have shown that the oxidant-induced reduction of cytochrome $\underline{b}$ in the presence of antimycin is inhibited by the Q
analogue 5-$\underline{n}$-undecyl-6-hydroxy-4,7-dioxobenzothiazole (UHDBT),
which inhibits the oxidation of the Rieske Fe-S protein by
cytochrome $\underline{c}_1$. Similarly, antimycin inhibits the reduction of
cytochrome $\underline{b}$ in the presence of cyanide and dibromothymoquinone which catalyses the auto-oxidation of QH$_2$ (61). (d) The
reduction of cytochrome $\underline{b}$ by succinate in succinate:ferricyto-
chrome $\underline{c}$ oxidoreductase is triphasic (62,63). An initial rapid
partial reduction (by Q$^{\cdot-}$ according to Fig. 2) is followed by
a rapid oxidation (according to Fig. 2 by Q$_c^{\cdot-}$ formed via the
Q formed by reduction of $\underline{b}$) and then finally by a slow reduction (63). The initial rapid phase of cytochrome $\underline{b}$ reduction
is faster than that of cytochrome $\underline{c}_1$ (according to Fig. 2
because the Fe-S cluster is first reduced); the final slow
reduction began when reduction of cytochrome $\underline{c}_1$ approached
completion (see below).

Table III. Correlation between amount of residual Rieske
            (2Fe-2S) cluster after destruction by different
            concentrations of BAL with fraction of cytochrome
            $\underline{b}$ that is rapidly reduced by succinate in the
            presence of antimycin.

[BAL] (mM)	[[2Fe-2S]] (relative)	Fraction of $\underline{b}$ rapidly reduced (%)
0	100	89
1	51	54
2	20	20
4	0	0

Data taken from (57). Submitochondrial particles inactivated by shaking with different concentrations of BAL
in the presence of oxygen, for 45 min at 25°C.

There is, in my opinion, overwhelming evidence in support of the left-hand side of the model in Fig. 2.

It is important to note that, according to this scheme, it is immaterial whether QH_2 is formed by reduction of Q by dehydrogenases on the inside (e.g. succinate) or on the outside (e.g. glycerol 1-phosphate) of the membrane. The critical point is that QH_2 is oxidized near the outer membrane. Thus the recent observation by Al Lehninger and colleagues (64) that the H^+/e ratio is the same with either succinate or glycerol 1-phosphate is perfectly compatible with the Q cycle, as depicted in Fig. 2, but not, as I understand them, with schemes in which the dehydrogenase is treated as a single-electron donor as in the formulations of Mitchell (65) and Trumpower (66).

3.   Cytochrome b-562 is oxidized by $Q^{\cdot-}$ in an antimycin-sensitive step. A specific antimycin-sensitive species of $Q^{\cdot-}$ has been identified by EPR spectroscopy by Yu et al. (62,67), Ohnishi and Trumpower (68), and Simon de Vries (69). It is not sensitive to BAL + O_2 (70). It has such a slow relaxation that it can be observed at room temperature. Observations at various pH values show unequivocably that it is in the anion form. The redox potentials of the various couples involving this semiquinone are listed in Table IV. The concentration of $Q_c^{\cdot-}$ can reach values equal to one half that of the monomer of QH_2: ferricytochrome c oxidoreductase (69). Since, as already mentioned, the concentration of free semiquinone in equilibrium with Q and QH_2 is far below this value, it must be concluded that $Q_c^{\cdot-}$ is bound to a specific site, presumably QP_c, the ubiquinone-binding protein present in QH_2:ferricytochrome c oxidoreductase (62). We call this species of bound ubisemiquinone $Q_c^{\cdot-}$ (it is referred to by Ohnishi and Trumpower (68) as SQ_c). It is critical to the mechanism that $Q_c^{\cdot-}$ be formed and reduced

near the matrix side of the membrane.

Table IV.   Redox potentials of various couples involving antimycin-sensitive species of ubisemiquinone $(Q_c^{\cdot-})$
observable by EPR.

Redox couple[*]	$E_{m,7}$	$dE_{m,7}/dpH$
	(mV)	(mV/pH)
$E(Q)/E(QH_2)$	84	-60
$E(Q^{\cdot-})/QH_{2_{tot}}$	233	-129
$Q_{tot}/E(Q^{\cdot-})$	-65	9

[*] $E(Q)$, $E(QH_2)$ and $E(Q^{\cdot-})$ refer to bound ubiquinone
species. Q_{tot} and $QH_{2_{tot}}$ refer to total (bound
and free species).

The data are from (69), which should be consulted for a description of the assumptions made in calculating these values.
$E_{m,7}$ refers to midpoint potential at pH 7 and 20°C.

4. Antimycin inhibits the oxidation of cytochrome $\underline{b}$ (37). Since
it affects the optical spectrum of cytochrome $\underline{b}$-562, the EPR
spectrum of ferricytochrome $\underline{b}$-562 and the E_m of this cytochrome (see Table II), without any effect on $\underline{b}$-566, it is
concluded that the antimycin-sensitive $Q_c^{\cdot-}$ oxidizes $\underline{b}$-562
rather than $\underline{b}$-566.

5. Since Q and QH_2 are in large excess over the concentration
of the respiratory proteins, and the equilibrium

$$Q + QH_2 \rightleftharpoons 2Q^{\cdot-} + 2 H^+ \qquad (1)$$

is very rapid, it is assumed that $Q_c^{\cdot-}$ will be formed by this
reverse dismutation in the vicinity of the $Q_c^{\cdot-}$ binding site.

6. The essential feature of Peter's Q-cycle hypothesis, namely that separate species of ubiquinone are involved in the reduction and oxidation of cytochrome b, is now proven by the three observations: (i) the Fe-S cluster-dependent (and, therefore, BAL-sensitive) reduction of cytochrome b in the presence of antimycin; (ii) the requirement of this cluster for the oxidation of QH_2; (iii) the direct demonstration of the antimycin-sensitive but BAL-insensitive species of $Q^{\cdot-}$. From the first two observations, the presence of a ubisemiquinone species, whose formation is dependent on an intact Fe-S cluster, is inferred. The third observation is direct evidence for the second species.

Our formulation differs, however, in one respect from Peter's. We conclude that the antimycin-sensitive oxidation of b-562 is brought about by the $Q_c^{\cdot-}/QH_2$ couple and not the $Q/Q_c^{\cdot-}$ couple. The main reason for this is that the $Q_c^{\cdot-}/QH_2$ couple is a more suitable oxidant for b-562 than the $Q/Q_c^{\cdot-}$ couple (cf. Tables II and IV). This is, however, not conclusive since, dependent on the binding constants of Q, QH_2 and $Q^{\cdot-}$, it is possible for the two couples bound to the enzyme to be equipotential. The triphasic reduction of cytochrome b indicating that reduction of b leads to the formation of an oxidant of b is also in favour of our formulation. However, the right-hand side of the scheme is not as firmly established as the left-hand side.

The antimycin-sensitive reduction of cytochrome b observed after destruction (39) or extraction (41) of the Fe-S protein and the slow reduction of cytochrome b after cytochrome c_1 reduction is complete (63) may perhaps be explained by reversal of the reaction

$$Q_c^{\cdot-} + b^{2+}\text{-}562 + 2H^+ \rightleftharpoons QH_2 + b^{3+}\text{-}562, \qquad (2)$$

although this would be expected to be relatively slow. Indeed,
this reaction would be more readily explainable on the basis
of Peter's formulation.

An alternative explanation is that $Q_c^{\cdot-}$ bound near the
b-562 haem can act both as donor and acceptor of electrons to
and from the haem, depending upon the redox state of the latter

$$Q_c^{\cdot-} + \underline{b}^{2+} + 2H^+ \rightleftharpoons QH_2 + \underline{b}^{3+} \qquad (3)$$

$$Q_c^{\cdot-} + \underline{b}^{3+} \qquad \rightleftharpoons Q + \underline{b}^{2+} \qquad (4)$$

Since the antimycin-resistant respiration, which leads to
reduction of O_2 to O_2^- (48), requires Q (71), it is most likely
due to autooxidation of the $Q^{\cdot-}$ species on the left-hand side
of the scheme. This explanation is supported by the fact that
the antimycin-insensitive respiration is sensitive to cyanide
(72).

It should be noted that a reverse dismutation reaction of
ubiquinone is not envisaged on the left-hand side of the scheme.
If this took place to an appreciable extent, the antimycin-
resistant respiration would be much faster than is found.
Indeed, one can determine an upper limit of the reversed dismutation by the amount by which H_2O_2, formed from O_2^- by action
of superoxide dismutase, exceeds 2/3 the amount of O_2 consumed
in the antimycin-resistant respiration. From the data of Boveris et al. (73), it can be calculated that the dismutation
does not exceed one-half of the antimycin-resistant respiration.

The lack of an appreciable reversed dismutation on the
left-hand side of the scheme implies that, in contrast to the
situation on the right-hand side, the semiquinone is not preferentially bound to a ubiquinone-binding protein in this region (cf. (65)). Perhaps the reactions here may be written

$$QH_2 + E \cdot [2Fe-2S]^{2+} \qquad \rightleftharpoons QH_2 \cdot E[2Fe-2S]^{2+} \qquad (5)$$

$$QH_2 \cdot E \cdot [2Fe-2S]^{2+} \qquad \rightleftharpoons Q^{\cdot-} \cdot E \cdot [2Fe-2S]^{1+} + 2H^+ \quad (6)$$

$$Q^{\cdot-} \cdot E \cdot [2Fe-2S]^{1+} + \underline{b}^{3+}566 \rightleftharpoons Q \cdot E \cdot [2Fe-2S]^{1+} + \underline{b}^{2+}566 \ (7)$$

$$Q \cdot E \cdot [2Fe-2S]^{1+} + \underline{c}_1^{3+} \qquad \rightleftharpoons Q \cdot E \cdot [2Fe-2S]^{2+} + \underline{c}_1^{2+} \quad (8)$$

$$Q \cdot E \cdot [2Fe-2S]^{2+} \qquad \rightleftharpoons Q + E \cdot [2Fe-2S]^{2+} \qquad (9)$$

where E represents the Rieske Fe-S protein.

Competing reactions would be

$$Q^{\cdot-} \cdot E \cdot [2Fe-2S]^{1+} \qquad \rightleftharpoons Q^{\cdot-} + E \cdot [2Fe-2S]^{1+} \qquad (10)$$

$$2Q^{\cdot-} + 2H^+ \qquad \rightleftharpoons Q + QH_2 \qquad (11)$$

$$E \cdot [2Fe-2S]^{1+} + Q \qquad \rightleftharpoons Q \cdot E \cdot [2Fe-2S]^{1+} \qquad (12)$$

$$E \cdot [2Fe-2S]^{1+} + QH_2 \qquad \rightleftharpoons QH_2 \cdot E \cdot [2Fe-2S]^{1+} \qquad (13)$$

$$Q^{\cdot-} \cdot E \cdot [2Fe-2S]^{1+} + O_2 \qquad \rightarrow Q \cdot E \cdot [2Fe-2S]^{1+} + O_2^- \quad (14)$$

Reaction 7 may normally be very rapid, so that little $Q^{\cdot-}$ will accumulate in the presence of a continuing supply of $\underline{b}^{3+}566$. In the presence of antimycin, however, $[2Fe-2S]^{1+}$ must be oxidized to regenerate $[2Fe-2S]^{2+}$ so that sufficient $Q^{\cdot-}$ can be formed to reduce all the cytochrome $\underline{b}$, the concentration of which is double that of the Fe-S protein. This is brought about by Reaction 8, and since oxidant keeps cytochrome $\underline{c}_1$ (also present in the same concentration as the Fe-S protein) oxidized, the oxidant-induced reduction of cytochrome $\underline{b}$ is explained. That the "oxygen effect" occurs even in the presence of 1 mM cyanide (31), a finding that made it impossible for me originally to accept the Wikström-Berden model, is now explained by the fact that the leak through cytochrome oxidase, although very slow in the presence of 1 mM cyanide, is fast

compared with the complete block of Reaction 2 by antimycin
which binds so exceptionally strongly.

This provides, too, a possible explanation of the reductant-induced inhibition of cytochrome b reduction (33), which
has a half-maximal effect at E_h = 225 mV at pH 7.5 (72), not
very far away from the E_m of the Fe-S cluster (285 mV). The
striking feature of this phenomenon is not just that b is more
slowly reduced in the presence of reductants of cytochrome c_1,
but that the fraction of rapidly reduced b declines with increasing reduction of the c_1 just as if the Fe-S cluster were
irreversibly destroyed (by BAL + O_2), i.e. it appears to be
irreversibly reduced, and no longer to be able to function as
an electron carrier between QH_2 and cytochrome c_1. This is
understandable on the basis of the above equations if reaction
15 cannot take place (74)

$$QH_2 \cdot E \cdot [2Fe-2S]^{1+} + c_1^{3+} \rightleftharpoons QH_2 \cdot E \cdot [2Fe-2S]^{2+} + c_1^{2+} \qquad (15)$$

This seems to be the case in chloroplasts (75).

As Mitchell already indicated in his first paper on the
Q cycle, the latter also satisfactorily explains the absence
of O_2-induced cytochrome b reduction in the presence of antimycin in submitochondrial particles prepared from a Q-deficient
yeast mutant (76). These particles contain an amount of Q less
than one half the concentration of cytochrome b.

The cytochrome b paradox is now essentially resolved. That
cytochrome b seemed in danger of not being admitted to the
cytochrome club, since it did not clearly reveal that it undergoes oxidation and reduction during its function, is explained
by the fact that its reductant is not QH_2 or a reduced flavoprotein, but the product of the oxidation of QH_2 by another
member of the chain. The question whether it precedes the Fe-S
protein or even cytochrome c_1, which appeared meaningful in

the context of the classical linear electron-transfer chain, is meaningless in the context of the Q cycle. The early observations of Keilin and Chance on the oxidation and slow reduction, respectively, of cytochrome b in the presence of cyanide is now explained by the poor supply of $Q^{\bullet-}$ on the left-hand side of the scheme under these conditions. The paradoxical oxidant-induced stimulation and reductant-induced inhibition of the reduction of cytochrome b are likewise explained, as is the "double-kill" experiment of Deul and Thorn (39), since in the Q cycle there are two pathways for reduction of b, one sensitive to BAL and the other to antimycin.

Most important of all, it provides a solution of the dilemma how a 2-eletron oxidation of substrate becomes a single-electron process when the cytochromes are reached. All reactions in the Q cycle are single-electron steps, and two turns of the cycle are necessary for the oxidation of one molecule of QII_2 by two molecules of ferricytochrome c as the following reactions (omitting the ubiquinone-binding reactions) show.

$$2(QH_2 + [2Fe-2S]^{2+} \rightleftharpoons Q^{\bullet-} + 2H_L^+ + [2Fe-2S]^{1+}) \qquad (16)$$

$$2(Q^{\bullet-} + \underline{b}^{3+}\text{-}566 \rightleftharpoons Q + \underline{b}^{2+}\text{-}566) \qquad (17)$$

$$2(\underline{b}^{2+}\text{-}566 + \underline{b}^{3+}\text{-}562 \rightleftharpoons \underline{b}^{3+}\text{-}566 + \underline{b}^{2+}\text{-}562) \qquad (18)$$

$$2([2Fe-2S]^{1+} + \underline{c}_1^{3+} \rightleftharpoons [2Fe-2S]^{2+} + \underline{c}_1^{2+}) \qquad (19)$$

$$2(\underline{c}_1^{2+} + \underline{c}^{3+} \rightleftharpoons \underline{c}_1^{3+} + \underline{c}^{2+}) \qquad (20)$$

$$QH_2 + Q \rightleftharpoons 2Q_c^{\bullet-} + 2H^+ \qquad (21)$$

$$2(Q_c^{\bullet-} + \underline{b}^{2+}\text{-}562 + 2H_R^+ \rightleftharpoons QH_2 + \underline{b}^{3+}\text{-}562) \qquad (22)$$

$$\text{Sum: } QH_2 + 2\underline{c}^{3+} + 4H_R^+ \rightleftharpoons Q + 2\underline{c}^{2+} + 4H_L^+ + 2H^+$$

In these equations, I have assumed that 2 protons per electron are withdrawn from the right-hand compartment (matrix) when $Q^{\cdot-}$ is reduced to QH_2 and are delivered to the left-hand compartment (inter-membrane space) when QH_2 is oxidized to $Q^{\cdot-}$. Since I am not (now) concerned with the mechanism of proton translocation and it is Peter's birthday, I am assuming that the two protons produced in the reverse dismutation reaction (21), that I have written as scalar protons in the sum reaction, are consumed in the cytochrome oxidase reaction. However, I have no evidence to support this assumption. Nor can I exclude the possibility favoured by Papa (77) and von Jagow (78) that cytochrome b functions as a proton pump.

However, I still cannot explain why NADH was a poorer reductant of cytochrome b than succinate under anaerobic conditions in my early experiments (20). Maybe the explanation is trivial, but it worries me.

FUNCTION OF CYTOCHROME b

According to the scheme in Fig. 2, cytochrome b functions as a transmembrane ubisemiquinone dismutase. Why is this useful? At first sight, a perfectly sensible classical-type electron-transfer chain between QH_2 and cytochrome c would be

$$QH_2 \rightarrow [2Fe-2S]^{2+} \rightarrow \underline{c}_1 \rightarrow \underline{c}$$

and we would write the reactions as

$$2(QH_2 + [2Fe-2S]^{2+} \rightleftharpoons Q^{\cdot-} + 2H^+ + [2Fe-2S]^{1+}) \qquad (23)$$

$$2([2Fe-2S]^{1+} + \underline{c}_1^{3+} \rightleftharpoons [2Fe-2S]^{2+} + \underline{c}_1^{2+}) \qquad (24)$$

$$2(\underline{c}_1^{2+} + \underline{c}^{3+} \rightleftharpoons \underline{c}_1^{3+} + \underline{c}^{2+}) \qquad (25)$$

$$2Q^{\cdot -} + 2H^+ \rightleftharpoons Q + QH_2 \qquad (26)$$

Sum: $QH_2 + 2\underline{c}^{3+} \rightleftharpoons Q + 2\underline{c}^{2+} + 2H^+$

Since the equilibrium of the dismutation lies far to the right, much free energy is made available in this reaction ($\Delta G_{\underline{o}}$ = 57 kJ). Since the reaction is very rapid and is non-enzymic, it is not easy to see how this energy could be utilized in the cell, unless, as Kröger (55) suggests, one molecule of $Q^{\cdot -}$ formed by reduction of Q by dehydrogenase reacts with a second molecule of $Q^{\cdot -}$ formed by oxidation of QH_2 with uptake of protons from the other side of the membrane from that to which protons are expelled during oxidation of QH_2. This seems to me to involve rather unlikely movements within the membrane of the unstable semiquinone. In the Q cycle, cytochrome b utilizes the energy.

How it does so is the next question. If we had thought of it when we gave a cytochrome b dimer a central role in the so-called chemical hypothesis of oxidative phosphorylation (47), I am sure that we could have incorporated this dismutation. However, it is now clear that the energy of the dismutation is utilized for the transmembrane translocation of electrons through the two-haem cytochrome b, against the electrical potential gradient. The energy thereby conserved is utilized for the translocation of protons.

Thus cytochrome b is far from paradoxical. It only appeared to be so in the context of the classical formulation of the respiratory chain, which I long ago likened to a random two-dimensional section of a three-dimensional object. Peter's Q cycle has given us the third dimension.

Q-BINDING PROTEINS

The discovery by Yu, Yu and King (79) of the Q-binding
proteins is of great importance in the context of the Q cycle.
The best studied is the 15-kD component of the succinate:Q
oxidoreductase, which is also present in certain preparations
(called b-c$_1$ complex (79)) of QH$_2$:cytochrome c oxidoreductase
(80) as well as in preparations of succinate:Q oxidoreductase
(81). This subunit, which has been shown to be essential for
the reduction of Q by succinate dehydrogenase, is very likely
the binding site of a second species of ubisemiquinone (SQ$_s$)
that has been identified by Ohnishi and Trumpower (68) in
preparations of succinate:ferricytochrome c oxidoreductase.
This is distinguished from what they call SQ$_c$ (Q$_c^{\cdot-}$ is our
nomenclature) in its faster relaxation, different line shape,
sensitivity to theonyltrifluoroacetone (TTFA) (82,62,68) and
resistance to antimycin.

The pathway of electrons from succinate to Q in this enzyme, which contains 2 or 3 Fe-S clusters, covalently bound
FAD and a low-potential cytochrome b (61) (coded for by the
nuclear genome (83)), is not known. It seems likely that SQ$_s$,
presumably bound to the 15-kD subunit, is an intermediate in
the reduction of Q to QH$_2$. It is conceivable, but in my opinion unlikely, that in the mitochondrion SQ$_s$ (or Q$_s^{\cdot-}$) bound
to succinate:Q oxidoreductase passes its electron directly to
Q in the QH$_2$:ferricytochrome c oxidoreductase, so that Q$_c^{\cdot}$ is
formed by the reaction

$$Q_s^{\cdot-} + Q \rightarrow Q + Q_c^{\cdot-} \tag{27}$$

instead of by

$$QH_2 + Q \rightarrow 2Q_c^{\cdot-} + 2\ H^+ \tag{28}$$

In any case, it would seem not to be the minimum hypothesis, since EPR shows that there is a stabilized semquinone in QH_2: ferricytochrome $\underline{c}$ oxidoreductase and it is reasonable to suppose that QH_2, Q and the equilibrium amount of free semiquinone would be in the region of the $Q^{\cdot -}$-binding site.

The subunit in QH_2:ferricytochrome $\underline{c}$ oxidoreductase responsible for binding $Q_c^{\cdot -}$ has not been identified. Yu and Yu (84) have found that two subunits of apparent molecular weight 37 000 and 17 000, respectively, according to SDS gel electrophoresis, are covalently labelled after irradiation of purified QH_2:cytochrome $\underline{c}$ oxidoreductase in the presence of the Q analogue 2,3-dimethoxy-5-methyl-6-{10[3-(4-azido-2-nitroanilino)-propionoxy]decyl}-1,4-benzoquinone. The larger subunit is very likely cytochrome $\underline{b}$ and it would be consistent with our reaction scheme if the Q analogue labelled the $Q^{\cdot -}$ (and Q)-reactive site near the $\underline{b}$-562 haem (right-hand side of scheme). However, it is not certain that the photo-affinity label would bind to this site since, according to our hypothesis, $Q_c^{\cdot -}$ is bound much more strongly to its binding site than Q or QH_2. Moreover, antimycin does not prevent binding of the photo-affinity label as would be expected if this represented labelling of the $Q_c^{\cdot -}$-binding site.

Indeed, one might expect it to be easier to identify this subunit by virtue of its strong antimycin binding. Since mutations affecting the mitochondrial genome for cytochrome $\underline{b}$ also lead to impaired antimycin binding, it has been concluded that the cytochrome $\underline{b}$ polypeptide contains the antimycin-binding site (84). However, an alternative explanation could be that the real antimycin-binding subunit is not assembled into membranes containing a defective cytochrome $\underline{b}$ (cf. (86)). Das Gupta and Rieske (87) have provided some, but not very impressive, evidence that the antimycin-binding site is on a 11.5 kD subunit.

Although in mitochondria most of the ubiquinone will not be bound to Q-binding proteins, a substantial fraction may be bound in the isolated enzymes of the respiratory chain and in submitochondrial particles from which all free Q has been extracted by pentane. Thus, in these preparations, addition of antimycin (88) or TTFA (89), by making bound Q free, can actually increase the rate of electron transfer from succinate to cytochrome c. This is, in fact, good support for the view that mobile Q acts as a carrier between the Q reductase and the cytochrome c reductase.

Q CYCLES AND b CYCLES

The Q cycle is also a b cycle. Cytochrome b cycles have also been proposed that are not Q cycles (47,78,90). That proposed by Wikström and Krab (90) is of particular interest, not only because it is a logical development of the scheme of Wikström and Berden (31), but also because it is identical with the scheme shown in Fig. 2, except that only one species of ubisemiquinone is involved. Like $Q^{\cdot-}$ in the left-hand side in our scheme, the semiquinone is formed by oxidation of QH_2 by the Fe-S cluster and like $Q_c^{\cdot-}$ in our scheme it is reduced by ferrocytochrome b-562 in an antimycin-sensitive reaction. The formation of the semiquinone by the reversed dismutation reaction shown in Fig. 2 is not envisaged in the b cycle of Wikström and Krab.

Since the only difference between our scheme and that of Wikström and Krab is the proposal in ours of two pools of semiquinone and in that of Wikström and Krab of a single pool, it is not surprising that most experimental findings can be

explained equally well by both schemes. However, in my opinion
(see, also, (59)), the experiment of Deul and Thorn and the
observations of an antimycin-sensitive $Q^{\cdot -}$ species can be explained only in terms of two pools. The argument for this conclusion will now be developed.

Wikström and Krab agree that their scheme operates "in
close association with a particular protein-bound species of
ubiquinone". In the context of our scheme, I have suggested
reactions in which the Fe-S protein functions as a (weak)
ubiquinone-binding protein. In the context of the Wikström-
Krab scheme, we should presumably postulate a separate Q-binding protein (E) that binds to QH_2, Q and $Q^{\cdot -}$. Oxidation by the
Fe-S cluster should then be written

$$E \cdot QH_2 + [2Fe-2S]^{2+} \rightarrow E \cdot Q^{\cdot -} + 2H^+ + [2Fe-2S]^{1+} \qquad (29)$$

Oxidation of the semiquinone would occur by the reactions

$$E \cdot Q^{\cdot} + \underline{b}^{3+}\text{-}566 \rightarrow E \cdot Q + \underline{b}^{2+}\text{-}566 \qquad (30)$$

and reduction by

$$E \cdot Q^{\cdot} + \underline{b}^{2+}\text{-}562 + 2H^+ \rightarrow E \cdot QH_2 + \underline{b}^{3+}\text{-}562 \qquad (31)$$

Since only one species of semiquinone is envisaged by Wikström
and Krab, $E \cdot Q^{\cdot}$ must correspond to the antimycin-sensitive $Q_c^{\cdot -}$.

In the absence of antimycin, but after destruction of the
Fe-S cluster, $\underline{b}$-562 could be reduced by the reaction

$$E \cdot QH_2 + \underline{b}^{3+}\text{-}562 \rightarrow E \cdot Q^{\cdot -} + 2H^+ + \underline{b}^{2+}\text{-}562 \qquad (32)$$

Since antimycin competes with QH_2 and $Q^{\cdot -}$ for E, $\underline{b}$-562
cannot be reduced by either $E \cdot Q^{\cdot -}$ (via $\underline{b}$-566) or $E \cdot QH_2$ in the
presence of antimycin. It could be conceivably reduced direct-
ly by free ubiquinol

$$QH_2 + \underline{b}^{3+}\text{-}562 \rightarrow Q^{\cdot -} + 2H^+ + \underline{b}^{2+}\text{-}562 \tag{33}$$

followed by dismutation of the semiquinone, but there would
be no reason to expect this reaction to be sensitive to destruction of the Fe-S cluster. Thus, the absence of b reduction
in the presence of antimycin after BAL treatment is not explained.

It is concluded, in agreement with Peter, that two pools
of semiquinone are necessary.

CONCLUDING REMARKS

In a letter dated July 28, 1975, Peter sent his first
version of the Q cycle (49) to me for comment. He added a
postscript "Do you think the 'Slater factor' might have something to do with the Q cycle?"

I did not think so at that time because I understood that
the proposal was to put Q between cytochromes $\underline{b}$ and $\underline{c}_1$, and
we had earlier found no evidence that BAL + O_2 affects ubi-
quinone. Now, I would answer: "Yes, indeed, and what is more,
I think that experiments in which the factor is destroyed by
treatment with BAL + O_2 have provided convincing evidence in
favour of the Q cycle as the mechanism of electron transfer
in the middle part of the respiratory chain."

Naturally, I am delighted that a reinvestigation of a
35-year-old problem (started when Peter was a youngster of 25)
would have provided the evidence that convinces me at any
rate of the correctness of his Q cycle, which like his chemiosmotic hypothesis was inductively conceived at a time when
there was little evidence in its favour.

Whether the Q cycle is the complete mechanism of proton

translocation I am not sure, but I know of no evidence against some at least of the protons being translocated exactly as envisaged by Peter.

I am happy to present this essay to Peter on the occasion of his 60th birthday. It was written mostly in the afternoons and evenings after a morning's skiing and I can give Peter the welcome news that at Scuol "60^{+}-ers" get 20% off the cost of their ski ticket.

Of course, I freely give Peter permission to look this gift horse (I mean the essay, not the ski ticket) in the mouth and to point out its imperfections.

REFERENCES

1. Keilin, D. (1925) Proc. Roy. Soc. B 98, 312-339.
2. Ball, E.G. (1938) Biochem. Z. 295, 262-264
3. Keilin, D. and Hartree, E.F. (1940) Proc. Roy. Soc. B 129, 277-306.
4. Slater, E.C. (1949) Biochem. J. 45, 1-8.
5. Green, D.E. and Hatefi, Y. (1961) Science 133, 13-19.
6. Hatefi, Y. and Galante, Y.M. (1980) J. Biol. Chem. 255, 5530-5537.
7. Marres, C.A.M. and Slater, E.C. (1977) Biochim. Biophys. Acta 462, 531-548.
8. Anterson, S., Bankier, A.T., Barrell, B.G., De Bruijn, M.H.L., Coulson, A.R., Drouin, J., Eperon, I.C., Nierlich, D.P., Roe, B.A., Sanger, F., Schreier, P.H., Smith, A.J.H., Staden, R. and Young, I.G. (1981) Nature 290, 457-465.
9. Nobrega, F.G. and Tzagaloff, A. (1980) J. Biol. Chem. 255, 9828-9837.
10. von Jagow, G., Schägger, H., Engel, W.D., Machleidt, W., Machleidt, I. and Kolb, H.J. (1978) FEBS Lett. 91, 121-125.
11. Rieske, J.S. (1976) Biochim. Biophys. Acta 456, 195-247.
12. Wikström, M.K.F. (1973) Biochim. Biophys. Acta 301, 155-193.
13. de Vries, S., Albracht, S.P.J. and Leeuwerik, F.J. (1979) Biochim. Biophys. Acta 546, 316-333.
14. DerVartanian, D.V., Albracht, S.P.J., Berden, J.A., van Gelder, B.F. and Slater, E.C. (1973) Biochim. Biophys. Acta 292, 496-501.
15. Borst, P. and Grivell, L.A. (1981) Nature 289, 439-440.
16. Lazowska, J., Jacq, C. and Slonimski, P.P. (1980) Cell 22, 333-348.
17. Wingfield, P., Arad, T., Leonard, K. and Weiss, H. (1979) Nature 280, 696-697
18. Enzyme Nomenclature. Recommendations (1978) of the Nomenclature Committee of the International Union of Biochemistry. Academic Press, New York, p. 595.
19. Keilin, D. (1929) Proc. Roy. Soc. B 104, 206-252.
20. Slater, E.C. (1950) Biochem. J. 46, 484-499.
21. Chance, B. (1952) Nature 169, 215-221.
22. Chance, B. (1954) in The Mechanism of Enzyme Action (W.D. McElroy and B. Glass, eds.), Baltimore, pp. 399-453
23. Chance, B. and Williams, G.R. (1955) J. Biol. Chem. 217, 409-427
24. Jackson, F.L. and Lightdown, J.W. (1958) Biochem. J. 69, 63-67.
25. Slater, E.C. and Colpa-Boonstra, J.P. (1961) in Haematin

Enzymes (J.E. Falk, R. Lemberg and R.K. Morton, eds.), Pergamon, Oxford, pp. 575-592.
26. Chance, B. (1952) 2e Congrès International de Biochimie, Paris, Résumés des Communications, p. 32, Declume, Lons-Le-Saunier.
27. Chance, B. (1958) J. Biol. Chem. 233, 1223-1229.
28. Chance, B. and Schoener, B. (1966) J. Biol. Chem. 241, 4567-4573.
29. Wegdam, H.J., Berden, J.A. and Slater, E.C. (1970) Biochim. Biophys. Acta 223, 365-373.
30. Wilson, D.F. and Dutton, P.L. (1970) Biochem. Biophys. Res. Commun. 39, 59-64.
31. Wikström, M.K.F. and Berden, J.A. (1972) Biochim. Biophys. Acta 283, 403-420.
32. Baum, H. and Rieske, J.S. (1966) Biochem. Biophys. Res. Commun. 24, 1-9.
33. Eisenbach, M. and Gutman, M. (1975) Eur. J. Biochem. 52, 107-116.
34. Slater, E.C. (1949) Biochem. J. 45, 14-30.
35. Yukushiji, E. and Okuniki, K. (1940) Proc. Imp. Acad. (Tokyo) 16, 299-302.
36. Slater, E.C. (1949) Nature 163, 532-533.
37. Potter, V.R. and Reif, A.E. (1952) J. Biol. Chem. 194, 287-297.
38. Keilin, D. and Hartree, E.F. (1955) Nature 176, 200-206.
39. Deul, D.H. and Thorn, M.B. (1962) Biochim. Biophys. Acta 59, 426-436.
40. Nishibayashi-Yamashita, H., Cunningham, C. and Racker, E. (1972) J. Biol. Chem. 247, 698-704.
41. Trumpower, B.L. (1976) Biochem. Biophys. Res. Commun. 70, 73-80.
42. Trumpower, B.L. and Edwards, C.A. (1979) J. Biol. Chem. 254, 8697-8706.
43. Rieske, J.S., Hansen, R.E. and Zaugg, W.S. (1964) J. Biol. Chem. 239, 3017-3022.
44. Slater, E.C. and de Vries, S. (1980) Nature 288, 717-718.
45. Slater, E.C. (1955) Proc. 3rd Intern. Congr. Biochem., Brussels, Academic Press, New York, pp. 264-277.
46. Slater, E.C. (1961) Symp. Genet. Biol. Italica 8, 309-329.
47. Slater, E.C. (1972) Harvey Lectures 66, 19-42.
48. Cadenas, E., Boveris, A., Ragan, C.I. and Stoppani, A.O.M. (1977) Arch. Biochem. Biophys. 180, 248-257.
49. Mitchell, P.D. (1975) FEBS Lett. 56, 1-6.
50. Mitchell, P.D. (1975) FEBS Lett. 59, 137-139.
51. van Ark, G. (1980) Electron Transfer through the Ubiquinol: Ferricytochrome $\underline{c}$ Oxidoreductase Segment of the Mitochondrial Respiratory Chain, Rodopi, Amsterdam.

52. Cox, G.B. and Gibson, F. (1974) Biochim. Biophys. Acta
    346, 1-25.
52a.Martius, C. (1955) Proc. 3rd Intern. Congr. Biochem.
    Brussels, Academic Press, New York, pp. 1-9
53. Kröger, A. and Klingenberg, M. (1973) Eur. J. Biochem.
    34, 358-368.
54. Albracht, S.P.J., van Verseveld, H.W., Hagen, W.R. and
    Kalkman, M.L. (1980) Biochim. Biophys. Acta 593, 173-186.
55. Kröger, A. (1976) FEBS Lett. 65, 278-280.
56. Trumpower, B.L. (1976) Biochem. Biophys. Res. Commun. 70,
    73-80.
57. Berden, J.A., de Vries, S. and Slater, E.C. (1981) in
    Functions of Quinone and Energy-Conserving Systems (B.L.
    Trumpower, ed.), Academic Press, New York, in the press
58. Malviya, A.N., Nicholls, P. and Elliott, W.B. (1980)
    Biochim. Biophys. Acta 589, 137-149.
59. Ksenzenko, M.Yu. and Konstantinov, A.A. (1980) Biochemis-
    try (U.S.S.R.) 45, 343-353.
60. Bowyer, J.R. and Trumpower, B.L. (1980) FEBS Lett. 115,
    171-174.
61. Surkov, S.A. and Konstantinov, A.A. (1980) FEBS Lett. 109,
    283-288.
62. Yu, C.A., Nagaoka, S., Yu, L. and King, T.E. (1980) Arch.
    Biochem. Biophys. 204, 59-70.
63. Jin, Y.-Z., Tang, H.-L., Li, S.-L. and Tsou, C.L. (1981)
    Biochim. Biophys. Acta in the press
64. Alexandre, A., Galiazzo, F. and Lehninger, A.L. (1980)
    J. Biol. Chem. 255, 10721-10730.
65. Mitchell, P. and Moyle, J. (1981) in Functions of Quinones
    and Energy-Conserving Systems (B.L. Trumpower, ed.),
    Academic Press, New York, in the press
66. Trumpower, B.L. and Katki, A.G. (1979) in Membrane Proteins
    in Energy Transduction (R.A. Capaldi, ed.), Dekker, New
    York, pp. 89-200.
67. Yu, C.A., Nagaoka, S., Yu, L. and King, T.E. (1978) Bio-
    chem. Biophys. Res. Commun. 82, 1070-1078.
68. Ohnishi, T. and Trumpower, B.L. (1980) J. Biol. Chem.
    255, 3278-3284.
69. de Vries, S., Berden, J.A. and Slater, E.C. (1980)
    FEBS Lett. 122, 143-148.
70. de Vries, S., Berden, J.A. and Slater, E.C. (1981) in
    Functions of Quinones and Energy-Conserving Systems
    (B.L. Trumpower, ed.), Academic Press, New York, in the press
71. Boveris, A. and Chance, B. (1973) Biochem. J. 134, 707-
    716.
72. Slater, E.C. (1961) in Intracellular Respiration: Phos-
    phorylation and Non-phosphorylating Oxidation Reactions

(E.C. Slater, ed.), Proc. 5th Intern. Congr. Biochem., Pergamon, Oxford, p. 360.
73. Boveris, A., Cadenas, E. and Stoppani, A.O.M. (1976) Biochem. J. 156, 435-444.
74. van Ark, G., Raap, A.K., Berden, J.A. and Slater, E.C. (1981) Biochim. Biophys. Acta, in the press.
75. Velthuys, B. (1981) in Function of Quinones in Energy-Conserving Systems (B.L. Trumpower, ed.), Academic Press, New York, in the press
76. de Kok, J. and Slater, E.C. (1975) Biochim. Biophys. Acta 376, 27-41.
77. Papa, S., Guerrieri, F. and Lorusso, M. (1974) BBA Library 13, 417-432.
78. von Jagow, G. and Engel, W.D. (1980) FEBS Lett. 111, 1-5.
79. Yu, L., Yu, C.A. and King, T.E. (1977) Biochem. Biophys. Res. Commun. 79, 259-265.
80. Yu, L. and Yu, C.A. (1980) Biochemistry 19, 3579-3585.
81. Ackrell, B.A.C., Bethany-Hall, M. and Kearney, E.B. (1980) J. Biol. Chem. 255, 2761-2769.
82. Konstantinov, A.A. and Ruuge, E.K. (1977) FEBS Lett. 81, 137-141.
83. Weiss, H. and Kolb, H.J. (1979) Eur. J. Biochem. 99, 139-149.
84. Yu, C.A. and Yu, L. (1980) Biochem. Biophys. Res. Commun. 96, 286-292.
85. Roberts, H., Smith, S.C., Marzuki, S. and Linnane, A.W. (1980) Arch. Biochem. Biophys. 200, 387-395.
86. Katan, M.B., van Harten-Loosbroek, N. and Groot, G.S.P. (1976) Eur. J. Biochem. 70, 409-417.
87. Das Gupta, U. and Rieske, J.S. (1973) Biochem. Biophys. Res. Commun. 54, 1247-1254.
88. Ernster, L., Lee, I.Y., Norling, B. and Persson, B. (1969) Eur. J. Biochem. 9, 299-310.
89. Trumpower, B.L. and Simmons, Z. (1979) J. Biol. Chem. 254, 4608-4616.
90. Wikström, M.K.F. and Krab, K. (1980) Current Topics in Bioenergetics 10, 51-101.

PATHWAYS OF ELECTRON TRANSFER IN THE CYTOCHROME b-c_1

COMPLEXES OF MITOCHONDRIA AND PHOTOSYNTHETIC BACTERIA[1]

John R. Bowyer[2] and Bernard L. Trumpower[3]

Department of Biochemistry
Dartmouth Medical School
Hanover, NH 03755

INTRODUCTION

The cytochrome b-c_1 complex of the mitochondrial respiratory chain is an oligomeric lipoprotein complex of the inner mitochondrial membrane, which transfers electrons from the membranous dehydrogenases to cytochrome c (1,2). For each electron passed through the b-c_1 complex, two protons are released to the electropositive, cytoplasmic side of the inner membrane and one proton is taken up from the electronegative, matrix side (3-5).

The photosynthetic bacteria, *Rhodopseudomonas sphaeroïdes* and *capsulata* appear to contain a b-c_1 complex analogous to that of mitochondria, and electron transfer through this complex is also accompanied by proton translocation across the energy transducing membrane (6-10). As discussed below, the bacterial b-c_1 complex is reduced

---

[1] Supported by NIH Research Grant GM 20379

[2] Present address: Department of Biochemistry and Biophysics, University of Pennsylvania Medical School, G-5, Philadelphia, PA 19104

[3] Established Investigator of the American Heart Association

V. P. Skulachev and Peter C. Hinkle (eds.), Chemiosmotic Proton Circuits in Biological Membranes
in honor of Peter Mitchell   ISBN 0-201-07398-6

Table I

Oxidation-Reduction Components in the Cytochrome b-c_1 Complexes of Mammalian Mitochondria and *Rhodopseudomonas sphaeroides*

Component	λ max (nm)	ε_m^1 (mv)	Ref.
Mitochondrial Cytochrome b-c_1 Complex			
Cytochrome b-566	566, 558	-100	(63)
Cytochrome b-562	562	+40, +135	(63)
Cytochrome c_1	553	+225	(63)
Iron-sulfur cluster	EPR resonance: g = 1.90	+280	Footnote[2]
Ubiquinol	-	+100 (n = 2)	(61,62)
Rhodopseudomonas sphaeroides Cytochrome b-c_1 Complex			
Cytochrome b-566	566, 559	-90	(47,64)
Cytochrome b-560	560	+50, +155	(47,64)
Cytochrome c_1	552	+290	(8)
Iron-sulfur cluster	EPR resonance: g = 1.90	+280	(65)
Ubiquinol	-	+155 (n = 2)	(43,44,50)

[1.] Midpoint potentials of the mitochondrial and bacterial components were measured at pH 7.2 and 7.0, respectively.

[2.] Unpublished results (J.R.B.) obtained with isolated succinate-cytochrome c reductase.

and reoxidized by a photochemical reaction center, the energy for this cyclic electron transfer being derived from light.

There is a striking similarity in the oxidation-reduction components of the b-c$_1$ complexes of mitochondria and these bacteria as indicated by Table 1. Both contain two spectrally and thermodynamically distinct b cytochromes, a membranous c$_1$ cytochrome having an absorption maximum and molecular weight distinct from the membrane-associated c or c$_2$ cytochrome, and an iron-sulfur protein characterized by an EPR resonance at g = 1.90. Both complexes also contain a bound ubiquinone. The properties of this quinone are deduced from the apparent potential dependency of the antimycin sensitive rate of cytochrome c$_1$ + c (c$_2$) rereduction following flash illumination. This ubiquinone may be identical to that which gives rise to a thermodynamically stable ubisemiquinone, SQ$_c$, (11).

Because of the extensive analogy between the mitochondrial and bacterial b-c$_1$ complexes, it is likely that the pathways of electron transfer and the associated mechanisms of proton translocation are similar and perhaps identical in these species. This review discusses electron transfer schemes postulated for these b-c$_1$ complexes and describes evidence for and against these schemes.

STUDIES WITH THE MITOCHONDRIAL b-c$_1$ COMPLEX

When antimycin is added to respiring mitochondria, it leads to increased reduction of ubiquinone and the b cytochromes and decreased reduction of cytochromes c and c$_1$ (12,13). If the iron-sulfur protein equilibrates with the c cytochromes under these conditions, these results support a linear scheme of electron transfer of the following type:

$$\text{succinate} \rightarrow Q \rightarrow [\underline{b}\text{-566}, \underline{b}\text{-562}] \overset{\textit{antimycin}}{-||} \rightarrow \text{ISP} \rightarrow \underline{c}_1 \rightarrow \underline{c}$$

This scheme does not account for the observation that when $\underline{c}_1$ is reduced, reduction of $\underline{b}$ by succinate or ubiquinol is inhibited by antimycin (2,14,15). Reoxidation of $\underline{c}_1$ results in "oxidant-induced" reduction of $\underline{b}$ (14-18). Chance has proposed that these redox reactions of cytochrome $\underline{b}$ result from a heme-heme interaction, in which oxidation of $\underline{c}_1$ increases the midpoint potentials of the $\underline{b}$'s, enabling their reduction by ubiquinol (18). Such a mechanism would presumably operate only in the presence of antimycin, since otherwise the reducibility of $\underline{b}$ is independent of the reduction status of $\underline{c}_1$ (19).

Further evidence against a simple linear scheme has been obtained with isolated succinate-cytochrome $\underline{c}$ reductase complex in which the cytochromes of the $\underline{b}$-$\underline{c}_1$ complex can be reduced via the associated dehydrogenase complex (2). With this preparation antimycin does not inhibit rapid reduction of cytochrome $\underline{c}_1$ when succinate is added to the fully oxidized complex, but does inhibit subsequent turnover of the complex (19). Rapid reduction of $\underline{c}_1$ in the presence of antimycin was also observed in mung bean mitochondria (20).

The iron-sulfur protein of the $\underline{b}$-$\underline{c}_1$ complex is essential for ubiquinol-cytochrome $\underline{c}$ reductase activity but not for succinate-ubiquinone reductase activity (21,22). Removal of the iron-sulfur protein from isolated succinate-cytochrome $\underline{c}$ reductase complex eliminates the otherwise rapid reduction of cytochrome $\underline{c}_1$ by succinate which is observed both in the absence or presence of antimycin (23,24). Removal of the iron-sulfur protein also eliminates the rapid reduction of cytochrome $\underline{b}$, but only in the presence of antimycin. In the

absence of antimycin, reduction of b is unaffected (23,24).
Removal of the iron-sulfur protein also blocks oxidant-induced
reduction of the b's (25). These results are especially difficult to reconcile with a linear scheme of electron transfer.

CYCLIC PROTONMOTIVE MECHANISMS

Mitchell's formulation of the protonmotive Q cycle (26-
28) accounted for oxidant-induced reduction of cytochrome b and
elegantly predicted the subsequently demonstrated effects on
electron transfer reactions within the b-c$_1$ complex resulting
from removal of the iron-sulfur protein (23). An important
feature of the Q cycle, shown in Fig. 1, is that there should

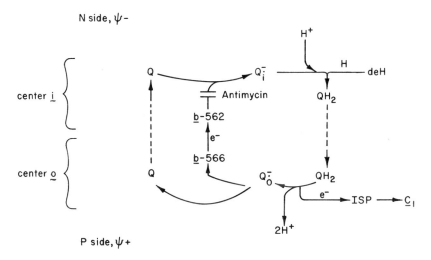

*Figure 1 Protonmotive Q cycle scheme for electron transfer from suc-
cinate dehydrogenase through the b-c$_1$ complex. The scheme depicts
electron transfer reactions in the forward direction under steady-
state conditions. During the first turnover, when succinate is
added to the oxidized complex, the dehydrogenase (deH) must reduce
ubiquinone to ubiquinol in an antimycin insensitive reaction. During
subsequent turnovers antimycin inhibits oxidation-reduction of b-562
by the ubiquinone/ubisemiquinone couple. The semiquinones are depicted in the anionic form, based on potentiometric studies of
ubisemiquinone in isolated b-c$_1$ complex (11,66).*

be two sites in the $\underline{b}$-$\underline{c}_1$ complex at which ubiquinone is involved, designated center $\underline{o}$ and center $\underline{i}$, topographically located at the electropositive and electronegative sides of the membrane, respectively. (For reviews, see refs. 28,29.)

At center $\underline{o}$ ubiquinol is oxidized to ubiquinone with release of 2 H^+ to the electropositive side of the membrane. One electron from ubiquinol is delivered to the iron-sulfur protein and thence to $\underline{c}_1$, hence the need for iron-sulfur protein for reduction of $\underline{c}_1$. The intermediate semiquinone then reduces $\underline{b}$-566, which in turn reduces $\underline{b}$-562. The electron on $\underline{b}$-562 is used, along with an electron delivered from the dehydrogenase, to reduce ubiquinone to ubiquinol at center $\underline{i}$. Of the 2 H^+ thus taken up from the electronegative side of the membrane, one comes from the substrate, which releases 1 H^+/e^- on oxidation. Antimycin inhibits reoxidation of $\underline{b}$-562, thus "trapping" electrons in the $\underline{b}$ cytochromes as the $\underline{c}$ cytochromes are oxidized.

In the absence of antimycin, the $\underline{b}$'s may be reduced by a reversal of the pathway by which they are normally reoxidized at center $\underline{i}$ (23). When this pathway is inhibited by antimycin, cytochrome $\underline{b}$ can only be reduced by $Q_o^{\bar{\cdot}}$, the formation of which requires iron-sulfur protein. That cytochrome $\underline{b}$ is not reduced by succinate in the presence of antimycin when the iron-sulfur protein and $\underline{c}_1$ are already reduced has been taken to indicate that ubisemiquinone is present in insignificant amounts at center $\underline{o}$ under these conditions. This implies that $Q_o^{\bar{\cdot}}$ is very unstable and can only be generated by ubiquinol oxidation, hence the requirement that the iron-sulfur protein and $\underline{c}_1$ must be oxidized prior to succinate addition.

Instability of the semiquinone means that the midpoint potential of the $Q_o^{\bar{\cdot}}/QH_2$ couple is likely to be higher than that of the iron-sulfur protein. If $Q_o^{\bar{\cdot}}$ is not rapidly removed

by electron transfer to b, ubiquinol oxidation is thermodynamically unfavorable. In this way antimycin would not inhibit
reduction of c$_1$ when succinate is added to the oxidized complex,
but would inhibit subsequent turnover of the complex in which
the b has become reduced during the first turnover.

Such a mechanism has two prerequisites. First, the
instability of $Q_o^{\bar{\cdot}}$ means that it is not bound very much more
tightly than Q or QH$_2$ at center o at equilibrium, but its
rate of dissociation from this site must be very slow. Second,
the loosely bound but slowly dissociating $Q_o^{\bar{\cdot}}$ must be unable to
react with oxidized iron-sulfur protein. Electron transfer to
the iron-sulfur protein and thence to c$_1$ in the presence of
antimycin would then be limited either by the rate of reoxidation of cytochrome b through the antimycin block, the rate of
dissociation of $Q_o^{\bar{\cdot}}$ from its binding site at center o, or the
rate of reaction between $Q_o^{\bar{\cdot}}$ and iron-sulfur protein.

There is no *a priori* reason why this last reaction
should not be rapid. Velthuys (30) has suggested that oxidation of reduced iron-sulfur protein by c$_1$ is inhibited when
$Q_o^{\bar{\cdot}}$ is present. It is conceivable that the "loosening" or
structural dislocation of the iron-sulfur protein which appears
to be an indirect consequence of antimycin binding to b-562
(for a review, see ref. 31) may make the oxidized iron-sulfur
cluster inaccessible to $Q_o^{\bar{\cdot}}$.

The original Q cycle does not account for the
observation that when the b cytochromes are fully reduced in
anaerobic mitochondria, addition of O$_2$ results in their oxidation by an antimycin sensitive pathway (14,18,32). In the
scheme of Fig. 1, oxidation of the c cytochromes would generate
$Q_o^{\bar{\cdot}}$ as a *reductant* for the already reduced b's, whereas the
experimental observations (14,18,32) require that an *oxidant*
is made available at center i. The scheme also imposes certain

kinetic constraints. Thus during one turnover of the b-c$_1$ complex, reoxidation of b-562 at center i should prevail over reduction of ubiquinone to ubiquinol by the dehydrogenase, otherwise an antimycin-like effect would be observed. Similarly, when succinate is added to the fully oxidized complex in the absence of antimycin, the pathway for b reduction which is linked to reduction of the iron-sulfur protein and cytochrome c$_1$ must prevail over the "antimycin sensitive" pathway through center i.

To account for these results, Mitchell (33) proposed that the fate of $\overline{Q_o^{\cdot}}$ depends on the redox poise of cytochrome b. If the b's are oxidized or only partially reduced, $\overline{Q_o^{\cdot}}$ acts as a *reductant* for b-566, as in oxidant-induced reduction thereof (14-18,34). If the b's are fully reduced, and only under these relatively unusual conditions, $\overline{Q_o^{\cdot}}$ would react at center i as an *oxidant* for b-562 in an antimycin sensitive reaction as shown in Fig. 2.

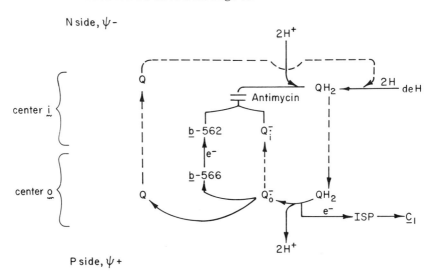

Figure 2 A hybrid scheme for electron transfer which differs from the protonmotive Q cycle in that ubisemiquinone generated by ubiquinol oxidation at center o acts as a reductant for b-566 or as an antimycin sensitive oxidant for b-562 at a separate site. Protonmotive consequences of this pathway are discussed in the text.

Conduction of $Q_o^{\bar{.}}$ to center $\underline{i}$ requires a specific mechanism
which ordinarily is inoperative and which prevents rapid dismutation of semiquinones generated at different center o's.

Wikström and Krab (35) proposed that a single species of
ubisemiquinone routinely alternates between being the reductant
and oxidant for the $\underline{b}$ cytochromes. One molecule of ubiquinol
is oxidized to ubiquinone with transfer of one electron to $\underline{c}_1$
via the iron-sulfur protein. The resulting semiquinone *reduces*
$\underline{b}$-562, possibly via $\underline{b}$-566. The quinone is then fully rereduced
by the dehydrogenase in an antimycin insensitive reaction. This
second molecule of ubiquinol is oxidized to semiquinone by the
same route as the first, but the resulting semiquinone then
oxidizes $\underline{b}$-562 in an antimycin sensitive reaction.

The "$\underline{b}$ cycle" (35) does not require coordinated
reduction of the ubisemiquinone couples by a $\underline{b}$ cytochrome and
the dehydrogenase, nor does it require $\underline{b}$-562 to function as a
dismutase in the ubiquinol-cytochrome $\underline{c}$ reductase reaction.
The $\underline{b}$ cycle accounts for antimycin sensitive oxidation of the
fully reduced $\underline{b}$ cytochromes, as does the restricted excursion
of $Q_o^{\bar{.}}$ (or $QH_o^{.}$) to center $\underline{i}$ in the Q cycle.

In the $\underline{b}$ cycle transmembranous oxidation-reduction
reactions of ubiquinone need not fully account for the observed
proton and charge translocation stoichiometries. To make up
for this shortfall, it has been proposed that the $\underline{b}$ cytochromes
translocate protons. A ligand mechanism which would link
proton translocation to oxidation-reduction of the $\underline{b}$'s is
thus notably missing.

STUDIES WITH THE PHOTOSYNTHETIC BACTERIAL $\underline{b}$-$\underline{c}_1$ COMPLEX

The membrane in which the photosynthetic bacterial $\underline{b}$-$\underline{c}_1$
complex is located also contains a pigment protein complex,
the photochemical reaction center. In response to a short

light flash the reaction center simultaneously generates a
high potential bacteriochlorophyll oxidant, $(BChl)_2^{+\cdot}$, and a
low potential ubisemiquinone anion reductant $(Q_I^{-\cdot})$, bound at
specific sites in the reaction center (36,37). The $(BChl)_2^{+\cdot}$
is rereduced by cytochrome c_2, a soluble protein analogous to
mitochondrial cytochrome c (8,9,38,39), and $Q_I^{-\cdot}$ is reoxidized
by another specifically bound ubiquinone, Q_{II} (40). These
reactions occur in less than 100 μs, which means that the reaction center provides both reducing and oxidizing equivalents
on a time scale considerably faster than the turnover time of
the b-c_1 complex. Bacterial c_1 appears to be oxidized by
cytochrome c_2 with $t_{\frac{1}{2}} \simeq 150$ μs (9,39). The iron-sulfur protein
donates electrons into the $c_1 + c_2$ "pool" on a similar time
scale (41). The latter reaction is inhibited by a ubiquinone
analogue, 5-n-undecyl-6-hydroxy-4,7-dioxobenzothiazole (41,42).

Following flash induced oxidation, reduction of $c_1 + c_2$
is only about 50% complete in the presence of antimycin. In
its absence, the remaining $c_1 + c_2$ becomes rereduced at a rate
which accelerates as the applied redox potential is lowered
below 200 mV ($t_{\frac{1}{2}} \sim 1$ ms at 100 mV) (43,44). If the b's are
oxidized before flash activation, then, in the presence of
antimycin, b-560 is reduced on flash excitation with a $t_{\frac{1}{2}} < 0.5$
ms at an applied potential of 100 mV (pH 7.0), following a lag
of 200 μs (45,46). Rapid reduction of b-566 has also been
observed (9,47). In the absence of antimycin, b-560 is
transiently reduced, and the kinetics of its reoxidation are
similar to those of the antimycin sensitive phase of $c_1 + c_2$
reduction (48,49).

There appears to be a 30-40% excess of reaction centers
over b-c_1 complex in the photosynthetic system (41,50), so
that some b-c_1 complexes may undergo more than one turnover
in the absence of antimycin following a single flash. In terms

of the data from the mitochondrial studies (19), this might explain the partial inhibition of c_1 + c_2 rereduction by anti-mycin. The rate of the slow phase of c_1 + c_2 reduction in the absence of antimycin would be limited by the antimycin sensitive reoxidation of b necessary to regenerate "kinetically competent" ubiquinol to complete the reduction of c_1 + c_2.

However, there is no evidence that electron transfer to c_1 + c_2 in the presence of antimycin includes any contribution from ubiquinol oxidation. This reaction is not significantly affected by ubiquinone extraction (51,52), nor by oxidation of ubiquinone before flash excitation (43,44,48, 50). In addition, a fraction of the "excess" reaction centers appears to be unavailable to react rapidly with c_2. It thus appears that incomplete rereduction of c_1 + c_2 in the presence of antimycin may be due to a substoichiometric level of reduced iron-sulfur protein before flash activation, and to the similar midpoint potentials of the three components (41).

It is generally considered then, that the rapid b reduction in the presence of antimycin is not linked to ubiquinol oxidation via the iron-sulfur protein, assuming the latter rapidly equilibrates with the c cytochromes under these conditions. The b is thought to be reduced by electrons delivered, possibly directly, from Q_{II} both in the presence and absence of antimycin. The kinetic similarity between the antimycin sensitive phases of c_1 + c_2 rereduction and b oxidation, and the similar acceleration of these rates at lower potential, led to the proposal that, in the absence of antimycin, ubiquinol oxidized by the iron-sulfur cluster generated an unstable semiquinone which oxidizes photo-reduced b-560 in an antimycin-sensitive reaction (45), like that proposed for the mitochondrial complex (33,35). Thus, following flash activation, in the presence of antimycin, cytochrome b is rapidly

reduced by Q_{II}, and ubiquinol oxidation by the iron-sulfur
protein cannot proceed because of the lack of a reaction
partner for the intermediate semiquinone.

Cytochrome b reduction linked to ubiquinol oxidation
by the iron-sulfur protein in the presence of antimycin may
be observable under certain conditions. If the c cytochromes,
ubiquinone, and presumably the iron-sulfur protein are reduced
in the presence of antimycin, and ferricyanide is added in the
dark, oxidant-induced reduction of b is observed (53). If,
under these same conditions, a weak flash is used to activate
only ~50% of the reaction centers, a partial recovery of the
antimycin sensitive phase of c_1 + c_2 rereduction is observed,
and these kinetics are similar to those of a phase of b reduction. This result was interpreted to indicate that the reaction
centers reduced b-560 via Q_{II}, leaving a fraction of the b-560
oxidized, and this could be reduced in an antimycin insensitive reaction linked to ubiquinol oxidation (54).

To explain the pathway in which b reduction appears to
be linked to the redox status of the iron-sulfur protein, Crofts
and coworkers (9) suggested that Q_{II} is unable to reduce b-560
for thermodynamic reasons unless the midpoint potential of the
latter is raised through a coulombic interaction with oxidized
iron-sulfur protein. Reduction of the iron-sulfur protein
would then indirectly inhibit b reduction.

This model appears not to explain the effects of
reduction or removal of the iron-sulfur protein in the mitochondrial b-c_1 complex. Succinate is able to reduce b-562
when c_1 and presumably the iron-sulfur protein are reduced,
but not in the presence of antimycin (2,15). The reduction
potential imposed by the addition of succinate ($\varepsilon_{m,7}$ = + 25 mV)
is low enough to reduce b-562 (Table 1), so that inhibition
by antimycin must be kinetic and not thermodynamic in this

system. In this model (9) removal of the iron-sulfur protein
would presumably mimic its reduction, since in both instances
b reduction becomes antimycin sensitive in the mitochondrial
system.

PARALLEL PATHWAYS

In the schemes illustrated, it has been assumed that
the b cytochromes act in series, and that the iron-sulfur protein and c_1 act in series. These serial reactions are by no
means proven and several schemes have recently appeared in
which pairs of components act in parallel, linked by reactions
with the ubiquinone/ubiquinol couple. On the basis of the
redox properties of Q_{II}, and the kinetics of b-566 and b-562
reduction following flash excitation of photosynthetic bacterial
membranes, it was suggested that the quinol form of Q_{II} delivers
two electrons into the b-c$_1$ complex on every alternate flash,
one to b-566 and the other to b-560 in parallel reactions (9).
It was also proposed that ubiquinol delivered one electron to
the iron-sulfur protein and the semiquinone intermediate
reduced c_1. In this way the iron-sulfur protein would be
required for c_1 reduction. This model does not simply explain
the potential-dependent acceleration of the rate of the antimycin sensitive phase of c_1 + c_2 reduction following flash
excitation (43,44,50) or antimycin insensitive c_1 reduction
in the mitochondrial complex (19,20).

A scheme (56) in which the ubiquinone/ubiquinol couple
reacts with the b-562/iron-sulfur protein pair, the b-566/
c_1 pair, and the b-562/b-566 pair appears unacceptable because
it does not require iron-sulfur protein for reduction of c_1
(23,24). von Jagow and Engel (57) proposed that the b's act

in parallel as redox driven proton pumps. They also observed
that treatment of an isolated cytochrome b dimer with urea
eliminates the redox potential difference between b-562 and
b-566, suggesting that there may be an interaction between
the two hemes, like that proposed for iron-sulfur centers
S-1 and S-2 in succinate dehydrogenase (58).

CONCLUSION

No single scheme adequately accounts for all of the
observations described here and elsewhere. Attempts to generate
a unifying model for the mitochondrial and photosynthetic bacterial complexes require a number of assumptions concerning
relative reaction rates and electrostatic/conformational
interactions between components of the complex. One possible
scheme, extending that of Fig. 2, postulates three pathways
for reduction of cytochrome b, two of which have been described
earlier. In order to explain the observations with photosynthetic bacteria it is necessary to postulate that Q_{II}, or an
additional quinone reduced by Q_{II}, may reduce b-562, perhaps
via b-566, in an antimycin insensitive reaction. This reaction must be linked, for kinetic and/or thermodynamic reasons,
to oxidation of the iron-sulfur protein. In the mitochondrial
complex, the requirement that the iron-sulfur protein is oxidized to permit subsequent b reduction would apply only in the
presence of antimycin. The pathway linked to ubiquinol
oxidation by the iron-sulfur protein must operate when
succinate is added to oxidized succinate-cytochrome c reductase
complex in the presence of antimycin (to account for c_1
reduction), presumably because it is kinetically faster under
these conditions.

This scheme requires some rather complex consequences
of antimycin binding and of oxidation of the iron-sulfur

protein (11,29,59,60). It is to some extent testable using
a system consisting of photosynthetic reaction centers and
mitochondrial or bacterial $\underline{b}-\underline{c}_1$ complex (61,62), omitting
cytochrome $\underline{c}$ or $\underline{c}_2$. In such a system, if cytochrome $\underline{c}$ ($\underline{c}_2$)
is not included, a reductant would be made available (Q_{II})
by flash excitation, but the possible complications resulting
from simultaneous oxidation of iron-sulfur protein and $\underline{c}_1$ by
the reaction center would be prevented. Cytochrome $\underline{b}$ reduction should then be antimycin sensitive. If reaction centers
are treated to prevent formation of a reductant on Q_{II}, then
$\underline{b}$ reduction should be insensitive to antimycin but require
the presence of ubiquinol before flash oxidation. Rereduction
of the iron-sulfur protein and $\underline{c}_1$ should then ensue with
kinetics similar to those of $\underline{b}$ reduction.

REFERENCES

1. Rieske, J.S. (1976) Biochim. Biophys. Acta 456, 195-247
2. Trumpower, B.L. and Katki, A. (1979) in Membrane Proteins
   in Energy Transduction (Capaldi, R.A., ed.), pp. 89-200,
   Marcell Dekker, New York
3. Mitchell, P. and Moyle, J. (1967) in Biochemistry of
   Mitochondria (Slater, E.C., Kaniuga, Z. and Wojtczak, L.,
   eds.), pp. 53-74, Academic Press, London
4. Lawford, H.G. and Garland, P.B. (1973) Biochem. J. 136,
   711-720
5. Alexandre, A. and Lehninger, A.L. (1979) J. Biol. Chem.
   254, 11555-11560
6. Crofts, A.R. and Wood, P.M. (1978) Curr. Topics Bioenerg.
   7, 175-244
7. Dutton, P.L. and Prince, R.C. (1978) in The Photosynthetic
   Bacteria, (Clayton, R.K. and Sistrom, W.R., eds.) pp. 525-
   570, Academic Press, New York
8. Wood, P.M. (1980) Biochem. J. 189, 385-391
9. Crofts, A.R., Meinhardt, S.W. and Bowyer, J.R. (1981) in
   Function of Quinones in Energy Conserving Systems
   (Trumpower, B.L., ed.) Academic Press, New York, in press
10. Prince, R.C., O'Keefe, D.P. and Dutton, P.L. (1981) in
    Photosynthetic Electron Flow and Phosphorylation (Barber,
    J., ed.) Elsevier/North Holland Biomedical Press, in press

11. Ohnishi, T. and Trumpower, B.L. (1980) J. Biol. Chem. 255, 3278-3284
12. Chance, B. (1952) Nature 169, 215-221
13. Keilin, D. and Hartree, E.F. (1955) Nature 176, 200-206
14. Erecinska, M., Chance, B., Wilson, D.F. and Dutton, P.L. (1972) Proc. Natl. Acad. Sci. U.S.A. 69, 50-54
15. Trumpower, B.L. and Katki, A. (1975) Biochem. Biophys. Res. Commun. 65, 16-23
16. Eisenbach, M. and Gutman, M. (1975) Eur. J. Biochem. 52, 107-116
17. Wikström, M.K.F. and Berden, J.A. (1972) Biochim. Biophys. Acta 283, 403-420
18. Chance, B. (1974) in Dynamics of Energy-Transducing Membranes (Ernster, L., Estabrook, R.W. and Slater, E.C., eds.) pp. 553-578, Elsevier, Amsterdam
19. Bowyer, J.R. and Trumpower, B.L. (1981) J. Biol. Chem. 256, 2245-2251
20. Rich, P.R. and Moore, A.L. (1976) FEBS Lett. 65, 339-344
21. Trumpower, B.L. and Edwards, C.A. (1979) J. Biol. Chem. 254, 8697-8706
22. Trumpower, B.L., Edwards, C.A. and Ohnishi, T. (1980) J. Biol. Chem. 255, 7487-7493
23. Trumpower, B.L. (1976) Biochem. Biophys. Res. Commun. 70, 73-80
24. Edwards, C.A. and Bowyer, J.R. (1981) in Function of Quinones in Energy Conserving Systems (Trumpower, B.L., ed.) Academic Press, New York, in press
25. Bowyer, J.R., Edwards, C.A. and Trumpower, B.L. (1981) FEBS Lett., 126, 93-97
26. Mitchell, P. (1975) FEBS Lett. 56, 1-6
27. Mitchell, P. (1975) FEBS Lett. 59, 137-319
28. Mitchell, P. (1976) J. Theor. Biol. 62, 327-367
29. Trumpower, B.L. (1981) J. Bioenerg. Biomembr., 13, 1-24
30. Velthuys, B.R. (1981) in Function of Quinones in Energy Conserving Systems, (Trumpower, B.L., ed.), Academic Press, New York, in press.
31. Trumpower, B.L. (1981) Biochim. Biophys. Acta, in press
32. Erecinska, M., Wagner, M. and Chance, B. (1973) Curr. Top. Bioenerg. 5, 267-303
33. Mitchell, P. (1981) in Oxidases and Related Redox Systems (King, T.E., Mason, H.S. and Morrison, M., eds.) Vol. 3, Pergamon, London, in press
34. Bowyer, J.R. and Trumpower, B.L. (1980) FEBS Lett. 115, 171-174
35. Wikström, M. and Krab, K. (1980) in Curr. Top. Bioenerg. (Sanadi, D.R., ed.) pp. 51-101, Academic Press, New York

36. Dutton, P.L., Prince, R.C. and Tiede, D.M. (1978)
    Photochem. Photobiol. 28, 939-949
37. Okamura, M.Y., Feher, G. and Nelson, N. (1981) in
    Integrated Approach to Plant and Bacterial Photosynthesis
    (Govindjee, ed.) Chapter 3, Academic Press, New York,
    in press
38. Prince, R.C., Baccarini-Melandri, A., Hauska, G.A.,
    Melandri, B.A. and Crofts, A.R. (1975) Biochim. Biophys.
    Acta 387, 212-217
39. Wood, P.M. (1980) Biochem. J. 192, 761-764
40. Wraight, C.A. (1979) Photochem. Photobiol. 30, 767-776
41. Bowyer, J.R., Dutton, P.L., Prince, R.C. and Crofts, A.R.
    (1980) Biochim. Biophys. Acta 592, 445-460
42. Bowyer, J.R., Tierney, G.V. and Crofts, A.R. (1979) FEBS
    Lett. 101, 207-212
43. Prince, R.C. and Dutton, P.L. (1977) Biochim. Biophys.
    Acta 462, 731-747
44. Crofts, A.R., Crowther, D., Bowyer, J.R. and Tierney, G.V.
    (1977) in Structure and Function of Energy Transducing
    Membranes (van Dam, K., and van Gelder, B.F., eds.)
    pp. 139-155, Elsevier/North Holland, Amsterdam
45. Evans, E.H. and Crofts, A.R. (1974) Biochim. Biophys.
    Acta 357, 89-102
46. Bowyer, J.R., and Crofts, A.R. (1981) Biochim. Biophys.
    Acta, in press
47. Bowyer, J.R., Meinhardt, S.W., Tierney, G.V. and Crofts,
    A.R. (1981) Biochim. Biophys. Acta 635, 167-186
48. Crofts, A.R., Crowther, D. and Tierney, G.V. (1975) in
    Electron Transfer Chains and Oxidative Phosphorylation
    (Quagliariello, E., Papa, S., Palmieri, E., Slater, E.C.
    and Siliprandi, N., eds.) pp. 233-241, North Holland,
    Amsterdam
49. Prince, R.C. and Dutton, P.L. (1975) Biochim. Biophys.
    Acta 387, 607-613
50. Prince, R.C., Bashford, C.L., Takamiya, K-I., van den Berg,
    W.H., and Dutton, P.L. (1978) J. Biol. Chem. 253, 4137-4142
51. Takamiya, K-I., Prince, R.C. and Dutton, P.L. (1979) J.
    Biol. Chem. 254, 11307-11311
52. Baccarini-Melandri, A., Gabellini, N., Rutherford, A.W.
    and Crofts, A.R. (1980) FEBS Lett., submitted
53. Dutton, P.L., and Prince, R.C. (1978) FEBS Lett. 91, 51-20
54. van den Berg, W.H., Prince, R.C., Bashford, C.L.,
    Takamiya, K-I., Bonner, W.D. and Dutton, P.L. (1979)
    J. Biol. Chem. 254, 8594-8604
55. Bowyer, J.R. and Crofts, A.R. (1978) in Frontiers of
    Biological Energetics Vol. I. (Dutton, P.L., Leigh, J.S.
    and Scarpa, A., eds.) pp. 326-333, Academic Press, New York

56. Malviya, A.N., Nicholls, P. and Elliott, W.B. (1980) Biochim. Biophys. Acta 589, 137-149
57. van Jagow, G. and Engel, W.D. (1980) FEBS Lett. 111, 1-5
58. Salerno, J.C., Lim, J., King, T.E., Blum, H. and Ohnishi, T. (1979) J. Biol. Chem. 254, 4828-4835
59. Rieske, J.S., Baum, H., Stoner, C.D. and Lipton, S.H. (1967) J. Biol. Chem. 242, 4854-4866
60. Petty, K., Jackson, J.B. and Dutton, P.L. (1979) Biochim. Biophys. Acta 546, 17-42
61. Packham, N.K., Tiede, D.M., Mueller, P. and Dutton, P.L. (1980) Proc. Natl. Acad. Sci. U.S.A. 77, 6339-6343
62. Matsuura, K., Packham, N., Tiede, D.M., Mueller, P., and Dutton, P.L. (1981) Biophys. J. 33, 102a
63. Dutton, P.L., Wilson, D.F. and Lee, C-P., (1970) Biochemistry 9, 5077-5082
64. Dutton, P.L. and Jackson, J.B. (1972) Eur. J. Biochem. 30, 495-510
65. Prince, R.C., Lindsay, J.G. and Dutton, P.L. (1975) FEBS Lett. 51, 108-111
66. Salerno, J.C., and Ohnishi, T. (1980) Biochem. J. 192, 769-781

THE Q CYCLE IN THE MITOCHONDRIAL RESPIRATORY CHAIN

Alexander Konstantinov, Wolfram S. Kunz
and Yuriy A. Kamensky

A.N. Belozersky Laboratory of Molecular Biology and
and Bioorganic Chemistry, Moscow State University
Moscow 117234, U. S. S. R.

INTRODUCTION. The second coupling site of the mitochondrial respiratory chain has long behaved more intricately than would be preferred by reviewers. The "Q cycle" scheme by Mitchell (1-4) is no exception to this rule. This advanced model integrates all the basic features of both redox and energy-coupling events at the second site and has proved helpful, at least as an operative scheme guiding further experiments in the field.

Whereas the schemes of Baum et al. (5) and Wikström and Berden (6) are recognized as precursors of Mitchell's hypothesis, it is probably not known to most readers that a model relevant to the Q cycle, with a special emphasis on the role of proton wells, was described independently by

---

Abbreviations: BAL, 2,3-dimercaptopropanol; CoQ, ubiquinone regardless of its redox state: QH_2SQ, Q-reduced, semi-quinone and oxidized forms of CoQ; FeS_R, the Rieske iron-sulfur centre; HOQNO, 2-alkyl-4-hydroxyquinoline-N-oxide; SMP, submitochondrial particles; TTFA, 2-thenoyltrifluoro-acetone; UHDBT, 5-n-undecyl-6-hydroxy-4,7-dioxobenzothia-zole; ΔE_h^{ATP} (x) an ATP-induced shift of redox potential of component x.

V. P. Skulachev and Peter C. Hinkle (eds.), Chemiosmotic Proton Circuits in Biological Membranes
in honor of Peter Mitchell   ISBN 0-201-07398-6

Liberman and co-workers (7) as part of a "chemielectric" version of protonmotive mechanism in the respiratory and photoredox chains (7-10).

The Q cycle can be divided into an electron flow diagram and protonmotive mechanism, which can be analyzed virtually independently from each other.

SEQUENCE OF ELECTRON TRANSFER

CoQ AS ELECTRON ACCEPTOR BY b CYTOCHROMES. The principal postulate of the Q cycle is that there is no direct redox contact between b and c cytochromes as has been believed traditionally (11-13, but see 14), so that CoQ is not only the reductant but also the oxidant for the b-566/b-562 dimer. The reduction of b cytochromes by CoQ is generally accepted (11-13,15). As to CoQ involvement in b cytochrome oxidation, it is corroborated in a rather general sense by the fact that most of the respiratory chain inhibitors which block oxidation of b cytochromes, e.g. antimycin, HOQNO, 2-alkyl-3-hydroxynapthoquinones (16) and many other related compounds (17-19), are CoQ structural analogs (presumably ubisemiquinone antagonists as discussed in (20)). In addition there are several reports that in CoQ-deficient respiratory (21,22) and photosynthetic (23) electron transfer chains inhibition by these compounds can occur above the b cytochromes.

THE 2 CoQ-REACTIVE CENTRES IN SITE 2; ROLE OF UBISEMIQUINONE. If ubiquinone operates on both the reducing and oxidizing sides of b cytochromes, there have to be 2 pathways of the reduction of these hemoproteins by CoQ. These 2 pathways

would correspond to forward and reversed directions of electron flow in site 2 and were assumed to be catalyzed by the
2 CoQ-reactive centres "o" and "i", respectively (4, Fig. 1).

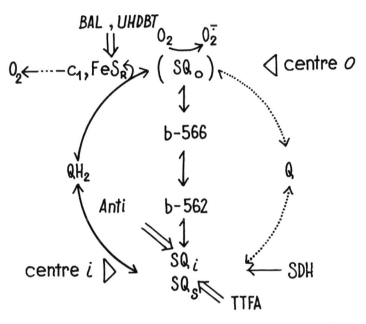

Fig. 1. Q cycle electron flow diagram. Migration of the
oxidized CoQ is depicted by a dotted line to distinguish it
from the flow of reducing equivalents. Three ubisemiquinone
species are shown: (i) stable SQ_s (a single molecule of a
coupled dimer) in succinate-CoQ reductase, (ii) stable SQ_i
associated with the CoQ-reducing site (centre i) of cytochrome
b.c_1 complex and (iii) putative unstable SQ_o which might
occur as an intermediate during the concerted oxidation of
QH_2 in centre o. It is to be emphasized that b cytochromes
(in centre i) and succinate dehydrogenase are capable of
reducing Q to QH_2 independently of each other (4) although
free cooperation between the enzymes is possible.

Junction of 2e and 1e transfer in the centres o and i.
Kinetically efficient and energy-efficient oxidation-reduction of the 2e carrier CoQ by the cytochrome chain comprised

of le centres requires that E_m of the consecutive redox steps QH_2 ---- SQ and SQ ---- Q be brought in accordance with the formal potentials of the metal redox centres serving as donor-acceptors in these reactions.   The problem of the 2e/le junction can be solved by virtue of (1) oxidation-reduction of CoQ by 2 redox centres with widely different E_m; presumably this type of reaction occurs in centre o (4).   (2) stabilization of ubisemiquinone, such that QH_2/SQ and SQ/Q couples acquire E_m values close to E_m of the QH_2/Q transition; consequently 2 electrons can be added to or taken from CoQ by the seme le redox centre.   Such a mechanism has been suggested for centre i (4).

SQ in centre o.

In centre o, an unstable semiquinone is formed transiently at the expense of QH_2 one-electron oxidation by a strong acceptor, most probably, FeS_R protein (24,25, see also 26,27). This ubisemiquinone (SQ_o) serves as a high-(redox)-energy intermediate which can reduce the low-potential heme b-566 and therefore must be protected from dismutation.   However, when concentration of ferric b-566 is low, e.g. in the antimycin-inhibited or energized state, SQ generated in centre o may become susceptible to side reactions.   Thus, as suggested in (28,29), autoxidation of the strongly reducing SQ_o (rather than of the stable SQ_i, 30) is the most likely source of the antimycin and HOQNO stimulated cyanide-sensitive O_2^- generation in site 2 (see 28,29 and references therein; Fig. 1).

   The concentration of SQ_o has to be rather low at equilibrium (4). However, massive accumulation of ubisemiquinone in centre o can be expected in the presence of antimycin and excess oxidant for c_1 cytochrome concurrently with extra-reduction of $\underline{b}$ cytochromes. Although an oxidant-induced increase of the ubisemiquinone ESR signal has been observed in SMP (31) and mitochondria (32), the effects appear to be considerably less than implied by straightforward Q cycle reasoning. It seems likely that antimycin not only inter-rupts the electron flow in centre $\underline{i}$ (4), but can also <u>directly</u> inhibit oxidation of QH_2 in centre $\underline{o}$ (see Fig. 6; 33,34); as has been long known for $CoQ-\underline{b}.\underline{c}_2$ oxidoreductase of photo-synthetic bacteria (35 and references therein). Strangely, this second inhibitory effect appears to be imposed only after heme $\underline{b}$-562 has been reduced in a first turnover of centre $\underline{o}$ (34,35).

<u>SQ in centre $\underline{i}$.</u>

In centre $\underline{i}$ of the Q cycle, SQ_i can be formed spontaneously from QH_2 and Q

$$Q_i + QH_{2i} \longleftrightarrow 2SQ_i; \; K_{eq} \; \sim 1$$

due to an appropriate stabilization of ubisemiquinone (4). There is considerable evidence concerning a stable ubisemi-quinone (31, 32,36-40) or ubisemiquinone pair (38,40-44) in succinate-CoQ reductase of the respiratory chain. This SQ_s is the target of TTFA (31,32,36,38-40,43) and carboxin (32, 44), and a polypeptide has been isolated (45-50) called "apo-Q-protein" (cf. 51) which might be involved in the tight binding of SQ_s. However, since QH_2-cytochrome $\underline{c}$ reductase activity is not sensitve to TTFA, it is unlikely that centre $\underline{i}$ of the $\underline{b}.\underline{c}_1$ complex and succinate-CoQ reductase share the same SQ-stabilizing domain.

At this time there are few data on the stable ubisemi-

quinone in the $\underline{b}.\underline{c}_1$ segment of the electron transfer chain
(52-54). The finding that a significant part of the easily
saturating ubisemiquinone ESR signal is sensitive to antimycin in SMP (31,37,55) and resolved succinate-cytochrome $\underline{c}$
reductase (39), together with a complete inhibition in the
$\underline{b}.\underline{c}_1$ complex (53,54), may indicate that this stable SQ is
indeed associated with centre $\underline{i}$ which is assumed to be the
antimycin inhibition site (1-4). The polypeptide of $\underline{b}.\underline{c}_1$
complex with M.W. 17,000, which has been long known to frac-
tionate (56-58) and assemble in the membrane (59) with $\underline{b}$
cytochromes and is labelled rather specifically by a photo-
active CoQ derivative (60), is a good candidate for SQ-
stabilizing component in centre $\underline{i}$.

It is not clear presently whether it is QH_2, SQ or
either of them that reduces $\underline{b}$ cytochromes in centre $\underline{i}$.
Since under highly reducing conditions reduction of $\underline{b}$ cytochromes becomes sluggish (the so-called "accessibility
barrier", 12,61,62), SQ_i may be the actual reducing species.
Accordingly, the "accessibility barrier" is overcome upon
alkalinization (12,61,62) concurrently with the increase of
SQ_i stability (32,39,55,63).

DISCRIMINATION BETWEEN THE BRANCHED AND (SEMI)CYCLIC MODELS
OF ELECTRON TRANSFER IN SITE 2. At this time there appears
to be general consensus that a simple linear sequence of
redox carriers in site 2 fails to explain "anomalous" features of $\underline{b}$ cytochromes oxidation-reduction in the presence of
antimycin such as "extra-reduction" (6,12), "dynamic control"
(64-67) as well as antimycin-insensitive oxidation of CoQ
(68) and reduction of cytochrome $\underline{c}_1$ (34) in single turnover

experiments. Although these effects fit the Q cycle nicely (4), it should be realized that the hypothesis of Wikström and Berden (6) accounted for all the above phenomena equally well. In fact, a unified diagrammatic presentation of the Q cycle and Wikström-Berden model (Fig. 2) enables one to see that the 2 schemes become indistinguishable in the antimycin-inhibited state. It is therefore important to concentrate on experiments which allow us to discriminate between the (semi) cyclic (4) and branched (6)[1] models of electron flow in site 2.

A crossover between b and c cytochromes induced by BAL and UHDBT.

According to both schemes in Fig. 2, inactivation of electron transfer through the QH_2-to-SQ-oxidizing branch of the respirator chain, e.g. at the FeS_R site, should abolish the antimycin + oxidant-induced extra-reduction of b cytochromes. Such a prevention of extra-reduction is indeed observed when the respiratory chain has been inhibited by BAL-treatment (6,70-73) or by a CoQ antagonist UHDBT (74), and the action of both these agents appears to be associated with FeS_R (27,75). Clear distinction between the branched and (semi)cyclic models in Fig. 2 can be made on the basis of BAL and UHDBT effects in the absence of antimycin (72,73). In the Wikström-Berden scheme, b cytochromes can be reduced by the CoQ-pool only by virture of the concerted QH_2 oxidation by FeS_R (reaction 1 in Fig. 2). Consequently, this reaction suppressed by BAL-

---

[1] An improved version of the scheme (6) is considered in which QH_2 is oxidized to SQ by FeS_R rather than b cytochromes (69).

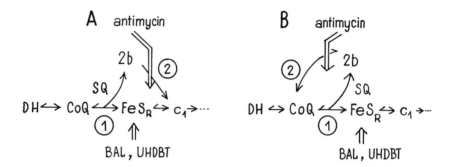

Fig. 2. The branched (A) and (semi)cyclic (B) models of
electron transfer in site 2. The BAL and UHDBT sensitive
concerted QH$_2$ oxidation (reaction 1) is common for both
schemes and corresponds to centre o catalyzed step in the Q
cycle. Reaction 2 makes the difference between the models:
in (B) it is readily reversible and allows for FeS$_R$-indepen-
dent second pathway of b cytochromes reduction catalyzed by
centre i.

treatment or UHDBT should result in a crossover between CoQ
and b cytochromes in the aerobic steady-state. As regards the
Q cycle, reversed electron transfer via centre i (reaction 2
in Fig. 2B) can keep the b cytochromes reduced despite inhibition of FeS$_R$. Accordingly, a crossover induced by BAL or
UHDBT would appear formally "between b and c cytochromes"
which is of course a purely phenomenological description of
the effect since there is no electronic communication between
b and c cytochromes in the Q cycle.

     That both BAL (70-73) and UHDBT (76) inhibit electron
transfer "between b and c cytochromes" has been observed experimentally and this fact provides a strong evidence in
favour of the (semi)cyclic model versus the branched one.

Antimycin inhibition site on the reducing side of b cytochromes.

Antimycin is considered traditionally to act on the oxidizing
side of b cytochromes (11-13). According to the linear or
Wikström-Berden model, this antibiotic can only enhance, never
inhibit, the reduction of cytochromes b by dehydrogenases! On
the other hand, inspection of the Q cycle shows that the antimycin inhibition site can appear on the reducing side of hemes
b-566 and b-562, if the oxidation of QH_2 in centre o is slow
compared to redox equilibration between b cytochromes and CoQ
via centre i.

That antimycin can hinder cytochrome b reduction by
succinate has been demonstrated under a variety of experimental
conditions in which the QH_2-to-SQ-oxidizing function of FeS_R
in centre o had been impaired by prereduction with ascorbate
(65,66), reversible extraction of the protein (77), or destruction of this FeS-centre by the BAL treatment (71-73).
Moreover, an antimycin-induced specific oxidation of cytochromes b-566 and b-562 has been shown in the cyanide-inhibited SMP treated aerobically with dibromothymoquinone in the
presence of succinate or NADH as substrates (78). None of
these results can be rationalized readily within the Wikström-
Berden-type scheme.

Thus, we can conclude that there is sufficient experimental evidence to discriminate between the branched and
(semi)cyclic models of electron flow in site 2 in favour of
the latter (cf. 69)[1].

---

[1] The "b cycle" model outlined recently by Wikström and Krab
(69) is in fact a (semi)cyclic scheme which does not differ
significantly from the Q cycle with respect to the electron
flow diagram.

ENERGY-LINKED EFFECTS

THE ATP-INDUCED OXIDATION-REDUCTION OF b CYTOCHROMES IN THE
RESPIRATORY CHAIN POISED WITH THE SUCCINATE/FUMARATE REDOX
BUFFER. An important piece of evidence for the Q cycle
electron flow diagram emerges from studies of the energy-
linked redox responses of b cytochromes. There is ample
evidence that energization of mitochondria or SMP under a
variety of conditions can increase the reduction of cyto-
chrome(s) b (12,79-81). The experiments, however, were
carried out either in the absence of redox buffer (e.g. 81) or
in the presence of redox-buffering mediators interacting with
the respiratory chain on both sides of the energy-conserving
span of site 2 (79,80), which does not allow tenable analysis
of the results (12,82).

A different experimental design, similar to that applied
previously to sites 3 (83) and 1 (84) and more or less suitable for thermodynamic interpretation (82), has been used in
this group. Thus, we have demonstrated the energy-linked
reduction of cytochrome b-556 in beef-heart SMP poised with
the succinate/fumarate couple (85,86, Fig. 3A), i.e. under the
conditions excluding interference from the reversed electron
flow across site 2 viewed in the classical sense.

Further experiments showed that the energy-linked reduction by succinate is not specific for b-556 but can also
involve heme b-562 (73,86), as evidenced by a shift of the
absorption maximum from 566 nm to 563-564 nm at higher redox
potentials (Fig. 3B).

On addition of antimycin to the reaction mixture, the
energy-linked reduction of b cytochomes was inhibited and

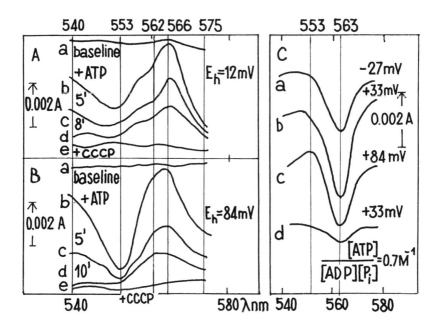

Fig. 3. Energy-linked responses of cytochromes in beef
heart SMP poised with the succinate/fumarate couple in the
absence (A,B) or in the presence (C) of antimycin. (A,B):
SMP (3.8 mg/ml) in a medium containing 20 mM of each MOPS,
Mes and Tris buffers pH = 7.5, 5 mM MgSO4, 4 mM KCN, 3 μM
rotenone, succinate/fumarate and sucrose up to 0.35 osM.
The baseline recorded (a), 2 mM ATP was added to the sample
and the spectra were scanned one after one of which 3 are
given in the figure (b,c,d). Finally, 3 μM CCCP was added to
both cuvettes (e). (C): conditions similar to (A,B) but SMP
(1.8 mg/ml) were supplemented with 1 μg/ml of antimycin. In
(a-c), 1.5 mM ATP was added to both cuvettes and 3 μM CCCP to
the reference; (d), as (b) but 2 mM ADP + 150 mM P_i present
and [ATP] = 0.2 mM. Energy-pressure decreased, the oxidation
of b-562 decays but still there is no evidence for b-566 response which ought to be relatively insensitive to ΔG_{ATP} at
this E_h. The measurements were made with an Aminco DW2a
instrument.

there occurred an ATP-induced oxidation of b-562 (Fig. 3C) without any measurable changes in the redox state of heme b-566 (cf. 12).

Table 1. Energy-Linked Responses of b Cytochromes in the Succinate/Fumarate-Poised SMP

Model	The Effect Predicted or Observed[1]			
	b-566	:	b-562	
	-anti	+anti	: -anti	+anti
Linear, "b_T" (11)	+	+	0	0
Linear, chemiosmotic (87)	0	0	-	-
Branched (6)	energy-linked effects not specified			
Q cycle (1-4)	+	0 or -[2]	0 or +[2]	-
Experiment (73,86, this paper)	+	0	0 or +[3]	-

[1] +, reduction; -, oxidation; 0, no effect. [2] Depending on the exact version of the model. [3] Depending on E_h, see the last paragraph before "Conclusions".

The effects of energization on the redox equilibrium between b cytochromes and succinate/fumarate buffer as observed experimentally or predicted by various models of site 2 are brought together in Table 1. One can see that the Q cycle is the only scheme qualitatively compatible with the experiment. Indeed, the "anomalous" antimycin-sensitive energy-driven reduction of hemes b-566 and b-562 by succinate is nicely explained by the reversed electron transfer via centre

i down $\Delta\psi$ or Δp (4,86)[1]; when centre i is blocked by antimycin, redox poise via centre o is operative which accounts
for the energy-linked oxidation of b-562.

PROTONMOTIVE MECHANISM; REDOX-LOOP OR PROTON-PUMP? In general, the Q cycle does not introduce any novel principle of
energy-transduction in site 2 and this scheme can be visualized in accordance with either of the extreme alternatives:
(i) pure redox-loop mechanism implying transmmembrane electron
transfer in the C → M direction, or (ii) pure proton pump with
electrogenic proton translocation across the membrane in the M
→ C direction being linked to scalar redox reactions. Conceivably, any compromise between these two extremes is possible (e.g., see 4). Transmembrane electron transfer requires
that metal electron carriers are located at the opposing sides
of the membrane or, more accurately, the complex $b.c_1$ insulating dielectric barrier. That hemes b-566 and b-562 represent
such an energy-conserving transmembrane redox couple has been
assumed in both linear (87) and cyclic (1-3) redox-loop
schemes of site 2.

Spatial topography of site 2

No doubt, the entire complex $b.c_1$ particle spans the membrane
and some evidence for a transmembrane location of some constituent subunits, notably cytochrome b dimer, have been

---

[1] Reoxidation of b cytochromes via centre o cannot counteract their energy-linked reduction by excess succinate via
centre i since the number of turnovers that the Q cycle can
run in the reversed direction is limited by the number of
e stored in the cytochromes c, c_1, a and FeS_R.

obtained (reviewed, 88). However, the meager knowledge of the
prosthetic group topography, if significant at all, argues
against rather than for the transmembrane arrangement of any
metal redox pair in site 2. In fact, all the 4 metal redox
centres proved more or less accessible from the C-aqueous
phase (although, except for heme c_1, not exposed at the surface) and inaccessible from the M-phase (89-93). Incidentally,
the CoQ-reducing site of succinate-ubiquinone reductase also
appears to be buried deeply inside the membrane or even located closer to the C-side (94), which can minimize the need for
spatial movement of redox equivalents in site 2.

Electrical topography of site 2

In order to evaluate the $\underline{b}$ cytochromes localization with
respect to energy-conserving step(s) in site 2, we attempted
to quantitate the ATP-induced shifts of redox equilibria
between cytochromes and succinate dehydrogenase.

In the first type of experiment we monitored a time-
dependent decay of the energy-linked responses of cytochromes
which occurred at fixed succinate/fumarate ratio due to ATP
being hydrolyzed (e.g., Fig. 3A,B). From each of the difference spectra scanned in series after an ATP addition,
energy-linked shift of redox potential ΔE_h^{ATP} was calculated
simultaneously for the $\underline{b}$-566 reduction and $\underline{c}_1 + \underline{c}$ oxidation
and the values obtained were plotted one vs another (Fig. 4).
The points fall on a straight line intercepting the origin
with a slope of 0.4. Thus the energy-linked reduction of heme
$\underline{b}$-566 by succinate is driven by less than 1/2 of the energy-
pressure across site 2 ($\Delta p - 60 \Delta pH$) as "sensed" by the redox
equilibrium between succinate dehydrogenase and cytochromes
$\underline{c}$.

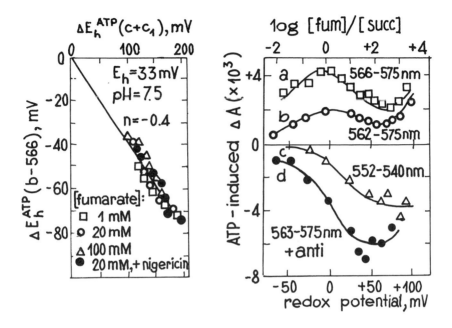

Fig. 4. Relationship between the magnitudes of the ATP-induced reduction of cytochrome b-566 and oxidation of cytochromes c_1 + c. Experiments similar to those in Fig. 3 A,B were carried out at E_h = 33 mV at 3 different concentrations of the succinate/fumarate buffer. Nigericin, 0.2 μg/ml.

Fig. 5. Energy-linked responses of cytochromes as a function of redox potential. Conditions, similar to Fig. 3 A,B. In (d), 1 μg/ml of antimycin added. SMP, 3.4 mg protein/ml. Parameters assumed. b-566: E_m, -55 mV; spectral contribution, 0.5 and 0.25 in (a) and (b), respectively. b-562: E_m, +50 mV; E_m (extra-reduced) in (d), +110 mV (95); contribution in (d), 0.75. c + c_1: E_m, 230 mV. Parameters fitted. (a and b), 2 components: (1) ΔE_h^{ATP} (b-566) = -85 mV and (2) energy-linked reduction of the both hemes b, switched on with E_m = 125 mV; (c) E_h^{ATP} (c + c_1) = 200 mV; (d) E_h^{ATP} (b-562) = 110 mV.

In the second type of experiment the ATP-induced res-
ponses of $\underline{b}$ and $\underline{c}$ cytochromes were measured as a function of
E_h imposed by the succinate/fumarate couple (Fig. 5; 73).   The
energy-linked oxidation of cytochromes $\underline{c}$ + $\underline{c}_1$ (curve c) corresponded to ΔE_h^{ATP} of 200 mV.   Regarding the cytochrome $\underline{b}$
reduction (curves a,b), the E_h profile reveals at least 2
components.   The bell-shaped part of the curves, centered
around 0 mV (pH = 7.5), is due to heme $\underline{b}$-556 reduction with
only small, if any, contribution from $\underline{b}$-562 with $E_{m\ 7.6}$ of +50
mV (86).   The computed magnitude of ΔE_h^{ATP} ($\underline{b}$-566) depended
somewhat on the choice of parameters used in curve fitting,
but always fell within the -50 to -90 mV range.   When compared
to ΔE_h^{ATP} ($\underline{c}$ + $\underline{c}_1$) of 200 mV, this value is in an excellent
agreement with the results of the experiment in Fig. 4 and
shows that electron transfer between heme $\underline{b}$-566 and centre $\underline{i}$
(and, even more so, between heme $\underline{b}$-566 and heme $\underline{b}$-562) is
controlled by not more than 1/2 of the membrane potential
(73).   Thus, at E_h below ca. 60 mV, heme $\underline{b}$-566 appears to be
located in the middle of the membrane and heme $\underline{b}$-562 near the
M-side in accordance with the preliminary considerations of
Mitchell (4).   Such an "electrical topography" implies that
after centre $\underline{i}$ has been blocked by antimycin, we should
observe energy-linked oxidation of $\underline{b}$-562 by approximately 200
mV and of $\underline{b}$-566 by some 100 mV via centre $\underline{o}$ with a concomitant
partial oxidation of $\underline{c}$ cytochromes.   In contrast, $\underline{b}$-562 oxidation by 100 mV (Fig. 5, d; 73) is the only energy-linked
effect seen unambiguously under these conditions (cf. Fig.
3C), which is now consistent with heme $\underline{b}$-562 being localized
near the middle of the membrane and heme $\underline{b}$-566 on its C-side
in the "electrical topography" map of site 2.   In addition,

again we encounter the signs of the antimycin inhibition site
between $\underline{c}$ cytochromes and CoQ in centre $\underline{o}$. One of the possible ways to rationalize these effects of antimycin is given in
Fig. 6. The situation is, however, further complicated by a
marked increase of $\underline{b}$ cytochrome energy-linked reduction at
positive E_h (Fig. 5 a,b). Both $\underline{b}$-566 and $\underline{b}$-562 seem to be
involved in the effect (e.g., see Fig. 3B) but the rise occurs
with $E_{m\ 7.5}$ of 120-130 mV (E_m/pH-dependence -60 mV, data not
shown) that is too high for these $\underline{b}$ cytochromes.

     One interesting possibility is that complex $\underline{b}.\underline{c}_1$ can
exist in 2 conformations in which the $\underline{b}$ cytochrome dimer
responds differently to energization. Transition to the more
"energy-sensitive" state is switched on by oxidation of a
redox centre with $E_{m\ 7}$ ca. 150 mV that might be a special
bound CoQ molecule (cf. 33) analogous to component Z in chromatophores (34). Enhanced energy-dependent reduction of both $\underline{b}$
cytochromes indicates the appearance of an additional electro-
genic step between heme $\underline{b}$-562 and centre $\underline{i}$ (or, less likely,
between centre $\underline{i}$ and succinate/fumarate). Although not shown
in Fig. 6, such an effect would be produced if oxidation of
the presumed bound quinone, e.g. X in Fig. 6, (i) opens the
centre $\underline{i}$-associated proton well and (ii) closes the input well
associated with cytochrome $\underline{b}$-562, i.e. gives rise to a state
analogous to the antimycin-inhibited state (Fig. 6, right)
except for electron (not hydrogen, as in Fig. 6, left) transfer between $\underline{b}$-562 and CoQ_i retained.

CONCLUSIONS

1. The sequence of electron transfer events in mitochondrial
site 2 is in much better agreement with the Q cycle electron

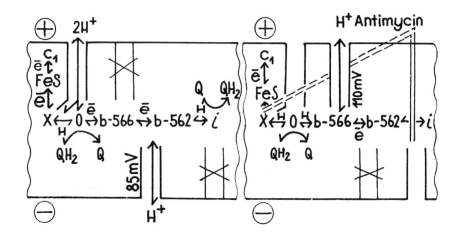

Figure 6. A modified Q cycle scheme. The following details
are added tentatively. Electron transfer mechanism. Antimycin not only blocks b-562 oxidation in centre i (4) but
also inhibits FeS_R reduction in centre o, the inhibition
imposed after at least 1 e has entered b cytochrome dimer.
Consequently, component X is added between QH_2 and FeS_R in
order to account for extra-reduction of b-566 in the presence
of antimycin. X might be a special FeS_R-bound CoQ. Energy-
transduction. 2 pairs of proton wells (input/output) are
postulated, one associated with b cytochrome dimer and
another with the CoQ-reactive centres o and i which can be in
fact 2 alternative states of the same CoQ-binding domain. Only
one proton well (input or output) of each pair can be opened
at the same time. Antimycin is shown to quench $b.c_1$ complex
in a conformation with the b cytochromes-associated output
well opened and the centre o-associated (output) well closed,
but this is not the only possible combination fitting our
data. QH_2/Q ratio is assumed to be kept constant by the
succinate/furmarate couple. The "electrical topography"
should not be related straightforwardly to the spatial one.

flow diagram than with the linear or branched (Wikström–Berden
type) models. Further development of the Q cycle is, nevertheless, required which should probably involve multiple
cooperative interactions between the individual redox and
protolytic steps within the $b.c_1$ complex ensemble. The effect
of antimycin on site 2, that is certainly more complex than
implied by the original Q cycle scheme, may provide a clue to
this problem.

2. Vectorial electrogenic H^+ translocation linked to redox
reactions of CoQ and b cytochromes can probably allow for a
more coherent picture of site 2 protonmotive function as compared to the pure redox-loop mechanism. Whether the H^+/e^- -
linkage is short-range "chemielectric" (7-10) (a proton-well
serviced machinery, 4,7-10) or long-range conformational – that
may be a problem of singular appeal for those involved in
solving the enigma of "proteoelectric" energy coupling.

ACKNOWLEDGEMENTS

We are much indebted to Dr. Alexander L. Drachev for curve
fitting program. Thanks are due to Profs. V.P. Skulachev and
E.A. Liberman for many helpful discussions, to Drs. M. Wikström
and B. Trumpower for the preprints of their papers, and to Ms.
T. Kheifets for correcting the English of the paper.

REFERENCES

1. Mitchell, P. (1975) FEBS Lett. 56, 1-6.
2. Mitchell, P. (1975) FEBS Lett. 59, 137-139.
3. Mitchell, P. (1975) in Electron Transfer Chains and
   Oxidative Phosphorylation (E. Quagliariello et al., eds)
   pp. 305-315, Elsevier, North-Holland, Amsterdam.
4. Mitchell, P. (1976) J. Theor. Biol. 62, 372-367.
5. Baum, H., Rieske, J.S., Silman, H.J. and Lipton, S.H.
   (1967) Proc. Natl. Acad. Sci. USA 57, 798-805.

142   ALEXANDER KONSTANTINOV et al.

6. Wikström, M.K.F. and Berden, J.A. (1972) Biochim.
    Biophys. Acta 283, 403-420.
7. Liberman, E.A., Arzumanjan, A.M., Valdimirova, M.A. and
    Tsofina, L.M. (1976) Biophysics (USSR) 21, 469-475.
8. Liberman, E.A. (1977) Biophysics (USSR) 22, 247-254.
9. Liberman, E.A. (1977) Biophysics (USSR) 22, 1115-1128.
10. Liberman, E.A. (1978) Biophysics (USSR) 23, 174-178.
11. Chance, B. (1972) FEBS Lett. 23, 3-20.
12. Wikström, M.K.F. (1973) Biochim. Biophys. Acta 301,
    155-193.
13. Rieske, J.S. (1976) Biochim. Biophys. Acta 456, 195-247.
14. Mitchell, P. (1966) Chemiosmotic Coupling in Oxidative
    and Photosynthetic Phosphorylation, Bodmin: Glynn
    Research Ltd.
15. Ernster, L. (1977) in Biomedical and Clinical Aspects
    of Coenzyme Q (K. Folkers and Y. Yamamura, eds.) p. 15-
    21.
16. Kaniuga, Z., Bryla, J. and Slater, E.C. (1969) in
    Inhibitors Tools in Cell Research (Bucher, Th. and Sies,
    H., eds.) pp. 282-300, Springer-Velag, Heidelberg.
17. Phelps, D.C. and Crane, F.L. (1975) Biochemistry 14,
    116-122.
18. Roberts, H., Choo, W.M., Smith, S.C., Marzuki, S.,
    Linnane, A.W., Porter, T.H. and Folkers, K. (1978) Arch.
    Biochem. Biophys. 191, 306-315.
19. Rieske, J.S. (1980) Pharm. and Ther. 11, 415-450.
20. Kostyrko, V.A. and Yaguzhinsky, L.S. (1979) Biochemistry
    (USSR) 44, 1884-1890.
21. Yu, L., Yu, C.A. and King, T.E. (1978) J. Biol. Chem.
    253, 2657-2663.
22. Downie, J.A. and Cox, G.B. (1978) J. Bacteriol. 133,
    477-484.
23. Baccarini-Melandri, A. and Melandri, B.A. (1977) FEBS
    Lett. 80, 459-464.
24. Trumpower, B.L. and Edwards, C.A. (1979) J. Biol. Chem.
    254, 8697-8706.
25. Turmpower, B.L., Edwards, C.A. and Ohnishi, T. (1980)
    J. Biol. Chem. 255, 7487-7493.
26. Malkin, R. and Posner, H.B. (1978) Biochim. Biophys.
    Acta 501, 552-554.
27. Bowyer, J.R., Dutton, P.L., Prince, R.C. and Crofts, A.R.
    (1980) Biochim. Biophys. Acta 592, 445-460.
28. Cadenas, E. and Boveris, A. (1980) Biochem. J. 188,
    37-51.

29. Grigolava, I.V., Ksenzenko, M. Yu., Konstantinov, A.A., Kerimov, T.M., Tikhonov, A.N. and Ruuge, E.K. (1980) Biochemistry (USSR) 45, 75-82.
30. Trumpower, B.L. and Simmons, Z. (1979) J. Biol. Chem. 254, 4608-4616.
31. Konstantinov, A.A. and Ruuge, E.K. (1977) FEBS Lett. 81, 137-141.
32. Grigolava, I.V., Ksenzenko, M. Yu., Konstantinov, A.A., Tikhonov, A.N. and Ruuge, E.K. (1981) Biochemistry (USSR) in press.
33. Packham, N.K., Tiede, D.M., Mueller, P. and Dutton, P.L. (1980) Proc. Natl. Acad. Sci. USA 77, 6339-6343.
34. Van den Berg, W.H., Prince, R.C., Bashford, C.L., Takamiya, K.-i., Bonner, W.D., Jr. and Dutton, P.L. (1979) J. Biol. Chem. 254, 8594-8604.
35. Bowyer, J.R. and Trumpower, B.L. (1981) J. Biol. Chem. 256, 2245-2251.
36. Ruuge, E.K. and Konstantinov, A.A. (1976) Biophysics (USSR) 21, 586-588.
37. Konstantinov, A.A. and Ruuge, E.K. (1977) Bioorg. Chem. (USSR) 3, 787-799.
38. Tikhonov, A.N., Burbaev, D.S., Grigolava, I.V., Konstantinov, A.A., Ksenzenko, M.Yu. and Ruuge, E.K. (1977) Biophysics (USSR) 22, 734-736.
39. Ohnishi, T. and Trumpower, B.L. (1980) J. Biol. Chem. 255, 3278-3284.
40. Salerno. J.C. and Ohnishi, T. (1980) Biochem. J. 192, 769-781.
41. Ruzicka, F.J., Beinert, H., Schepler, K.L., Dunham, W.R. and Sands, R.H. (1975) Proc. Natl. Acad. Sci. USA 72, 2886-2890.
42. Ingledew, W.J., Salerno. J.C. and Ohnishi, T. (1976) Arch. Biochem. Biophys. 177, 176-184.
43. Ingledew, W.J. and Ohnishi, T. (1977) Biochem. J. 164, 617-620.
44. Ackrell, B.A.C., Kearney, E.B., Coles, C.J., Singer, T.P., Beinert, H., Wan, Y.-P. and Folkers, K. (1977) Arch. Biochem. Biophys. 182, 107-117.
45. Yu, C.A., Yu, L. and King, T.E. (1977) Biochem. Biophys. Res. Commun. 78, 259-265.
46. Yu, C.A., Yu, L. and King, T.E. (1977) Biochem. Biophys. Res. Commun. 79, 939-949.
47. Yu, C.A. and Yu, L. (1980) Biochim. Biophys. Acta 591, 409-420.
48. Yu, C.A. and Yu, L. (1980) Biochemistry 19, 3579-3585.

49. Yu, L. and Yu, C.A. (1980) Biochim. Biophys. Acta 593, 24-38.
50. Vinogradov, A.D., Gavrikov, V.B. and Gavrikova, E.V. (1980) Biochim. Biophys. Acta 592, 13-27.
51. Hatefi, Y. and Galante, Y.M. (1980) J. Biol. Chem. 5530-5537.
52. Siedow, J.H., Powers, S., de la Rosa, F. and Palmer, G. (1978) J. Biol. Chem. 253, 2392-2399.
53. Yu, C.A., Nagoaka, S., Yu, L. and King, T.E. (1978) Biochem. Biophys. Res. Commun. 82, 1070-1078.
54. Yu, C.A., Nagoaka, S., Yu, L. and King, T.E. (1980) Arch. Biochem. Biophys. 204, 59-70.
55. De Vries, S., Berden, J.A. and Slater, E.C. (1980) FEBS Lett. 122, 143-148.
56. Rieske, J.S. (1967) Methods Enzymol. 10, 239-245.
57. Gellerfors, P. and Nelson, B.D. (1975) Eur. J. Biochem. 52, 433-443.
58. Yu, L., Yu, C.A. and King. T.E. (1977) Biochim. Biophys. Acta 495, 232-247.
59. Katan, M.B., van Harten-Loosbroek, N. and Groot, G.S.P. (1976) Eur. J. Biochem. 70, 409-417.
60. Yu, C.A. and Yu, L. (1980) Biochem. Biophys. Res. Commun. 96, 286-292.
61. Lee, I.Y. and Slater, E.C. (1972) Biochim. Biophys. Acta 256, 587-593.
62. Lee, I.Y. and Slater, E.C. (1972) Biochim. Biophys. Acta 283, 223-233.
63. Trumpower, B.L. (1981) J. Bioenerget. Biomembr. 13, 1-24.
64. Eisenbach, M. and Gutman, M. (1975) Eur. J. Biochem. 52, 107-116.
65. Trumpower, B.L. and Katki, A. (1975) Biochem. Biophys. Res. Commun. 65, 16-23.
66. Trumpower, B.L. and Katki, A.G. (1979) In Membrane Proteins in Energy Transduction (Capaldi, R.A., ed.) pp. 89-200, Marcel Dekker Inc., New York.
67. Gutman, M. (1980) Biochim. Biophys. Acta 594, 53-84.
68. Chance, B. (1974) In Dynamics of Energy Transducing Membranes (Ernster, L., Estabrook, R.W. and Slater, E.C., eds.) pp. 553-578, Elsevier, Amsterdam.
69. Wikström, M.K.F. and Krab, K. (1980) Curr. Top. Bioenerget. 10, 51-101.
70. Slater, E.C. (1949) Biochem. J. 45, 14-30.
71. Deul, D.H. and Thorn, M.B. (1962) Biochim. Biophys. Acta 59, 426-436.

72. Ksenzenko, M.Yu. and Konstantinov, A.A. (1980) Bio-
     chemistry (USSR) 45, 343-354.
73. Konstantinov, A.A., Kamensky, Yu.A., Ksenzenko, M.Yu.
     and Surkov, S.A. (1980) EBEC Reports, vol. 1, pp. 63-64.
74. Bowyer, J.R. and Trumpower, B.L. (1980) FEBS Letts.
     115, 171-174.
75. Slater, E.C. and de Vries, S. (1980) Nature (London)
     288, 717-718.
76. Trumpower, B.L. and Haggerti, J.G. (1980) J. Bioenerget.
     Biomembr. 12, 151-164.
77. Trumpower, B.L. (1976) Biochem. Biophys. Res. Commun.
     70, 73-80.
78. Surkov, A.S. and Konstantinov, A.A. (1980) FEBS Lett.
     109, 283-288.
79. Berden, J.A., Opperdoes, F.R. and Slater, E.C. (1972)
     Biochim. Biophys. Acta 256, 594-599.
80. Dutton, P.L. and Wilson, D.F. (1974) Biochim. Biophys.
     Acta 346, 165-212.
81. Wilson, D.F. and Erecinska, M. (1975) Arch. Biochem.
     Biophys. 167, 116-128.
82. Walz, D. (1979) Biochim. Biophys. Acta 505, 279-353.
83. Hinkle, P. and Mitchell, P. (1970) J. Bioenerget. 1,
     45-60.
84. Gutman, M., Beinert, H. and Singer, T.P. (1975) In
     Electron Transfer Chains and Oxidative Phosphorylation
     (Quagliariello, E. et al., eds.) pp. 55-62, Elsevier/
     North Holland, Amsterdam.
85. Konstantinov, A.A. and Kamensky, Yu.A. (1974) 9th FEBS
     Meeting, Budapest, Abstracts, p. 267.
86. Kamensky, Yu.A., Konstantinov, A.A. and Jasaitis, A.A.
     (1975) Biochemistry (USSR) 40, 1022-1031.
87. Mitchell, P. (1972) FEBS Symp. 28, 353-370.
88. Mitchell, P. (1980) Ann. N.Y. Acad. Sci. 341, 564-584.
89. Case, G.D. and Leigh, J.S. (1976) Biochem. J. 160,
     769-783.
90. Kiselev, A.V. and Konstantinov, A.A. (1976) Bioorg.
     Chem. (USSR) 2, 253-258.
91. Grigolava, I.V. and Konstantinov, A.A. (1977) FEBS
     Lett. 78, 36-40.
92. Grigolava, I.V. and Konstantinov, A.A. (1979) Bio-
     chemistry (USSR) 44, 1329-1332.
93. Ohnishi, T. and Blum, H. (1980) EBEC Reports, vol. 1,
     71-72.
94. Merli, A., Capaldi, R.A., Ackrell, B.A.C. and Kearney,
     E.B. (1979) Biochemistry 18, 1393-1400.

95. Kamensky, Yu.A., Artzatbanov, V.Yu., Shevchenko, D.V.
     and Konstantinov, A.A. (1979) Dokl. Acad. Nauk SSSR
     249, 994-997.

CONSTITUTION OF "THE b-c_1 COMPLEX"[*]

Tsoo E. King

Department of Chemistry and Laboratory of Bioenergetics
State University of New York at Albany
Albany, New York   12222

The b-c_1 complex can be defined in two ways. First,
it can be considered to be the complex which is able to reconstitute with soluble SDH[1] to physically and functionally
form the so-called succinate-cytochrome c reductase (1, 2)
for electron transfer[2] from succinate to cytochrome c.
Second, the b-c_1 complex can be defined as the QH_2-c reduc-
tase--Complex III (Green and coworkers ($cf.$ 3)), which cannot reconstitute with soluble SDH (2). The complex by the
first definition also shows QH_2-c reductase activity ($e.g.$ 2).
This paper uses the first definition. The constituents of
the b-c_1 complex are not quite completely known, and its
sequence is the subject of more conjecture, whereas the mechanism or mode of electron (hydrogen) transfer is practically
completely unknown--it may or may not involve tunneling.

---

[*]Dedicated to Dr. Peter Mitchell, also an ardent poet.

[1]Abbreviations used: HPLC, high performance liquid
chromatography; ISP, an iron-sulfur protein (the Rieske protein); PAGE, polyacrylamide gel electrophoresis; Q, ubiquinone (coenzyme Q): QH_2, reduced Q (the numerical subscript
of Q denotes a Q with a particular number of isoprene units,
subscripts i and o for Q used in the Q cycle refer to Q on
the matrix and cytoplasmic sides of mitochondrial inner
membrane, respectively: QP, ubiquinone bound proteins: QP-C,
a QP required in the cytochrome b-c_1 region: QP-S, the QP
which receives electron (hydrogen) directly from SDH· SDS,
sodium dodecyl sulfate: SDH, succinate dehydrogenase.

V. P. Skulachev and Peter C. Hinkle (eds.), Chemiosmotic Proton Circuits in Biological Membranes
in honor of Peter Mitchell   ISBN 0-201-07398-6

Presently, it is generally agreed that the complex contains cytochrome c_1, two or even three b cytochromes, and an iron-sulfur protein, the so-called Rieske protein. The existence of specific quinone binding proteins is not yet unanimously agreed upon (cf. 5). QP-S has been shown by isolation and OP-C by evidence from various lines, particularly EPR spectrometry. Are there more respiratory carriers in this segment in addition to these? The question cannot be unequivocally answered.

CYTOCHROME c_1. Cytochrome c_1 has been solubilized and isolated by many methods (cf. 6, 7). We have developed two methods (8, and references cited therein) for solubilization: one uses β-mercaptoethanol, cholate and ammonium sulfate, and the other only 2% cholate and ammonium sulfate. One sample of c_1, about 50% pure, prepared by the second method, has been used by workers in the Johnson Foundation who reported

---

[2]For convenience, the term electron transfer is used to denote the transfer of electron, hydrogen, proton, or whatever species is indeed involved. The terms succinate-cytochrome c reductase, QH_2-c reductase, and so on, do not necessarily mean the rigid and permanent existence of such entities in mitochondria and are used here only for convenience in writing. Likewise, the respiratory chain should not be considered literally as a chain of beads made of respiratory carriers, but as complexes distributed in the inner membrane, and the respiratory members individually, or in groups, possess lateral diffusion in the bilayer of phospholipid (cf. 4 for further discussion).

the E_m value at near neutral pH, is very close to that found
in mitochondria or submitochondrial particles (9). In the
beginning, we found that c_1 samples prepared by either method
showed two bands in polyacrylamide gel electrophoresis in
dissociating media (PAGE). One band corresponding to about
29,000 molecular weight contains heme, whereas the other
which is equivalent to approximately 15,000 does not contain
heme. A few years ago, we found (10) the ratio of these
two bands is not always 1:1 as originally reported (8, see
references given therein). The isolated samples are always
stored in cholate-free medium and show pentameric form by
the usual hydrodynamic method.

The isolated heme-containing subunit still possesses
the ascorbate-reducing property and its complete amino acid
sequence has been determined (11) as shown in Fig. 1 of
Ref. 11. It has certain similarities with the sequence
of c, such as the nearness of the heme group to the amino
terminal region and linkage of the heme with two cysteine
residues (12). However, c_1 shows some characteristics of
its own, notably the concentration of hydrophobic and basic
amino acids, especially leucine, in the carboxyl terminal:
no acidic amino acids in the last 42 residues; and the
appearance of some distinct sequences, such as 5 pro-pro
doublets, 1 pro-x-pro-x-pro-x-pro sequence, as well as a
number of leu-leu, arg-arg, glu-glu, ala-ala, asp-asp, and
met-met doublets. Since the sequence was announced just
last December, the significance of these characteristics is
yet to be investigated.

Cytochrome c_1 shows no resemblance to sequences from
the subunits of cytochrome oxidase so far reported (4, 10, 13).

Recently, two methods (14, 15) have been reported for
modifying our procedure for c_1 preparation by introduction

of deoxycholate in the solubilization mixture. These methods
are said to yield the monomeric form of c_1 which shows only
one band in PAGE. We have had difficulties reproducing either
method. Robinson and Talbert (15) apparently did not use
preparative HPLC and details have not been presented. At
any rate, neither Dr. C. H. Kim, nor other workers of our
laboratory, have been able to obtain the same results as
König, *et al.* (14) have claimed; namely, the preparation of
c_1 in our hands still shows two bands in PAGE. Likewise,
she has been unsuccessful in reproducing the high yield
(40%) as well as distinct elution patterns as reported (14)
even after private communication with Dr. van Gelder concerning precautions required, which we have strictly taken
(16). The fault naturally belongs to us, with the difference
being, perhaps, that some steps of operation were not explicit
enough in their published paper at the time we attempted to
reproduce the method. However, our modification (to be published) of the Dutch method (14), using the deoxycholate and
β-mercaptoenthol method, does give a monomeric c_1 with truly
one band on PAGE except that the yield is very low, *viz.*, at
present, in the neighborhood of 10%. We believe that we have
found the reasons for discrepancy in the results obtained by
the Dutch school and those by ours. They will be discussed
elsewhere.

Preliminary results show that absorption spectra of
monomeric c_1 obtained at near liquid nitrogen temperature
are different from that of "two band" c_1 from our original
method (8). Likewise, the remarkable increase of the Cotton
effect in the Soret region of the c_1-c complex formed with
"two band" c_1 (17) is not observed when monomeric c_1 is used.
Indeed, monomeric c_1 does not form the complex with c. (10).

One more serious problem comes into the picture, and

this is the molecular weight of detergent-free cytochrome
c_1. By calculation from the heme content as reported by
König, et al. (although the hydrodynamic method gives 45,000
(14), the molecular weight should be about 31,000; but, from
the amino acid sequence of the c_1 obtained by the original
methods (8), it is only 27,874 including the heme group (11).
Is it possible that a polypeptide was cleaved off while obtaining a sample for our amino acid sequencing? According
to Robinson and Talbert (15), the absorption decreases in
the presence of deoxycholate and with time. Thus, The heme
content calculated from absorption spectra may be an underestimate. Moreover, the amino and carboxyl terminals of the
"one band" c_1 prepared by the modified method are the same
(10) as those reported (11). Regardless of the plausibility
of the arguments, we are checking the complete sequencing
of our monomeric c_1 prepared by the new method.

IRON SULFUR PROTEIN. A nonheme iron protein in the b-c_1
region was first isolated by Rieske, et al. (18). Naturally,
it lacks biological function because the protein is succinyl-
ated during isolation. In 1972, Racker and coworkers (19)
found that two oxidation factors are essential for the oxidation of succinate in their system. At least one of the
oxidation factors has been purified, characterized, and reconstituted with the particles which contain all components
for the oxidation of succinate by cytochrome c except the
oxidation factor by Trumpower and his colleagues (20-22).
Significantly enough, the oxidation factor has been found
to be a nonheme iron protein, evidently the same as the
unmodified Rieske protein in situ with molecular weight of
24,500. At present, the method of preparation of the iron
sulfur protein is rather tedious and the yield low. Succinate-cytochrome c reductase, 3.6 g, which is prepared from

10 kg, or more, of beef heart can yield only 1.7 mg of the
the purified protein with 1.3% yield.

b CYTOCHROMES. All preparations of cytochromes reported
are not identical with b cytochromes *in situ* or show any
biological activity (regarding the latter), however, see
(24). Since the early 1960's, our laboratory has attempted
to isolate cytochrome b, without significant success. This
task is further complicated by definitive evidence reported
for the existence of multiple b cytochromes.

Recently, we have isolated two b cytochromes from succinate-cytochrome c reductase which is prepared by a modified method (25) of our previous preparation (1). The
isolation procedure (25), after the reductase is solubilized
by Triton X-100 alone, involves principally five steps of
chromatography on: (a) anaerobic hydroxylapatite, (b) DEAE
cellulose, (c) hydroxylapatite, (d) Sephacryl, and (e)
phospho-cellulose columns. In the first step, two distinct
b cytochrome fractions are obtained—one is a small fraction
containing cytochrome b of "Complex II type" (24) and the
other fraction is a major b_{561-2} type. After the latter
fraction is further purified following the fourth step, two
protein bands in Weber-Osborn or Swank-Munkres type PAGE gel
electrophoresis are observed at 38,000 and 14,000 positions.

Application of the Ferguson plot (26) substantiates the
existence of these bands. The parent proteins of these peptides have been estimated to have molecular weights of about
75,000 (b_L) and 55,000 (b_s) by gel permeation method and
their subunits confirmed by PAGE. The last step of chromatography separates these fractions. The fraction b_L is
apparently a dimer of the 38,000 subunit whereas b_s is a
tetramer of the 14,000 subunit. Isoelectric focusing of the

fraction obtained after the fourth step in Triton shows two
distinct red bands with pI of 5.8 and 6.3. Both fractions
contain protoheme and are free of lipid, but a part of the
protoheme has been lost during isolation. Heme can be replenished by addition of exogenous protohematin. Only
limited amounts of exogenous heme equivalent to the amount
of the calculated content are taken up by both fractions.
The absorption spectra of heme-replenished b_L and b_s are the
same as shown in Fig. 1. It is significant to note that b
dissociated from c_1 always shows an α—maximum at 561-2 nm;
no sample with the peak at 566 has ever been obtained by any
solubilization method used to dissociate c_1.

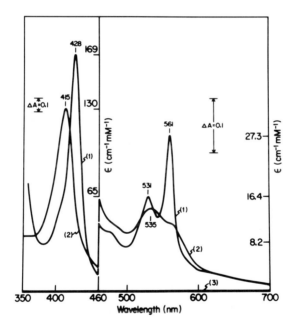

Fig. 1   The absorption spectra of isolated b cytochromes in
         which heme is replenished. Cytochrome b_L and b_s
         show the same spectra. Curve 1 is the reduced form,
         curve 2, the oxidized form, curve 3, base line.

UBIQUINONE PROTEINS (OP). Our evidence from various lines
suggests the existence of at least three ubiquinone proteins
in the respiratory chain. Two of them exist in the b-c_1
region. The one, OP-S, which accepts electron directly from
succinate dehydrogenase, has been isolated with contamination
by only a very small amount of cytochrome b. QP-S has been
reconstituted with succinate dehydrogenase to functionally
and physically form succinate-Q reductase as reported from
our laboratory. Another, OP-C, exists in the b-c_1 region
and is in the process of isolation, and has not been completely purified. However, evidence beyond a reasonable
doubt (30-32) suggests that it can serve as a respiratory
carrier and stabilize the ubisemiquinone.

OP-C can be demonstrated upon addition of catalytic
amounts of SDH and OP-S to the cytochrome b-c_1-III complex
by the formation of a stable Q-radical at room temperature
(30-32). The stable radical of QP-C can also be shown in
the cytochrome b-c-II complex with a catalytic amount of
SDH, and it is completely sensitive to antimycin A. In this
system OP-S radical cannot be demonstrated (vide infra)
(33). The difference between the b-c_1-II and the b-c_1-III
complexes is the existence of QP-S in the former but not in
the latter (30-32). The antimycin sensitive QP-C radical
which is demonstrated in the b-c_1-II complex in the presence
of a catalytic amount of SDH gives $g = 2.0046 \pm 0.0003$ at
~ 9 GHz with no resolved hyperfine structure. The line width
of this signal, estimated between the derivative extrema, is
8.1 ± 0.5 Gauss at room temperature. Under these conditions
when the radical formed with suitable amount of fumarate-
succinate mixture is examined in a Q band EPR spectrometer,
a prominent anisotropic EPR spectrum is observed at room
temperature; three g values are obtained at 2.0064, 2.0054
and 2.0021. It shows a field separation between derivative

extrema of 26 ± 1 Gauss at room or ice (∿ 0°C) temperature.
This observation indicates that the OP-C radical is strongly
immobilized since a freely tumbling radical would not show
anisotropy and would show resolved hyperfine structure, and
substantial line shape changes upon change of temperature (34).

This signal can be completely abolished by addition of
antimycin at equimolar concentration of cytochrome c_1. However, in the presence of excess exogenously added Q_2 some
residual Q radical remains (35) apparently because antimycin
competes with Q (36, 37). Evidence from other lines shows
no QP-S radical is involved although sufficient amount of
QP-S is present in the $b\text{-}c_1\text{-}II$ complex. Indeed, numerous
attempts failed to show radicals of the purified QP-S.

However, when the amount of SDH is increased, another
EPR signal, which is not sensitive to antimycin, appears at

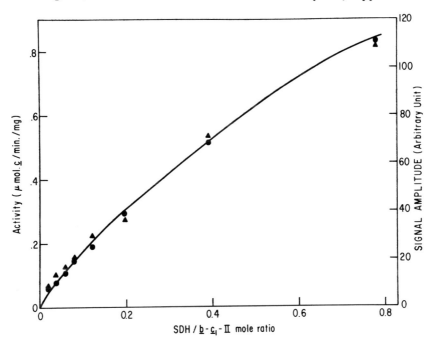

Fig. 2.   Demonstration of QP-S radical (△) and its correla-
          tion with reconstituted succinate-c activity (·) (33).

$g = 2.00$ at room temperature as well as at 77°. The line
is found to be approximately 11 Gauss at room temperature.
The amplitude of this signal is proportional to the SDH
added to the b-c_1 complex. The signal amplitude parallels
the enzymic activity of the reconstituted system as shown
in Fig. 2. It might be noted that the line width of this
signal gradually increases when more and more SDH is added.
This observation is due evidently to spectral overlapping
with the flavin semiquinone radical of SDH, which possesses
lower amplitude intensity than that of the ubisemiquinone.
The interpretation of this observation and additional evidence are detailed elsewhere (33).

ADDITIONAL REMARKS.   Since the Q cycle was first proposed
in 1975 by Mitchell (38-39) and further later refinements
(40, 41), a number of intriguing questions (42) of the
chemiosmotic theory have been resolved and the theory
greatly strengthened, because the confusion of the location
of the active sites of Q in the respiratory chain was explained and clarified.   Later, Trumpower (43) found that
one-turnover reduction of cytochrome c_1 in the succinate-
cytochrome c reductase and in mitochondria is not inhibited
by antimycin.   These and other results prompted Trumpower,
$et.$ $al.$ (5, 43-45) to conclude that the linear respiratory
chain is not applicable to their observations and he modified the original Q cycle of Mitchell by introducing ISP
(21) as a pivotal point in the transfer of electrons from
QH_2 to c_1 ($cf.$ Fig. 7 of Ref. 44).   The reduced ISP transfers
electrons to c_1 and, with $QH_0^•$ to b_{566}, either simultaneously
or consecutively, and at the same time protons are released.
It seems unlikely that our QP-C radical can serve $QH_i^•$ as
well as $QH_0^•$.   The existence of a second QP-C is not surprising.   At any rate, a conclusion can be made that <u>at least</u>

two Q-proteins exist in the b-c_1 complex, *viz.*, QP-S and QP-C. The only physiologically active form of Q is protein-linked Q and the specificity of the proteins determines the site where QP acts (*e.g.*, 45). At the same time, the protein stabilizes the Q radicals since the dismutation constant of free Q radicals is about 10^{10} favoring the non-radical form (40). The definitive information of the respiratory members required and the sequence of electron transfer depend finally on experiments of reconstitution with all active components and the study of the rapid reaction kinetics of the reconstituted system comparable to the intact one.

Acknowledgment. I acknowledge with gratification the experimental collaboration of Drs. H. Matsubara and S. Wakabayashi of Osaka University and Drs. K. Kawai, C. H. Kim, M. Seaman, S. Nagoaka, C. P. Scholes, Y. H. Wei, S. Yoshida, C. A. Yu, L. Yu and Z. P. Zhang of this university. This work was defrayed by grants from NIH and the American Cancer Society.

REFERENCES

1. King, T. E. and Takemori, S. (1964) J. Biol. Chem. 239, 3559-3569.
2. Yu, C. A., Yu, L., and King, T. E. (1974) J. Biol. Chem. 249, 4905-4910.
3. Green, D. E., Wharton, D. C., Tzagoloff, A., Rieske, J. S. and Brierly, G. P. (1965) in Oxidases and Related Redox Systems (T. E. King, et al., eds.) Vol. 2, pp. 1032-1076, John Wiley & Sons, New York.
4. King, T. E. (1978) in Membrane Proteins (P. Nicholls, et al., eds.) pp. 17-31, Pergamon Press, Oxford.
5. Trumpower, B. L. and Katki, A. (1979) in Membrane Proteins (R. A. Capaldi, ed.) pp. 89-200, M. Dekker Inc., New York.
6. Wainio, W. W. (1970) The Mammalian Mitochondrial Respiratory Chain, pp. 233-249; 249-255, Academic Press, New York.
7. Lemberg, R. and Barrett, J. (1973) Cytochromes, pp. 58-121; 212-216, Academic Press, New York.
8. King, T. E. (1978) in Methods Enzymology, Vol. 53, pp. 181-191.
9. Dutton, P. L., Wilson, D. F., and Lee, C. P. (1970) Biochemistry 9, 5077-5082.
10. Unpublished observation from this laboratory.
11. Wakabayashi, S., Matsubara, H., Kim, C. H., Kawai, K., and King, T. E. (1980) Biochem. Biophys. Res. Commun. 97, 1548-1554.
12. Margoliash, E. and Schejter, A. (1966) Adv. in Protein Chemistry 21, 113-286.
13. Tanaka, M., Haniu, M., Zeitlin, S., Yasunobu, K. T., Yu, C. A., Yu, L. and King, T. E. (1975) Biochem. Biophys. Res. Commun. 66, 1194-1200; Yasunobu, K. T., Tanaka, M., Haniu, M., Sameshima, M., Reimer, N., Eto, T., King, T. E., Yu, C. A., Yu, L., and Wei, Y. H. (1979) in Cytochrome Oxidase (T. E. King, et al., eds.) pp. 91-101, Elsevier/North Holland, Amsterdam; Tanaka, M., Haniu, M., Yasunobu, K. T., Yu, C. A., Yu, L., Wei, Y. H. and King, T. E. (1979) J. Biol. Chem. 254, 3879-3885; Tanaka, M., Yasunobu, K. T., Wei, Y. H. and King, T. E. (1981) J. Biol. Chem., in press.
14. König, K. W., Schilder, L. T. M., TerVoort, M. J. and van Gelder, B. F. (1980) Biochim. Biophys. Acta 621, 283-295.
15. Robinson, N. C. and Talbert (1980) Biochem. Biophys. Res. Commun. 95, 90-96.
16. Van Gelder, R. F. (1981) Private Commun., Feb. 17, 1981.
17. Chiang, Y. L. and King, T. E. (1979) J. Biol. Chem. 254, 1845-1853.

18. Rieske, J. S., MacLennon, D. H. and Coleman, R. (1964)
    Biochem. Biophys. Res. Commun. 15, 338-345.
19. Nishibayashi-Yamashita, H., Cunningham, C., and Racker,
    E. J. (1972) J. Biol. Chem. 247, 698-704.
20. Trumpower, B. L. and Edwards, C. A. (1979) FEBS Lett.
    100, 13-16.
21. Trumpower, B. L. and Edwards, C. A. (1979) J. Biol.
    Chem. 254, 8697-8706.
22. Trumpower, B. L., Edwards, C. A. and Ohnishi, T. (1980)
    J. Biol. Chem. 255, 7487-7493.
23. Von Jagow, G. and Sebald, W. (1980) Ann. Rev. Biochem.
    49, 281-314.
24. Hatefi, Y. and Galante, Y. M. (1980) J. Biol. Chem. 255,
    5530-5537.
25. Yoshida, S. and King, T. E., in preparation.
26. Ferguson, K. A. (1964) Metab. Clin. Exp. 13, 985-1002.
27. Yu, C. A., Yu, L. and King, T. E. (1977) Biochem. Bio-
    phys. Res. Commun. 78, 259-265.
28. Yu, C. A., Yu, L. and King, T. E. (1977) Biochem. Bio-
    phys. Res. Commun. 79, 939-946.
29. Yu, C. A. and Yu, L. (1980) Biochim. Biophys. Acta 591,
    409-420.
30. Yu, C. A., Nagaoka, S., Yu, L. and King, T. E. (1978)
    Biochem. Biophys. Res. Commun. 82, 1070-1078.
31. Yu, C. A., Nagaoka, S., Yu, L. and King, T. E. (1980)
    Arch. Biochem. Biophys. 204, 59-70.
32. Nagaoka, S., Yu, L., and King, T. E. (1981) Arch. Bio-
    chem. Biophys., in press.
33. Wei, Y. H., Scholes, C. P. and King, T. E. (1981) Bio-
    chem. Biophys. Res. Commun., in press.
34. Das, M. R., Connor, H. D., Keniart, D. S. and Freed, J.
    H. (1970) J. Am. Chem. Soc. 92, 2258-2268.
35. King, T. E. (1981) in Quinones in Energy Coupling (B. L.
    Trumpower, ed.) Academic Press, in press.
36. Takemori, S. and King, T. E. (1964) Science 144, 852-853.
37. Takemori, S. and King, T. E. (1964) J. Biol. Chem. 239,
    3546-3558.
38. Mitchell, P. (1975) FEBS Lett. 56, 1-6.
39. Mitchell, P. (1976) FEBS Lett. 59, 137-139.
40. Mitchell, P. (1976) J. Theor. Biol. 62, 327-367.
41. Mitchell, P. (1979) Science 206, 1148-1159.
42. Greville, G. D. (1969) Curr. Topics. of Bioenerg. 3, 1-78.
43. Trumpower, B. L. (1981) J. Bioenerg. & Biomem. 13, 1-23.
44. Bowyer, J. R. and Trumpower, B. L. (1981) J. Biol. Chem.
    256, 2245-2251.
45. King, T. E. (1980) in New Horizons in Biological Chem-
    istry, a Festschrift for Professor K. Yagi (M. Koike,
    et al., eds.) pp. 121-134, Japan Scientific Societies
    Press, Tokyo.

STRUCTURAL AND KINETIC APPROACHES TO ELECTRON TRANSFER OXYGEN REACTION AND ENERGY CONSERVATION IN CYTOCHROME OXIDASE[1]

Britton Chance

Johnson Research Foundation, University of Pennsylvania
Philadelphia, PA 19104

The confluence of the variety of new experimental results on the structure and function of cytochrome oxidase now brings more sharply into focus the structural factors which may govern energy conservation in site 3 of the respiratory chain. This site is one on which most structural information is available and which has the greatest possibilities for energy conservation.

The key questions relating structure to function are well known: How are electrons transported; How is oxygen reduced; How is energy conserved. Some of the answers are available: 1. Electrons are transported in part, if not completely, by tunneling mechanisms either nuclear or electronic (1,2) 2. Oxygen is reduced in a series of intermediates (3) of which peroxide is the most stable and the most interesting from the energetic standpoint (4,5); and 3. Bond making and bond breaking events in the redox cycle of the oxidase (6) afford coupling between the redox state of the oxidase and structural parameters of the active center and

---

[1]Supported by NIH Grants GM-27308 and HL-18708.

V. P. Skulachev and Peter C. Hinkle (eds.), Chemiosmotic Proton Circuits in Biological Membranes
in honor of Peter Mitchell   ISBN 0-201-07398-6

of the protein itself, a variety of couplings for which
there had previously been little direct evidence. Two
mechanisms summarizing current views are first, a structure
based reaction mechanism of electron transfer, and second,
two structural models--one indicating electron transfer possibilities (6) and the other emphasizing energy conservation
possibilities (7).

The chemical mechanism of the oxidase is depicted in
Figure 1. The use of modern biophysical techniques identifies
the reactive center of cytochrome oxidase as an iron-copper
binuclear complex of spacing of 3.75 $\overset{o}{A}$ with a bridge sulfur
atom in the oxidized state, but not in the reduced state (6)
(Eqs. 1 and 2). Thus, a cyclic reaction mechanism shows the
acceptance of a pair of electrons by the redox center at
physiological temperatures from cytochrome c via cytochrome
a and its associated copper, Cu_a, and at low temperatures

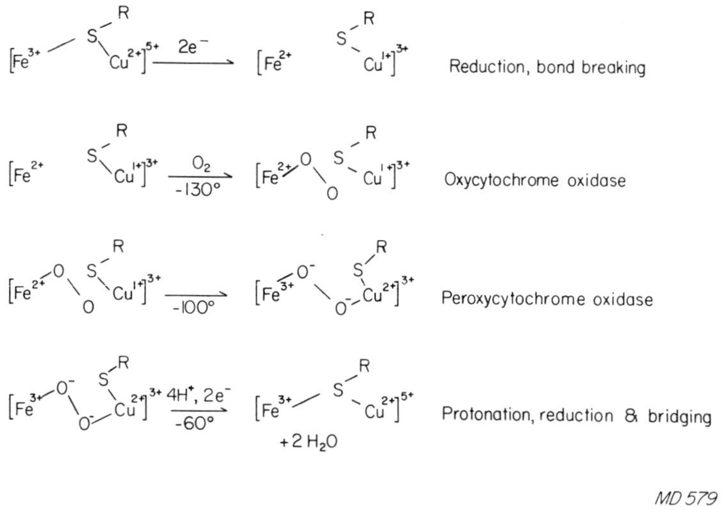

Reduction, bond breaking

Oxycytochrome oxidase

Peroxycytochrome oxidase

Protonation, reduction & bridging

MD 579

Fig. 1. Structure-based reaction mechanism for cytochrome
        oxidase.

directly from cytochrome c by an electron tunneling reaction
(8). This yields the ferrous-cuprous complex with the S bond
broken and the active site clear for reaction with oxygen
(Eq. 2). In the second step at low temperatures, liganding
of the iron and oxygen leads to a stable, highly dissociated
intermediate, whose structure fits the analogous liganded
form of hemoglobin and myoglobin. Under these conditions
cytochrome oxidase behaves like these well known oxygen
transport hemoproteins. Electron transfer to oxygen from
the iron copper couple reaction appears to be nearly simultaneous (the μ superoxo intermediate appears at a low concentration) and the peroxo form is observed (9). This compound
is stable over a wide range of temperatures (-130 to -50°)
but may exist in a number of structural states depending upon
whether the dioxygen bond is broken and the iron acquires
higher valence states. Reduction of peroxide to water is
expected from thermodynamic considerations and occurs in a
two-step, two-electron reaction at higher temperatures where
electron donation from cytochrome a, or indeed cytochrome c,
by a tunneling reaction, completes oxygen reduction and re-
establishes the iron copper bond. The redox cycle of bond
making and bond breaking (Eq. 4) then continues.

The structure of the molecule in the active site is
depicted in Figure 2 where the latest in Frey's data [per-
sonal communication and (10)] are melded with the structural
data to give an approximate location of the two irons and
two coppers of cytochrome oxidase with respect to the oxidase
molecule, and the oxidase molecule with respect to the membrane. Resonance energy transfer locates hemes a and a_3 at
$\sim$25 $\overset{\text{o}}{\text{A}}$ from the iron atom of cytochrome c (11), which in turn
is electrostatically bound to the membrane here indicated to

CYTOCHROME OXIDASE

CYTOPLASMIC - SIDE

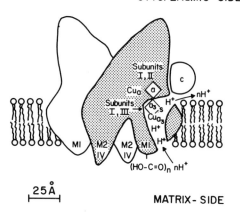

25Å

MATRIX- SIDE

MD 593

Fig. 2.   Structure of redox sites of cytochrome oxidase (6)
in relation to molecular structure of Frey (10)
which illustrates the dimer from M1, M2 and the exposed subunit IV. Most parts are crudely drawn to
scale except for the channel width.

be near the junction of the oxidase molecule and the lipid
membrane. Heme a and Cu_a are outside of magnetic interaction and EXAFS determinable distances (> 5 Å) while heme a_3
and Cu_a are closely knit in the ferromagnetically coupled
center at 3.75 Å just beyond the confines of the iron pyrrole-
nitrogen distances (2.0 Å) (6). The two cysteine residues of
subunit II (12), together with its stellacyanin/azurin-like
amino acid sequence, identify heme a_3, Cu_{a_3} with subunit II
(12). Since proton pumping is involved in cytochrome oxidase
function and subunit III may contain the appropriate channel
(13), a close association of II and III is suggested. Heme a
and Cu_a could, according to the sulfur amino acid content of
the subunits, be in either subunits I or II (14). The distance between heme a and heme a_3 perpendicular to the plane

of the membrane, as determined by anomalous scattering (15),
is about 10 $\overset{\circ}{A}$ as indicated here--an appropriate distance for
an electron tunneling mechanism. Since cytochrome c is
observed to tunnel electrons to cytochrome oxidase at low
temperatures, the distance between it and heme a_3 is indicated to be only slightly larger than the distance to heme a.
The distance of heme a and heme a_3 from the cytochrome c
binding site can also be determined by dysprosium broadening
of the epr signals (16) which suggests an approximation of
heme a to the cytosolic side of the membrane as indicated
here and a somewhat larger distance for heme a_3. Evidence
on the disposition of heme a_3 with respect to the membrane
plane is afforded by the accessibility of the subunit II
cysteine to attack by sulfhyryl reagents from the membrane
plane (Capaldi, R., personal communication). Whether this
suggests entry of the reagents through the channel (see discussion below), or preferential permeation of SH reagents
over dysprosium, is not known at the present time.

The relationship of this mechanism to charge separation
and transport is suggested by the ion pump channel indicated
(out of scale) in Figure 2 and drawn in more detail in
Figure 3 (7). Insofar as Figure 2 is concerned, the main
feature of the channel is that heme a_3, Cu_{a_3} are directly
involved in the process.

One of the few charge separation mechanisms that is
consistent with the biological functions of cytochrome oxidase in transporting 3 to 4 hydrogen ions across the membrane per electron transferred is based upon a hypothesis
previously proposed for chromatophores (17), namely that a
structural change in the redox center activates peripheral
groups on the protein (18,19). We propose that cytochrome

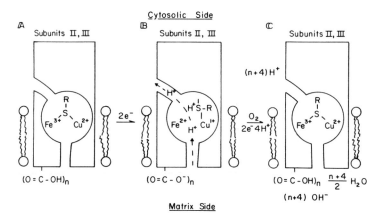

Fig.3.   An illustration of the redox center's function in
charge separation by the Membrane Bohr Effect.

oxidase operates as a similar pump where the structural
changes of the reaction redox center, which vastly exceed in
magnitude those observed in liganding of hemoglobin ($\sim$0.07 A)
(20,21), cause the pK changes of multiple groups either on
the periphery of the protein, as indicated, or in the transmembrane channel (presumably subunit III)(7).   Step A represents the resting state where the carboxyl group is protonated and the iron and sulfur bridge is intact; no water
space exists in the environment of the redox center and the
gate is thereby effectively closed.   Reduction of cytochrome
oxidase from the ferric-cupric couple to the ferrous-cuprous
couple causes a large conformation change.   In addition, an
appropriate change of peripheral groups can alter their
environment and a passage through the open gate.   Also,
change of pK's result in n protons (n $\geq$ 1) to be released
into the channel and translocate through the open gate to
the opposite side of the membrane.   Whether or not the

sulfur atom itself participates in this reaction by binding protons is not inconsistent with, but is not proved by, the available data. Addition of two more electrons and four hydrogen ions completes the reaction, restoring the closure of the gate by the reestablishment of the iron-sulfur copper bond in the ferric-cupric couple. The peripheral groups are reprotonated releasing n hydroxyl ions on the matrix side, corresponding to the n hydrogen ions on the cytosolic side. Since oxygen is reduced to water, four additional hydrogen ions per dioxygen molecule or one per electron are taken up on the matrix side. Since the observed H^+/e value is n = 4 (22), three H^+ will travel by the channel and one by asymmetric O_2 reduction per electron or 12 + 4 per dioxygen molecule. Obviously, small alterations of the number of groups that change pK's would initiate the need for the 4 H^+ obtained from the dioxygen reduction. Possibilities exist for many variations of this scheme and appropriate values of n depend only upon the net difference of the pK changes on one side of the membrane and one on the other.

Coupling between cytochrome oxidase and the f_1. Structural coupling between the f_1 ATPase and the cytochrome oxidase is made possible by interaction between the redox center, heme a_3, Cu_{a_3}, and the periphery of the oxidase protein, particularly subunit III with its corresponding member in the ATPase (23), thereby permitting localized charge separation mechanisms to function in the energy coupling reaction. In the absence of structural information on the relationship of subunits III and II in cytochrome oxidase and the corresponding coupling in the f_1 ATPase, it is premature to speculate about the nature of the juxtaposition of these subunits and the coupling of structural changes between them. However, this last link in the chain of research towards an appropriate solution for the energy coupling mechanism will come as structure determinations proceed.

REFERENCES

1. DeVault, D. and Chance, B. (1966) Biophys. J. $\underline{6}$(6), 825-847.
2. Chance, B., DeVault, D.C., Frauenfelder, H., Marcus, R.A., Schrieffer, J.R. and Sutin, N. (eds.) (1979) Tunneling in Biological Systems, Academic Press, New York.
3. Chance, B., Saronio, C. and Leigh, J.S. (1975) J. Biol. Chem. $\underline{250}$(24),9226-9237.
4. George, P. (1956) in Currents in Biochemical Research (Green, D.E., ed.) Interscience Press, Inc., New York, p. 388.
5. Taube, H. (1965) J. Gen. Phys. $\underline{49}$(1),29-49.
6. Powers, L., Chance, B., Ching, Y. and Angiollilo, P. (1981) Biophys. J. $\underline{34}$. In press.
7. Chance, B., Powers, L. and Ching, Y. (1981) in Mitochondria Microsomes (Lee, C.P., Schatz, A. and Dallner, A., eds.) Addison-Wesley Co., Reading, Mass. In press.
8. Chance, B., Waring, A. and Powers, L. (1979) in Cytochrome Oxidase (King, T., Orii, Y., Chance, B. and Okunuki, K., eds.) Elsevier/North Holland, Amsterdam, pp. 353-360.
9. deFonseka, K. and Chance, B. (1980) Biochem. J. $\underline{185}$(2), 527-530; and deFonseka, K. and Chance, B., Biophys. J. In press.
10. Frey, T., Chan , S.H.P. and Shatz, G. (1978) J. Biol. Chem. $\underline{253}$(12),4489-4495.
11. Vanderkooi, J.M., Glatz, P., Casadei, J. and Woodrow, G.V. (1980) Eur. J. Biochem. $\underline{110}$(1),189-196.
12. Steffens, G.J. and Buse, G. (1979) Hoppe-Seyler's Z. Physiol. Chem. $\underline{360}$,613-619.
13. Krab, K. and Wikstrom, M. (1979) Biochim. Biophys. Acta 548(1),1-15.
14. Buse, G. and Steffens, G.J. (1978) Hoppe-Seyler's Z. Physiol. Chem. $\underline{359}$, 1005-1009.

15. Stamatoff, J., Blasie, J.K., Tavarmina, A., Pechance, J., Dutton, P.L., Erecinska, M., Eisenberger, P. and Brown, G. (1981) Bull. of Am. Phys. Soc. 36(3),266. Abstr. No. DC1.
16. Blume, H., Cusanovich, M., Sweeney, W. and Ohnishi, T. (1981) J. Biol. Chem. 256(5),2199-2206.
17. Chance, B., Crofts, A., Nishimura, M. and Price, B. (1970), Eur. J. Biochem. 13,364-374.
18. Bohr, C., Hasselbach, K.A. and Krogh, A. (1904) Scand. Arch. Physiol. 16,402.
19. Hess, B. and Kurschmitz, D. (1978) in Frontiers of Biological Energetics (Dutton, P.L., Leigh, J.S. and Scarpa, A., eds.) Academic Press, New York. pp. 257-264.
20. Eisenberger, P., Shulman, R.G., Brown, G.B. and Ogawa, S. (1976), Proc. Natl. Acad. Sci. USA 73,491-495.
21. Perutz, M. (1969) The Croonian Lecture, Proc. Royal Soc. B., 173,130-140.
22. Lehninger, A. (1980) First Eur. Bioenerg. Conf., Urbino, Italy. (Abstract).
23. Pedersen, P.L. and Hullihen, J. (1978) J. Biol. Chem. 253(7),2176-2183.

THE PROTONMOTIVE FUNCTION OF CYTOCHROME OXIDASE

Mårten Wikström

Department of Medical Chemistry, University of
Helsinki, SF-00170 Helsinki 17, Finland

INTRODUCTION

Since 1977 the protonmotive function of cytochrome oxidase (EC 1.9.3.1) has been subject of a fundamental controversy. Based on experiments with intact mitochondria, submitochondrial particles and cytochrome oxidase liposomes it was
then proposed that this respiratory chain complex generates
protonmotive force (pmf) by redox-linked proton translocation
(1-3). Since cytochrome oxidase does not contain redox carriers of the classical H-transfer type, but electron transfer
centres only (two haems and two coppers per $\underline{aa}_3$ monomer), true
proton translocation would have to take place by a mechanism
quite different from from the group translocation or redox
loop type of mechanism proposed earlier to explain generation
of pmf by the respiratory chain (see e.g. 4).

The proposal of cytochrome oxidase as a redox-linked
proton pump has more recently received experimental support
from work in several laboratories (reviewed in 3,5). The
strongest and in my opinion conclusive proof has come from
the studies of the isolated and purified enzyme incorporated

V. P. Skulachev and Peter C. Hinkle (eds.), Chemiosmotic Proton Circuits in Biological Membranes
in honor of Peter Mitchell   ISBN 0-201-07398-6

into liposome membranes (2,6-11).

The object of this minireview is to discuss the significance of the most recent work on the protonmotive function of cytochrome oxidase. It seems that our knowledge of the molecular mechanics by which the oxidase generates pmf may have recently increased considerably. The new data may also open the way for a view according to which cytochrome oxidase may, in fact, function both as a proton pump and as a directly coupled generator of pmf. Both these functions contribute equally to the overall energy transduction by the enzyme.

PROTON-ELECTRON COUPLING

Linkage between redox and protolytic events is an obvious requirement in a redox-coupled proton pump. In a minimum model the pump must consist of a redox centre to which an acid/base group is coupled. Both elements should exhibit specific properties with discrete input and output states, making them susceptible to experimental analysis (3,12,13). The H^+-e^- coupling may be expressed as a pH-dependence of the midpoint redox potential (E_m) of the redox centre, as found for the haem system in cytochrome oxidase (14-17). If cytochrome oxidase functioned merely as an electron translocator (18), there would be no obvious reason for such H^+-e^- linkage.

The phenomenon of H^+-e^- coupling in electron carriers has been termed a "redox Bohr effect" (19). We have avoided this terminology because the analogy to the Bohr effect in haemoglobin is poor (ligand binding to haem iron, not oxidoreduction, is linked to protolysis), and may therefore give a misleading impression of the underlying molecular events. It may be emphasised that a pH-dependent E_m simply means that the pK of an acid/base group anywhere in the redox protein (or, indeed, in the prosthetic group) changes upon a change in the redox state of the electron carrier. This phenomenon is not sufficient to account for redox-linked proton translocation, nor is it absolutely necessary in such a system. Yet, the phenomenon is expected to facilitate the operation of a proton pump kinetically (13).

IDENTIFICATION OF THE REDOX CENTRE OF THE PUMP

There is now an impressive amount of evidence for the idea that the haem of cytochrome $\underline{a}$ is the redox centre of the proton pump. This evidence stems, in part, from the biphasic electron transfer kinetics of this cytochrome (13), and in part from the nature of H^+-e^- coupling, to be described below. Moreover, the previous indications for cytochrome $\underline{a}_3$ having such a role (see 2,3), due to the energy-linked shift in its spectrum, have been removed more recently by the demonstration that this effect is due to partial reversal of the reactions of O_2 reduction to water (20).

Artzatbanov et al. (16) made the important observation that, not only is oxidoreduction of cytochrome $\underline{a}$ linked to protolysis in cyanide-inhibited cytochrome oxidase, but H^+ uptake and release coupled to oxidoreduction of cytochrome $\underline{a}$ is confined only to the matrix or M side of the mitochondrial membrane under such conditions. We have confirmed this finding under slightly improved conditions (17,21). This sidedness of the redox-linked acid/base group is almost diagnostic for its involvement in proton translocation, in which it is expected to shuttle between two states (input and output) in protonic contact with the M and C (cytoplasmic) sides of the membrane, respectively (3,12,13). This finding thus supports the view that cytochrome $\underline{a}$ is the redox centre of the pump, but further evidence has been obtained more recently (see below).

THE ROLE OF SUBUNIT III IN PROTON TRANSLOCATION

Outgoing from the finding that the mitochondrially syn-
thesised subunit III of cytochrome oxidase may be removed from
the enzyme without significantly affecting electron transfer
activity or main spectral properties (22), we have recently
tested in greater detail how the properties of the enzyme may
change on removal of this subunit.

In contrast to some preliminary findings (23), it is
now clear that although the subunit III-free enzyme is active
in electron transfer and shows good respiratory control (i.e.
uncoupler-induced acceleration of O_2 consumption) after reconstitution into liposomes, it lacks the H^+-translocating property. Thus the characteristic H^+ extrusion (see 6-11) is
lacking (24), and the K^+/e^- ratio of K^+ uptake in the presence of valinomycin is near 1 (25). With the reconstituted intact enzyme the K^+/e^- ratio was confirmed to be near 2 (8-10).

These findings lead to some important conclusions.
First, a central role of subunit III in proton translocation
is clearly indicated, supporting the interpretation of independent data on the binding of dicyclohexyl carbodiimide (DCCD)
to the enzyme (11,26,27). Further strong evidence favouring
this notion is reported below.

Secondly, the data show that the subunit III-free enzyme still generates pmf even though the proton pump is apparently removed or inoperative, but with the energy-transducing
efficiency cut by about one half. It is interesting that the
removal of subunit III apparently causes a local uncoupling of
electron transfer and H^+ translocation without a generalised
increase in the permeability of the liposome membranes for H^+.
This suggests that subunit III may have a specific role in

H^+-e^- coupling of the proton pump so that its removal creates molecular "slipping" after which electron transfer is allowed without being linked to H^+ translocation.

Thirdly, these results suggest a specific role of the haem a_3/copper centre in generation of pmf, as discussed in the next section.

THE ROLE OF THE HAEM a_3/Cu CENTRE IN GENERATION OF PMF

Since "local uncoupling" of the proton pump does not abolish generation of pmf (see above), it seems clear that the haem a_3/Cu centre receives the electrons and protons required in the reduction of O_2 to water from opposite sides of the membrane. Since the electrons are derived from cytochrome c on the C side, it follows that the protons must be taken from the M side. This is the mechanism proposed previously by Mitchell (see e.g. 18) to account entirely for pmf generation by cytochrome oxidase. To date this proposal has remained ambiguous, however, due to the simultaneous functioning of the proton pump (cf. 1,2,28).

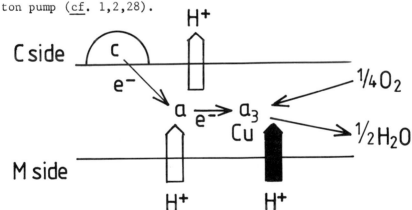

Fig.1.Generation of pmf by cytochrome oxidase

H^+ translocation linked to oxidoreduction of cytochrome a (thick white arrows) constitutes the proton pump. Pmf is also generated by the function of the a_3/Cu centre in accepting e^- from the C side and H^+ (black thick arrow) from the M side.

We conclude that the generation of pmf by cytochrome oxidase takes place by two separate mechanisms coupled in series rather independently of one another. (i) The proton pump is linked to the redox function of cytochrome a and requires specifically the cooperation with subunit III, (ii) the directly coupled "annihilation" of electrons and protons from opposite sides of the membrane is catalysed by the a_3/Cu centre in the reduction of O_2 to water. This conclusion is summarised schematically in Fig. 1.

This hypothesis may have interesting evolutionary implications. The proton pump could be a more recent development to enhance the efficiency of energy conservation. In this respect it is intriguing that the isolated enzyme from Paracoccus lacks the analogue of subunit III, does not carry out H^+ translocation, but shows excellent respiratory control after reconstitution (29; cf. properties of the subunit III-free mammalian enzyme). Since the oxidase in Paracoccus membranes was recently shown to contain the H^+ pump (30) it is possible that an analogue of subunit III is lost on isolation of the enzyme. Alternatively,however, the H^+ pump function might be modulated in this micro-organism depending, for instance, on growth conditions.

TENTATIVE LOCALISATION OF THE ACID/BASE GROUP

The acidic groups responsible for the pH-dependence of E_m of the aa_3 and b cytochromes have not so far been identified. Their identification may be of great importance if they are indeed crucial in the protonmotive mechanisms of the aa_3 and bc_1 complexes, as proposed previously (3,31).

Fig. 2 shows that the normally observed pH-dependence of the E_m of cytochrome a is abolished on removal of subunit III from the enzyme (25). This strongly suggests that the

H^+-e^- coupling of cytochrome $\underline{a}$ is lost.

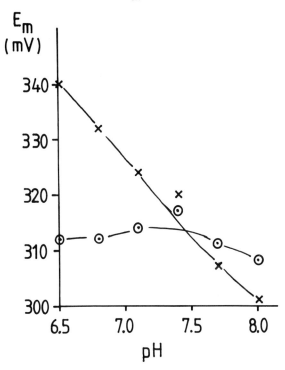

Fig.2. <u>The pH-dependence of the E_m of cytochrome a. The effect of removal of subunit III.</u>

Cytochrome oxidase with (x-x) or without (o-o) subunit III was isolated and purified as described previously (22-24). The E_m was determined in the presence of cyanide and a mixture of ferri- and ferrocyanide essentially as described in (16). For details, see (25).

Together with the finding that removal of subunit III abolishes the H^+-translocating function, this discovery strongly favours the proposal that cytochrome $\underline{a}$ is intimately involved in the mechanism of the proton pump. The simplest explanation for the lost pH-dependence is that the redox-linked acid/base group is located in subunit III. This would mean that the H^+-e^- coupling takes place between different polypeptide

chains. However, at present it is not possible to rule out
the alternative that removal of subunit III changes the structure enough to alter or abolish H^+-e^- coupling between the
haem of cytochrome $\underline{a}$ and an acid/base group on a subunit other
than III.

The result of Fig. 2 may contain further information on
the nature of the acid/base group. Since the main change in
E_m on removal of subunit III occurs at acidic pH this residue
is likely to be one that is charged in the protonated state
and uncharged when deprotonated. Together with the pH range
where the E_m is a function of pH in the intact enzyme (Fig. 2;
$\underline{cf}$. 16), this would point towards a histidine residue. Preliminary experiments have shown that DCCD does not consistently
change the pH-dependence of the E_m in the system of Fig. 2.
Thus the DCCD-sensitive glutamyl residue of subunit III (11)
is unlikely to be the redox-dependent acid/base group of the
proton pump.

CONCLUSION

The notion of a proton pump type of mechanism in cytochrome oxidase has received considerable further support since
its discovery in 1977. By comparison, the mechanisms of generation of pmf are almost completely unknown for the $\underline{bc}_1$ and
NADH dehydrogenase segments of the respiratory chain. The most
recent work has led to the conclusion that cytochrome $\underline{a}$ and
subunit III are essential components of the proton pump. The
latter may contain the essential redox-linked acid/base group
and is, in any case, more involved in the mechanism of H^+
translocation than merely by forming a channel of passive H^+
conductance. The haem $\underline{a}_3$/Cu centre also contributes to generation of pmf by accepting the electrons and protons necessary
for O_2 reduction to water from opposite sides of the membrane.

If this hypothesis is correct, cytochrome oxidase functions both as a proton pump and, simultaneously, as proposed by Mitchell. The two functions contribute equally to overall conservation of redox energy by this intriguing enzyme. It is hoped that this finding may help to reconcile the remnants of controversy on the protonmotive function of cytochrome oxidase.

REFERENCES

1.   Wikström,M.(1977) Nature (Lond.) 266, 271-273.
2.   Wikström,M. & Saari,H. (1977) Biochim. Biophys. Acta 462, 347-361.
3.   Wikström,M. & Krab,K. (1979) Biochim. Biophys. Acta 549, 177-222.
4.   Mitchell,P.(1979) Eur. J. Biochem. 95, 1-20.
5.   Wikström,M. & Krab,K.(1980) Curr. Top. Bioenerg. 10, 51-101.
6.   Krab,K. & Wikström,M. (1978) Biochim. Biophys. Acta 504, 200-214.
7.   Casey,R.P., Chappell,J.B. & Azzi,A.(1979) Biochem. J. 182, 149-156.
8.   Sigel,E. & Carafoli,E.(1979) J. Biol. Chem. 254, 10572-10574.
9.   Sigel,E. & Carafoli,E. (1980) Eur. J. Biochem. 111, 299-306.
10. Coin,J.T. & Hinkle,P.C. (1979) in (Lee,C.P. et al., eds.) Membrane Bioenergetics, Addison-Wesley, Reading, Mass., pp. 405-412.
11. Prochaska,L.J., Steffens,G.C.M., Buse,G., Bisson,R. & Capaldi, R.A. (1981) Biochim. Biophys. Acta, in press.
12. Wikström,M.,Krab,K. & Saraste,M. (1981) Annu. Rev. Biochem. 50, 623-655.
13. Wikström,M., Krab,K. & Saraste,M. (1981) Cytochrome Oxidase - A Synthesis, Academic Press, London,in press.
14. Wilson,D.F., Lindsay,J.G. & Brocklehurst,E.S.(1972) Biochim. Biophys. Acta 256, 277-286.
15. Van Gelder,B.F., Van Rijn, J.L.M.L., Schilder,G.J.A. & Wilms,J. (1977) in (K. Van Dam & B.F. Van Gelder, eds.) Structure and Function of Energy-Transducing Membranes, Elsevier/North-Holland Biomedical Press, Amsterdam, pp. 61-68.
16. Artzatbanov,V.Yu., Konstantinov,A.A. & Skulachev,V.P. (1979) FEBS Lett. 87, 180-185.

180   MÅRTEN WIKSTRÖM

17. Wikström,M.(1981) in (C. Ho & W.C. Eaton,eds.) Inter-
    action Between Iron and Proteins in Oxygen and Electron
    Transport, Elsevier, New York, in press.
18. Mitchell,P. & Moyle,J.(1979) in (T.E. King et al., eds.)
    Cytochrome Oxidase, Elsevier/North-Holland Biomedical
    Press, Amsterdam, pp. 361-372.
19. Papa,S.(1976) Biochim. Biophys. Acta 456, 39-84.
20. Wikström,M.(1981) Proc. Natl.Acad. Sci.U.S.A., in
    press.
21. Wikström,M. & Krab,K. (1979) in (Y. Mukohata & L.
    Packer,eds.) Cation Flux Across Biomembranes, Academic
    Press, New York, pp. 321-329.
22. Penttilä,T., Saraste,M. & Wikström,M.(1979) FEBS Lett.
    101, 295-300.
23. Saraste,M., Penttilä,T., Coggins,J.R. & Wikström,M.
    (1980) FEBS Lett. 114, 35-38.
24. Saraste,M., Penttilä,T. & Wikström,M.(1981) Eur. J.
    Biochem. 115, 261-268.
25. Penttilä,T. & Wikström,M.(1981) in (F. Palmieri et al.,
    eds.) Vectorial Reactions in Electron and Ion Transport
    in Mitochondria and Bacteria, Elsevier/North-Holland
    Biomedical Press, in press.
26. Casey,R.P., Thelen,M. & Azzi,A.(1979) Biochem. Biophys.
    Res. Commun. 87, 1044-1051.
27. Casey,R.P., Thelen,M. & Azzi,A.(1980) J. Biol. Chem.
    255, 3994-4000.
28. Wikström,M. (1981) in (C.P. Lee et al., eds.) Mito-
    chondria and Microsomes, Addison-Wesley, Reading,
    Mass., in press.
29. Ludwig,B.(1980) Biochim. Biophys. Acta 594, 177-189.
30. Van Verseveld,H.W., Krab,K. & Stouthamer,A.H. (1981)
    Biochim. Biophys. Acta, in press.
31. Wikström,M.(1972) in (G.F. Azzone et al., eds.) Bio-
    chemistry and Biophysics of Biological Membranes,
    Academic Press, New York and London, pp. 147-164.

BIOGENESIS OF THE MITOCHONDRIAL PROTON TRANS-

LOCATING SYSTEM

Gottfried Schatz

Biocenter, University of Basel, CH-4056 Basel
Switzerland

INTRODUCTION

Electron transport-linked phosphorylation in bacteria,
chloroplasts and mitochondria is effected by the precise interplay between electron-and proton translocating circuits
which are now partly known. This new knowledge is a milestone
for bioenergetics and membrane biology, but it also presents
a formidable challenge to workers trying to understand how
these circuits are synthesized. Where are the individual components of these circuits made and how are they assembled and
properly positioned within the membrane where they function?
Complete answers to these questions are still far away but
some partial answers are nevertheless available. In this brief
survey I will try to review some recent key discoveries on
how the mitochondrial inner membrane is formed in living
cells.

V. P. Skulachev and Peter C. Hinkle (eds.), Chemiosmotic Proton Circuits in Biological Membranes
   in honor of Peter Mitchell   ISBN 0-201-07398-6

THE MITOCHONDRIAL GENETIC SYSTEM

Mitochondria contain their own genetic system that consists of a relatively small (usually circular) DNA and a complete machinery for replicating, transcribing and translating the genetic information residing in this DNA (1-3). Every component of this mitochondrial genetic system seems to be different from its corresponding counterpart in the nucleo-cytoplasmic system. For example, it has been known for more than a decade that protein synthesis on mitochondrial and extramitochondrial (i.e. cytoplasmic) ribosomes is blocked by different inhibitors (1). The unique features of the mitochondrial genetic system have now been impressively underscored by studying the nucleotide sequence and the transcription of mitochondrial DNA (3). The mitochondrial genomes from human placenta and bovine heart (4, 5) have been completely sequenced and extensive sequence information is available on mitochondrial DNAs from yeast (6), Neurospora (7) and Aspergillus (8). These genomes are represented by the circles shown in Fig. 1. It can be seen that the mitochondrial genomes from humans, Aspergillus and the yeast Saccharomyces cerevisiae differ greatly in size and gene arrangement, but code for almost the same types of products. All of them code for the mitochondrial RNA species, for the three large subunits of cytochrome oxidase, the apoprotein of cytochrome b and for the 20,000 dalton subunit (subunit VI) of the oligomycin-sensitive ATPase complex. The mitochondrial DNA of yeast codes, in addition, for the DCCD-binding protein (subunit IX) of the ATPase complex. All of the mitochondrial protein products are integral membrane proteins functioning in electron- or proton transfer

within the mitochondrial inner membrane. In addition to the
genes mentioned above, human mitochondrial DNA contains at
least eight long "uninterrupted reading frames" (termed URFs)
which might represent genes for as yet unidentified mitochondrial protein products (Table 1).

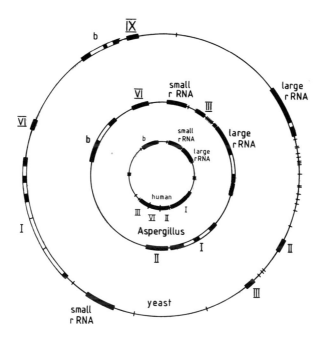

Fig. 1. The mitochondrial genomes of Saccharomyces,
        Aspergillus and humans
        The different sizes of the circles are approximately
        proportional to the sizes of the DNA molecules. The
        blocks superimposed on the circles represent genes for
        ribosomal RNAs or proteins. Filled blocks signify exons,
        open blocks introns. The short thin lines represent
        tRNA genes. The unidentified open reading frames (URFs)
        on human - or Aspergillus mitochondrial DNA are not
        shown.

I, II and III: subunits I, II and III of cytochrome
oxidase; VI and IX: subunits VI and IX associated with
the F_o- moiety of the oligomycin-sensitive ATPase complex. (Subunit IX is often termed "DCCD-binding protein"); b: cytochrome b apoprotein.

Table 1. Genes on human mitochondrial DNA

Genes coding for	Product
RNA	16 S RNA of mitochondrial ribosomes 12 S RNA of mitochondrial ribosomes 22 different tRNAs
Protein	Cytochrome oxidase subunit I Cytochrome oxidase subunit II Cytochrome oxidase subunit III ATPase subunit VI Cytochrome b
?	8 Uninterrupted reading frames (URFs) which could be genes for as yet un- identified protein products.

Even though the mitochondrial DNA molecules from humans and yeast code for roughly the same types of products,
they differ vastly in the way their genes are arranged and
transcribed. Human mitochondrial DNA is among the most com-
pact genomes known; individual genes are either immediately
adjacent to each other or separated by only very short
stretches of "intergenic" DNA. Also, intervening sequences
within genes ("introns") seem to be absent. Most of the genome appears to be transcribed as a single polycistronic RNA
which is then processed to individual RNA components by precise endonucleolytic cleavages (9). In some cases, the termination codon of the resulting mRNA has to be completed by
post-transcriptional polyadenylation. Most human mitochondrial mRNAs species contain very little, if any, untranslated

sequences at either end (9, 3).

In contrast, yeast mitochondrial DNA is roughly five times larger than human mitochondrial DNA and contains extensive AT-rich non-coding sequences between genes (10). At least two protein genes (those for cytochrome b and cytochrome oxidase subunit I) have "introns". Some of these introns feature long sequences uninterrupted by termination codons; one such intron within the cytochrome b gene of yeast appears to code for a mitochondrial polypeptide involved in the processing of cytochrome b pre-mRNA (11). Most of the biochemical details of these fascinating phenomena still remain to be worked out. It is also puzzling that some yeast strains may lack certain introns without any noticeable effect on the expression of the genes from which these introns had been lost (3, 10).

Perhaps the most surprising result emanating from sequencing mitochondrial DNA molecules is the finding that the genetic code used by mitochondria is slightly different from that which had so far been considered "universal" (12-16). There are even differences in codon assignments between mitochondria from different species! For example, the codon UGA (which is normally read as "stop" in bacteria and the eucaryotic nuclear genetic system) is read as the amino acid tryptophan, the codon AUA can be read as methionine or initiation rather than the amino acid isoleucine etc. Obviously, these findings have important implications for trying to retrace the evolutionary origin of mitochondria.

The structural characterization of mitochondrial genomes is one of the most exciting recent developments in molecular biology. Nevertheless, the enormous differences

between the genomes of different types of mitochondria
suggest that structural studies on mitochondrial DNA molecules
will not readily uncover the general principles by which mitochondria are assembled in vivo. More direct information on
this point comes from recent experiments on the import of
extramitochondrially-synthesized polypeptides into mitochondria.

IMPORT OF PROTEINS INTO MITOCHONDRIA

Table 1 shows clearly that the mitochondrial genetic
system manufactures only a very small part of the several
hundred polypeptides which make up a mitochondrial organelle.
The vast majority of these polypeptides are coded by nuclear
genes, synthesized on extramitochondrial polysomes and imported into the mitochondria (1). How is an extramitochon-
drially-made polypeptide directed towards the organelle, how
does it move across one or both mitochondrial membranes to
its correct intramitochondrial location and how is this transport driven and regulated?

Research in several laboratories indicates that polypeptides destined to be imported into mitochondria are initially synthesized as precursors (17-19). Most of these precursors are between 2,000 and 6,000 daltons larger than the
corresponding mature proteins found inside the mitochondria,
but some precursors differ from the corresponding mature polypeptides only by conformation, not by molecular weight. These
precursors can be identified by translating total mRNA in a
heterologous cell free protein synthesizing system in the

presence of radioactive amino acids, isolating the radiolabeled precursor by immune precipitation with specific anti-
sera and characterizing it by SDS-polyacrylamide electrophoresis followed by radioautography (Figure 2).

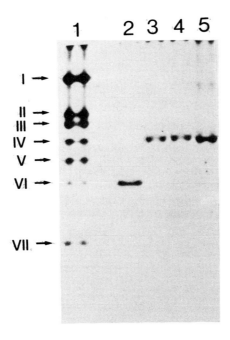

Fig. 2. The nuclearly-coded subunit VI of yeast cytochrome
oxidase (MW = 12,700) is made as a 20,000 dalton precursor. 1, uniformly labeled mature yeast cytochrome
oxidase; 2, mature subunit VI; 3, subunit VI precursor
accumulating in yeast cells whose intramitochondrial
ATP level had been lowered by the uncoupler CCCP (20);
4 and 5, subunit VI precursor synthesized in a reticulocyte lysate in the presence of ^{35}S-methionine; 5,
same as 4 and 5 except that _in vitro_ synthesis was
done in the presence of N-formyl-^{35}S-methionine-tRNA$_f$
to label only the N-terminus of the nascent subunit
VI precursor chain. See ref. 21 for details. The
Roman numerals indicate the seven cytochrome oxidase
subunits. The figure represents a photograph of the
fluorogram made from a dried SDS-polyacrylamide gel
slab.

Synthesis in the form of larger precursors has been demonstrated for several dozen mitochondrial polypeptides, many of
them being part of the mitochondrial proton-translocating
system. Such polypeptides include subunits IV, V and VI of
cytochrome oxidase, the alpha, beta and gamma subunits of the
F_1 ATPase and several subunits of the cytochrome bc_1 complex, including cytochrome c_1 itself (17). When the in vitro
synthesized precursors are incubated with isolated mitochondria under conditions preventing simultaneous protein synthesis,
the precursors are imported into the mitochondria with high
efficiency (Table 2) and cleaved to their mature size by specific intra-mitochondrial proteases (22, 23).

Table 2. Import of F_1 β-subunit precursor into isolated mitochondria

LYSATE (precursor)	-PROTEASES		+PROTEASES	
	pellet	supt.	pellet	supt.
100%	81%	7%	63%	0%
100%	87%	21%	71%	0%

The β-subunit of yeast F_1 was synthesized in a reticulocyte
lysate in the presence of ^{35}S-methionine, protein synthesis
was stopped and the radiolabeled precursor was incubated with
isolated yeast mitochondria essentially as described in ref.
23. The mitochondria were then reisolated by centrifugation
and an aliquot of the mitochondrial pellet and the supernatant
was digested with trypsin and chymotrypsin to reveal β-subunit
that had been imported into mitochondria and thereby become

resistant to externally added proteases. The amount of radiolabeled β-subunit was determined by quantitative immune precipitation followed by radioautography and densitometry
(S. Gasser, unpublished).

Peter Böhni has purified a matrix-localized soluble protease

that cleaves precursors of those proteins that are transported

either across or into the mitochondrial inner membrane (ref.

24, Figure 3).

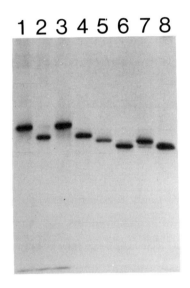

Fig. 3. Maturation of the precursors to the F_1 α- and β-subunit by a purified protease from the yeast mitochondrial matrix. The radiolabeled, in vitro-synthesized
precursors were incubated with the soluble protease
and the products identified by immunoprecipitation,
SDS-polyacrylamide gel electrophoresis and fluoro-
graphy. 1 and 5, pre α and pre β, respectively; 2 and
6, after incubation with the protease; 3 and 7, after
incubation with the protease in the presence of
o-phenanthroline. 4 and 8, mature α- and β-subunit,
respectively. (Peter Böhni, unpublished).

Proteins transported into the intermembrane space are cleaved by an additional protease which has not been characterized. The matrix-localized processing protease is specifically inhibited by chelators such as o-phenanthroline and nucleoside triphosphates such as GTP. Unpublished data by Susan Gasser and Günther Daum from our laboratory show that in vitro import of different radiolabeled precursors into mitochondria occurs into the correct intramitochondrial spaces.

Transport of cytoplasmically-made mitochondrial precursor polypeptides into the organelles requires the presence of ATP within the mitochondrial matrix (20; Susan Gasser, unpublished); if isolated mitochondria are incubated with radiolabeled precursors in the absence of ATP or in the presence of ATP+ atractylate, they stop importing and processing the precursors. This is a dramatic demonstration of energy dependence of trans-membrane movement of polypeptides. Exactly how ATP is used to drive the polypeptides across the membrane barrier is not known except that present evidence argues against the possibility that ATP is used to set up a membrane potential. We are currently favoring the possibility that ATP induces the phosphorylation of a membrane protein which is involved in polypeptide import.

In the case of cytochrome c_1, Akira Ohashi and Jane Gibson (unpublished) could show that the import of the precursor polypeptide is followed by a complex series of maturation steps which have been partly dissected with the use of specific inhibitors and mutations. As briefly outlined in Figure 4, the cytochrome c_1 apoprotein is initially made outside the mitochondria as a heme-less precursor which is then imported across the outer membrane and at least partly across

the inner membrane in an energy-dependent translocation step
which can be blocked in living cells by appropriate concentrations of the uncoupler CCCP.

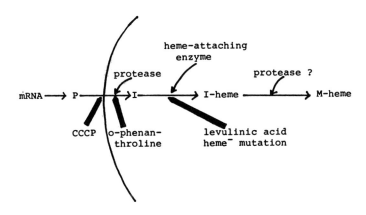

Fig. 4. Suggested maturation pathway for yeast cytochrome c_1.
        See text for details (Akira Ohashi and Jane Gibson,
        unpublished). M = mature apoprotein

The precursor is processed to a slightly smaller polypeptide
(I-form) by the o-phenanthroline-sensitive matrix protease
whereupon the resulting I-form is fitted with a heme group.
Attachment of heme appears to trigger a conformational change
which results in a second (presumably proteolytic) processing
event which generates the mature cytochrome c_1 protein containing a covalently-bound heme group. Attachment of heme and,
as a consequence, processing to the mature form can be prevented by blocking heme synthesis with levulinic acid or by
employing yeast mutants which are unable to synthesize heme.
The three forms of the cytochrome c_1 polypeptide indicated in
Figure 4 are shown as radiolabeled polypeptide bands in the

acrylamide gel of Figure 5.

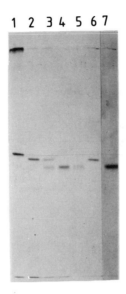

Fig. 5. Two-step, heme dependent maturation of yeast cyto-
      chrome c_1. A photograph of a fluorographed SDS-poly-
      acrylamide gel slab is shown.
      1, apocytochrome c_1, precursor (P-form) made in vitro;
      2, partially processed form (I-form) accumulated in a
      heme-deficient yeast mutant; 3, 4 and 5, same as 2
      except that the prelabeled heme-less mutant was chased
      for 30, 60 and 120 min in the presence of the heme-
      precursor delta-aminolevulinic acid; 6, same as 2 ex-
      cept that the prelabeled mutant was chased for 120 min
      in the absence of delta-aminolevulinic acid; 7, mature
      cytochrome c_1 (M-form). (Akira Ohashi and Jane Gibson,
      unpublished).

The conversion of the various cytochrome c_1 polypeptides

during the maturation process is documented by the pulse-chase

experiment depicted in Figure 6. Since the cytochrome c_1 pre-

cursor is processed by a matrix-localized soluble protease

we must conclude that a least part of the precursor is
initially transported all the way across the mitochondrial
inner membrane even though the final product, cytochrome $\underline{c}_1$,
is localized on the outer face of that membrane.

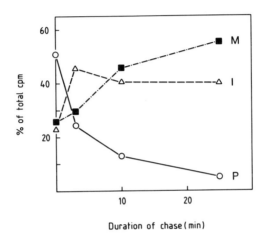

Fig. 6. The P-form of apocytochrome $\underline{c}_1$ is the precursor to the
        I- and M-forms $\underline{in}$ $\underline{vivo}$. Yeast cells were grown over-
        night in the presence of $^{35}SO_4$, pulse-labeled with
        ^{3}H-leucine and chased with unlabeled leucine. At the
        indicated times, the cells were rapidly denatured in
        10 % trichloroacetic acid, the various cytochrome $\underline{c}_1$
        polypeptides were isolated by immunoprecipitation and
        SDS-polyacrylamide gel electrophoresis and the ^{3}H/^{35}S-
        ratio of each form was determined. (Jane Gibson, un-
        published).

Since most imported mitochondrial proteins are initially made
as precursors, it is tempting to speculate that the (presumably) N-terminal extensions function as specific ligands for
some receptors on the mitochondrial surface. However, the
situation may be mere complex than that since several laboratories have found that the mature forms of aspartate amino-

transferase and malate dehydrogenase (two imported matrix enzymes) can spontaneously enter isolated mitochondria (25-27).
This process is clearly non-physiological since, in vivo,
aspartate amino transferase is made as a precursor (28) which
is probably cleaved to the mature size only after it has at
least partly reached the matrix space (24). Nevertheless,
these model systems may offer important information on the
molecular mechanism of protein import into mitochondria.

We are currently trying to identify receptor proteins
on the outer face of the mitochondrial outer membrane which
govern the import of cytoplasmically-synthesized precursor
polypeptides into the various mitochondrial compartments.
Another promising line of study attempts to purify and char-
acterize the different mitochondrial proteases that are involved in the correct maturation of imported precursor polypeptides. The most important, but also the most difficult
problem is the translocation step itself. At the moment we
have no idea how a polypeptide can move across a biological
membrane. Ignorance on this point is almost as profound as
that on the mechanism of proton translocation across the
mitochondrial inner membrane! Both problems must now be
attacked by characterizing and isolating the membrane components that are involved in the translocation phenomena.

ACKNOWLEDGEMENT

This article is dedicated with admiration and affection
to Peter Mitchell on occasion of his sixtieth birthday.
The studies from our laboratory quoted in this article
were supported by grants 3.606.80 and 3.212.77 from the Swiss
National Science Foundation.

REFERENCES

1. Review: Schatz, G. and Mason, T. L. (1974) Annu. Rev.
    Biochem. 43, 51-87.
2. Review: Borst, P. and Crivell, L. A. (1978) Cell 15,
    705-723.
3. Abstracts: Slonimski, P., Borst, P. and Attardi, G.
    (eds.) (1981) Mitochondrial Genes, Cold Spring Harbor
    Laboratory, Cold Spring Harbor, N. Y.
4. Anderson, S., Bankier, A. T., Barrell, B. G., De Bruijn,
    M. H. L., Coulson, A. R., Drouin, J., Eperon, I. C.,
    Nierlich, D. P., Roe, B. A., Sanger, F., Schreier, P.
    H., Smith, A. J. H., Staden, R. and Young, I. G. (1981)
    Nature 290, 457-465.
5. Review: Borst, P. and Grivell, L. (1981) Nature 290,
    443-444.
6. Bonitz, S. G., Coruzzi G., Thalenfeld, B. E.,
    Tzagoloff, A. and Macino, G. (1980) J. Biol. Chem. 255,
    11927-11941.
7. Van den Boogaart, P., Samallo, J., Van Dijk, S. and
    Agsteribbe, E. (1981), see ref. 3, p. 105.
8. Köchel, H. G. and Küntzel, H. (1981), see ref. 3,
    p. 103.
9. Ojala, D., Montoya, J. and Attardi, G. (1981) Nature
    290, 470-474.
10. Symposium: Kroon, A. M. and Saccone, C. (eds.) (1980)
    The Genetic Function of Mitochondrial DNA Elsevier/
    North Holland.
11. Lazowska, J., Jacq, C. and Slonimski, P. (1980) Cell
    22, 333-348.
12. Barrell, B. G., Bankier, A. T. and Druin, J. (1979)
    Nature 282, 189-194.
13. Macino, G., Coruzzi, G., Nobrega, F. G., Li, M. and
    Tzagoloff, A. (1979) Proc. Natl. Acad. Sci. USA 76,
    3784-3785.
14. Fox, T. D. (1979) Proc. Natl. Acad. Sci. USA 76,
    6534-6538.
15. Heckman, J. E., Sarnoff, J., Alzner-de Weerd, B.,
    Yin, S. and Raj Bandary, U. L. (1980) Proc. Natl. Acad.
    Sci. USA 77, 3159-3163.

16.   Barrell, B. G., Anderson, S., Bankier, A. T.,
        De Bruijn, M. H. L., Chen, E., Coulson, A. R., Drouin,
        J., Eperon, I. C., Nierlich, D. P., Roe, B. A., Sanger,
        F., Schreier, P. H., Smith, A. J. H., Staden, R. and
        Young, I. G. (1980) Proc. Natl. Acad. Sci. USA 77,
        3164-3166.
        Bonitz, S. G., Berlani, R., Coruzzi, G., Li, M.,
        Macino, G., Nobrega, F. G., Nobrega, M. P., Thalenfeld,
        B. E. and Tzagoloff, A. (1980) Proc. Natl. Acad. Sci.
        USA 77, 3167-3170
17.   Review: Neupert, W. and Schatz, G. (1981) Trends
        Biochem. Sci. 6, 1-4.
18.   Review: Schatz, G. (1979) FEBS LETTERS 103, 201-211.
19.   Harmey, M. A. and Neupert, W. (1979) FEBS LETTERS 108,
        385-389.
20.   Nelson, N. and Schatz, G. (1979) Proc. Natl. Acad. Sci.
        USA 76, 4365-4369.
21.   Lewin, A. S., Gregor, I., Mason, T. L., Nelson, N. and
        Schatz, G. (1980) Proc. Natl. Acad. Sci. USA 77,
        3998-4002.
22.   Maccechini, M. L., Rudin, Y., Blobel, G. and Schatz, G.
        (1979) Proc. Natl. Acad. Sci. USA 73, 343-347.
23.   Maccechini, M. L., Rudin, Y. and Schatz, G. (1979)
        J. Biol. Chem. 254, 7468-7471.
24.   Böhni, P. Gasser, S., Leaver, C. and Schatz, G. (1980)
        in Structure and Expression of the Mitochondrial Genome
        (Kroon, A. M. and Saccone, C., eds.) pp. 423-433,
        North Holland, Amsterdam.
25.   Marra, E., Doonan, S., Saccone, C. and Quagliariello, E.
        (1978) Eur. J. Biochem. 83, 427-435.
26.   Hubert, P., Crémel, G., Rendon, A., Sacko, B. and
        Waksman, A. (1979) Biochemistry 18, 3119-3126.
27.   Strasberg, P. M., Webster, K. A., Patel, H. V. and
        Freeman, K. B. (1979) Can. J. Biochem. 57, 662-665.
28.   Sonderegger, P., Jaussi, R. and Christen, P. (1980)
        Biochem. Biophys. Res. Commun. 94, 1256-1260.

BACTERIAL CYTOCHROME OXIDASES -- SOME PROPERTIES AND PROTON PUMP ACTIVITY

Nobuhito Sone

Department of Biochemistry, Jichi Medical School,
Minamikawachi-machi, Tochigi, Japan 329-04

INTRODUCTION

Respiratory systems of bacteria show great diversity, especially in the terminal oxidase. Most aerobic gram-positive bacteria have a-type cytochrome oxidase. Although most gram-negative bacteria contain o-type or d-type cytochromes instead, a group of gram-negative bacteria is known to contain a-type cytochrome oxidase (1,2). One such bacterium, Paracoccus denitrificans, has a respiratory chain very similar to mitochondria, and has been proposed to be related to an ancestor of mitochondria (3). Recent reports on purification of cytochrome oxidases from several species of bacteria including P. denitrificans have shown that bacterial a-type cytochrome oxidases contain only two subunits (4-10), much simpler than the seven subunits of mitochondrial cytochrome oxidases (11). The diversity of the bacterial terminal oxidases and simplicity of their structures are in contrast to H^+-ATP synthetases which are very similar in all prokaryotic and eukaryotic species. This article will review the structures of bacterial cytochrome oxidases and show H^+ pump activity in the cytochrome oxidase from thermophilic bacterium PS3. These studies have been guided by Peter Mitchell's penetrating and fruitful chemiosmotic theory (12,13).

V. P. Skulachev and Peter C. Hinkle (eds.), Chemiosmotic Proton Circuits in Biological Membranes
in honor of Peter Mitchell   ISBN 0-201-07398-6

STRUCTURE OF BACTERIAL CYTOCHROME OXIDASES

Until recently terminal oxidases of bacteria were
analyzed mainly by spectrophotometry (1,14). In these few
years $\underline{a}$-type cytochrome oxidases have been purified to near
homogeneity from several species of bacteria and their
structural properties have been reported, as shown in Table
I (also 15). The list only covers $\underline{a}$-type cytochrome oxidases,

TABLE 1. Some Properties of Bacterial Cytochrome Oxidases.

Organism	Subunit M.W (K) I	II	Minimum M.W/heme $\underline{a}$ (K)	Suggested number I	II	heme a	Cu	heme c	Ref.
Thermophilic bacterium PS3	56*	38(c)	80	1 (2)	1 (2)	1 (2)	1 (2)	1 (2)	4,20
Thermus thermophilus	55	33(c)	100	2 1	2 1	2 2	2 2	1 1	6 10
Paracoccus denitrificans	45 55**	28	37	1	1	1	2	0	7 15
Nitrobacter agilis	51*	31	41	1	1	2	2	0	5,9
Thiobacillus novellus	32	23	–	2	2	2	2	0	5,8

 * Obtained from Ferguson plot.
** Suggested by the data of DNA code.

although purification of other terminal oxidases, an $\underline{o}$-type
from $\underline{Vitreoscilla}$ (16,17) and cytochromes b-d complex from
$\underline{Escherichia}$ $\underline{coli}$ (18) have been reported.

Subunit Structure - Two kinds of subunits are found in all
five cytochrome oxidases. The molecular weights of larger
subunits (subunit I) are around 50,000 and several show
abnormal behavior on polyacrylamide gel electrophoresis with
dodecyl sulfate (SDS-PAGE). This behavior consists of a
broad band on gels without urea (7), abnormal extrapolated Rf
values at 0% acrylamide (9) and coagulation upon boiling with
SDS (7). PS3 oxidase shows all these properties (N. Sone,
unpublished). The molecular weights of subunit II ranged
from 23,000 to 38,000. In the case of T. thermophilus and
PS3 these bands contained c-type heme covalently bound (4,6).
Subunit II's of P. denitrificans and of PS3 are reported to
cross-react immunologically with yeast subunit II (15).

Prosthetic Groups - All these bacterial a-type oxidases show
absorption peaks at 442-445 nm (Soret band) and 604-605 nm (α
band) and contain heme a and copper as the mitochondrial
oxidases do. In the case of the enzymes from P. denitrificans
and N. agilis the heme a contents were as high as 27 and 25
nmol/mg protein, respectively. The content of Cu were 1 to
1.5-fold of heme a contents. A preparation from T. thermophilus contains 24 nmol heme a and 26 ng atoms Cu per mg of
protein (10). Lower contents of heme a and Cu are reported
in the cases of PS3, T. thermophilus and T. novellus.

Based on the contents of these prosthetic groups and
subunit molecular weights, the minimum structural unit for
the individual bacterial cytochrome oxidase are also suggested
in Table 1.

Addition of CO to mitochondrial oxidases results in a
shift of the absorption band of the reduced form, which have
been interpreted to be due to cytochrome a_3 (19). All

bacterial cytochrome oxidases other than from PS3 are reported
to show a similar CO-difference spectrum (with a trough at
445 nm and peak at 430 nm) and are thus classified as aa_3-
type. The CO-difference spectrum of PS3 oxidase was somewhat
different (with a trough at 435 nm and peak at 417 nm), being
rather similar to that of cytochrome o (20). Rapid kinetics
of rebinding of CO after flash photolysis of CO-complex of
PS3 oxidase at room temperature, however, suggest that the
abnormal spectrum of CO-complex is partly due to weak cytochrome a_3-like behavior of heme a chromophore as well as the
existance of cytochrome o-like pigment (N. Sone and Y. Orii,
unpublished). The amount of cytochrome o was below 1/5 that
of heme a and its possible role in cytochrome oxidase activity is under investigation.

Structural Resemblance to Mitochondrial Cytochrome Oxidases –
Cytochrome oxidase from mitochondria is know to consist of
seven subunits (11). The three largest polypetides are coded
for by mitochondrial DNA (21). Although the molecular
weights of mitochondrial subunits I (35,800) and II (24,100)
from beef heart (23) are somewhat smaller than bacterial
subunits I and II (Table 1), they seem homologous since they
share the characteristic behavior in SDS-PAGE of subunit I
(22) and immunological cross reaction occurs between yeast
subunit II and P. denitrificans subunit II or PS3 subunit II
(15). Winter et al. have reported that mitochondrial subunit
I bears half of the heme a (showing cyt. a properties) and
subunit II, half of the heme a (showing cyt. a_3 properties)
and most of the Cu after SDS-PAGE under the carefully designed
conditions (23). Thus the two-subunit bacterial oxidases no
longer seem surprising.

　　　Evidence suggesting that subunit III of mitochondrial

oxidase functions as an H^+ channel was recently reported (24). It is still not clear whether bacterial oxidase has subunit II or not. Ludwig did not find subunit III in his preparations from P. denitrificans, but he speculated that subunit III may be associated less tightly and was therefore lost (15). In the case of PS3 cytochrome oxidase, one band (around 20 K daltons) with about 10% of the total staining intensity was observed in many preparations (N. Sone, unpublished).

CHEMIOSMOTIC COUPLING IN PS3 OXIDASE. Because of the great diversity of the respiratory systems of bacterial and of the simplicity of the subunit structure, it is of interest to examine how these bacterial oxidases can convert redox energy into chemiosmotic energy.

Electron Transport and Proton Pump - Four models seem possible as in the case of mitochondrial oxidase:

    (A) Cytochrome oxidase is an electron translocating loop as Mitchell originally proposed (12).

    (B) The redox reaction occurs on the outer side of the membrane to which H^+ permeates through an H^+-channel (H^+-well model; 13).

    (C) Cytochrome oxidase pumps H^+ in addition to (A).

    (D) Cytochrome oxidase pumps H^+ in addition to (B) as Wikström proposed (25). Two H^+ per electron come through an H^+ channel to the redox center.

To try to distinguish between these possibilities, we have studied proton and charge transport by proteoliposomes reconstituted from purified PS3 oxidase and soybean phospholipids (PS3 oxidase vesicles) (N. Sone and P.C. Hinkle, in preparation).

H^+/e and K^+/e Ratios - As shown in Fig. 1A, H^+ ejection
occured when a small amount of yeast ferrocytochrome c was
added to PS3 oxidase vesicles. The lower trace (Fig. 1B)

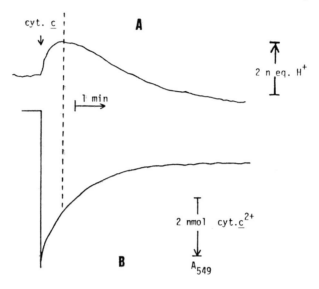

Fig. 1. Measurement of H^+ ejection (A) and cytochrome c
oxidation (B) upon addition of reduced cytochrome c pulse.
Proteoliposmes (50 μl) were suspended in 2 ml of the reaction
medium containing 25 mM K_2SO_4, 2.5 mM $MgSO_4$, 0.1 mM potassium
morpholinopropane sulfonate (MOPS) and 0.1 μg/ml valinomycin
at 25°C. Addition of reduced yeast cytochrome c was 3.8
nmoles. The pH change (6.6 - 6.7) was recorded with a Corning
combination pH electrode M10. Proteoliposomes were prepared
by the freeze-thaw methods (26) as follows; acetone-washed
soybean phospholipids (27) in 1 ml of 10 mM K-MOPS buffer (pH
6.6) containing 0.1 mM EDTA and 2 mM dithiothreitol were
sonicated for 3 min at 25°C. PS3 cytochrome oxidase (0.12 -
0.15 mg was then added and sonicated briefly (6 - 10 s). The
mixture in the test tube was quickly frozen and then thawed,
followed by a brief sonication of 10 or 20 s. The freeze-
thaw-sonication cycle was then repeated once more.

shows the time course of oxidation of added cytochrome $\underline{c}$. Because of the relatively slow oxidation rate, the maximal H^+ ejection was reached at 45 s after the addition of cytochrome $\underline{c}$, when 1.5 nmoles were oxidized. This H^+ ejection was not observed when the uncoupler SF6847 (3.4 μM) was present (not shown). Although the H^+/e ratio was around 0.4 in this experiment, a higher H^+/e ratio around 0.8 was observed when ferrocytochrome $\underline{c}_{552}$ from $\underline{T}$. $\underline{thermophilus}$, a better substrate for PS3 oxidase, was used as a reductant. Figure 2A shows the relationship between the size of the ferrocytochrome c_{552} pulse and H^+/e values observed. These uncorrected H^+/e values are close to 1 when pulse sizes are sufficiently small.

The amount of charge transported across the membrane during cytochrome c oxidation can be determined by the movement of K^+ in the presence of valinomycin. Effects of the size of oxygen pulses on K^+/e ratio are summarized in Fig. 2B. The ratios tend toward a value of 2 when the pulse sizes are small, indicating that two charges move across the membranes per one electron transfer.

Effects of DCCD - Dicyclohexylcarbodiimide (DCCD) is known to inhibit H^+ translocation of $F_o \cdot F_1$ by binding to the DCCD-binding proteolipid which forms a proton channel through membranes. Casey et al. have reported that DCCD, at relatively high concentrations, can also block H^+ pumping activity of mitochondrial cytochrome oxidase (24). Fig. 3 shows the effects of DCCD on H^+ ejection, H^+ permeability and oxidation rate of PS3 oxidase vesicles. To reduce side effects of DCCD in the solution, vesicles were centrifuged through a column of Sephadex G-50 (1 ml) after the incubation with DCCD. A relatively long incubation time was necessary for

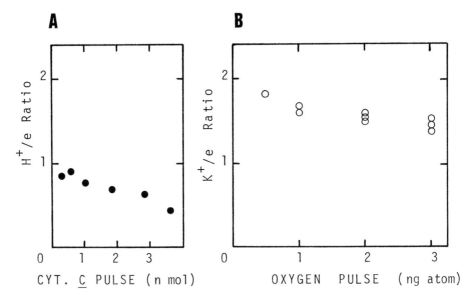

Fig. 2. H^+/e values upon cytochrome c_{552} pulse (A) and K^+/e values upon oxygen pulse (B). A, T. thermophilus cyt. c552 (kindly donated by Dr. Hon-nami) was used as an electron donor under the conditions given in figure 1. B, K^+ concentration was measured with a cation electrode (Beckman #39047) under anaerobic conditions at 25°C. PS3 oxidase vesicles (100 µl) depleted of K^+ by the centrifuged-column method (28) were suspended in the reaction medium containing 50 mM choline-Cl, 2.5 mM $MgSO_4$, 2 mM Na-Pi (pH 6.7) and 1 mM NaCl, 0.1 mM K_2SO_4, 4 mM Na·ascorbate, 16 µM yeast cyt. c and 0.3 ng/ml valinomycin.

complete inhibition of H^+ pump activity of PS3 oxidase, as was the case for mitochondrial oxidase (24). No significant effect of DCCD was seen on H^+ permeability or oxidizing activity.

The effect of DCCD on charge-separating activity of PS3 oxidase was also tested. Part of K^+ uptake (K/O = 10) still survived when H^+ ejection was almost completely blocked (H^+/e = 0.03) by the incubation with 2 mM DCCD for 130 min.

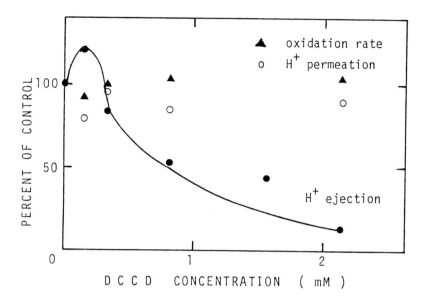

<u>Fig. 3.</u>   Effects of DCCD concentration on H^+ pump activity of
PS3 cytochrome oxidase vesicles.   PS3 oxidase vesicles (100
µl) mixed with 11 µl of 100 mM Tricine·NaOH (pH 7.6) and 5 µl
of methanol solution of DCCD were incubated for 130 min at
20°C.   After removal of low molecular weight substances by
the centrifuged-column method (28), H^+ pump activity was
measured as shown in Fig. 1.   The H^+ permeation activity was
measured as a rate of H^+ extrusion upon addition of valinomycin and the oxidase activity as the rate of proton uptake
due to cytochrome <u>c</u> oxidation in the presence of SF 6847.

A possible interpretation of these results is that two
charge separations occur with one electron transfer reaction;
one of which is due to DCCD-sensitive H^+ pumping and another
due to the electron translocation across the membrane
(Mitchell's electron loop).   Thus model C is most consistent
with these observations.

The effect of DCCD on H^+-pumping and charge-separating
activities of mitochondrial oxidase vesicles were also examined.   Figure 4 shows that DCCD-treated vesicles in which
H^+ ejection was almost entirely eliminated, accumulated K^+
upon addition of an oxygen pulse.   So model C seems applicable to both mitochondrial and bacterial a-type oxidases.

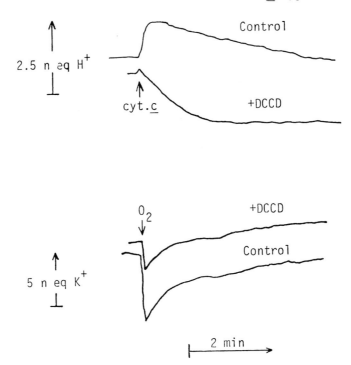

Fig. 4.   Effects of DCCD on H^+ ejection and K^+ uptake by
mitochondrial oxidase vesicles.   Treatment with DCCD was
carried out as described in the legend for figure 3 except
the incubation time was 150 min.   The amount of yeast ferrocytochrome c was 1.8 nmoles in (A) and the size of oxygen
pulse was 3 ng atoms in (B).   Mitochondrial oxidase vesicles
were prepared by the cholate-dialysis method as described
in (29), except that 4 nmoles of the oxidase (in heme a)
were used for the preparation of 1 ml of the vesicles.
Other conditions were the same as in figure 2.

SUMMARY

Bacterial a-type cytochrome oxidases have heme a and Cu
as prosthetic groups on two different subunits which probably correspond to the two mitochondrially coded large
subunits.

Research on energy conserving reactions of cytochrome
oxidase from thermophilic bacterium PS3 showed that electrogenic proton pumping does occur in addition to transmembrane
electron flow.

Some other bacterial oxidases have also been reconstituted into proteoliposomes. Paracoccus oxidase vesicles are
reported to show respiratory control (7) and to pump H^+ at a
value of 0 - 0.2 H^+/e (15). Thermus oxidase as well as PS3
oxidase, when reconstituted, generate a membrane potential
as much as -240 mV during T. thermophilus c_{552} oxidation (N.
Sone and K. Hon-nami, to be published).

The possible roles of cytochromes o and d in chemiosmotic processes is not clear (30). Cytochrome o may not be
a proton pump but a transmembrane electron loop (31). Partial
purification of the b-o complex has been attained from E.
coli (32).

In conclusion, studies on bacterial cytochrome oxidases
seem fruitful and should provide new and possibly different
examples of electron and proton circuits in membranes.

ACKNOWLEDGEMENT

I want to thank Drs. B. Chance, P.C. Hinkle, T. Yonetani
and Y. Kagawa for their valuable discussion and support.

REFERENCES

1. Smith, L. (1978) Methods Enzymol. 53, 202-212.
2. Okunuki, K. and Yamanaka, T. (1976) "Microbial Cytochromes" (in Japanese), Kohdan-sha, Tokyo.
3. John, P. and Whatley, F.R. (1977) Biochim. Biophys. Acta 436, 129-153.
4. Sone, N., Ohyama, T. and Kagawa, Y. (1979) FEBS Lett. 106, 39-42.
5. Yamanaka, T., Fujii, K. and Kamita, Y. (1979) J. Biochem. 86, 821-824.
6. Fee, J.A., Choc, M.G., Findling, K.L., Lorence, R. and Yoshida, T. (1980) Proc. Natl. Acad. Sci. USA 77, 141-151.
7. Ludwig, B. and Schatz, G. (1980) Proc. Natl. Acad. Sci. USA 77, 196-200.
8. Yamanaka, T. and Fujii, K. (1980) Biochim. Biophys. Acta 591, 53-62.
9. Yamanaka, T. and Kamita, Y. (1981) J. Biochem., 89, 265-273.
10. Hon-mani, K. (1980) Seikagaku (in Japanese) 52, 854.
11. Cabral, F. and Schatz, G. (1978) J. Biol. Chem. 253, 4396-4401.
12. Mitchell, P. (1966) Biol. Rev. 41, 445-502.
13. Mitchell, P. (1979) Eur. J. Biochem. 95, 1-20.
14. Castor, L.R.N. and Chance, B. (1959) J. Biol. Chem. 234, 1587-1592.
15. Ludwig, B. (1981) Biochim. Biophys. Acta, 594, 177-189.
16. Webster, D.A. and Liu, C.Y. (1974) J. Biol. Chem. 249, 4257-4260.
17. Tyree, B. and Webster, D.A. (1978) J. Biol. Chem. 253, 6988-6991.
18. Reid, G. and Ingledew, W.J. (1980) FEBS Lett. 109, 1-4.
19. Keilin, D. (1966) The History of Cell Respiration and Cytochrome, Cambridge University Press, London.
20. Sone, N. and Kagawa, Y. (1979) in Third Internat. Symp. on Oxidases and Related Redox Systems (King, T.E. et al., eds), in press, Pergamon Press, Oxford.
21. Schatz, G. and Mason, T.L. (1974) Ann. Rev. Biochem. 43, 51-87.
22. Capaldi, R.A., Bell, R.L. and Branchek, T. (1977) Biochem. Biophys. Res. Commun. 74, 425-433.
23. Winter, D.B., Bruyninckx, W.J., Foulke, F.G., Grinich, N.P. and Mason, H.S. (1980) J. Biol. Chem. 255, 11408-11414.

24. Casey, R.P., Chappel, J.B. and Azzi, A. (1980) J. Biol. Chem. 255, 3994-4000.
25. Wikström, M. and Krab, K. (1979) Biochim. Biophys. Acta 549, 177-222.
26. Kasahara, M. and Hinkle, P.C. (1976) Proc. Natl. Acad. Sci. USA 73, 396-400.
27. Sone, N., Yoshida, M., Hirata, H. and Kagawa, Y. (1977) J. Biochem. 81, 519-528.
28. Penefsky, H. (1979) Methods Enzymol. 56, 527-530.
29. Coin, J.T. and Hinkle, P.C. (1979) in Membrane Bioenergetics (Lee, C.P. et al., eds), 405-412, Addison-Wesley, Reading.
30. Stouthamer, A.H. (1980) Trends Biochem. Sci. 5, 164-166.
31. Mogi, T. and Anraku, Y. (1979) Abstracts of Meeting of Japan Bioenergetics Group, 5, 90-91.
32. Kita, K. and Anraku, Y. (1981) Biochem. Internat. 2, 105-112.

NITRATE REDUCTASE

Peter B. Garland

Department of Biochemistry, Medical Sciences Institute,
University of Dundee, Dundee DD1 4HN, Scotland, U.K.

INTRODUCTION

My first contact with Peter Mitchell was in the Spring
of 1952, when along with some two hundred other undergradu-
ates at Cambridge I attended his lectures in what was quaintly
known as "half-subject" Biochemistry. I certainly recall
the style, and more surprisingly, some of the content: the
dreaded Donnan equilibrium, and transport in Staphylococcus
aureus. That Peter Mitchell should have gone on to win 26
years later the Nobel Prize in Chemistry would not perhaps
have surprised his youthful audience. His interest in biological membranes and the desire to bind physico-chemical
mechanisms was evident then even to us. But I would have
dismissed as wild fantasy any suggestion that in the years
ahead his work would have influenced my own (whatever that
was to be) or that I would have the pleasure and honour of
contributing in 1981 to a volume commemorating his scientific
achievements.

V. P. Skulachev and Peter C. Hinkle (eds.), Chemiosmotic Proton Circuits in Biological Membranes
in honor of Peter Mitchell   ISBN 0-201-07398-6

211

My introduction to chemiosmosis came in the late
sixties, at Bristol, where Brian Chappel was providing elegant experimental evidence for the substrate permeases of
mitochondria and for the mechanism of ionophore action (1,2).
My own interest then was in mitochondrial fatty acid oxidation. A microbiology graduate, Ann Light, introduced yeasts
and chemostats to my laboratory in 1967, and out of some
iron-limitation studies came the finding that the presence
or absence of site 1 energy conservation was under phenoty-
pic control (3). So we had to take bioenergetics seriously,
to read Mitchell's monographs (4,5), and to plan our work
on chemiosmotic principles. (Other hypotheses were less
than helpful in experimental design). It seemed to us that
microbial systems could offer particular advantages for
studying respiratory driven proteon translocation, because
the composition of their respiratory chains was capable of
being altered in many ways. By contrast, animal mitochondria
are somewhat invariant. In 1972 I was joined at Dundee by
Bruce Haddock, who introduced me to bioenergetic studies of
prokaryotic organisms. Bacteria offer a much wider natural
variety and freedom to manipulate respiratory chains both
genetically and phenotypically than do yeasts. Another
important but unexpected advantage arises from the relative
simplicity of some bacterial proton-translocating respiratory systems, at least when compared with mammalian systems
on the basis of number and variety of polypeptide chains.

More specifically, we chose to study the respiratory
nitrate reductase of the cytoplasmic membrane of Escherichia
coli as a system that might well give important information
on the mechanism of respiratory driven proton-translocation.
It was already known that nitrate respiration could support

oxidative phosphorylation (6,7), and available information
(8-13) on the respiratory components indicates a relatively
small number of components acting between ubiquinone and
nitrate, namely, a b-type cytochrome and nitrate reductase
itself, which is a molybdenum containing iron-sulphur protein containing two types of polypeptide chain, the α and β
subunits. Synthesis of the b-type cytochrome and nitrate
reductase is derepressed under anaerobic growth conditions
by the presence of nitrate. The detergent solubilized enzyme contains very variable amounts of the b-type cytochrome,
giving rise on SDS-PAGE gels to a third subunit (γ) in addition to the α and β subunits.

CHEMIOSMOTIC PROPERTIES OF NITRATE REDUCTASE

Stoichiometry

        Given that the oxidation of ubiquinol by nitrate via
nitrate reductase and the associated b-type cytochrome is
proton-translocating, then the stoichimetry ($\rightarrow H^+/e^-$ ratio)
becomes an important indicator of possible mechanisms. A
value of 1 is consistent with a simple chemiosmotic loop or
many other mechanisms. Values other than 1 would not sustain
the idea of a loop. Our own observations over several years
strongly favoured an $\rightarrow H^+/e^-$ ratio of 1.0 for the oxidation
of endogenous or exogenous ubiquinol by nitrate and the
nitrate reductase system (14,15).

Physical topography

        Structural studies using covalent labelling methods
show that the α and β (18) subunits of nitrate reductase are

accessible at the cytoplasmic face of the cytoplasmic membrane, whereas the γ subunit (b-cytochrome) is at the periplasmic face (16,17). Thus the proteins of the nitrate reductase system are collectively transmembranous, even if any
single one is not.

Functional topography

The sites for nitrate reduction (19,20), scalar H^+
consumption and artifical electron donors such as reduced
flavin mononucleotide or Benzyl Viologen radical are at the
cytoplasmic face (21,23). By contrast, Diquat radical reduces nitrate reductase via cytochrome b at the periplasmic
face (2,3). Thus the nitrate reductase system can effect a
transmembranous electron flow from the b-cytochrome (accepts
electrons from Diquat radical at the periplasmic face) to
nitrate reductase (donates electrons to nitrate at the cytoplasmic face).

The source of the translocated protons

In a simple chemiosmotic loop H^+ as such is not translocated. The apparent translocation of H^+ arises from transmembranous electron flow between two protolytic oxidoreduct-
ions on opposite sides of the membrane, one generating and
the other consuming H^+. By contrast, a conformationally
driven proton pump would accept H^+ from one side of the membrane and eject it on the other: the energy to do so must
come from the oxidoreduction reaction. Discrimination
between these two mechanisms - chemiosmotic or conformational - can be made by suitable choice of the reductant for the
oxidoreduction. In the case of the nitrate reductase system
we were able to use ubiquinol (donates $2H^+$ and $2e^-$), reduced

phenazine methosulphate (donates $1H^+$ and $2e^-$) or Diquat
radical (donates e^- only). The corresponding H^+/e^- ratios
predicted by a chemiosmotic loop are 1.0, 0.5 and zero respectively when measuring pH in the external phase, and that
is what we observed (15). There was therefore no evidence
for proton pumping driven by the oxidative flow of electrons
from donor to cytochrome b, nitrate reductase and nitrate.
For these reasons we concluded that the nitrate reductase
system is organised as a simple chemiosmotic loop (15).

HIGHLY ORGANIZED MEMBRANES

     If the respiratory chain enzymes and the proton-
translocating ATPase are organised into complexes, or packed
shoulder-to-shoulder into their membrane, then the way is
open for alternative hypotheses in which protons still
couple oxidation to phosphorylation, but not through a transmembrane proton circuit: localized proton circuits may be
envisaged instead (24). One way of investigating this possibility of organization is to measure the rotational diffusion coefficients (D_R) of respiratory components or of the
ATPase. The rotation of membrane proteins is considered to
be uniaxial, around an axis normal to the membrane (25).
D_R is strongly dependent on molecular size, decreasing as
the square of the molecular radius traversing the bilayer
(26). Early work by Junge using laser flash photolysis
indicated that mitochondrial cytochrome oxidase does not
rotate in the membrane over a time scale of many msecs, implying considerable immobility (27,28). By contrast, a rotational relaxation time of say 50 - 500µsec would be reas-

onable for a molecule the size of cytochrome oxidase rotating around the normal to a fluid bilayer. Although lateral
diffusion coefficients in the membrane (D_L) are only weakly
dependent on molecular size (26), they bear very directly
on the role and kinetic competence of diffusional collision
in respiration and oxidative phosphorylation (29).

In view of the significance of D_R and D_L values, I
set up a laser flash photolysis system (30) to study the
former (by transient dichroism) and a laser-microscope apparatus (31,32) for the latter (by fluorescent photobleaching
recovery). In agreement with Cherry and colleagues (33),
we find that cytochrome oxidase in ox heart mitochondria
can rotate freely in the 200 - 500µs time range at 37°,
although intramembrane aggregation and slower mobility is
readily produced (34). In E. coli we find fast rotational
relaxation times (50 - 150µs) for cytochromes o and d
(34,35). Concerning lateral mobility in E. coli, we could
not repeat (36) the observations of Kepes et al (37), who
had concluded on indirect evidence that there is highly
restricted protein diffusion in the cytoplasmic membrane.
In addition, we have obtained approximate values of D_L for
(uncharacterized) proteins of the cytoplasmic membrane by
two methods: either time resolved distribution on warming
of freeze fracture particles (35), or fluorescence photobleaching recovery of fluorescently labelled giant spheroplast membranes (38). In both cases D_L is about 10^{-10} cm^2
s^{-1}, which is typical for most reports of protein mobility
in membranes. Thus so far our data for the cytoplasmic
membrane of E. coli are in keeping with a fluid mosaic, not
a heavily organised array of respiratory complexes. Indeed,
a fluid mosaic was to be expected from studies of phospho-

lipid diffusional rates (39).

Interestingly, as an example of the circuitous way in
which developments are often made, these chemiosmotic pre-
occupations with movement of protein in membranes have led
to the development of new methods of measuring D_R, either
by depolarization of phosphorescence (40) at a sensitivity
of about 10^{12} molecules or, more recently, by a fluorescence
depletion method sensitive to as little as 10^3 molecules (41).
The applications of these powerful new methods lie mainly
outside bioenergetics, but are consistent with the Mitchellian view that bioenergetics is an exercise in membrane
structure and function.

OUTLOOK

Progress on the primary structure of bacterial respiratory enzymes can be fast if recombinant DNA methods and
gene sequencing are used. Fuller characterization of the
location of peptide domains in, across or peripheral to the
lipid bilayer is also very possible. Thus the structural
work can follow quite predictable approaches. Nevertheless,
it would be surprising if controversy concerning H^+/e^- ratios
does not arise even in apparently well documented bacterial
systems. There is the risk of underestimating the ratios
in pulsed oxidant or reductant methods if fast H^+ backflow
can occur through permease systems. Fortunately, mutants
lacking various permeases are readily available, and were
used for example to indicate that phosphate transport in
E. coli was not interfering with estimates of H^+/e ratios.
Finally, a prediction of conformational proton pump models
is that mutants are possible that have retained an apparently

218   PETER B. GARLAND

normal oxidoreduction behaviour of a respiratory pathway
but have lost the ability to drive H$^+$ translocation by the
oxidoreduction concerned. Testing this prediction would
seem to be both feasible and fruitful.

ACKNOWLEDGMENTS

I am indebted to numerous colleagues who have contributed to work referred to from our institute. I am also
indebted to the Medical Research Council and the Royal
Society for support.

REFERENCES

1.   Chappell, J. B. and Haarhoff, K. N. (1967) in Bio-
      chemistry of Mitochondria (Slater, E. C., Kaniuga, Z.
      and Wotzjak, L., eds.) pp. 75-91, Academic Press,
      London.
2.   Chappell, J. B. and Robinson, B. H. (1968) Biochem.
      Soc. Symp. 27, 123-133.
3.   Light, P. A., Ragan, C. I., Clegg, R. A. and Garland,
      P. B. (1968) FEBS Lett. 1, 4-8.
4.   Mitchell, P. (1966) Chemiosmotic Coupling in Oxida-
      tive and Photosynthetic Phosphorylation, Glynn
      Research Ltd., Bodmin.
5.   Mitchell, P. (1968) Chemiosmotic Coupling and Energy
      Transduction, Glynn Research Ltd., Bodmin.
6.   Ota, A., Yamanaka, T. and Okunuki, T. (1965) J. Bio-
      chem. 55, 131-135.
7.   Ota, A. (1965) J. Biochem. 58, 137-144.
8.   Ruiz-Herrera, J. and DeMoss, J. A. (1969) J. Bacter-
      iol. 99, 720-729.
9.   Forget, P. (1974) Eur. J. Biochem. 42, 325-332.
10.   Enoch, H. G. and Lester, R. L. (1974) Biochem.
      Biophys. Res. Commun. 61, 1234-1241.
11.   Enoch, H. G. and Lester, R. L. (1975) J. Biol. Chem.
      250, 6693-6705.
12.   Clegg, R. A. (1976) Biochem. J. 153, 533-541.

13.   Wallace, B. J. and Young, I. G. (1977) Biochim.
       Biophys. Acta 461, 84-100.
14.   Garland, P. B., Downie, J. A. and Haddock, B. A.
       (1975) Biochem. J. 152, 547-559.
15.   Jones, R. W., Lamont, A. and Garland, P. B. (1980)
       Biochem. J. 190, 79-94.
16.   Boxer, D. H. and Clegg, R. A. (1975) FEBS Lett. 60,
       54-57.
17.   MacGregor, C. H. and Christopher, C. R. (1978) Arch.
       Biochem. Biophys. 185, 204-213.
18.   Graham, A. and Boxer, D. H. (1980) FEBS Lett. 113,
       15-20.
19.   Jones, R. W., Ingledew, W. J., Graham, A. and
       Garland, P. B. (1978) Biochem. Soc. Trans. 6, 1287-
       1289.
20.   Kristjansson, J. K. and Hollocher, T. C. (1979) J.
       Bacteriol. 137, 1227-1233.
21.   Jones, R. W. and Garland, P. B. (1978) Biochem. Soc.
       Trans. 6, 416-418.
22.   Kemp, M. B., Haddock, B. A. and Garland, P. B. (1975)
       Biochem. J. 148, 329-333.
23.   Jones, R. W. and Garland, P. B. (1977) Biochem. J.
       164, 199-211.
24.   Williams, R. J. P. (1961) J. Theoret. Biol. 1, 1-17.
25.   Cherry, R. J. (1979) Biochim. Biophys. Acta 559,
       289-327.
26.   Saffman, P. G. and Delbrück, M. (1975) Proc. Natl.
       Acad. Sci. U.S. 42, 3111-3113.
27.   Junge, W. and DeVault, D. (1975) Biochim. Biophys.
       Acta 408, 200-214.
28.   Kunze, U. and Junge, W. (1977) FEBS Lett. 80, 429-434.
29.   Hochli, M. and Hackenbrock, C. R. (1979) Proc. Natl.
       Acad. Sci. U.S. 76, 1236-1240.
30.   Garland, P. B. and Moore, C. H. (1979) Biochem. J.
       183, 561-572.
31.   Axelrod, D., Koppell, D. E., Schlesinger, J., Elson,
       E. and Webb, W. W. (1976) Biophys. J. 16, 1055-1069.
32.   Garland, P. B. (1981) Biophys. J. 33, 481-482.
33.   Kawato, S., Siegel, E., Carafoli, E. and Cherry, R. J.
       (1980) J. Biol. Chem. 255, 5508-5510.
34.   Johnston, K., Reid, G. and Garland, P. B. (unpub-
       lished work).
35.   Garland, P. B., Davison, M. T. and Moore, C. H. (1979)
       Biochem. Soc. Trans. 7, 1112-1114.
36.   Cadenas, E. and Garland, P. B. (1979) Biochem. J.
       184, 45-50.

37.   Autissier, F. and Kepes, A. (1971) Biochim. Biophys.
        Acta 249, 611-615.
38.   Davison, M. T. and Garland, P. B. (unpublished work).
39.   Sackman, E., Träuble, H., Galla, H.-J. and Overath,
        P. (1973) Biochemistry 12, 5360-5368.
40.   Moore, C. H., Boxer, D. H. and Garland, P. B. (1979)
        FEBS Lett. 108, 161-166.
41.   Johnson, P. and Garland, P. B. (1981) FEBS Lett.
        in press.

ON THE MOLECULAR MACHINE OF PHOTOSYNTHESIS:

OVERVIEW AND SOME RECENT RESULTS

H.T. Witt

Max-Volmer-Institut für Biophysikalische und
Physikalische Chemie, Technische Universität
Berlin, Strasse des 17. Juni 135, 1000 Berlin
12, Germany

1. Overview

Results and methods which we contributed for insights into the concept of photosynthesis have been reviewed in 1979 in Ref. (1). Some results obtained by
us since 1979 are subject of this report and are outlined in paragraphs 2-4. The topics are: 1. Large
membrane layers as possible tools for analysis of membrane enzyme complexes; 2. Nature of the steady state
potential and its structural consequences; 3. Model for
the regulation of the rate of phosphorylation. In the
first paragraph some basic results are reviewed briefly
for the understanding of the following (for specific
literature references concerning the results mentioned
in this overview see (1)).

Fig. 1 shows the current scheme of the electron
transport, the coupled protolytic reactions, and phosphorylation with respect to energetics, kinetics, vectors of reactions, and structure. These reactions take
place in the membrane of partially interconnected

V. P. Skulachev and Peter C. Hinkle (eds.), Chemiosmotic Proton Circuits in Biological Membranes
in honor of Peter Mitchell   ISBN 0-201-07398-6

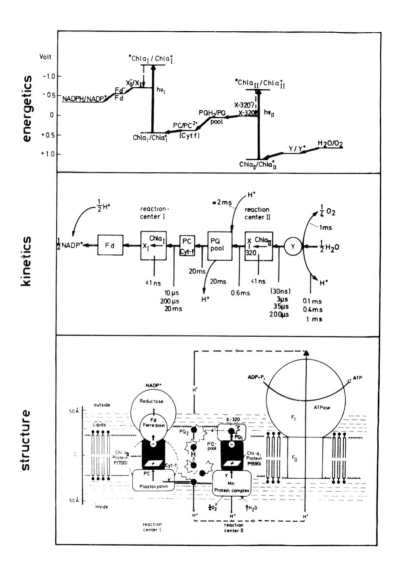

Fig. 1   Scheme of energetics, kinetics, vectors,
and organizations within the functional
membrane of photosynthesis (1).

vesicles, the so-called thylakoids. About 200 electron
transport chains are embedded in the membrane of one
thylakoid. On absorption of light quanta within two
special reaction centers, I and II, of each electron
transport chain, a vectorial electron transfer from inside to outside takes place. These two unidirectional
redox processes establish a transmembrane electric field
and an electric potential difference, $\Delta\Psi$. The generation of this field and vectorial charge separation,
resp. have been detected by electrochromic absorption
changes (2,3). The electron donors are $Chl\text{-}a_I$ and
$Chl\text{-}a_{II}$. They are both located at the membrane inside
and become oxidized, while the corresponding two electron acceptors located at the outside become reduced.
The electron shifts occur with a half rise time faster
than 20 ns and even faster than 1 ns. Protolytic reactions of the two negative charges at the outside and
two positive ones at the inside lead to a translocation
of 2 H^+ from the outside to the inside in the following
way. The oxidizing equivalent from $Chl\text{-}a_{II}$ is transferred to the watersplitting enzyme, which leads to H_2O
oxidation coupled with oxygen evolution and proton release. The electron ejected from $Chl\text{-}a_{II}$ is transferred
to the acceptor at the outside which is a special plastoquinone, X320 or PQ_I and further, via a second PQ_{II} to
a plastoquinone pool, PQ, whereby a proton is picked up
from the outside. The plastoquinone pool electroneutrally translocates a hydrogen (proton plus an electron) to
the inner space. The plastoquinone is oxidized within
20 ms by the oxidized $Chl\text{-}a_I$ via different intermediates
(PC, Cyt-f) so that a further proton is simultaneously

released at the inside within 20 ms. This 20 ms reaction time is the rate-determining step of the overall reaction of photosynthesis. The ejected electron from Chl-a$_I$ is finally transferred via intermediates to NADP$^+$. Under special reaction conditions, the translocation of a third proton across the membrane by the so-called Q cycle has been postulated and observed.

The translocation of H$^+$ across the membrane results in a transmembrane pH difference. Thereby, a transmembrane electrochemical potential difference of protons is generated. Its magnitude is in a single turnover $\Delta\Psi$ = 50 mV and Δ pH $\leq$ 0,1; in the steady state $\Delta\Psi$ = 0 - 80 mV and Δ pH = 3 - 1,7, depending on the salt concentration (see para 2).

The proton efflux via the ATPase driven by the electrochemical potential difference is coupled with ATP synthesis (4). The overall reaction can be described according to Mitchell by the following equations:

$$ADP + P_i + nH^+_{in} \rightleftarrows ATP + nH^+_{out} + H_2O \qquad (1)$$

The free enthalpy change is given by

$$\Delta G = n \, \Delta G_{H^+} + G_p \lesseqgtr 0 \qquad (2)$$

n = number of H$^+$ translocated per ATP synthesized/hydrolyzed (< ATP synthesis, > ATP hydrolysis, = equilibrium) with

$$\Delta G_{H^+} = - \{2.3 \, RT \, \Delta \, pH + F \, \Delta\Psi\} \qquad \text{and} \qquad (3)$$

$$\Delta G_p = {}^o \Delta G_p + RT \, \ln ATP/ADP \cdot P \qquad (4)$$

Our contributions to the above outlined concept of the
photosynthesis machine and, with respect to the results
reported in this article, are based mainly on four
methodical advances:

1. The repetitive pulse technique (5,6) which provides
a high sensitivity and time resolution for optical,
electrical, and chemical signals.
2. The electrochromic method (2,3) by which the elec-
trification and organization of the membrane as well as
the phosphorylation have been analyzed.
3. Membrane excitation by external electric fields (7)
through which problems have been solved which was not
possible by light excitation.
4. Transformation of vesicles into large membrane
layers (8) making areas accessible which were otherwise shielded by the vesicular structure. Results
about this item are reported in the next paragraph.

2. Large membrane layers as possible tool for characterization, separation, and isolation of membrane enzyme
complexes

With respect to the vectorial reactions and
especially to those taking place at the inside of the
membrane and in the inner space, resp., it would facilitate examinations if the membrane could be transformed
into a planar interface, with the inside open to a
macroscopic aqueous compartment. In this way, complexes
located towards the membrane inside as e.g., the Chl-a_{II}
protein and the watersplitting Mn enzyme, are directly
accessible for measurements and manipulations. In black
lipid membranes "fixed" on circular apertures < 1 mm^2,

the material is suitable only for electrical but not
optical and chemical measurements. For the latter at
least about 10^5 times larger planes are necessary. We
have developed a technique which enables us to transform the membranes of thylakoid vesicles into such large,
flat areas (256 cm^2) in form of (a) "fluid" thylakoid
layers and (b) "rigid" layers, without a loss of activity (8). Chloroplast solutions of spinach were injected
into a heptane/water interface using a thin glass capillary. Through this process the chloroplasts are spread
at the interface. This spreading can be monitored
through measuring the interfacial tension. A comparison
of the data on the density of chlorophyll in thylakoids
and at the interface, respectively, suggests that
probably predominantly monolayers are formed at the
interface. These have been called "fluid" layers.
"Rigid" layers are made by immersing hydrophobic glass
plates into the heptane phase, all the way through the
fluid layer into the aqueous subphase, which causes the
"fluid" layer to gather on the hydrophobic plate. The
activities on the rigid layer are practically quantitatively the same as those of thylakoids in solutions
(see Fig. 2). Moreover, it was found that the activities of the rigid layers are maintained about eight
times longer than those of thylakoids in solutions.
This may be due to an increased immobilization of the
enzymes at the solid plate.

The fluid layer is inactive, in contrast to the
rigid layer. This might be explained by complexes of
the electron transport chain which have been separated
from each other in the fluid layer. When adding arti-

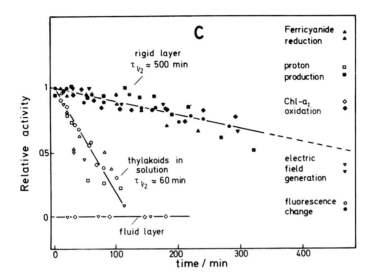

Fig. 2   Activities of thylakoids in solution, in
          fluid layers, and on rigid layers as a
          function of time (8).

ficial electron donors or acceptors, the activities
should then appear. This has been observed. Since the
rigid layer obtained from the fluid layer is fully
active, the separated complexes of the fluid layer are
obviously reintegrated when the fluid layer is transformed into a rigid one.

1. The open state of the layers allows measurements
and manipulations at enzymes located – under normal
conditions – at the inner side of the closed system.
For instance, the Chl-a$_{II}$ protein complex and the water
splitting Mn-enzyme complex, both located at the thylakoid inside (see Fig. 1), are probably located – at least
in parts – at the open side towards the aqueous phase in
the fluid as well as in the rigid layer. This improves

possibilities for direct measurements of the O_2 evolution, H^+ release, etc., and the exchange of the natural complexes with artificial systems as organic dyes (instead of the active chlorophyll) and metal oxides (instead of the watersplitting enzyme complex).

2. The separated complexes in the fluid layers – perhaps even separated protein complexes – could possibly be isolated in electrophorese set up in the plane of the fluid layer or vertically to it.

3. Injection of thylakoid material together with artificial lipids could result in a further separation. This may lead to an increased possibility for isolation.

4. Attacking the fluid layer with detergents under these conditions may result in a better isolation of enzyme complexes than is normally the case when detergents are applied to closed vesicles for isolation.

5. Supported by the eight times increased lifetime of the activities in the rigid layer, isolation of the immobilized enzymes through use of such detergents could be attempted which otherwise would deactivate the short-lived enzymes in thylakoid vesicles.

3. Nature of the steady state potential and its structural consequences

In a first stage the transfer of an electron from the inside to the outside of the thylakoid membrane generates a transmembrane electric potential difference, $\Delta\Psi$, detected through the electrochromic changes of the accessory pigments (3). The voltage set up by the charge separation in a single turnover is approximately 50 mV.

Subsequent protolytic reaction with the separated
charges leads to proton transport into the inner thylakoid space (see para 1). The main part of these transported protons ($\approx$ 99%) is bound by natural buffers in
the inner space. In saturating continuous light in the
steady state, an acidification of the inner thylakoid
with a pH decrease of about three pH units takes place,
e.g., from 8 to 5 (9). Due to the proton binding, the
charge density of the inner thylakoid space is shifted
towards more positive values. The buffer groups may be
located either at the inner membrane surface (Gouy-
Chapman type) or within the inner thylakoid space
(Donnan type). The steady state potential was first
interpreted by Rumberg et al. as being based on a
Donnan type (10a) but finally interpreted as based on
the Gouy-Chapman type (10b). Whether the Gouy-Chapman
or Donnan type is realized has been clarified by the
different dependencies of the steady state potential
on the ion concentration (11,19).

We have shown that the steady state potential
difference is ~5 mV at 20 mM KCl and changes to 80 mV
when the ionic concentration is changed to 1 mM (11)(see
Fig. 3). The theoretical dependence of the potential
difference on the ion concentration according to a Gouy-
Chapman mechanism (dashed line) and Donnan mechanism
(solid line), resp., has been calculated according to
the following data from the literature (surface charge
densities in the dark, $\sigma_d = 5 \cdot 10^{-4}$ e/$\mathring{A}^2$, space charge
density $\bar{A_d} = 30$ mM, regarding an internal volume V_{in}/Chl=
10 l/Chl). The steady state voltage is fairly well
fitted by the theoretical Donnan trace, regarding the

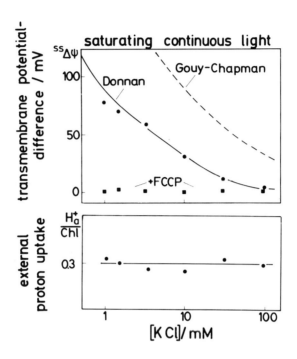

Fig. 3   Steady state potential difference (top)
          and H⁺ translocation (bottom) on depend-
          ence of the KCl concentration (11).

measured salt independent uptake of 0.3 H⁺/Chl. Consequences of this result with respect to (a) the structure of the inner thylakoid phase, and (b) the energization of the membrane, are the following:

        (a) The observed Donnan mechanism can be explained
only if the buffer groups are distributed within the
whole inner thylakoid space. These groups may be (a)
residues of the proteins which are embedded in the
membrane and which project into the inner thylakoid
space (see Fig. 4) and (b) proteins attached to the
membranes as e.g. plastocyanine. From electronmicro-

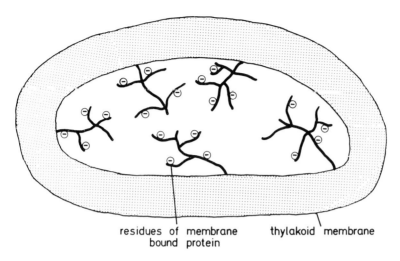

residues of membrane   thylakoid membrane
bound protein

Fig. 4   Protein residues in the inner thylakoid
         space (11).

scopic studies of the size of the membrane proteins
(100-200 Å), it is possible to conclude that the buffer
groups may be distributed over the whole inner space,
if the lateral axis of the thylakoids is smaller than
400 Å. The latter would correspond to an inner thylakoid volume of ≲ 20 l/MChl. Salt dependent volumes of
this order have been measured. A change of the buffer
group concentration by volume change through concentration change of sucrose should cause a decrease of the
Donnan potential which has been observed (11,19).

     (b) If one assumes that the electrochemical poten-
tial of the protons is constant within the outer and
inner phase in the steady state, the pH gradient from
the outer to the inner phase must become salt dependent
in the opposite direction to the salt dependence of the
electric potential difference. This means that the
measured ΔpH 3 and $\Delta \Psi$ = 5 mV at 20 mM KCl must change

to Δ pH = 1.8 and $\Delta\Psi$ = 80 mV at 1 mM KCl. This phenomenon may explain divergences of the H^+ potential reported
in the literature and is of importance with regard to
the energetic consideration of phosphorylation (see
para 4, eq. (2)).

4. Model for the regulation of the rate of phosphory-
lation and its proof

The chemiosmotic theory provides predictions concerning the energetic coupling between the electron
transport chain and the ATPase (4), but not such concerning the kinetics and chemical mechanism of ATP synthesis/
hydrolysis. As the chemiosmotic theory is now widely
accepted, efforts have been made by us to examine the
kinetics of phosphorylation (for references see (12)).
The mechanism is based on the following properties
(12,13):

1. Only the activated ATPase is open for proton
currents, j_H+, either outwards (phosphorylation) or,
$-j_H+$, inwards (hydrolysis).
2. The fraction of activated ATPases, E_a, depends on
ΔG_H+.
3. The extent and direction of j_H+ depends on ΔG_H+,
H_{in}^+, H_{out}^+, ADP, ATP, and P_i (see Fig. 5).
4. The rate of phosphorylation is a product of j_H+ and
E_a.

Under physiological conditions it results that, with
increasing ΔG_H+ the ATPase, E, starts to be activated
when j_H+ has already changed from negative to positive
values. Therefore, at these conditions, only phosphorylation takes place and the apparent irreversibility of

the ATPase can be explained in this way (see Fig. 6).
But, it also follows from the model that, under extreme
conditions e.g., very high ATP concentration, the mechanism works automatically and soundly in the opposite
direction, i.e., in the direction of hydrolysis. The
model fits the observed rates and their dependencies
on ΔG_H^+. It is experimentally shown that the assumptions made are acceptable.

The catalyst, the ATPase enzyme E, is kinetically
inhibited under non-energized conditions and transformed
into its activated state, E_a, if a transmembrane $\Delta\Psi$ and
ΔpH, resp., is induced:

$$(\Delta\Psi, \Delta pH)$$

$$E_i \underset{k_{-1}}{\overset{k_1}{\rightleftarrows}} E_a \qquad\qquad (5)$$

Therefore, it seems reasonable to assume that protons
are involved in the activation step. In the following,
the number of protons which may be involved in the activation is called b, in contrast to n which is the number
of protons involved in phosphorylation. Only the influence of ΔpH and $\Delta\Psi$ on the activation/deactivation process is regarded in the following. The influence of
other parameters is neglected in as far as the calculations are not in contrast to the experiments. The free
enthalpy change for activation may be given by (12,13):

$$b\,\Delta G_H^+ + \Delta G_E \underset{>}{\overset{<}{}} 0 \qquad\qquad (6)$$

b = number of H^+ involved in activation; ΔG_H^+, see eq.
(3); ΔG_E = free enthalpy change for activation (< acti-

vation, > deactivation, = equilibrium)

$$\Delta G_E = - RT \ln K_E^o + RT \ln \frac{E_a}{E_i}$$
(7)

$K_E^o = k_1^o / k_{-1}^o$ equilibrium constant under non-energized conditions, i.e., at $\Delta G_H^+ = 0$. It follows from eqs. (6) and (7), under energized conditions, at equilibrium

$$\frac{E_a}{E_i} = \frac{k_1}{k_{-1}} = \frac{k_1^o}{k_{-1}^o} \exp \left[\frac{-b \Delta G_H^+}{RT} \right]$$
(8)

The activation by Δ pH and $\Delta\Psi$ may occur, e.g., through the binding of H_{in}^+ and OH_{out}^- to the enzyme

$$E_i + b H_{in}^+ + b OH_{out}^- \underset{k_{-1}}{\overset{k_1}{\rightleftharpoons}} E_a$$
(9)

or through an H^+ translocation via the ATPase

$$E_i + b H_{in}^+ \underset{k_{-1}}{\overset{k_1}{\rightleftharpoons}} E_a + b H_{out}^+$$
(10)

In both cases the fraction of activated enzymes is

$$\frac{E_a}{E_t} = \frac{e^x}{1 + e^x} \quad , \quad x = \ln K_E^o - \frac{b \Delta G_H^+}{RT}$$
(11)

(E_a, activated enzymes; E_t, total enzymes)

In the activated state, ATP synthesis and ATP hydrolysis can be catalyzed depending on the sign of $n \Delta G_H^+ + \Delta G_p$ (see eq. (2)).

$$\text{ADP} + P_i \overset{(\Delta pH, \Delta \Psi, E_a)}{\rightleftharpoons} \text{ATP}$$
(12)

In this mechanism the rate of ATP synthesis/hydrolysis
is regulated by the energetics of the catalytic reaction
and by the fraction of activated ATPases. The interaction of the phosphorylating proton flux (see eq. (1))
with the activated enzyme and the coupling of both with
phosphorylation and hydrolysis, resp., can be described
by a mechanism depicted in Fig. 5 (12,13). In this
scheme in which the explicit formulation of enzyme substrate complexes is omitted, the proton flux through
one activated ATPase, $j_{H^+} = \overset{\circ}{H}^+/E_a$ as a function of ΔpH
($\Delta\Psi = 0$) is

$$\frac{j_{H^+}}{j_{H^+}^{max}} = \frac{1 - \exp\left\{\dfrac{n\,\Delta G_{H^+} + \Delta G_p}{RT}\right\}}{1 + \left[1 + \left(\dfrac{H^+_{out}}{K'_{out}}\right)^n\right]\left(\dfrac{K'_{in}}{H^+_{in}}\right)^n + \left(\dfrac{H^+_{out}}{K''}\right)^n} \tag{13}$$

K'_{out}, K'_{in}, and $K'' = f(k_{1,2,3,4}, k_{-(1,2,3,4)})$. For
details see references (12,13). The rate of phosphorylation is given by

$$V_p = \frac{1}{n}\, j_{H^+} \cdot E_a = \frac{1}{n}\, j_{H^+} \cdot \frac{e^x}{1 + e^x} \cdot E_t \tag{14}$$

In general, V_p – the rate of ATP synthesis and hydrolysis,
resp. – is the product of j_{H^+} (dotted line) and E_a (large
dotted line) (see Fig. 6). The product is depicted as a
solid line. For the sake of simplicity, two extreme
cases are discussed (see Fig. 6).

V_p may be regulated only through E_a, because j_{H^+}
is already constant or only through j_{H^+} because E_a is

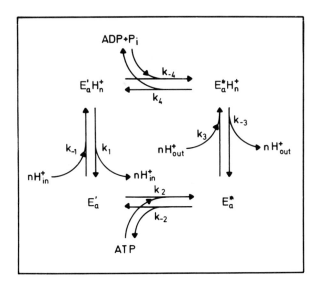

Fig. 5   Simplified reaction scheme for the phosphorylating H^+ influx/efflux and ATP synthesis/
hydrolysis; E'_a, $E'H^+_n$, E^*_a, and E^*_a non-speci-
fied complexes containing bound substances
such as ADP, P, and ATP (12,13).

already constant. The dotted curves show the dependence
of the phosphorylating proton flux per activated ATPase,
j_{H^+}, on ΔpH ($\Delta \Psi = 0$) with an appropriate choice of
parameters. The two examples are based on two different
ΔG_p values, 34 kJ and 65 kJ, corresponding to an equi-
librium ΔpH_{eq} (at $j_{H^+} = 0$) at $\Delta pH_{eqI} = 2$ and $\Delta pH_{eqII} =$
3.7 (see eqs. (2)-(4)). The large-dotted curve shows the
dependence of the fraction of activated ATPases, E_a, on
ΔpH as described by eq. (11). Under conditions of
$\Delta pH_{eqI} = 2$, the model predicts that V_p is regulated by
the dependence of the fraction of activated ATPases on
ΔpH (range I), i.e., V_p increases with ΔpH as determined by $E_a = f(\Delta pH)$ (large-dotted curve), i.e., V_p does

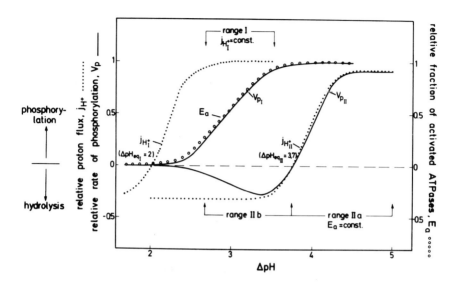

Fig. 6   Proton flux, j_{H^+}, fraction of activated
         ATPases, E_a, and rate of ATP synthesis/
         hydrolysis as a function of ΔG_{H^+} ($\Delta\Psi = 0$)
         calculated for two different ΔG_p values,
         corresponding to ΔpH_{eq} 2 and 3.7.
         Details see text (12,13).

not depend on the ADP/ATP ratio; this effect has been
observed. Under conditions of ΔpH_{eqII} = 3.7 practically all ATPases are activated and the Δ pH dependence
above Δ pH 3.7 is, on the whole, determined by the
dependence of j_{H^+} on Δ pH (range IIa). Below Δ pH 3.7
the dependence of the rate is determined by the product
of E_a and j_{H^+} (range IIb). Therefore, with decreasing
Δ pH, the rate of ATP hydrolysis increases at first
(due to the increase of the coupled inward proton flux –
j_{H^+}) and then decreases (due to the decrease of E_a).
Such an effect has been observed.

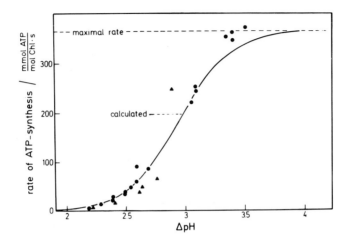

Fig. 7   Rate of ATP synthesis as a function of
Δ pH. calculated curve (eq. (14')) with
b = 2, ln K_E^O = -13.6 (12,13,14).

Obviously, as a consequence of the outlined mechanism (eq. (14)) ATP hydrolysis occurs only at relatively
high ATP concentrations, i.e., at relatively high ΔG_p
values. This might explain the apparent irreversibility
of the ATPase.

To check the functional dependence of the rate, $V_{p'}$
on Δ pH as evaluated in the kinetic model
the calculated curves are compared in Fig. 7 with
measured data (14). The calculation of the curves
according to eq. (14) is based on the assumption that
j_{H^+} is practically constant and that the rate of phosphorylation, V_p, is regulated by the Δ pH dependence of
the fraction of activated ATPases (see Fig. 6, range I).
The parameters used to fit the data are ln K_E^O = - 15.6
and b = 2 and accordingly, ΔG_E^O = 38.6 kJ (see eq. (7)).
Theory and experiment match rather well.

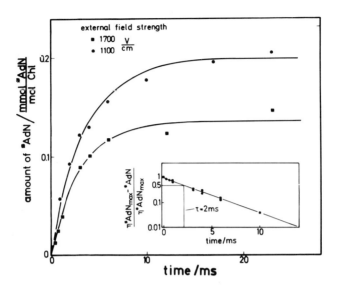

Fig. 8   Adenine nucleotides released as a function
         of the duration of external field pulses
         at two different field strengths.   Inset:
         log plot of the time course (15).

To check whether the activation of the ATPase is
regulated by $\Delta\Psi$ or/and Δ pH, the following experiments
have been carried out. Tightly bound adenine nucleotides, AdN, are released upon energization of the
membrane. The amount released indicates the number of
ATPases which have changed their conformation. It is
assumed that this conformation change is coupled with
the activation of the ATPase.

First, it remains to be seen whether at all the
rate of AdN-release and conformational changes, resp.,
are comparable to the rate of ATP synthesis.

Fig. 8 shows the time resolved ^{x}AdN release obtained by external voltage pulses at two different

field strengths. A half rise time of 2 ms is observed, independent of the magnitude of energization (15). The initial rate of this [x]AdN release is practically the same as the rate of ATP synthesis under identical conditions. Therefore, the [x]AdN release is sufficiently fast to be an initial step coupled with the activation of the ATPase. Thus, it can be assumed that the amplitude of the AdN release indicates the fraction of activated ATPases, i.e., $\eta = E_a/E_t$.

After these clarifications, the dependence of the activation on $\Delta\Psi$ and Δ pH can be evaluated (16). Fig. 9, bottom left, shows the dependence of the fraction of "activated" ATPases, η , on $\Delta\Psi$ pulses of 30 ms duration. A non-linear increase of the fraction of active ATPases with $\Delta\Psi$ is found. Fig. 9, left center, shows the amount of ATP depending on $\Delta\Psi$ changes of 30 ms duration. About six times more ATP is generated than [x]AdN is released. The amount of ATP per "activated" ATPase, i.e., ATP per [x]AdN released, is depicted for different $\Delta\Psi$ values at the top of Fig. 9, left. As one can see, this ratio is independent of $\Delta\Psi$ in a range where both ATP synthesis and AdN release change by a factor of about 10. Division of this ratio, $ATP/n \cdot E_t$, by the pulse duration, Δ t, gives the rate of ATP synthesis per activated ATPase, j_H+/n, i.e., the turnover number of the ATPase (200 s^{-1}) (scale at the right side) (see eq. (15)).

Similar results have been obtained upon energization with Δ pH pulses using the rapid mixing quenched flow method (17) (see Fig. 9, right).

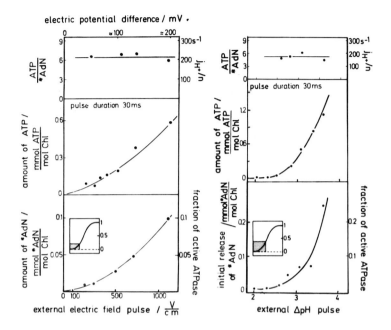

Fig. 9   Left: Amount of AdN released (bottom) and
          ATP generated (center) and rate of phos-
          phorylation per active ATPase (top) as a
          function of the external electric field
          strength and potential $\Delta\Psi$ (Δ pH = 0), resp.
          (16). Right: as a function of Δ pH
          ($\Delta\Psi$ = 0) (17).

These results provide evidence that the rate of
ATP synthesis is controlled by the activation step as
described above. It is assumed that the fraction of
activated ATPases, η , is identical with the activated
fraction present in the steady state, i.e., $\eta \approx E_a/E_t$.
For the turnover of the ATPase is follows from eq. (14)
and Fig. 9:

$$1/\tau_{ATP} = \frac{V_p}{E_a} = \frac{j_H^+}{n} = \frac{ATP}{\eta \cdot E_t \cdot \Delta t} \approx 200 \ s^{-1} \qquad (15)$$

i.e., the production time for one ATP is:

$$\tau_{ATP} \approx 5 \text{ ms} \tag{15'}$$

Furthermore, $j_H{}^+/n$ is practically independent of $\Delta\Psi$ and Δ pH. Only E_a/E_t depends on both parameters as described in eq. (11): $E_a/E_t = f(\Delta\Psi, \Delta pH)$. This implies that the dependence of the rate of ATP synthesis on Δ pH and $\Delta\Psi$ reflects the dependence of the number of activated ATPases on Δ pH and $\Delta\Psi$. Obviously, the change into the activated state under normal phosphorylating conditions occurs only at such a high $\Delta\Psi$ and/or Δ pH that $j_H{}^+$ has already reached its maximum constant value (see Fig. 6, range I). If all ATPases are activated, i.e., $E_a/E_t = 1$, then $v_p^{max} = j_{H^+}^{max} / n = 200$ ATP/$CF_1 \cdot$s should be observed. Rates between 200 – 320 ATP/$CF_1 \cdot$s have, in fact, been reported (14,18) and have been shown to approach saturation (see Fig. 7).

For the synthesis of one ATP, n protons must be translocated from the inside to the outside (see eq.(2)), and it is reasonable to assume that these protons pass only through the activated ATPases. The phosphorylating proton flux at the thylakoid membrane, H_p^+, can be then described by

$$\overset{\circ}{H}{}_p^+ = n \cdot V_p = j_{H^+} \cdot E_a \tag{16}$$

Since a maximum of about 200 ATP is generated per second per active ATPase, the corresponding maximum proton current through an active ATPase (n = 3) is

$$j_{H^+}^{max} = 600 \text{ H}^+/\text{s} \tag{16'}$$

The above-described activation of the ATPase may
be described as a gating process for the phosphorylating proton flux, j_H^+ (16).

ACKNOWLEDGEMENTS
I am most grateful to Ms. D. DiFiore, Dr. P. Gräber, G. Schatz,
Dr. E. Schlodder, and Mr. R. Tiemann for their contributions to the results described in this report. I am
also indebted to the Deutsche Forschungsgemeinschaft
for the financial support provided.

244   H. T. WITT

REFERENCES

1. Witt, H.T. (1979) Biochim. Biophys. Acta 505,
    335-427.
2. Witt, H.T. (1967) in Fast Reactions and Primary
    Processes in Chemical Kinetics (Nobel Symposium V)
    (Cleasson, S., ed.), pp. 261-316, Almqvist and
    Wiksell, Stockholm; Interscience Publ., New York.
3. Junge, W. and Witt, H.T. (1968) Z. Naturforsch.
    23b, 244-254.
4. Mitchell, P. (1966) Biol. Rev. 41, 445-502.
5. Witt, H.T. (1967) in Fast Reactions and Primary
    Processes in Chemical Kinetics (Nobel Symposium V)
    (Cleasson, S., ed.), pp. 81-97, Almqvist and
    Wiksell, Stockholm; Interscience Publ., New York.
6. Rüppel, H. and Witt, H.T. (1970) Methods Enzymol.
    16, 316-380.
7. Witt, H.T., Schlodder, E. and Gräber, P. (1976)
    FEBS Lett. 69, 272-276.
8. Witt, H.T. and DiFiore, D. (1981) FEBS Lett. in
    press.
9. Rumberg, B. and Siggel, U. (1969) Naturwiss. 56,
    130-132.
10a. Schröder, H., Muhle, H. and Rumberg, B. (1971)
    Proc. II International Congress on Photosynthesis,
    Stresa, 919-930.
10b. Rumberg, B. and Muhle, H. (1976) Bioelectrochem.
    Bioenerg. 3, 393-403.
11. Tiemann, R. and Witt, H.T. (1981) in press.
12. Schlodder, E., Gräber, P. and Witt, H.T. (1981)
    in press.
13. Gräber, P. and Schlodder, E. (1981) in press.
14. Rumberg, B. and Heinze, Th. (1980) Ber. Bunsen-
    ges. Phys. Chem. 84, 1055-1059.
15. Schlodder, E. and Witt, H.T. (1981) Biochim.
    Biophys. Acta 635, 571-584.
16. Gräber, P., Schlodder, E. and Witt, H.T. (1977)
    Biochim. Biophys. Acta 461, 426-440.
17. Schatz, G.H., Schlodder, E. and Gräber, P. (1980)
    Proc. of the 5th Intern. Congress on Photosynthesis,
    Kallithea, Greece
18. Pick, U., Rottenberg, H. and Avron, M. (1974)
    FEBS Lett. 48, 32-36.
19. Tiemann, R., DiFiore, D. and Witt, H.T. (1979)
    in Abstracts of Poster Presentation, Annual Meet-
    ing of the Deutsche Ges. f. Biophysik (Adam, G. and
    Stark, G., eds.), p. 70, Springer, Berlin

PLASTOQUINONE FUNCTION AND A POSSIBLE Q-CYCLE

IN PHOTOSYNTHETIC ELECTRON TRANSPORT

David Crowther and Geoffrey Hind

Biology Department, Brookhaven National Laboratory,
Upton, New York 11973, USA

It is generally accepted that the photosynthetic
electron transfer chain of chloroplasts is arranged across
the thylakoid membrane to cause the light-driven translocation of protons from the stroma (exterior) to the lumen
(interior). The review by Trebst (1) provides an excellent
description of the classical "Z" scheme of light driven
electron flow, in which plastoquinone is thought to serve as
the hydrogen carrying arm of a Mitchellian redox loop between photosystem II (PS II) and photosystem I (PS I). Such
a scheme predicts a H^+/e^- stoichiometry of 2 for "linear"
electron transport from H_2O to $NADP^+$ which, given a H^+/ATP
ratio of 3, would provide insufficient ATP for steady state
CO_2 fixation, wherein a ratio of 3 ATP:2 NADPH is required.
Pseudocyclic (O_2 evolution by PS II and rereduction by PS I)
and PS I-driven cyclic electron flows have been proposed to
redress this shortfall. Recent evidence suggests, however,

V. P. Skulachev and Peter C. Hinkle (eds.), Chemiosmotic Proton Circuits in Biological Membranes
in honor of Peter Mitchell   ISBN 0-201-07398-6

that the "Z" scheme even with such additions is an oversim-
plified view of chloroplast electron transfer. Additional
complexities that are now recognized centre on the function
of plastoquinone A (PQ), particularly in the manner of its
oxidation by the cytochrome b/f complex, and the possible
involvement of a Q-cycle in chloroplast electron flow.
Evidence that thylakoid quinones other than plastoquinone A
(2) have any specialized function in chloroplast electron
flow is inadequate. We will consider PQ involvement in two
sections: first, its reduction to plastoquinol (PQH_2) by PS
II and second, its interactions with the cytochrome b/f
complex and PS I. There is good physiological justification
for such separate treatment, as the majority of PQ-reducing
PS II reaction centers (PS II-α) occur in the regions where

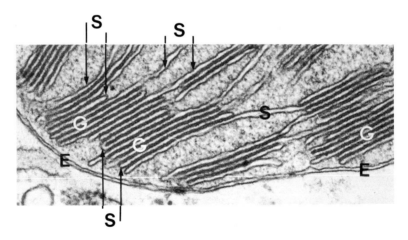

Fig. 1.   Partial section of Potamogeton chloroplast. The
           double envelope (E) bounds the stroma which con-
           tains thylakoids partly appressed in grana
           stacks. The proposed lateral heterogeneity of
           thylakoid membranes (3) places PS II-α units in
           membrane regions within the grana stacks (G) and PS
           II-β, PS I, cytochromes b/f and ATPase in stroma-
           exposed membrane areas (S). 60,000 X.

thylakoid lamellae are structured into grana whereas most
PS I and probably cytochrome b/f units are found in the
stroma lamellae with the PS II-β centres (3) (see Fig. 1).

PLASTOQUINONE REDUCTION BY PHOTOSYSTEM II.

Photosystem II-α centres.   In mature, wild-type chloroplasts, PS II-α centres comprise ~65% of the chloroplast PS
II (4,5). The PS II-α complex contains two acceptor PQ's,
one tightly bound primary acceptor ("Q") and a secondary
acceptor ("R" or "B") (6). An EPR signal attributed to a
semiquinone-iron complex has been reported (7) and thus the
PS II-α acceptor structure mirrors that of the purple non-
sulphur photosynthetic bacterium Rhodopseudomonas spheroides
(8). The mechanism of PQ reduction resembles that reported
for quinone reduction by such bacterial reaction centres, in
that Q is reduced to an anionic semiquinone form following a
single turnover flash then the electron is transferred to the
secondary quinone ("R"), reducing it to semiquinone, R^- (9).
A second flash again produces Q^- which reduces R^- to quinol.
Although the spectra of Q^- and R^- suggest anionic semiquinone
species, protons are taken up between flashes; neither the
group(s) responsible for the uptake of H^+ nor the mechanism
of protonation to form PQH_2 are known. Recent work has
suggested that, following reduction to the (protonated)
quinol, R is itself released from the complex (10) rather
than remaining bound and transferring 2 reducing equivalents
to another PQ molecule from a distinct pool. A third, high
potential, acceptor has been reported in PS II but its
function is unknown (11).

PS II-β centres   PS II-β centres are located in the stroma
lamellae, do not show the R/R⁻ oscillations, have an acceptor
Em considerably more positive than that of the PS II-α
acceptor and have smaller antennae than α centres (4,5,9,
12). It is unclear whether β centres are immature α centres
or are complete and essential for normal photosynthesis.

PLASTOQUINOL OXIDATION

Oxidation by isolated cytochrome b/f complexes.   A complex
analagous to mitochondrial complex III may be isolated from
chloroplasts; the purest active preparations contain 5 polypeptides of M_r's 34, 33, 23.5, 20 and 17.5 kD by SDS gel
analysis with optical spectra indicating 2 cytochromes b_{563}
per f (13).   Cytochrome f haem is associated with one or both
of the larger subunits and cytochrome b_{563} haem probably with
the third subunit; the fourth may be a PQ binding protein,
and the smallest the Rieske 2Fe:2S centre (G. Hauska, personal communication).   Light-driven cytochrome f oxidation and
cytochrome b_{563} reduction were seen when this complex was reconstituted into liposomes with PS I particles (14); similar
results have been obtained with less pure cytochrome b_{563}/f
complex containing some PS I, in which titration with DBMIB
produced increasing and parallel inhibitions of the extents
of cytochrome b_{563} photoreduction and cytochrome f photooxidation (15).   These results appear to show an oxidant induced
cytochrome b reduction similar to that seen with mitochondrial complex III (16) but as all published experiments showing
cytochrome b_{563} reduction have relied on the presence of PS I
this conclusion is equivocal; if a true oxidant induced
reduction of cytochrome b_{563} occurs, it should be demonstrable (as in the mitochondrial complex) by chemical oxidation

in the absence of PS I, thus removing any possibility of cytochrome b_{563} reduction by the reducing side of PS I.

Oxidation in situ.   Plastoquinol is oxidised in vivo by PS I via plastocyanin (PC), cytochrome f and (probably) the Rieske Fe:S centre. Rereduction of $P700^+$ by PC occurs in three kinetic phases with more than 90% attributable to the two fastest (halftimes of ~20 μs and ~200 μs) in unbroken thylakoids (17). The relative amplitudes of these rapid phases depend on the ion type and concentration and on the osmolarity of the medium; screening of membrane surface negative charge seems important (17). $P700^+$ rereduction does not give rise to a kinetic phase of the electrochromic effect (18) and so differs from $P870^+$ rereduction by cytochrome c_2 in Rps. spheroides (19). Rereduction of oxidised PC by cytochrome f proceeds with two apparent phases of ~100 μs and ~600 μs halftimes following a 30-50 μs lag time from the flash; the similar redox midpoint potentials of PC and cytochrome f (20) and the reported excess of the former (21) suggest that the extent of cytochrome f photooxidation seen following a single turnover flash would be considerably less than the amount of $P700^+$ rereduced, and indeed values of around 40% of the expected P700 yield have been observed (22). Cytochrome f is then rereduced by plastoquinol in a DBMIB sensitive reaction; high concentrations of DBMIB additionally cause the appearance of a slow phase of cytochrome f oxidation (23) -- also seen in the presence of o- or batho-phenanthrolines (23,24) -- with a substantial lowering of the midpoint potential of the Rieske centre and a shift of its EPR spectrum (25,26), so demonstrating a close relationship between the DBMIB binding site (presumably the same as the plastoquinol binding site) and the Rieske centre. UHDBT does not cause such a dramatic

effect on the Rieske EPR signal, but can readily displace
DBMIB and inhibit rereduction of the Rieske centre; neither
UHDBT nor DBMIB inhibit photooxidation of the centre (26).

Concurrent with cytochrome f rereduction following a
single turnover flash may occur a slow rise in the electrochromic pigment bandshift, P518, equal in amplitude to the
fast rise originating from electron transfer within the PS I
reaction centre. This slow rise (P518$_s$, or "phase b") is
claimed as evidence of a transmembrane electrogenic reaction
occurring in dark electron flow (6,27,28) in analogy with the
slow carotenoid bandshift seen in several species of photosynthetic bacteria (19); proposals that it directly reflects
the deposition of protons into the lumen (29) seem unjusti-
fied as no kinetic phases corresponding to the liberation of
protons by the water splitting complex of PS II are seen. If
P518$_s$ does indeed reflect a third transmembrane charge separation (the other two arising in the PS I and PS II reaction
centres) then a third proton uptake (from the stroma) and release (into the lumen) might be expected when P518$_s$ is seen,
and indeed such "extra" H^+ release into the lumen has been
reported (30). P518$_s$ is observed only on reduction of cytochrome f by plastoquinol; there is no kinetic phase of P518
corresponding to the reported rapid rereduction phase (23,24)
suggesting that both the Rieske centre and cytochrome f are
located near the inner surface of the thylakoid membrane.
P518$_s$ is seen, with the extra H^+ and cytochrome f rereduction, on alternate, even number, flashes from a dark state
with all PQ initially oxidized (31,32) since plastoquinol,
the necessary donor, is released by PS II only on alternate
flashes. In Chlorella cells in the presence of reductant, an
inversion of P518$_s$ oscillations (i.e. maxima on odd-numbered

flashes) has been reported (32), presumably due to reduction
of R to R$^{\bar{}}$ in the dark before the flash sequence.

   A specially bound quinone "U" in the cytochrome b/f
complex (analogous to "Q_z" of Rps. spheroides) has been proposed (28,32,33) to account for the redox properties of
P518$_s$, which shows an apparent Em somewhat more positive than
that of the PQ pool (27,34). Inhibition of PQH$_2$ oxidation by
quinone analogues or iron chelators might then result from
competitive displacement of U or modification of its binding
site (on the Rieske Fe:S protein?) respectively. A recent
report suggests that U may exchange rapidly with "free" PQ
(24) as claimed for the quinone R of PS II (10), although
other work has indicated only a small pool of PQ interacting
rapidly with PS II and the cytochrome b/f complex (27,34).

   Suggestions have been made that the reductant for
cytochrome b$_{563}$ may be semiquinone generated from UH$_2$ by
single electron reduction of cytochrome f, as cytochrome b$_{563}$
reduction is seen (with cytochrome f rereduction and P518$_s$)
on the second flash of a sequence starting with PQ initially
oxidized (31) and is inhibited (along with cytochrome f
rereduction and P518$_s$) by quinone analogues under a variety
of conditions (27,28,35-37). In spinach chloroplasts,
though, cytochrome b$_{563}$ reduction following a flash is
apparently faster than cytochrome f rereduction and the rise
of P518$_s$, while its reoxidation is considerably slower than
these (28); the kinetics of cytochrome b turnover in
Chlorella are also apparently unrelated to cytochrome f
turnover and P518$_s$ (27). It is possible that these kinetic
discrepancies may result from simultaneous oxidation and
reduction of one or both cytochromes, with further complications arising from the equilibrium of cytochrome f with PC;
additional experiments are needed to settle this issue.

More work is also required to elucidate the role of multiple cytochrome $\underline{b}$ haems: although cytochrome $\underline{b}_{563}$ is present at double the concentration of cytochrome $\underline{f}$ in the chloroplast and in fragments, the extent of its flash-induced reduction is not greater than the extent of cytochrome $\underline{f}$ oxidation (22,28,31), and although digitonin fractionated PS I/cytochrome $\underline{b/f}$ particles contain a low potential cytochrome $\underline{b}_{559}$ (38) this is not present in purer cytochrome $\underline{b/f}$ particles (13) and no evidence for its turnover in plastoquinol oxidation has been obtained (28). In Chlorella a claim has been made that a redox centre (Fe:S protein?) with a weak optical signal and an Em of about −50 mV is reduced in parallel with cytochrome $\underline{f}$ (32), but biochemical identification of such a component is not yet available.

POSSIBLE MECHANISMS OF ELECTRON TRANSFER.

The observations described above have led to several proposals (6,27,28,36) for possible mechanisms of electron transfer in the cytochrome $\underline{b/f}$ complex based on, or similar to, the general Q-cycle scheme presented by Mitchell (39). All of these schemes assume that $P518_s$ indicates the movement of an electron across the dielectric barrier of the thylakoid membrane from the inner to the outer edge, rather than the transfer of a positive charge (such as H^+) in the opposite direction, as might occur with a "membrane Bohr effect" or similar process; if this assumption is correct, then the electron transfer across the membrane must be followed by an electroneutral return of a reducing equivalent as $H^{\bullet}$, after uptake of H^+ at the outer surface (Fig. 2). The carrier responsible for such $H^{\bullet}$ movement would be plastoquinol and thus a PQ reductase should function at the thylakoid outer

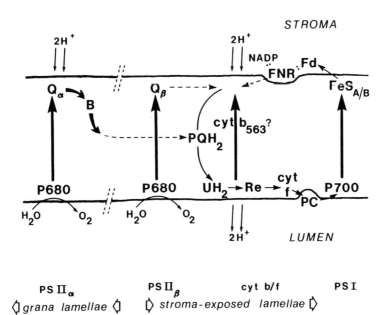

Fig. 2. Possible Q-cycle mechanisms in chloroplast electron
         flow. Pigment-protein complexes are identified
         below the scheme. Upward arrows show electrogenic
         steps. Proton fluxes due to water splitting and
         NADP reduction are not shown. Q, B and U are
         thought to be bound forms of plastoquinone (PQ).
         Re: Rieske high potential Fe:S centre.

surface. For such a mechanism to function efficiently in
purely linear electron flow, both electrons needed for PQ
reduction would have to be derived from oxidation of UH_2 at
the inner side of the membrane; in this case a dismutation
between cytochrome b/f complexes (or equilibration between
them by mobile carriers such as PQ and PC has to be proposed
(6,31) since no oscillations of cytochrome b_{563} reoxidation
are seen (31) -- these would be expected if the complexes
behaved as discrete entities.

An alternative to dismutation is electron input to the PQ reductase from a source at the thylakoid exterior such that each electron crossing the membrane from within can be matched by one from the outer face in the manner of the Q-cycle (39). Two electron sources are possible given the reported partitioning of PS I, PS II-α, PS II-β and the cytochrome b/f unit: the acceptor complex of PS II-β and ferredoxin:NADP oxidoreductase (FNR). The PS II-β acceptor is apparently a single-electron transferring complex with an Em of $\sim$ +120 mV, n=1 (12, cf. 4,9) and is sensitive to DCMU despite a lack of the "two electron gate" found in PS II-α centres (9); these properties make it a possible single electron donor to the reducing side of a Q-cycle but, though such function would explain the PS II stimulation of P518$_s$ generation on multiple flashes (27,34), the less than 1:1 stoichiometry of PS II-β to P700 (and presumably cytochrome b/f units) in normal chloroplasts (4) makes this pathway seem less likely. FNR is a flavin-containing dehydrogenase which in the isolated form can be reduced by NADPH to a stable semiquinone with an Em$_7$ of -320 mV (40). In spinach thylakoids, NADPH-driven reductions of PS II acceptors and intersystem components have been demonstrated (41,42); these reductions are catalysed by FNR and are sensitive to inhibitors of this enzyme (41,43). Spectroscopic (44) and inhibitor (43) studies have led to the suggestion that FNR is the branch point between linear and cyclic electron flow pathways. A Q-cycle may then be easily visualized, with FNR serving in the manner of the "i" side dehydrogenase in the mitochondrial cristae membrane (39).

These three possible PQ reduction pathways are not mutually exclusive and simultaneous operation of all three could occur, the relative rates being controlled by the redox

states of PQ and NADP pools and the stromal and luminal pH
values. This sort of flexibility would allow the chloroplast
to vary the rates of ATP and NADPH production to suit its
metabolic needs (45). A more positive switching mechanism
similar to the coupling factor and PS II antenna chlorophyll-
protein phosphorylations (46) might also operate.

Inhibition of the Q-cycle might be expected if the
transthylakoid $\Delta\psi$ and/or ΔpH were too high, and inhibition of
P518$_s$ by high ΔpH in chloroplasts (22) and high Δp in
Chlorella (27) has been observed. It seems likely that high
$\Delta\psi$ inhibits transmembrane electron movement, while low luminal pH (high ΔpH) might prevent oxidation of UH$^\cdot$ by raising
the Em of U/UH$^\cdot$ (when the pH falls below the pK of the
semiquinone -- pK $\sim$ pH 5-6? (15)) so that reduction (of cytochrome $\underline{b}_{563}$?) is unfavourable; dismutation of UH$^\cdot$ or
oxidation of cytochrome $\underline{b}_{563}$ might then occur to regenerate
quinol. The extra H$^+$ translocation of the Q-cycle would be
lost in both cases, as proposed for mitochondria (47).

ACKNOWLEDGEMENTS

Thanks are owed to Drs. Barber, Bendall, Bouges-
Bocquet, Hauska, Malkin, Rich, Telfer, Velthuys and their
colleagues for providing preprints and some unpublished
observations. Dr. M.C. Ledbetter kindly furnished the
electron micrograph for Figure 1. This work was supported by
the United States Department of Energy.

REFERENCES

1.   Trebst, A. (1974) Ann. Rev. Plant Physiol. 25, 423-458
2.   Crane, F.L., Henninger, M.D., Wood, P.M. and Barr, R.
     (1966) in Biochemistry of Chloroplasts (Goodwin, T.W.,
     ed.) Academic Press, New York, pp. 133-151
3.   Anderson, J.M. (1981) FEBS Lett. 124, 1-10

4. Melis, A. (1981) in Function of Quinones in Energy
    Conserving Systems (Trumpower, B., ed.), Academic
    Press, New York, (in press)
5. Thielen, A.P.G.M. and van Gorkum, H.J. (1981)
    Biochim. Biophys. Acta 635, 111-120
6. Velthuys, B.R. (1980) Ann. Rev. Plant Physiol. 31,
    545-567
7. Nugent, J.H.A., Diner, B.A. and Evans, M.C.W. (1981)
    FEBS Lett. 124, 241-244
8. Wraight, C.A. (1979) Photochem. Photobiol. 30, 767-776
9. van Gorkum, H.J. (1981) in Function of Quinones in
    Energy Conserving Systems (Trumpower, B., ed.),
    Academic Press, New York, (in press)
10. Velthuys, B.R. (1981) FEBS Lett. (in press)
11. Bowes, J.M. and Crofts, A.R. (1980) Biochim. Biophys
    Acta 590, 373-384
12. Horton, P. (1981) Biochim. Biophys. Acta 635, 105-110
13. Hurt, E. and Hauska, G. (1981) Eur. J. Biochem. (in
    press)
14. Hauska, G., Orlich, G., Samoray, D., Hurt, E. and
    Sane, P.V. (1981) in Proc. 5th. Intl. Cong. on
    Photosynthesis (Akoyunoglou, G., ed.) Intl. Science
    Services, Jerusalem (in press)
15. Rich, P.R. and Bendall, D.S. (1981) ibid.
16. Rieske, J.S. (1976) Biochim. Biophys. Acta 456,
    195-247
17. Haehnel, W., Pröpper, A. and Krause, H. (1980)
    Biochim. Biophys. Acta 593, 384-399
18. Junge, W. (1975) in Proc. 3rd. Intl. Cong. on
    Photosynthesis (Avron, M. ed.) Elsevier, Amsterdam,
    pp. 273-286
19. Wraight, C.A., Cogdell, R.J. and Chance, B. (1978)
    in The Photosynthetic Bacteria (Clayton, R.K. and
    Sistrom, W.R., eds) Plenum, New York, pp. 471-511
20. Wood, P.M. (1974) Biochim. Biophys. Acta 357, 370-379
21. Plesničar, M. and Bendall, D.S. (1970) Biochim.
    Biophys. Acta 216, 192-199
22. Slovacek, R.E., Crowther, D.and Hind, G. (1980)
    Biochim. Biophys. Acta 592, 495-505
23. Koike, H., Satoh, K. and Katoh, S. (1978) Plant Cell
    Physiol. 19, 1371-1380
24. Velthuys, B.R. (1981) in Function of Quinones in
    Energy Conserving Systems (Trumpower, B., ed.),
    Academic Press, New York, (in press)
25. Chain, R.K. and Malkin, R. (1979) Arch. Biochem.
    Biophys. 197, 52-56

28. Crowther, D. and Hind, G. (1980) Arch. Biochem.
     Biophys. 204, 568-577
29. Hope, A.B. and Moreland, A. (1980) Aust. J. Plant
     Physiol. 7, 699-711
30. Velthuys, B.R. (1980) FEBS Lett. 115, 167-170
31. Velthuys, B.R. (1979) Proc. Nat. Acad. Sci. USA, 76,
     2765-2769
32. Bouges-Bocquet, B. (1980) FEBS Lett. 117, 54-58
33. Bouges-Bocquet, B. (1981) in Proc. 5th. Intl. Cong. on
     Photosynthesis (Akoyunoglou, G., ed.) Intl. Science
     Services, Jerusalem (in press)
34. Crowther, D. and Hind, G. (1981) in Function of
     Quinones in Energy Conserving Systems (Trumpower, B.,
     ed.), Academic Press, New York, (in press)
35. Olsen, L.F., Telfer, A. and Barber, J. (1980) FEBS
     Lett. 118, 11-17
36. Malkin, R. (1981) in Proc. 5th. Intl. Cong. on
     Photosynthesis (Akoyunoglou, G., ed.) Intl. Science
     Services, Jerusalem (in press)
37. Telfer, A. and Barber, J. (1981) ibid.
38. Rich, P.R. and Bendall, D.S. (1980) Biochim. Biophys.
     Acta 591, 153-161
39. Mitchell, P. (1976) J. Theoret. Biol. 62, 327-367
40. Keirns, J.J. and Wang, J.H. (1972) J. Biol. Chem.
     247, 7374-7382
41. Mills, J.D., Crowther, D., Slovacek, R.E., Hind, G.,
     and McCarty, R.E. (1979) Biochim. Biophys. Acta
     547, 127-137
42. Malkin, R. and Chain, R.K. (1980) Biochim. Biophys.
     Acta 591, 381-390
43. Shahak, Y., Crowther, D., and Hind, G. (1981) Biochim.
     Biophys. Acta (in press)
44. Bouges-Bocquet, B. (1978) FEBS Lett. 94, 95-99
45. Hind, G., Crowther, D., Shahak, Y., and Slovacek, R.E.
     (1981) in Proc. 5th. Intl. Cong. on Photosynthesis
     (Akoyunoglou, G., ed.) Intl. Science Services,
     Jerusalem (in press)
46. Horton, P., Allen, J.F., Black, M.T., and Bennett, J.
     (1981) FEBS Lett. 125, 193-196
47. Mitchell, P. (1980) in Oxidases and Related Redox
     Systems (King, T.E., Mason, H.S., and Morrison, M.,
     eds.) Vol. 3, Pergamon Press, London (in press)

FLASH ACTIVATED ELECTRON AND PROTON TRANSLOCATION

THROUGH THE UBIQUINONE-CYTOCHROME $\underline{c}$ OXIDOREDUCTASE

OF MITOCHONDRIA AND PHOTOSYNTHETIC BACTERIA

Katsumi Matsuura and P. Leslie Dutton

Department of Biochemistry and Biophysics
University of Pennsylvania
Philadelphia, PA   19104
U.S.A.

INTRODUCTION

Flash-activatable cyclic electron transfer systems composed of photochemical reaction center protein (RC), with ubi-
quinone-cytochrome $\underline{c}$ (Q-$\underline{c}$) oxidoreductase and $\underline{c}$-type cytochrome
have provided much information about the nature of the electron
and proton transfer in biological membranes. In this report, we
shall focus on the electron and proton transfer in Q-$\underline{c}$ oxido-
reductases from the photosynthetic bacterium Rhodopseudomonas
sphaeroides studied in vivo and from mitochondria studied in vitro as a hybrid construction comprising Q-$\underline{c}$ oxidoreductase
(beef heart), cytochrome $\underline{c}$ (horse heart), and RC (Rps. sphaeroides).

The respective Q-$\underline{c}$ and Q-$\underline{c}_2$ oxidoreductase of mitochondria and Rps. sphaeroides are equipped with similar redox
components with comparable redox midpoint potentials at pH 7.0

V. P. Skulachev and Peter C. Hinkle (eds.), Chemiosmotic Proton Circuits in Biological Membranes
   in honor of Peter Mitchell   ISBN 0-201-07398-6

259

(E_{m7}) as shown in Fig. 1. Furthermore, recent work has established that they display parallel flash activated electron
transfer reactions (1-3). Thus we are now in a position to
examine in more detail the individual steps of electron transfer in the Q-c oxidoreductase of mitochondria using the
approaches that have been applied to the Q-c oxidoreductase
of Rps. sphaeroides for several years (4-12).

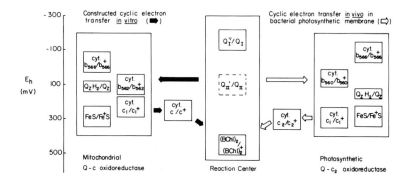

Fig. 1   Redox components in cyclic electron transfer of Rps.
sphaeroides and in vitro constructed system.

As shown in Fig. 1 the activated RC provides the Q-c
oxidoreductase with a single reducing equivalent via the Q
complement of the RC, and a single oxidizing equivalent via
cytochrome c. In the work presented here, flash activated
oxidation and reduction reactions of cytochromes b and c are
studied in Q-c oxidoreductase adjusted to various redox
states[1] prior to activation following the guidelines recently
presented by O'Keefe and Dutton (11).

[1]Experiments were done in an anaerobic cuvette in the pres-
ense of redox mediators used to monitor and control the redox
state of the components of the system. Redox equilibrium
between electrodes, mediators, and protein bound components
was generally established on a minutes timescale.

RECOGNITION OF A Q_Z TYPE COMPONENT. Fig. 2A shows flash induced oxidation-reduction kinetics of mitochondrial cytochromes c and b. At E_h 150 mV the flash elicits rapid cytochrome b reduction and slow re-oxidation, and rapid cytochrome
c oxidation followed by slow re-reduction. However as the E_h
is lowered (see trace at 60 mV) the re-oxidation of cytochrome
b becomes faster, and there is parallel behavior in the rereduction of cytochrome c. The E_h dependence of the similar
initial rates of ferrocytochrome b oxidation and ferricytochrome c reduction (Fig. 2B) describes an n=2 Nernst curve
with an $E_{m7.8}$ at 75 mV. The E_m value has a -60 mV/pH unit
dependency in the range pH 6.3 to 8.5; the E_{m7} value is 115 mV.
These properties (see Fig. 1) are analogous to those of a redox

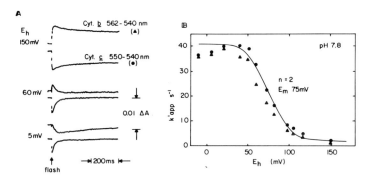

Fig. 2 Flash induced oxidation-reduction kinetics of cytochromes b and c (A) and E_h dependence of initial
rates of cytochrome b oxidation and cytochrome c reduction (B) in the hybrid system. The system contains mitochondrial Q-c oxidoreductase (Complex III,
prepared as in ref. 17) (4 μM in c_1), horse heart
cytochrome c (6 μM) and RC (0.6 μM) in 10 mM Tris-
HCl, pH 7.8 together with a small amount of detergents, cholate and LDAO, that came with the protein
preparations. Redox mediators used were 0.1 mM
$FeSO_4$ with 3.3 mM EDTA, 10 μM DAD, and 10 μM pyocyanine. The flash is >90% saturating and is <10 μs
in duration, allowing a single turnover.

component, Q_zH_2/Q_z, identified as a ubiquinone in a special environment in the Q-$\underline{c_2}$ oxidoreductase of <u>Rps. sphaeroides</u> (6-9).

Scheme I $\underline{b}_{562}$ $Q_z^{\cdot}$ Q_zH_2 $\rightarrow$ FeS $\rightarrow \underline{c}_1 \rightarrow \underline{c}$

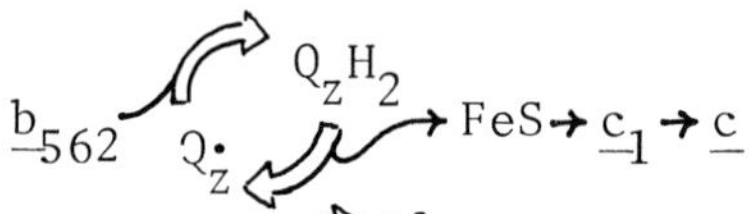

Scheme II $Q_I \rightarrow Q_{II}$ Q_y $Q_y^{\cdot}$ $\underline{b}_{562}$

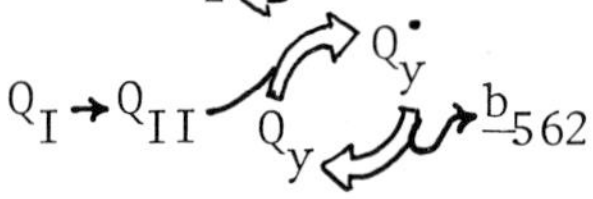

Scheme III $\underline{b}_{562}$ $\underline{b}_{566}$ Q_z $Q_z^{\cdot}$ Q_zH_2 $\rightarrow$ FeS $\rightarrow \underline{c}_1 \rightarrow \underline{c}$

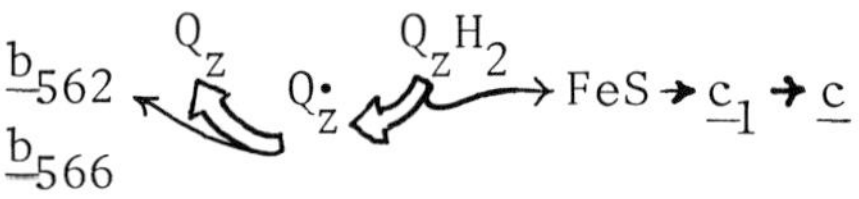

Scheme IV $\underline{b}_{562}$ (red) $\underline{b}_{566}$ Q_z $Q_z^{\cdot}$ Q_zH_2 $\rightarrow$ FeS $\rightarrow \underline{c}_1 \rightarrow \underline{c}$

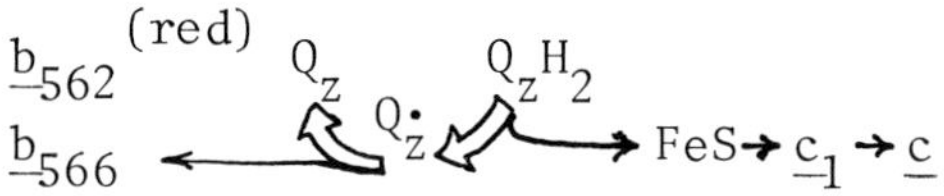

Four partial reactions of electron transfer in Q-$\underline{c}$ oxidoreductase suggested by flash-activated experiments at various ambient redox potentials prior to activation. Solid arrows represent electron transfer between redox components. Open arrows indicates the changes of redox states of the quinones which are the focus of attention in the text.

LINEAR ELECTRON TRANSFER FROM CYTOCHROME $\underline{b}_{562}$ <u>VIA</u> Q_z TO CYTOCHROME $\underline{c}$. Starting with cytochrome $\underline{b}_{562}$ reduced (trace taken at 5 mV; Fig. 2A) the flash elicits rapid cytochrome $\underline{c}$ oxidation followed by millisecond re-reduction that matches cytochrome $\underline{b}_{562}$ oxidation. The electron transport sequence is considered to be that shown in Scheme I. Since $\underline{b}_{562}$ oxidation matches cytochrome $\underline{c}$ reduction, the reactions involving Q_z are seen as the rate limiting step. Note that the re-reduction of cytochrome $\underline{b}_{562}$ after this sequence (Fig. 2A) is slow despite the low redox state of the system. The same results have been obtained <u>in vivo</u> with <u>Rps. sphaeroides</u> (11).

REDUCTION OF CYTOCHROME b_{562} VIA REDUCING SIDE OF RC; RECOG-
NITION OF ANOTHER QUINONE SPECIES? By omitting cytochrome c
from the system we abolish the oxidizing equivalent that
would be presented to the Q-c oxidoreductase. Starting in
the presence of ferricytochrome b_{562} and Q_z (i.e., Q_z oxidized)
(trace taken at E_h 140 mV; Fig. 3A) cytochrome b_{562} is reduced
milliseconds after the flash and the re-oxidation is slow as
was encountered under similar conditions in Fig. 2A. However

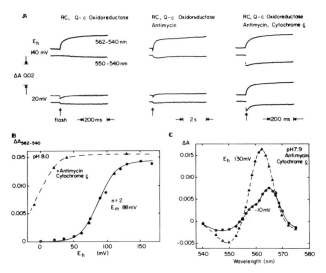

Fig. 3   Kinetics (A), E_h dependence (B) and spectra (C) of
         cytochrome b reduction in RC and Q-c oxidoreductase
         with and without cytochrome c and antimycin. (A) 4
         μM (in c_1) Q-c oxidoreductase, 1 μM RC were mixed
         in 3 mM Tris-HCl pH 8.0 and redox mediators as in
         Fig. 2. 8 μM cytochrome c and 20 μM antimycin were
         present where indicated. 550-minus-540 nm measure-
         ments are for cytochrome c and c_1 changes which are
         only seen in the presence of cytochrome c. (B) E_h
         dependence of extent of cytochrome b reduction 200
         ms after flash activation in the mixture of RC and
         Q-c oxidoreductase without (●) and with cytochrome
         c and antimycin (▲). (C) Spectra of flash-induced
         cytochrome b reduction in the complete system with
         antimycin at different E_h values.

in contrast to Fig. 2A, an increase in the rate of re-oxidation of flash reduced cytochrome b_{562} is not seen when Q_zH_2 (i.e., Q_z reduced) is present; nor is net oxidation of cytochrome b_{562} encountered when it is reduced prior to the flash (trace at 20 mV; bottom left of Fig. 3A). This is consistent with Scheme I in which the source of cytochrome b_{562} oxidation is flash oxidized cytochrome c acting through the $Q_zH_2/Q_z^{\cdot}$ couple. However we unexpectedly find that the E_h dependence of the flash induced cytochrome b_{562} reduction does not follow the Nernst curve of cytochrome b_{562} (E_{m8} 40 mV; n=1); it follows an E_{m8} of about 90 mV (n=2). Since this value is some 30 mV higher than that of the Q_zH_2/Q_z couple we might tentatively suggest that it may represent another quinone (we shall tentatively call it Q_y) which acts as a $Q_y^{\cdot}/Q_y$ couple between Q_{II} and cytochrome b_{562} as shown in Scheme II. It has to be concluded that when already reduced to Q_yH_2 prior to the flash single electron transport to cytochrome b_{562} is impeded; this may be the reason for the slow re-reduction of flash oxidized cytochrome b_{562} in Scheme I. Similar results to those in this section have been obtained in vivo with cytochrome c_2 depleted membranes of Rps. sphaeroides (data not presented).

REDUCTION OF CYTOCHROME b_{562} AND CYTOCHROME b_{566} VIA THE OXIDIZING SIDE OF THE RC; "OXIDANT INDUCED REDUCTION". In contrast to the reductive route of cytochrome b reduction when Q_z is oxidized prior to activation (Fig. 2A 150 mV, and Fig. 3A 140 mV[2]), an oxidative route for cytochrome b reduction is possible when Q_z is reduced as shown in Fig. 3A, 20 mV.

[2]At 140 mV antimycin slows down cytochrome b reduction rate when there is no cytochrome c there about ten times (note that the timescale in the middle traces of Fig. 3A is different from others). Reason unknown.

As described in the previous section, no cytochrome b reduction can be observed in the system without cytochrome c at
20 mV both in the absence and presence of antimycin (Fig. 3A,
left and middle bottom). However, on addition of cytochrome c
to the system, the flash elicits cytochrome b reduction
as well as rapid oxidation of cytochrome c followed by partial
re-reduction (Fig. 3A, right bottom). Because of the pronounced
effect of the cytochrome c addition and the kinetic similarity
between the cytochrome b reduction and the cytochrome c rereduction (Fig. 3A, right bottom), there is good reason to believe that cytochrome b reduction under these conditions is at
least in part caused by oxidative side reactions as Schemes
III and IV[3]. When more than 80% of cytochrome b_{562} is already
reduced before activation the flash reduced species is predominantly cytochrome b_{566} (Fig. 3C, -10 mV), whose spectrum
is quite different from that taken at 130 mV which is dominated by b_{562}. At E_h 20 mV, the spectrum shows the mixture of
b_{566} and b_{562} reduction (data not presented).

In Rps. sphaeroides in the presence of antimycin, flash
induced cytochrome b_{560} and b_{566} reduction is observed without
concomitant reduction of cytochrome c even when Q_z is reduced.
Therefore, it would appear that an electron from the reducing
side (Q_{II}) is available for cytochrome b_{560} and b_{566} even when
Q_z is reduced prior to activation. However, the following
observations suggest that all cytochrome b reduction is at
least initiated by the "oxidant-induced" route when Q_zH_2 is
present before activation.

---

[3]Only because no clear evidence is available for direct electron transfer between cytochrome b_{562} and b_{566}, we depicted
the schemes in parallel separately instead of in series as
$Q_z \rightarrow b_{566} \rightarrow b_{562}$ or $Q_z \rightarrow b_{562} \rightarrow b_{566}$.

1) There is no flash induced cytochrome $\underline{b}$ reduction in Rps. sphaeroides preparations without cytochrome $\underline{c}_2$ when Q_z is reduced (data not presented).

2) With subsaturating flash (30% saturation) in the presence of antimycin (8) or near saturating flash in the presence of diphenylamine and antimycin (data not presented) quantitative parallel reductions of cytochrome $\underline{b}$ and $\underline{c}$ are observed following the flash in Rps. sphaeroides.

3) When Q_zH_2 is present, UHDBT inhibits cytochrome $\underline{b}$ reduction at exactly the same concentration which inhibit the FeS $\rightarrow \underline{c}_1$ reaction (12).

4) pH dependence of cytochrome $\underline{b}$ reduction rate when Q_z is reduced is similar to cytochrome $\underline{c}$ re-reduction rate, but has opposite tendency to pH dependence of cytochrome $\underline{b}$ reduction rate when Q_z is oxidized (data not presented; some suggestions in ref. 12).

LOCATION OF THE ELECTROGENIC REACTIONS.   The transmembrane electrogenic reaction associated with Q-$\underline{c}$ oxidoreductase has been studied using electrochromic bandshift of intrinsic carotenoid pigments as a "voltmeter" in the in vivo system of Rps. sphaeroides (4, 7, 13).   The electrogenic reaction, which is antimycin sensitive and kinetically separable from rapid electrogenic reactions associated with the RC, is coincident with the oxidation (trace taken at -50 mV) but not reduction (trace at 180 mV) of cytochrome $\underline{b}_{560}$ (analogous to mitochondrial $\underline{b}_{562}$; see Fig. 1) as shown in Fig. 4A and has been shown in ref. 5 and 11.   Comparison of the E_h dependence of the changes from 0.3 ms to 5 ms of both reactions (Fig. 4B and C) substantiates the conclusion that oxidation of cytochrome $\underline{b}_{560}$, but not reduction of cytochrome $\underline{b}_{560}$, is associated with the

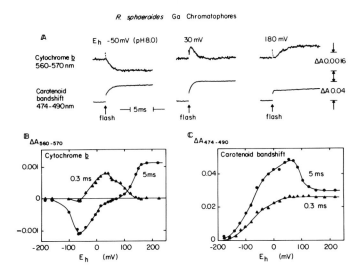

Fig. 4   Comparison of cytochrome b redox changes and electrogenic reactions (carotenoid bandshift) in chromatophores of Rps. sphaeroides Ga. Chromatophores (BChl,
40 μM) were suspended in 10 mM Tris-HCl, pH 8.0 and
100 mM KCl. 5 μM each of DAD, PMS, PES, pyocyanine
and 2 hydroxy-1,4-naphthoquinone were present as redox
mediators. 10 μM valinomycin was also added in the
cytochrome b measurements. [Cytochrome b kinetics in
the absence of valinomycin after the first flash is
similar to that in the presence of valinomycin but requires a correction for bacteriochlorophyll red shift
(11)]. (B) and (C) E_h dependence of time resolved extents of the changes after the flash activation.

electrogenic reaction. In a direct study on the reaction
sequence of Scheme III, evidence suggests (8) that an electrogenic reaction does not occur in Rps. sphaeroides under conditions that promote this reaction sequence. Thus the electrogenic reaction appears to be coupled to the oxidation of
cytochrome b_{560}.

THE ANTIMYCIN INHIBITOR SITE. The effects of antimycin on the
Q-c oxidoreductase are manifold. In Rps. sphaeroides it in-

duces a red shift in the α-band of cytochrome b_{560} (8) and
leads to the inhibition of cytochrome b oxidation, the electrogenic reaction and proton (H^+_{II}) binding and at least
partial inhibition of cytochrome c reduction. In the mitochondrial system, although electrogenic reactions and H^+ binding have not yet been examined following single turnover activation, antimycin induces a red shift in the α-band of cytochrome b_{562} and elicits responses in the flash activated
kinetics of cytochromes b and c that are similar to the photosynthetic counterparts. An additional effect in mitochondria
is the destabilization of a semiquinone which may be Q_z (13).
Because one antimycin molecule binding per Q-c oxidoreductase
is enough for all the effects (8) the site of action of antimycin is considered to affect cytochrome $b_{560(562)}$ oxidation
and whatever is coupled to it. Indeed the primary effect of
antimycin may not be the electron transfer inhibition itself,
but a coupled reaction (2).

THE UHDBT INHIBITOR SITE. In Rps. sphaeroides UHDBT has been
shown to inhibit flash activated electron transfer from FeS
to cytochrome c (10). Similarly we have shown (data not
presented) with the mitochondrial Q-c oxidoreductase that
UHDBT inhibits the reduction of flash oxidized cytochrome c.
The effects of UHDBT are consistent with Scheme I (no cytochrome b_{562} oxidation starting with cytochrome b_{562} reduced
before activation) and Schemes III and IV (no oxidant induced
reduction of either cytochrome b_{562} and b_{566}) (see 12 for
Rps. sphaeroides). We also observed reactions in Scheme II
were not inhibited so strongly as reactions in Scheme I, III,
and IV in the mitochondrial system.

CONCLUSIONS

1.   The Q-c (c_2) oxidoreductase from mitochondria and Rps. sphaeroides are remarkably similar when activated by the RC; though differences in detail are expected we believe that two systems can usefully be considered interchangeably.

2.   Cytochrome b can be reduced in two ways: by reducing side route (Scheme II) or by oxidizing side route (Scheme III). In Rps. sphaeroides we have also known that neither of these electron transfer routes includes an electrogenic step (see ref. 8). The electrogenic step(s) in Rps. sphaeroides appear to occur as a result of cytochrome b_{560} oxidation, and it seems reasonable to consider that the same will be true for cytochrome b_{562} oxidation in mitochondria.

3.   The conclusion on the location of the electrogenic step deserves considerations in respect to current models of electron and proton transfer in Q-c oxidoreductase. Q-cycle schemes (15) which have cytochrome b_{562} reduction as the electrogenic step may not fit the above conclusion. In "linear" schemes (5), oxidant induced reduction should lead to a reversed electrogenic reaction. In the ideas of electrogenic H^+ pump associated with the b-cytochromes (16), there is a restriction that the actual electrogenic step will not occur until the oxidation of cytochrome b_{562}. A proton pump model in which Q_z is the functional redox element has been constructed at least to be consistent with the above conclusion (2, 3).

ACKNOWLEDGMENTS

    We are grateful to Ms. Angela Smallwood for preparations of Q-c oxidoreductase, RC and chromatophores, to Ms. Peggi Mosley for preparing the manuscript, and to Drs. D. O'Keefe, R. Prince, J. Bowyer, D. Tiede, and N. Packham for suggestions and discussions. Supported by NIH PHS GM 27309.

REFERENCES

1 Packham, N.K., Tiede, D.M., Mueller, P., and Dutton, P.L. (1980) Proc. Natl. Acad. Sci. USA 77, 6339-6343
2 Matsuura, K., Packham, N.K., Tiede, D.M., Mueller, P., and Dutton, P.L. (1981) in Function of Quinones in Energy Conserving Systems (Trumpower, B.L., ed.), Academic Press, NY, in press
3 Matsuura, K., Packham, N.K., Tiede, D.M., Mueller, P., and Dutton, P.L. (1981) Biophys. J. 33, 102a
4 Jackson, J.B. and Dutton, P.L. (1973) Biochim. Biophys. Acta 325, 102-113
5 Crofts, A.R., Crowther, D., and Tierney, G.V. (1975) in Electron Transfer Chains and Oxidative Phosphorylation (Quagliariello, E., ed.), pp. 233-241, North Holland, Amsterdam
6 Prince, R.C., Bashford, C.L., Takamiya, K., van den Berg, W.H. and Dutton, P.L. (1978) J. Biol. Chem. 253, 4137-4142
7 Bashford, C.L., Prince, R.C., Takamiya, K., and Dutton, P.L. (1979) Biochim. Biophys. Acta 545, 223-235
8 van den Berg, W.H., Prince, R.C., Bashford, C.L., Takamiya, K., Bonner, W.D., Jr. and Dutton, P.L. (1979) J. Biol. Chem. 254, 8594-8604
9 Takamiya, K., Prince, R.C., and Dutton, P.L. (1979) J. Biol. Chem. 254, 11307-11311
10 Bowyer, J.R., Dutton, P.L., Prince, R.C. and Crofts, A.R. (1980) Biochim. Biophys. Acta 592, 445-460
11 O'Keefe, D.P. and Dutton, P.L. (1981) Biochim. Biophys. Acta 635, 149-166
12 Bowyer, J.R. and Crofts, A.R. (1981) Biochim. Biophys. Acta, in press
13 Jackson, J.B. and Crofts, A.R. (1969) FEBS Letts. 4, 185-189
14 Ohnishi, T. and Trumpower, B.L. (1980) J. Biol. Chem. 255, 3278-3284
15 Mitchell, P. (1976) J. Theor. Biol. 62, 327-367
16 Wikström, M. and Krab, K. (1980) Curr. Topics in Bioenergetics 10, 51-101
17 Rieske, J.S. (1967) Methods in Enzymology 10, 239-245

INTRAMEMBRANE VS. TRANSMEMBRANE pH GRADIENTS IN PHOTOPHOSPHORYLATION[1]

Richard E. McCarty

Section of Biochemistry, Molecular and Cell Biology
Division of Biological Sciences
Cornell University
Ithaca, NY 14853

Within ten years of its original formulation (1), Peter Mitchell's chemiosmotic theory (2) describing the coupling between light-driven electron flow and ATP synthesis in chloroplast thylakoid membranes had been accepted by most investigators of photophosphorylation. This relatively rapid acceptance is not too surprising since a number of the early experiments that provided evidence for the concept that artificial electrochemical proton gradients can drive phosphorylation were carried out with thylakoids (3,4). In the past decade, excellent evidence for the role of transmembrane electrochemical gradients in photophosphorylation has accumulated (5,6).

The viewpoint, first set forth by Williams (7), that protons localized within the membrane are used for ATP

---

[1] Supported by NSF Grant PCM79-11476.

V. P. Skulachev and Peter C. Hinkle (eds.), Chemiosmotic Proton Circuits in Biological Membranes
in honor of Peter Mitchell   ISBN 0-201-07398-6

synthesis increased in popularity during the middle 1970's.
Robertson and Boardman (8) postulated that protons are
carried from the outer aqueous phase to a hydrophobic region
within the membrane via plastoquinone. They further proposed that the protons could combine with a small, lipophilic molecule which by rapid lateral diffusion could carry
protons to the sites of ATP synthesis. In principle, protons
could also be carried on fixed negative charges on the
interior surface of the thylakoid membrane. On the basis of
experiments with acetic anhydride modification of thylakoid
membrane proteins (9,10), Dilley and his coworkers have
proposed that protons released by the oxidation to water to
oxygen are released in a domain that is not readily accessible to protons released by the actions of photosystem I.
Finally, an extensive study of the onset of phosphorylation
by Ort et al. (11,12) led to the conclusion that protons may
be used by the ATPase complex in ATP synthesis before they
appear in the intrathylakoid aqueous compartment.

    In this brief article, I will discuss experiments con-
ducted with thylakoids, that deal with the protons in membrane controversy. On the balance, there appears to be no
unequivocal evidence that intramembrane protons gradients
participate in photophosphorylation. Fillingame's recent
review (13) contains a discussion of the protons in membrane
controversy for other coupling membranes.

ONSET OF PHOTOPHOSPHORYLATION AND ΔpH

    As early as 1970, photophosphorylation was studied with
different regimes of flashing light and Junge (14) concluded
that a mimimum critical electrochemical potential gradient

is required for photophosphorylation. Reasoning that the
onset of ATP synthesis should correlate to the rise of the
electrochemical proton gradient, Ort et al. (11,12) investigated the amount of ATP formed as a function of flash
duration. The rise time of the transmembrane electric
potential difference ($\Delta\psi$) is fast (15) and since $\Delta\psi$ can
drive ATP synthesis (16) the onset of ATP synthesis would
also be expected to be rapid. In agreement with this
notion, Ort and Dilley (11) and later Vinkler et al. (17)
and Davenport and McCarty (18) found that ATP synthesis
proceeds promptly after initiation of illumination. A short
lag is noted, however. This lag may be attributed at least
in part to the conversion of the ATPase complex to a form
active in ATP synthesis (19). For reasons that are unclear,
Chow et al. (20) observed a longer lag.

In the presence of valinomycin and K^+ or of anions
known to permeate thylakoid membranes rapidly, Ort et al.
(11,12) observed that about 40 to 50 ms was required before
phosphorylation commenced. Under these conditions, the
development of $\Delta\psi$ would be discouraged and in chemiosmotic
terms, the transmembrane proton activity gradient (ΔpH)
would provide the driving force for ATP synthesis. This
view is consistent with the sensitivity of photophosphorylation to nigericin (17). At short times, nigericin which
catalyzes an electroneutral exhange of H^+ for K^+, has little
effect on photophosphorylation. In longer periods of
illumination, however, phosphorylation is very sensitive to
nigericin.

So far the results are readily interpreted within the
framework of the chemosmotic hypothesis. It was, however,
somewhat surprising that the lag time for the development of

ATP synthesis in the presence of valinomycin and K^+ was only 50 ms. Assuming an H^+/e stoichiometry of two for electron transport from water to a photosystem I electron acceptor such as methyl viologen, and an average rate of electron transport of 1000 $\mu eq \cdot hr^{-1} \cdot mg$ chlorophyll^{-1}, approximately 0.4 s would be required to accumulate 200 neq of H^+ from the medium. At external pH of 8.0, H^+ uptake of 200 neq·mg chlorophyll^{-1} is often observed. Most of these protons are sequestered by buffering groups on the thylakoid membrane. Thus, a relatively massive accumulation of protons is required to generate a significant ΔpH.

An increase in the internal buffering capacity should cause a longer delay of the onset of ATP synthesis, provided valinomycin and K^+ were present. Phosphorylation driven by $\Delta\psi$ should be independent of the buffering capacity. Ort et al. (12) showed that a number of buffers including Tris, phosphate and imidazole can equilibrate across the thylakoid membrane. A rough calculation of the time required to overcome this buffering by these reagents can be made. Under conditions where a lag on the order of seconds was expected, Ort et al. (12), observed that the buffers caused a further delay in the onset of ATP synthesis of only a few milliseconds. They therefore concluded that protons can be used by the ATPase complex before they equilibrate with the internal thylakoid aqueous compartment.

This conclusion has been challenged. The amounts of ATP formed in very short periods of illumination are small. To increase the amount of ATP made, Ort et al. (11,12) used multiple flashes separated by a dark period of 15 s. Although they concluded that 15 s was long enough to allow the ΔpH generated in the previous flash to decay completely, this conclusion appears to be incorrect. Chow et al. (20) monitored ΔpH using the internal pH-indicating dye neutral red and the flurorescent amines, atebrine and N-(1-napthyl) ethylene diamine. Although whether the response of these indicators gives a quantative estimate of the rise of ΔpH may be questioned, there is little doubt that ΔpH gradually rises during sequential flash activation. With flashes of only 1 ms separated by a 20 s dark time, a significant ΔpH as was detected by the quenching of the fluorescence of the amines. A disturbing feature of these experiments, however, was that 2 mM imidazole, a permeant buffer, did not delay the development of ΔpH. Moreover, phosphorylation had very little effect on the ΔpH monitored by these reagents. However, even when a slowly responding technique was used, the flash regime used by Ort et al. (11,12) was found to generate significant ΔpH values (18).

Another indication that ΔpH increased with flash number is that the amount of ATP synthesized per flash is not independent of the number of flashes given, but increases with increasing flash number (18).

Thus, it seems likely that multiple flash activation as used by Ort et al. (11,12) would result in an underestimation of the time required for phosphorylation to start. Experiments with single flashes support this conclusion. Chow et al. (20), who used the luciferin/luciferase system to measure ATP synthesis, found a 0.4 s lag when valinomycin and K^+ were present. Vinkler et al. (21) and Davenport and McCarty (18) detected lags of similar magnitudes. These lags are consistent with the time required to generate ΔpH. Moreover, permeant buffers increased the lag in these single flash experiments as predicted if ΔpH drives ATP synthesis

(18,21). A comparison of the lags obtained by the different groups is given in Table 1. Some variation in the lag is to be expected since it depends on a number of factors including temperature, light intensity, passive proton permeability of the membrane and internal buffering capacity.

Table 1. Lag times observed in the onset of ATP synthesis

Conditions	Flash Regime	Approximate Lag (ms)	Ref.
Control	multiple	5	(12)
valinomycin and K^+	multiple	40	(12)
2 mM imidazole	multiple	5	(12)
imidazole + valinomycin and K^+	multiple	50	(12)
Control	single	150	(20)
valinomycin and K^+	single	400	(20)
Control	single	<10	(21)
valinomycin and K^+	single	100	(21)
2 mM imidazole + valinomycin and K^+	single	250	(21)
Control	single	<10	(18)
valinomycin and K^+	single	230 – 630	(18)
2 mM imidazole + valinomycin and K^+	single	1300 – 1600	(18)

Data were obtained at high light intensity, in the pH range of 7.8 - 8.0 and using methylviologen as the electron acceptor.

Thylakoids form substantial amounts of ATP in the dark after they have been illuminated in the presence of a mediator of electron flow (3). That this post-illumination ATP synthesis is driven by ΔpH is supported by a number of different kinds of experiments. Vinkler et al. (21) used post-

illumination ATP formation as a measure of the time required
to generate a transmembrane ΔpH sufficient to drive phosphorylation. In the presence of valinomycin and K^+, post-
illumination ATP synthesis and photosphosphorylation showed
very similar lags. Moreover, permeant buffers increase the
lags for the onset of both phosphorylation reactions by a
similar extent. Thus, the single flash experiments give
clear support for transmembrane pH gradients as the driving
force for photophosphorylation.

Chow et al. (20) also measured the rate at which phosphorylation, assayed in the presence of valinomycin and K^+,
decays after switching off the light. They reasoned that
ATP synthesis should stop abruptly if it is being driven by
a small pool of intramembrane protons, but that it should
last a longer time if the larger pool of protons on the
thylakoid interior is involved. Unfortunately, the scatter
in the data points was such that an accurate determination
of the post-illumination ATP synthesis could not be made.
This approach, however, may not be a satisfactory one for
differentiating between the possibilities. Illumination
induces an ATPase activity which decays in the dark (22) and
this fact will obscure the true rate of ATP synthesis. In
addition, phosphorylation is apparently sharply dependent on
ΔpH (23) and a drop in ΔpH of only 0.1 unit should cause a
decrease in photophosphorylation rate of 50%.

CHEMICAL MODIFICATION

Acetic anhydride has little effect on photosystem II-
dependent electron transport in the light or the dark. If,

however, uncouplers were present, the treatment of thylakoids with 3.5 mM acetic anhydride in the dark for 45 s
resulted in substantial inhibition of oxygen evolution.
Uncouplers also increased by 20-40% the incorporation of
acetate into the thylakoids incubated with acetic anhydride
in the dark and the extent of the inhibition was correlated
with the extent of the enhancement of incorporation (10).
Acetic anhydride reacts with unprotonated amino groups in
addition to other functional groups in proteins. By increasing the pH in the environment of lysine residues required in some way for activity, uncouplers could increase
the proportion of these residues in the reactive, unprotonated form.

Illumination in the presence of uncouplers, at concentrations which are sufficient to elicit anhydride inhibition but which do not abolish proton uptake, prevented the
inhibition of photosystem II-dependent electron transport
(10). In the presence of low uncoupler concentrations,
cyclic electron flow around photosystem I failed to protect.
The action of photosystem II and associated oxygen evolution
was blocked by dichlorophenyl dimethyl urea. In the absence
of this inhibitor, light protection was observed. The
extent of proton uptake, measured with a pH electrode, were
adjusted to be equal for the two conditions of electron
transport by varying the light intensity.

An uncoupler stimulation of incorporation of [^{3}H]-
acetate into a hydrophobic protein of 8,000 molecular weight
was also reported (9). This protein may be the dicylco-
hexylcarbodiimide-reactive protein of the F_o portion of the
chloroplast ATPase complex which acts as a transmembrane
proton channel.

If the protection afforded by illumination is caused by
protonation of essential NH_2 groups, these results could
mean that the protons formed by water oxidation are released
at a site not readily approached by protons formed inter-
nally by the action of photosystem I. It is, however, very
difficult to exclude the possibility that changes in the
conformation of proteins elicited more directly by photosystem II electron transport are the cause of the differential modification by the anhydride. For example, the activity of a protein kinase bound to thylakoid membranes is
influenced by the oxidation state of plastoquinone (24).
Moreover, the inhibition could be influenced by the presence
of the dichlorophenyl dimethyl urea which was present when
the effects of photosystem I alone were determined, but
absent when the effects of both photosystems were assayed.

Protons formed by the two photosystems appear to be
equivalent in their effects on delayed fluorescence of
photosystem II (25). Moreover, protons from photosystem II
are released very rapidly. Using neutral red as an indicator
of the internal pH, Junge (14) estimated that water protons
are released within 1 ms after a brief flash. In inverted
thylakoids Tiemann, Renger and Gräber (personal communication) showed that proton release into the suspending medium,
as monitored by changes in the absorbtion of bromocresol
purple, occurred with a half-time of 600 µs after a 250 µs
lag.

The rates of ATP synthesis driven by electrochemical
proton gradients generated artificially across thylakoid
(26) and submitochondrial particle (27) membranes are at
least as fast as those driven by electron flow. Thus,
transmembrane gradients are kinetically competent to drive

phosphorylation. In addition, photophosphorylation is extremely sensitive to gramicidin, which forms a transmembrane ion channel. In the presence of 1 mM NH_4Cl and at saturating light intensity, full uncoupling of photophosphorylation occurs at 10-20 nM gramicidin, an amount equivalent to 1 gramicidin per 3 to 6 x 10^3 chlorophyll molecules or 1 gramicidin per 4 to 7 ATPase complexes. At lower light intensity, photophosphorylation is even more sensitive to gramicidin.

In summary, the evidence suggests that transmembrane gradients drive ATP synthesis in chloroplast thylakoids. There may be compartments or wells within the thylakoid membrane with high local proton concentrations which do not equilibrate rapidly with the internal proton pool. However, the relevance of these domains to photophosphorylation remains to be established. It should be emphasized, however, that the fact that transmembrane gradients are involved in ATP synthesis does not exclude the possibility that a special mechanism(s) for proton conductance within the membrane exists.

REFERENCES

1. Mitchell, P. (1961) Nature 191, 144-48.
2. Mitchell, P. (1966) Biol. Rev. Cambridge Philos. Soc. 41, 445-502.
3. Hind, G. and Jagendorf, A.T. (1963) Proc. Natl. Acad. Sci. US 49, 715-722.
4. Jagendorf, A.T. and Uribe, E. (1966) Proc. Natl. Acad. Sci. US 55, 170-177.
5. Avron, M. (1978) FEBS Lett. 96, 225-232.
6. Portis, A.R. Jr. and McCarty, R.E. (1976) J. Biol. Chem. 251, 1610-1617.
7. Williams, R.J.P. (1962) J. Theor. Biol. 3, 209-229.

8. Robertson, R.N. and Boardman, N.K. (1975) FEBS Lett. 60, 1-6.
9. Prochaska, L.J. and Dilley, R.A. (1978) Biochem. Biophys. Res. Commun. 83, 664-672.
10. Baker, G.A., Bhatnagar, D. and Dilley, R.A. (1980) Biochemistry 20, 2307-2315.
11. Ort, D.R. and Dilley, R.A. (1976) Biochim. Biophys. Acta 449, 95-107.
12. Ort, D.R., Dilley, R.A. and Good, N.E. (1976) Biochim. Biophys. Acta 449, 108-124.
13. Fillingam, R.H. (1980) Ann. Rev. Biochem. 49, 1079-1113.
14. Junge, W. (1970) Eur. J. Biochem. 14, 582-592.
15. Junge, W. (1977) Ann. Rev. Plant Physiol. 28, 503-536.
16. Witt, H.T., Schlodder, E. and Gräber, P. (1976) FEBS Lett. 69, 272-276.
17. Vinkler, C., Avron, M. and Boyer, P.D. (1979) FEBS Lett. 96, 129-134.
18. Davenport, J.W. and McCarty, R.E. (1980) Biochim. Biophys. Acta 589, 353-357.
19. Harris, D.A. and Crofts, A.R. (1978) Biochim. Biophys. Acta 502, 87-102.
20. Chow, W.S., Thorne, S.W. and Boardman, N.K. (1978) in Frontiers of Biological Energetics (P.L. Dutton, J.S. Leigh and A. Scarpa, eds) Vol. 1, pp 287-296, Academic Press, New York.
21. Vinkler, C., Avron, M. and Boyer, P.D. (1980) J. Biol. Chem. 255, 2263-2266.
22. Jagendorf, A.T. and Hind, G. (1963) in Photosynthetic Mechanism of Green Plants, pp 599-610. National Academy of Sciences: National Research Council Publication 1145.
23. Portis, A.R. Jr. and McCarty, R.E. (1974) J. Biol. Chem. 249, 6250-6254.
25. Bowes, J.M. and Crofts, A.R. (1978) Z. Naturforsch. 33C, 271-275.
26. Smith, D.J., Stokes, B.O. and Boyer, P.D. (1976) J. Biol. Chem. 251, 4165-4171.
27. Thayer, W.S. and Hinkle, P.C. (1975) J. Biol. Chem. 250, 5336-5342.

BACTERIORHODOPSIN PHOTOCYCLE AND STOICHIOMETRY

Walther Stoeckenius, Richard H. Lozier,

and Roberto Bogomolni

Department of Biochemistry and Cardiovascular Research
Institute, University of California,
San Francisco, CA 94143

INTRODUCTION. Bacteriorhodopsin (bR) is found in crystalline patches – known as the purple membrane – in the cell membrane of halobacteria. It is a retinylidene protein of 26000 molecular weight and functions as a light-driven proton pump. Its retinal chromophore causes a strong broad absorbance band in the green region of the spectrum. In purple membrane that has been exposed to light, the absorbance maximum is at 568 nm and the molar extinction coefficient is $\varepsilon = 63000 \ M^{-1}cm^{-1}$. The amino acid sequence of the protein is known and low dose electron microscopy has shown that its polypeptide chain traverses the membrane in seven α-helical segments. A short N-terminal segment is exposed on the external surface and a 17 amino acid long C-terminal segment occurs on the cytoplasmic surface. The highly negatively charged lipids of the membrane are arranged in the typical bilayer. The retinal, which is bound

V. P. Skulachev and Peter C. Hinkle (eds.), Chemiosmotic Proton Circuits in Biological Membranes
in honor of Peter Mitchell   ISBN 0-201-07398-6

as a protonated Schiff base to the ε-amino group of a lysine
residue is apparently buried in the protein interior and not
readily accessible from the aqueous environment on either side
of the membrane. The isolated purple membrane is obtained in
the form of crystalline sheets, which contain approximately
75% by weight bacteriorhodopsin and virtually no other protein. A small contamination with other surface membrane components is usually found, but typically does not amount to
more than a few percent. Lipid vesicles can be formed by the
incorporation of additional lipid into the purple membrane or
by the complete solubilization of bR and reconstitution with a
wide variety of natural and synthetic membrane lipids. Typically the preferential orientation of bR in the vesicles is
the opposite of that found in the bacterial cell, i.e. in
intact cells or envelope vesicles illumination causes proton
translocation out of the cell, while in lipid vesicles protons
are translocated into the lumen. In intact cells the energy
of the resulting electrochemical gradient is used for the synthesis of ATP, the generation of other ion gradients, the
transport of amino acids and presumably also locomotion. In
lipid vesicles photophosphorylation has been demonstrated
after incorporation into the bR-vesicles of the H^+-ATPase from
mitochondria, chloroplasts or other bacteria. A more detailed
account and references can be found in several recent reviews
(1-6).

Several light-induced reactions of bR are known. When
purple membrane suspensions are kept in the dark the absorbance decreases by 15% and the absorption maximum shifts to
558 nm. At the same time the all-trans retinal of the light-
adapted purple membrane isomerizes to a 1:1 mixture of 13-cis
and all-trans. This is known as dark-adaptation. At room

temperature and neutral pH dark-adaptation is a slow process
with a half time of approximately 40 min. The reverse process, light-adaptation, occurs much faster (7,8). However
light-dark adaptation cannot account for the observed proton
translocation unless an extremely high stoichiometry is
assumed. Reasonable stoichiometries require a fast cyclic
photoreaction.

Both the 13-cis and all-trans retinal-containing bR
species do indeed undergo rapid cyclic reactions in the light
but it appears that only the all-trans bR translocates protons
(9,10). We shall therefore confine this review to light-
adapted purple membrane.

THE BACTERIORHODOPSIN PHOTOCYCLE. A unique model for the photocycle of light-adapted bacteriorhodopsin (bR_{570}^{LA}) can not be
determined directly from the observed absorbance changes.
Possible models can be based on light-induced absorbance
changes measured either kinetically using rapid kinetic optical absorption spectroscopy (11) or by scanning optical
absorption spectroscopy of purple membrane samples containing
intermediates trapped at low temperatures (see, e.g., references 12-14). However, in addition to the measured absolute
absorbance and absorbance changes, an estimate of the fraction
of the sample converted from bR_{570}^{LA} to the first intermediate
($x_{cycling}$) and a tentative model are needed to search for a
model consistent with the data. In our early work (12) we
assumed an unbranched unidirectional cycle and calculated the
fraction cycling from the maximal transient absorbance change
near 570 nm. This requires the further assumption that all of

the material cycling accumulates transiently in the "M_{412}" intermediate and that its absorbance does not overlap with bR_{570}^{LA} in the 570 nm region of the spectrum. We then proposed (12) a cycle

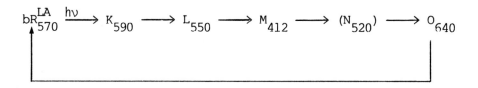

where the subscripts represent the calculated absorption maxima (in nanometers) for the intermediates. Calculated quantum efficiencies for the cycle depend on this model (15,16) and/or additional assumptions (13,17,18). Even in our early work (12) we noted that our assumptions were not quantitatively correct. Many papers have appeared which attempt to overcome the difficulties with this relatively simple model (for a recent review, see reference 6). However, a rigorous test of the proposed models with the available data has not been done. We have developed methods for more rigorous testing of proposed photocycle models. We extract the fundamental rate and amplitude parameters from the raw data (11,13,19) and test the consistency of specific models with the extracted parameters and additional explicitly stated assumptions such as "extinction coefficients must not be negative" and "the fraction cycling must not exceed unity" (19,20). Although we found no completely satisfactory model for a cycle which would fit our data (only unidirectional unbranched and unidirectional simply branched models were tested so far (20)), many features of the cycle proposed in 1975 (12) were confirmed.

Several authors have measured the kinetics of release and

uptake of protons from purple membrane during the photocycle using pH-indicating absorption or fluorescence dyes (12,21-23) or flash calorimetry (24). Except for a paper by Dencher and Wilms (22) there is general agreement that proton release precedes proton uptake and roughly correlates with the formation and decay of the M_{412} intermediate. There is quantitative disagreement, however. We (12,23) reported that the proton release is significantly slower than the rise of the 400 nm absorbance change whereas Ort and Parson (24) find the proton release to be faster than the absorbance change of bR at pH < 7.5 and slower than the absorbance change of bR at pH > 7.5. Chance et al (21) noted no difference in kinetics between the proton and absorption signals. These apparent discrepancies may be due to the different experimental conditions used in each case. Chance et al used much lower temperatures (-28 and $-40^{o}C$) and Dencher and Wilms lower pH (pH = 5.0) than the other authors. Dencher and Wilms reported that proton uptake preceded proton release and was kinetically similar to the rise and decay of O_{640} measured at 620 nm. We have never observed net proton uptake by purple membrane in flash experiments (reference (25) and other unpublished experiments attempting to reproduce Dencher and Wilm's result).

STOICHIOMETRY. The lack of a definitive model for the photocycle of light-adapted bR poses the most serious problem in all efforts to determine the stoichiometry of proton translocation by bR and to understand the energy transduction mechanism. While it is in principle possible to determine the number of protons translocated per absorbed photon ($\phi_{H}+$)

independent of such a model closed vesicular systems have to be used and these are necessarily less well defined in their physical properties than isolated purple membrane. The errors in the measured values of ϕ_H+ are large. It is usually not obvious to what extent differences in results may be attributed to light scattering effects, differences in ionic permeability, imperfect orientation of bR, presence of other pigments, differences in surface potential or differences in bR itself induced by the different environments. Moreover, measuring ϕ_H+ is valuable in determining the efficiency of light energy conversion, but is of little help in exploring its mechanism, for which we also need to know the quantum efficiency for cycling (ϕ_{cyc}). Most investigators determine ϕ_{cyc} by measuring the maximal absorbance change near 400 nm and calculating the molar concentration of M_{412} usually using a molar extinction coefficient for the absorbance change near 400 nm of $\Delta\varepsilon = 23000 \ M^{-1}cm^{-1}$ (23). The ratio of protons translocated to molecules of M intermediate generated, H^+/M, is then assumed to be equal to the number of protons translocated in one cycle (S_H+). For the time being we shall ignore the obvious problems arising from our incomplete knowledge of the photocycle, especially of branches in the cycle, which does not allow us to show conclusively that such a determination of M_{412} measures the molecules cycling. We shall furthermore use the quantum efficiency for cycling of 0.25 - 0.3 determined in several laboratories (15, 16) to calculate S_H+ when we compare experiments where ϕ_H+ rather than H^+/M has been measured. (However, as noted above, the reported values for ϕ_{cyc} are model dependent.) The number of protons translocated S_H+ is usually measured in closed systems in one or both compartments either with a pH electrode or by the absorbance

or fluorescence change of an indicator dye. Some investigators have used light-induced electric currents, or light-
induced conductivity or volume changes to estimate the number
of protons released or translocated balancing the obvious
advantages against the limitations of these techniques. A
critical analysis of these techniques is beyond the scope of
this review (see reference 11 for detailed discussion on H^+
stoichiometry measurements using indicator dyes). Most investigators have taken care to avoid the obvious pitfalls and the
remaining errors are probably small compared to those caused
by the problems mentioned earlier. In open systems $\phi_{H}+$ and
$S_{H}+$ can be determined directly only if the release and uptake
of protons do not overlap in time during the photocycle and if
no additional protons which are not transported across the
membrane are released and taken up during the photocycle (Bohr
protons).

   We divide the results to be discussed into seven groups
according to the experimental systems used. 1) Intact cells,
2) Cell envelopes, 3) Lipid vesicles containing bacteriorhodopsin, 4) Planar films containing bacteriorhodopsin,
5) Purple membrane sheets in suspension, 6) Ordered arrays
of purple membrane sheets, 7) Modified purple membrane
suspensions.

1) Intact Cells. Intact cells offer the advantage that one
may assume perfect orientation of the pigment in a native
environment and less unspecific "leakiness" of the permeability barrier than in other closed systems. The strong light
scattering and the presence of other pigments cause technical
difficulties but these can largely be overcome. More serious

is the problem that pH and potential gradients across the cell membrane exist even in starved anaerobic cells in the dark, which might change ϕ_{cyc} or S_H+, and that the light-induced proton outflow rapidly triggers inflows of protons. The first inflow usually occurs through the ATPase and through a second channel still unidentified in its function (Helgerson and Stoeckenius, submitted for publication). These can be blocked by phloretin or dicyclohexylcarbodiimide (DCCD) and triphenyl-tin chloride ($SnPh_3Cl$). The preexisting gradients can be reduced by manipulating the cell permeability with ionophores and changing external ion concentrations. Most investigators have tried to measure the initial rates of proton ejection and photon absorption simultaneously to obtain ϕ_H+ and then calculated S_H+ from ϕ_{cyc} obtained in other experiments (26–28). However, H^+/M has also been measured (29).

All investigators report similar results, with S_H+ values near 2.0 for the slightly acidic cell suspensions in the high salt medium necessary for cell survival. The actual numbers obtained in different experiments range from 1.3 to 2.6. Experimental errors are most likely to result in low estimates. The only obvious causes of a high estimate are an underestimate of ϕ_{cyc}, an overestimate of the buffering capacity (due possibly to a contribution to the buffering from the interior of the cell for the acid pulse calibrations but not for the time-resolved flash experiments), or an increasing dissociation of acidic surface groups during the course of illumination. The latter effect has been postulated to occur and will be discussed in more detail later. It should manifest itself in complex kinetics of the proton ejection, which are not observed and we think it is a highly unlikely proposition. Careful measurements of ϕ_{cyc} in intact cells have not been reported in detail but the flash experiments of Govindjee et al (29) measuring H^+/M also gave values very close to 2.0. Hartmann et al (26) used $\phi_{cyc} = 0.8$ and concluded that only 1 H^+ was translocated per cycle. However, their measured value of 0.4 to 0.6 for ϕ_{H^+} is perfectly in line with all other reported experiments and yields values of 1.3 to 2.0 for S_{H^+} when the now generally accepted ϕ_{cyc} ~0.3 is used.

Only Renard and Delmelle have measured ϕ_{H^+} over a range of pH values in intact cells, and report that S_{H^+} dropped from 2.1 to 0.9 between pH 6.0 and pH 8.0. An increase in the preexisting protonmotive force with increasing pH has not been observed and they suggest that the observed decrease in cycling rate with increasing pH could explain the result. This conflicts with their observation that the rate of proton outflow increases linearly with light intensity; cycling time can, therefore, not be limiting (although they do not explicitly state that this also holds for high pH values). If light saturation at higher pH values and a pH dependence of ϕ_{cyc} can be ruled out, a decrease of S_{H^+} with increasing pH will have to be accepted. From a physiologic point of view an obvious need exists for a control mechanism to prevent excessive alkalinization of the cell interior when cells in slightly alkaline brine are exposed to bright light, a condition likely to occur in their natural environment.

2) Cell Envelopes. These preparations usually obtained by sonication and subsequent differential centrifugation have the advantage that the composition of the internal and external medium can be controlled but some misorientation of bacteriorhodopsin and/or "leakiness" causes problems. The

leakiness may range from the presence of proton-specific channels caused by the loss of the ATPase headpiece (which is con-
trollable by the addition of DCCD) to the complete permeability of broken vesicles. Nevertheless, in the only determination we are aware of the values for ϕ_{H^+} are similar to those
obtained in cells, 0.58 to 0.71, yielding S_{H^+} values of 1.9 to
2.8 assuming ϕ_{cyc} = 0.25 to 0.3 (27). Again the most likely
errors would lead to an underestimate of S_{H^+}.

3) Lipid Vesicles. Misorientation of bR is the most serious
problem in lipid vesicles. The techniques usually used yield
preparations where the preferential orientation of bR is
inside-out with a very small internal volume. Reliable data
cannot be expected from initial rate measurements. Flash
spectroscopy with indicator dyes shows that a small acidification precedes the larger alkalinization of the outside medium.
This acidification has been attributed to the minority of
right-side-out bR molecules and was used to correct the
results for the misorientation (23,29). We calculate H^+/M =
1.25 from our earlier data at low ionic strength (23); Govindjee et al (29) find H^+/M = 2.3 using, however, a slightly
higher molar extinction coefficient of $\Delta\epsilon$ = 30000 $M^{-1}cm^{-1}$.
They also tested the ionic strength dependence of this value
and found no change between 10 mM and 100 mM KCl, the highest
concentration used.

4) Planar Films. These systems have the advantage that conditions on both surfaces of the membrane can be independently
controlled, and concentration changes, potentials and currents

can be measured with high sensitivity and good time resolution by electrodes. However, to measure ϕ_{H^+} (or H^+/M) the amount and orientation of the bacteriorhodopsin present must be known. The only system in which the latter condition is fulfilled is that of Korenbrot (30) which consists of purple membrane fragments embedded in a lipid bilayer and resting on a thin, highly permeable nitrocellulose support film. The concentration of the purple membrane and its orientation are determined by electron microscopy and the concentration confirmed by absorbance measurements. At pH 5.8 the initial rate of photocurrent rise increases linearly with light intensity and measurements with the film directly applied to a pH electrode show that all of the current is accounted for by the protons accumulating on the glass electrode surface. These data should exclude cooperativity of pumping and contributions of Bohr protons due to net protonation changes on the membrane surface at least for the conditions tested. Unfortunately, due to an arithmatic error the reported value of $S_{H^+} \sim 2.0$ is ten times to high. The low stoichiometry actually observed is presumably caused by the relatively high permeability of the planar film assembly (J.I. Korenbrot personal communication).

5) <u>Purple</u> <u>Membrane</u> <u>Sheets</u> <u>in</u> <u>Suspensions</u>. Many more experiments have been done with this preparation than with any of the others. Even though this is an "open" system translocated protons can be detected if after a short actinic flash their release and uptake from opposite sides of the membrane can be time-resolved or if a deprotonated intermediate can accumulate under photosteady state conditons. While the optical

conditions for measuring photointermediate concentrations and
pH indicator dye changes are far better than in any of the
systems discussed above, the limitations of purple membrane
suspensions are nevertheless severe and mainly for three obvious reasons. Firstly, the isolated membrane sheet may differ
fundamentally from the purple membrane patch embedded in the
cell membrane or artificial lipid bilayer. We think this is
unlikely because the photoreaction cycle appears to be essentially the same in all systems tested. Secondly, protons from
protonation changes of groups which are not part of the
proton-conducting path across the membrane (i.e. Bohr protons)
may obscure the appearance and disappearence of the transported protons. Thirdly, release and uptake of translocated
protons on opposite sides of the membrane may be simultaneous
or near simultaneous processes and, therefore, not be detectable at all in an open system, or yield values which are too
low. The appearance of Bohr protons and the timing of transported proton release and uptake should depend on conditions
such as pH and ionic strength. It is, therefore, not surprising that the reported results vary much more widely than in
any of the other systems. In most cases protons released (or
taken up) per molecule of M intermediate formed (H^{+}/M) was
measured directly either after a flash or under photosteady
state conditions and the reported values range from 500 to 0.
The extreme values have been obtained in photosteady state
experiments but no values significantly above 2.0 resulted
from flash experiments. Furthermore, at acidic pH a proton
uptake rather than release was observed in the photosteady
state (31,32) and an uptake of protons preceded their release
in flash experiments (22). In photosteady state conditions
the change from release to uptake is usually seen between pH 5

and 6 and at temperatures between $0^{\circ}C$ and room temperature.
It can, however, occur at higher pH when the temperature is
raised (33). One would expect low pH to accelerate the uptake
and high pH to accelerate the release of transported protons
at the membrane surfaces. Moreover, proton uptake before
release in flash experiments or net uptake in the photosteady
state are obtained under conditions which favor the accumulation of intermediate O in the photoreaction cycle, and O is
presumably a reprotonated species. (However, we have not been
able to detect net proton uptake during the photocycle under
conditions which favor the accumulation of O.) The results
are, therefore, at least qualitatively easily understood and
it seems unnecessary to invoke the participation of Bohr protons. However, it follows that to determine S_{H^+} in purple
membrane suspensions one should work at pH and temperature
conditions where release and uptake are well separated. Complications arise at pH 4.0 due to the formation of a new bacteriorhodopsin species (34-36) and only the high pH range is
of physiologic significance. We shall, therefore, limit our
discussion to experiments carried out in the near neutral and
slightly alkaline pH range. Also in this region, ϕ_{cyc} and the
rate of cycling are essentially ionic strength- and pH-
independent.

The extremely high H^+/M values of up to 500 have all been
reported by Caplan's group at the Weizmann Institute and
explained as due to Bohr protons. Very few details on the
technically difficult experiments are given, which involve
measuring absorbance changes in the 10^{-3} O.D. range in
strongly scattering, aggregating membrane suspensions (32,37-
39). We have tried to repeat these experiments and obtained
H^+/M values in the range 0.2 to 2.0. As far as we know, no

other reports have confirmed the high values reported by
Caplan's group. We are at loss to explain them and shall not
consider them here any further. A review of these results can
be found in (3).

The first S_H+ values were obtained from flash experiments
with purple membrane suspensions at low ionic strength and
with low light intensities (12,23). The release and uptake of
protons were found to be slightly slower than the formation
and decay of M_{412} respectively. The experimental value of
$H^+/M = 0.7$, when corrected for the overlap in release and
uptake, yielded $S_H+ = \sim 1$. The experimental value was soon
confirmed by others for comparable conditions not only in
flash but also in photosteady state experiments (29,40,41).
However, the later results also revealed that the measured S_{H+}
values strongly depend on experimental conditions, especially
on ionic strength. Increasing the salt concentration
increases S_{H+} to about twice the value found at low salt and
the effect saturates between 0.2 M and 0.4 M NaCl or KCl.
Kuschmitz and Hess using photosteady state measurments of M
and ΔpH in addition report an effect of light intensity and
their values range from 0.33 at low ionic strength and light
saturation to 3.0 at low light intensity and high ionic
strength (Hess, personal communication). A similar effect of
light intensity was observed by Ort and Parson (40) in flash
experiments and explained as due to photoreaction of intermediate K which is known to cause rapid reformation of bR_{570}
without translocation of protons. This explanation does not
hold for the results of Hess and Kuschmitz, who measured H^+/M,
unless photoproducts of intermediates contribute to the absorbance at the wavelength where M is measured. This seems possible because at high light intensities under photosteady

state conditions photoproducts of later intermediates in the
photoreaction cycle can be expected to appear. Hess and
Kuschmitz, however, attribute the light intensity as well as
the ionic strength effects at least partly to Bohr protons and
propose that three different proton pools exist, which can
contribute protons to the translocating groups and exchange
protons with the medium. They show that, given light-
activated dissociable surface groups, the ionic strength
effects in a first approximation fit the classic Gouy-Chapman
theory. They also report differences in the H^+/M ratio and M
decay kinetics at high but not at low ionic strength under
prephotosteady state conditions. They explain these observations by assuming a proton pool from which M is reprotonated,
but which cannot be replenished fast enough from the medium,
so that after a small number of photocycles it becomes rate-
limiting and delays proton release and M decay. This means
that, at least at high ionic strength, photosteady state and
flash experiments are not comparable, a notion also strongly
expounded by Caplan's group (37).

However, this explanation of the observations encounters
a number of difficulties. As already pointed out by Ort and
Parson groups releasing or binding Bohr protons whould have to
shift their pK_a from > 7.8 to < 6.0 when transferred from
10 mM to 200 mM KCl. Also, the results obtained with planar
films (30) and lipid vesicles (29) so far fail to show any
evidence for Bohr protons. Finally, we have carried out photosteady state and flash experiments with the same preparation
at low ionic strength, varying light intensity (over a limited
range) and pH. We found H^+/M = 0.6 at pH 7.8 (figure 1), a
result not significantly different from our earlier flash
experiments (12, 23). There was no light intensity effect

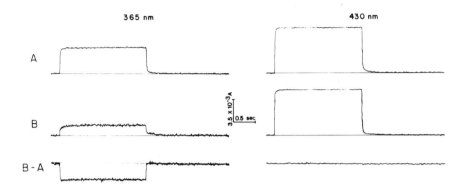

Fig. 1 Light-induced absorbance changes of purple membrane
(2.7 μM in bR) in aqueous suspensions (pH 7.8, 21°C)
without (A) and with (B) the pH indicator 7-
hydroxycoumarin (~10^{-4} M). Measurements were made at
365 nm to observe proton release (B-A) and at 430 nm
to determine M concentration. The actinic light
source was a 450 W Xenon lamp with heat reflecting
filters and a broad band interference filter
(575+/-25 nm). The actinic light was turned on and
off with an electromechanical shutter (opening and
closing time ~1 msec). The traces are the average of
32 pulses at a repetition rate of 0.2 Hz.

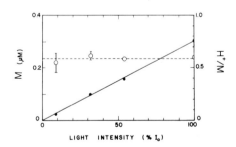

Fig. 2 Concentration of M in the photostationery state (left
ordinate) and H^+/M (right ordinate) versus light
intensity, from the data of fig. 1 and additional
experiments at lower light intensities. M concentra-
tion was calculated assuming $\Delta\varepsilon_{430}$ = 23000. H^+/M was
calculated using the above and the observed ΔA_{365} in
trace A-B (fig. 1) and the ΔA_{365} of sample B induced
by acid and alkali pulses (data not shown).

above the error limits of our experiment (see figure 2); the M
kinetics in flash and photosteady state experiments were
indistinguishable. Our own experiments with purple membrane
suspended at high salt concentrations have not yielded reliable results so far. Another attractive possibility to
account for the salt effect is provided by the proposition
which Kell (42) used to explain the large discrepancy which
can often be observed in mitochondria and chromatophores
between measured proton motive force and ATP synthesis. Based
on electrode theory he proposes that protons ejected from a
membrane can be trapped in a potential well at the negatively
charged membrane surface but have a high lateral mobility.
This would explain why Govindjee et al observed no effect of
ionic strength on H^+/M in lipid vesicles where the highly
negatively charged purple membrane lipids have mostly been
replaced by egg lecithin, which carries no net charge. Should
the pH effect observed by Renard and Delmelle (28) prove to be
a true change in stoichiometry, the salt effect could be
attributed to the same mechanism. The purple membrane is
obviously uniquely suited to further test this theory.

6) Ordered Arrays of Purple Membrane Sheets. Preparations
with nearly perfect parallel alignment of the sheets all facing in the same direction can be obtained by exposing suspensions to electric fields or by collecting on a support suc-
cesive layers of a surface film containing purple membrane
sheets embedded in a monomolecular lipid film (32,43,44). In
aqueous suspension and in fully hydrated multilayers photocycle reaction kinetics are readily measured and show no
dramatic change from unoriented suspensions. With electrodes

on both sides of the ordered membrane stacks light-induced
charge movements may also be followed. Keszthelyi and Ormos
(64) used pulsed electric fields synchronized with laser
flashes and found a net movement of one elementary charge over
10 nm per bR molecule cycling. Since the membrane is only
5 nm thick they conclude that two protons are moved across the
membrane in one cycle.

7) Modified Purple Membrane. The kinetics of the photoreaction cycle can be profoundly modified while only minor changes
occur in the absorption spectrum of bR. One of the most sensitive reactions appears to be the decay of M, which often
seems to be significantly retarded. (It should be noted, however, that it is also the most easily observed reaction and in
most cases no systematic investigation of the other reactions
has been reported). Thus M can accumulate in significant concentrations even at physiologic temperatures and relatively
low light intensities. There is no a priori reason why S_H^+
should not be affected when the photocycle kinetics are
changed, but whether or not it actually changes is of considerable interest. H^+/M measurements for two such preparations
have been reported. Bakker and Caplan (45) partially delipidated purple membrane with cholate and substituted a variety
of natural and synthetic lipids. If the ratio of lipid to bR
is not much larger than in purple membrane the preparations
retain their sheet structure and do not close up to form vesicles. The experiments were carried out at salt and buffer
concentrations of 150 mM to 300 mM. The H^+/M values observed
are highly pH-dependent in the range of pH 5.0 to 8.5 and
decrease with increasing temperature. Maximal values for

dipalmitoylphosphatidylcholine-substituted purple membrane reached values of 1.5. The experiments are complicated by the only partially reversible formation of a species absorbing maximally at 470 nm with unknown photoreactivity.

Addition of the cyclic depsipeptides valinomycin and beauvericin in combination and in a 1:1 molar ratio to bacteriorhodopsin causes a large increase in the photosteady state accumulation of M and a parallel increase in medium acidification. The effect is independent of medium pH between pH 5.6 and 7.8 and requires a small amount of K^+. The H^+/M value is 0.2 in 3 mM KCl but increases to 0.7 if salt is added. The increase saturates at ~75 mM NaCl but divalent cations are considerably more effective and 10 μM $La(NO_3)_3$ is sufficient for a maximal response (46). The authors assume an allosteric effect of salt on the release site for the translocated proton. It is, however, known that La^{3+} in μM concentrations inhibits proton pumping but only when added to the cytoplasmic side of the purple membrane (47). It is, therefore, more likely that the measured H^+/M ratio results from an overlap of proton release and uptake and that the increase caused by La^{3+} is due to an inhibition of proton uptake.

CONCLUSIONS. The rather wide range of measured S_H^+ values could reflect a variable stoichimetry of the proton pump. There is no obvious reason to assume that it must be fixed; it could conceivably not even be an integer. However, in the closed systems discussed, where presumably only transported protons are measured, most recent experiments yield S_H^+ values close to 2.0. A notable exception is Renard and Delmelle's value of ~1.0 at alkaline pH, which clearly needs further study. On the other hand, in nearly all of the experiments with purple membrane suspensions, an underestimate of S_H^+ is much more likely than an overestimate and the usually used molar extinction coefficient of $\Delta\varepsilon = 23000$ $M^{-1}cm^{-1}$ to calculate M concentration or $\phi_{cyc} = 0.3$ to calculate S_H^+ may also give slightly low values. S_H^+ values higher than 2.0 can, therefore, not be dismissed lightly. The values determined in purple membrane suspensions vary even more widely. The lower values can readily be explained by time overlap between the release and uptake of protons or in photosteady state experiments by the presence of photocycle intermediates other than M_{412}; a contribution by Bohr protons need not be invoked, and there is recent experimental evidence against it. The higher values are, therefore, the more significant ones and most of them are close to 2.0, in good agreement with measurements on closed systems. Again there is the significantly higher value of 3.0 reported by Kuschmitz and Hess for low light intensity and high ionic strength, which is not readily explainable as an artifact.

Whether S_H^+ is variable remains to be seen. The cell clearly has a need to control the rate of pumping, but the decrease in the rate of cycling at alkaline pH and the photoreactions of intermediates may suffice to accomplish this. If the pump is tightly coupled one would also expect it to slow down under a load and this has been experimentally demonstrated (reference 48 and Dancshazy and Helgerson, unpublished results). If the pump is tightly coupled at least under low load conditions one would also like to think that S_H^+ is an integer, but this is not necessarily so. One can postulate, for instance, that during a photoreaction cycle one proton is

moved completely and another one only partially across the
membrane. This would require differences in successive
cycles, which though unlikely can not be ruled out. More
likely are branching points in the cycle, which can totally or
partially short circuit the H^+ translocation, and the decrease
of S_H^+ from 2.0 to 1.0 at alkaline pH is a strong argument
that such branching does occur. Nevertheless, the most important result of the data reviewed is that the available evidence presently suggests that at least two protons are
translocated in every complete photocycle in high salt solutions and near neutrality.

The stoichiometry S_H^+ is, of course, crucial for our
efforts to understand the mechanism of this proton pump. The
observation that more than one proton may be translocated in
one photoreaction cycle severely affects our ideas about the
mechanism of proton pumping in bR. Most of the many tentative
models advanced so far are more or less extensive modifications of an early rough model proposed by us but not explicitly published until 1978 (49,50). It was based on the
observation that the Schiff base is transiently deprotonated
during the photoreaction cycle (51) and assumed an isomerization of the chromophore to provide the driving force and
prevent backreactions. The postulated transient isomerization
was later confirmed experimentally (52-54). The proton conduction to and from the Schiff base was attributed to two
chains (or limited networks) of hydrogen-bonded groups connecting the Schiff base to either the cytoplasmic or the
external membrane surface depending on the isomeric configuration. Schulten (55,56) has carried out detailed calculations
for energy barriers and pK changes during isomerizations of
the chromophore. He demonstrated the feasibility of the

pumping mechanism and reasonable agreement of calculated with observed kinetics and absorbance changes. Nagle and collaborators (57,58) have developed the theory for proton conduction across membranes by hydrogen-bonded chains and shown that several mechanisms based on such "proton wires" may drive an uphill transport of protons. Lewis et al (59) postulated that a second lysine and an arginine residue were involved in the protonation changes at the Schiff base. Their model also takes account of the observation that a proton transfer reaction may occur in the protein before Schiff base deprotonation (60). However, this mechanism is not compatible with recent resonance Raman data on ^{15}N-lysine substituted purple membrane (61).

These models are attractive because they can explain how protons are translocated without large conformational changes in the protein, which are a priori unlikely because of the protein lattice structure in purple membrane and because no large changes in chromophore angle occur during the photocycle (13). They cannot account, of course, for the translocation of more than one proton in one photoreaction cycle. However, even before the stoichiometry problem arose, certain other difficulties became obvious. A fast light-driven back-reaction from M_{412} to bacteriorhodopsin is difficult to account for (62) and a search for possible proton wires in bacteriorhodopsin have failed so far to turn up any sufficiently long structures (63). Most seriously, Keszthelyi and Ormos (64) observed that charge movement through the membrane appeared to be synchronized with the absorbance changes during the photoreaction cycle, which is clearly incompatible with a model postulating the existence of permanent proton wires connecting the Schiff base to both surfaces.

The latter difficulty can be overcome if one replaces the permanent proton wires by short segments which are formed and broken in the appropriate sequence during the photocycle. The higher stoichiometry may be explained by assuming that the pK of a second group close to the Schiff base may also be changed during the chromophore isomerization. A model based on the observation that a transient deprotonation of a tyrosine residue occurs during the photocycle (65, 66) has been proposed (62). The recent observation that a migration of the Schiff base from one lysine residue to another may occur during the photocycle (67, 68) could also be used to construct models with a stoichiometry of 2 H^+ per cycle still using the general principles we originally invoked. Models that do not postulate that the Schiff base proton is the transported proton can, of course, explain higher stoichiometries quite readily. For instance Nagle's model of driving proton translocation in a proton wire through protein conformational changes could easily add a second "wire". A similar but much less detailed proposition by Dunker and Marvin (63) offers the same advantage. However, at present it seems best to await the completion and confirmation of new results, such as the possible transimination reaction of retinal during the photocycle and the considerably improved structural data (69, 70), before serious further attempts in model building are undertaken.

This work was supported by NIH grant GM-27057 and NASA grant NSG-23206.

REFERENCES

1. Stoeckenius, W., Lozier, R.H. and Bogomolni, R.A. (1979) Biochim. Biophys. Acta 505, 215-278.
2. Stoeckenius, W. (1980) Account. Chem. Res. 13, 337-344.
3. Eisenbach, M. and Caplan, S.R. (1979) in Current Topics in Membranes and Transport (F. Bonner, A. Kleinzeller, ed.), pp. 165-250, Academic Press, New York NY.
4. Lanyi, J.K. (1978) Microbiological Reviews 4, 682-706.
5. Lanyi, J.K. (1980) in Membrane Proteins in Energy Transduction (R.A. Capaldi, ed.), pp. , Marcel Dekker, New York NY.
6. Ottolenghi, M. (1980) Adv. Photochem. 12, 97-200.
7. Sperling, W., Carl, P., Rafferty, C.N. and Dencher, N.A. (1977) Biophys. Struct. Mech. 3, 79-94.
8. Casadio, R. and Stoeckenius, W. (1980) Biochemistry USA 19, 3374-3381.
9. Ohno, K., Takeuchi, Y. and Yoshida, M. (1977) Biochim. Biophys. Acta 462, 575-582.
10. Lozier, R.H., Niederberger, W., Ottolenghi, M., Sivori-novsky, G. and Stoeckenius, W. (1978) in Energetics and Structure of Halophilic Microorganisms (S.R. Caplan, M. Ginzburg, ed.), pp. 123-141, Elsevier/North-Holland Biomedical Press, Amsterdam, The Netherlands.
11. Lozier, R.H. (1981) Methods in Enzymology, in press.
12. Lozier, R.H., Bogomolni, R.A. and Stoeckenius, W. (1975) Biophys. J. 15, 955-962.
13. Lozier, R.H. and Niederberger, W. (1977) Fed. Proc. 36, 1805-1809.
14. Becher, B., Tokunaga, F. and Ebrey, T.G. (1978) Biochemistry USA 17, 2293-2300.
15. Goldschmidt, C.R., Kalisky, O., Rosenfeld, T. and Ottolenghi, M. (1977) Biophys. J. 17, 179-183.
16. Becher, B. and Ebrey, T.G. (1977) Biophys. J. 17, 185-191.
17. Goldschmidt, C.R., Ottolenghi, M. and Korenstein, R. (1976) Biophys. J. 16, 839-843.
18. Hurley, J. and Ebrey, T. (1978) Biophys. J. 22, 49-66.
19. Lozier, R.H. and Nagle, J.F. (1980) Fed. Proc. 39, 1964.
20. Nagle, J.F., Parodi, L.A. and Lozier, R.H. (1981) Biophys. J., accepted for publication.
21. Chance, B., Porte, M., Hess, B. and Oesterhelt, D. (1975) Biophys. J. 15, 913-917.
22. Dencher, N. and Wilms, M. (1975) Biophys. Struct. Mech. 1, 259-271.

23. Lozier, R.H., Niederberger, W., Bogomolni, R.A., Hwang, S.B. and Stoeckenius, W. (1976) Biochim. Biophys. Acta 440, 545-556.

24. Ort, D.R. and Parson, W.W. (1978) J. Biol. Chem. 253, 6158-6164.

25. Lozier, R.H., Niv, H., Hwang, S.B., Havel, P., Bogomolni, R.A. and Stoeckenius, W. (1979) Biophys. J. 25, 77a.

26. Hartmann, R., Sickinger, H.D. and Oesterhelt, D. (1977) FEBS Lett. 82, 1-6.

27. Bogomolni, R.A., Baker, R.A., Lozier, R.H. and Stoeckenius, W. (1980) Biochemistry USA 19, 2152-2159.

28. Renard, M. and Delmelle, M. (1980) Biophys. J. 32, 993-1006.

29. Govindjee, R., Ebrey, T.G. and Crofts, A.R. (1980) Biophys. J. 30, 231-242.

30. Korenbrot, J.I. and Hwang, S.B. (1980) J. Gen. Physiol. 76, 649-682.

31. Fischer, U.C. and Oesterhelt, D.O. (1980) Biophys. J. 31, 139-146.

32. Eisenbach, M., Garty, H., Klemperer, G., Weissmann, C., Tanny, G. and Caplan, R. (1977) in Bioenergetics of Membranes (L. Packer, ed.), pp. 119-128, Elsevier/North-Holland Biomedical Press, New York NY.

33. Garty, H., Klemperer, G., Eisenbach, M. and Caplan, S.R. (1977) FEBS Lett. 81, 238-242.

34. Lozier, R.H., Chae, Q., Mowery, P.C. and Stoeckenius, W. (1978) in Energetics and Structure of Halophilic Microorganisms (S.R. Caplan, M. Ginzburg, ed.), pp. 297-301, Elsevier/North-Holland Biomedical Press, Amsterdam, The Netherlands.

35. Mowery, P., Lozier, R., Chae, Q., Tseng, Y., Taylor, M. and Stoeckenius, W. (1979) Biochemistry USA 18, 4100-4107.

36. Fischer, U. and Oesterhelt, D. (1979) Biophys. J. 28, 211-230.

37. Caplan, S.R., Eisenbach, M. and Garty, H. (1978) in Energetics and Structure of Halophilic Microorganisms (S.R. Caplan, M. Ginzburg, ed.), pp. 49-66, Elsevier/North Holland Biomedical Press, Amsterdam, The Netherlands.

38. Klemperer, G., Eisenbach, M., Garty, H. and Caplan, S.R. (1978) in Energetics and Structure of Halophilic Microorganisms (S.R. Caplan, M. Ginzburg, ed.), pp. 291-296, Elsevier North/Holland Press, Amsterdam, The Netherlands.

39. Eisenbach, M., Garty, H., Bakker, E.P., Klemperer, G., Rottenberg, H. and Caplan, S.R. (1978) Biochemistry USA 17, 4691-4698.

40. Ort, D.R. and Parson, W.W. (1979) Biophys. J. 25, 341-353.
41. Hess, B. and Kuschmitz, D. (1978) in Frontiers of Biological Energetics (P.L Dutton, J.S. Leigh, A. Scarpa, ed.), pp. 257-264, Academic Press, New York NY.
42. Kell, D.B. (1978) Biochim. Biophys. Acta 549, 55-99.
43. Keszthelyi, L. (1980) Biochim. Biophys. Acta 598, 429-436.
44. Hwang, S.B., Korenbrot, J.I. and Stoeckenius, W. (1978) Biochim. Biophys. Acta 509, 300-317.
45. Bakker, E.P. and Caplan, S.R. (1978) Biochim. Biophys. Acta 503, 362-379.
46. Avi-Dor, Y., Rott, R. and Schnaiderman, R. (1979) Biochim. Biophys. Acta 545, 15-23.
47. Drachev, L.A., Frolov, V.N., Kaulen, A.D., Liberman, E.A., Ostroumov, S.A., Plakunova, V.G., Semenov, A.Y. and Skulachev, V.P. (1976) J. Biol. Chem. 251, 7059-7065.
48. Hellingwerf, K. (1979) Doctoral Thesis.
49. Kozlov, I.A. and Skulachev, V.P. (1977) Biochem. Biophys. Acta 463, 29-89.
50. Stoeckenius, W. (1978) in Energetics and Structure of Halophilic Microorganisms (S.R. Caplan, M. Ginzburg, ed.), pp. 185-198, Elsevier/North Holland Press, Amsterdam, The Netherlands.
51. Lewis, A., Spoonhower, J., Bogomolni, R.A., Lozier, R.H. and Stoeckenius, W. (1974) Proc. Natl. Acad. Sci. USA 71, 4462-4466.
52. Pettei, M.J., Yudd, A.P., Nakanishi, K., Henselman, R. and Stoeckenius, W. (1977) Biochemistry USA 16, 1955-1959.
53. Tsuda, M., Glaccum, M., Nelson, B. and Ebrey, T.G. (1980) Nature 287, 351-353.
54. Braiman, M. and Mathies, R. (1980) Biochemistry USA 19, 5421-5428.
55. Schulten, K. (1978) in Energetics and Structure of Halophilic Microorganisms (S.R. Caplan, M. Ginzburg, ed.), pp. 331-334, Elsevier/North-Holland Biomedical Press, New York NY.
56. Orlandi, G. and Schulten, K. (1979) Chem. Phys. Lett. 64, 370-374.
57. Nagle, J.F. and Morowitz, H.J. (1978) Proc. Natl. Acad. Sci. USA 75, 298-302.
58. Nagle, J.F., Mille, M. and Morowitz, H.J. (1980) J. Chem. Phys. 72, 3959-3971.
59. Lewis, A., Marcus, M.A., Ehrenberg, B. and Crespi, H. (1978) Proc. Natl. Acad. Sci. USA 75, 4642-4646.

60. Applebury, M.L., Peters, K.S. and Rentzepis, P. (1978) Biophys. J. 23, 375-382.
61. Rothschild, K.J., Argade, P.V., Kawamoto, A.H. and Herzfeld, J. (1980) Fed. Proc. 39, 1964.
62. Kalisky, O., Ottolenghi, M., Honig, B. and Korenstein, R. (1981) Biochemistry USA 20, 649-655.
63. Dunker, A.K. and Marvin, D.A. (1978) J. Theoret. Biol. 72, 9-16.
64. Keszthelyi, L. and Ormos, P. (1980) FEBS Lett. 109, 189-193.
65. Bogomolni, R.A., Stubbs, L. and Lanyi, J.K. (1978) Biochemistry USA 17, 1037-1041.
66. Hess, B. and Kuschmitz, D. (1979) FEBS Lett. 100, 334-340.
67. Ovchinnikov, Y.A., Abdulaev, N.G., Tsetlin, V.I. and Zakis, V.I. (1980) Bioorgan. Chem (USSR) 9, 1427-1429.
68. Katre, N., Wolber, P., Stroud, B. and Stoeckenius, W. (1981) Proc. Natl. Acad. Sci. USA in press.
69. Agard, D., and Stroud, R. (1981) J. Mol. Biol. in press.
70. Hayward, S. and Stroud, R. (1981) Biophys. J. in press.

STRUCTURE-TOPOGRAPHIC ANALYSIS OF BACTERIORHODOPSIN
BY MEANS OF PROTEOLYTIC ENZYMES

Yuri A. Ovchinnikov

Shemyakin Institute of Bioorganic Chemistry,
USSR Academy of Sciences, Moscow, USSR

INTRODUCTION

The 1978 Nobel Prize in Chemistry awarded to Peter
Mitchell was in recognition of his chemiosmotic hypothesis.
The study of bacteriorhodopsin and photophosphorylation in
halophilic microorganisms has proved brilliantly these
ideas. As is well known, bacteriorhodopsin functions as a
light-driven proton pump establishing a considerable pH
gradient across the membrane. The energy of this gradient
is used by the cell, particularly for the synthesis of ATP,
in complete agreement with Mitchell's hypothesis.

Elucidation of the mechanism of bacteriorhodopsin as a
proton pump is impossible without knowledge of its primary
structure and the topography of its polypeptide chain in the
membrane. Determination of the bacteriorhodopsin primary
structure (1) laid the basis for investigations of the protein three-dimensional structure. Experiments on limited
proteolysis of purple membranes by proteolytic enzymes
(Trypsin, Chymotrypsin and Papain) were a decisive factor in
this determination. This paper gives a detailed description
of these studies.

V. P. Skulachev and Peter C. Hinkle (eds.), Chemiosmotic Proton Circuits in Biological Membranes
in honor of Peter Mitchell   ISBN 0-201-07398-6

TRYPSIN - Analysis of trypsin action on bacteriorhodopsin
was carried out by electrophoresis in polyacrylamide gel in
the presence of sodium dodecyl-sulfate. In the course of
the reaction bacteriorhodopsin was transformed into a product of higher electrophoretic mobility. From the supernatant obtained after hydrolysis and centrifugation of
membranes a nine-membered peptide was isolated by thin-layer
chromatography on cellulose. Using Edman degradation the
following amino acid sequence was determined for this peptide: Ala-Gly-Asp-Gly-Ala-Ala-Ala-Thr-Ser (233-247) (Fig.
1). The peptide was the C-terminal protein fragment which
was formed as a result of the splitting of the bond Ser-Ala
(237-238). This bond is not hydrolyzed by trypsin with the
peptide Ala-Ile-Phe-Gly-Glu-Ala-Glu-Ala-Pro-Glu-Pro-Ser-Ala-
Gly-Asp-Gly-Ala-Ala-Ala-Thr-Ser which was isolated from
tryptic hydrolyzate of the delipidated bacteriorhodopsin.
The surface charge of the membrane probably alters the
trypsin specificity as shielding the surface charge with
0.15 M NaCl or 0.1 M ammonium bicarbonate buffer, pH 8.4,
inhibits the hydrolysis of the bond 237-238 of the bacteriorhodopsin molecule. (Trypsin activity on synthetic substrates
is well preserved under these conditions) (2).

α-CHYMOTRYPSIN - The treatment of purple membranes with
chymotrypsin digests the protein into two large fragments
(Fig. 1). There were no amino acids and peptides in the
supernatant obtained after membrane centrifugation. The
mixture formed after delipidation was subjected to Edman
automatic degradation. The amino acid sequence found is
Gly-Gly-Glu-Gln-Asn. The C-terminal amino acids: serine
and phenylalanine were established by hydrazinolysis. The

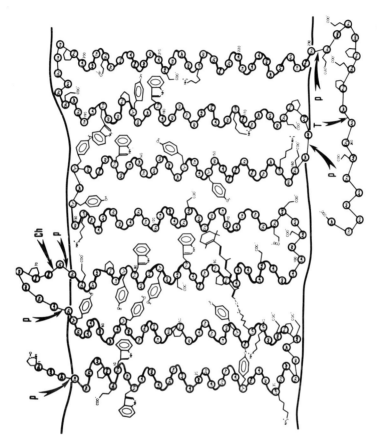

Figure 1. Disposition of the polypeptide chain of bacteriorhodopsin in the native purple membrane.

data obtained and information on bacteriorhodopsin structure
points to the fact that α-chymotrypsin cleaves only the bond
Phe-Gly (71-72). Even an increase of α-chymotrypsin concentration in the reaction medium (enzyme/membrane 1:1 mg/mg)
does not result in new bacteriorhodopsin fragments.

PAPAIN - A short treatment (2 hr) of purple membranes with
papain in an enzyme/membrane ratio of 1:200 (mg/mg) leads to
the splitting of 17 amino acids from the C-terminal region of
bacteriorhodopsin (231-247). From the supernatant obtained
after membrane centrifugation three peptides p-1, p-2, p-3
were isolated by chromatography and electrophoresis on cellulose thin layer plates. Using Edman degradation the following
amino acid sequences were established: Asp-Gly-Ala-Ala-Ala-
Thr-Ser (241-247), Ala-Pro-Glu-Pro-Ser-Ala (234-240) and Glu-
Ala-Glu (231-233). The C-terminal amino acid residue, glycine, was determined by hydrazinolysis on the fragment remaining in the membrane, while under the same conditions
serine was the C-terminal residue of the native protein. Thus
at least five C-terminal amino acids of bacteriorhodopsin
(243-247) can be split off by carboxypeptidase A, the region
237-238 is accessible to trypsin, while the 17 amino acids
split off with papain are most likely exposed into aqueous
medium.

The kinetics of bacteriorhodopsin hydrolysis with
papain in an enzyme/membrane ratio 1:20 (mg/mg) has shown that
the protein is transformed into a "heavy" fragment H'
(Fig. 2), identical with the one described above. This
fragment in its turn is cleaved in time into two other fragments - middle M and light L, which have correspondingly

glycine and isoleucine as N-terminal amino acids.

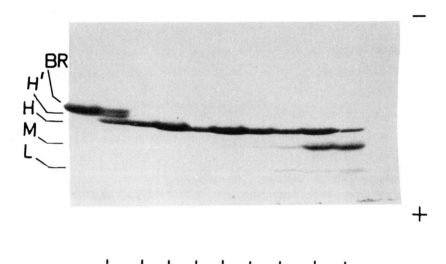

Analysis of amino acid cleavage in the process of hydrolysis of the fragment H' with papain is also confirmed by the structure analysis of the peptides isolated from the supernatant after membrane centrifugation.

Three peptides p-4, p-5, p-6 were isolated from the supernatant by peptide mapping on cellulose plates. Using Edman degradation there were established amino acid sequences of peptides p-4, p-5:Leu-Thr (66-67) and Val-Pro-

Phe-Gly (69-72) correspondingly. Pyroglutamic acid was found
as the N-terminal amino acid residue of peptide p-6 (treatment of the peptide with 1N NaOH or 1N HCl in MeOH, 48 hr,
20°). The peptide structure Glu-Ala-Gln (1-3) was determined
by means of Edman degradation with identification of PTH
derivatives of amino acids (3). The heavy fragment cleavage
to form M and L was successfully carried out with the use of
an enzyme/membrane ratio 1:2 (mg/mg) for 20 hr. The C-terminal amino acids:glycine and threonine were established by
hydrazinolysis on the mixture of middle and light fragments.
The fragments were separated by preparative electrophoresis
in polyacrylamide gels in the presence of sodium dodecyl-
sulfate. The N-terminal amino acid sequences for each fragment
were determined by automatic analysis.

For the middle fragment: ...Gly-Glu-Gln-Asn-Pro-
                           Ile-Tyr-Trp-Ala-Arg-Tyr-
                           Ala-Asp-Trp-Leu-Phe-Thr-
                           Thr-Pro-Leu

For the light fragment: Ile-Thr-Gly-Arg-Pro-Glu-
                          Trp-Ile

Analysis of the sequences of the isolated fragments and
information obtained on the bacteriorhodopsin primary structure permitted the localization of the sites of papain action:
Gln-Ile (3-4) and Gly-Gly (72-73). In order to determine the
fragment which splits off from the membrane upon papain
cleavage, the mixture of the middle and light fragments was
subjected to cyanogen bromide digestion. In particular,
peptides Leu-Leu-Gly-Tyr-Gly-Leu-Thr (61-67) and Leu-Leu-Gly-
Tyr-Gly (61-65) were isolated from the soluble part of hydrolyzate by gel-chromatography on Sephadex G-50 (superfine).

The results obtained indicate that the region of the bacteriorhodopsin molecule between Gly-65 and Gly-73 (Leu-Thr-Met-
Val-Pro-Phe-Gly) is cleaved in the course of papain action.

Membrane treatment with papain for 7 days in an enzyme/
bacteriorhodopsin ratio of 1:20 (mg/mg) leads to appearance
of a new band in polyacrylamide gel. The preparation also
contains the middle and light fragments. Glycine, isoleucine
and methionine were obtained as a result of the N-terminal
analysis of the fragment mixture; the C-terminal analysis by
hydrazinolysis gave glycine, serine and threonine. The
fragment mixture was subjected to Edman degradation after
delipidation. Besides the amino acid sequences already
found there was a new one Met-Arg-Pro. Thus the data on the
primary structure show that the cleavage of the bond Ser-Met
(161-162) takes place. This bond is not easily accessible
to protease. It should be noted that the papain treatment
resulting in the cleavage of the bond 3-4, site 68-72 and
removal of 17 C-terminal amino acids has no effect on the
functioning of bacteriorhodopsin as a proton pump (4).

Data obtained on bacteriorhodopsin proteolysis con-
triubted to elucidation of the protein primary structure.
Study of the papain fragments gave data on the disposition
of cyanogen bromide peptides. Determination of the primary
structure and the results on the investigation of limited
proteolysis of bacteriorhodopsin permitted a determination
of protein topograpy in the membrane. Taking into account
that the N- and C-terminal regions of the protein (20 amino
acids) are exposed to the membrane surface, each of the
seven segments with their junctions according to Henderson's
model (5) should contain on an average 32 amino acids. The
polypeptide fragment 65-73, susceptible to proteases, is

located between segments 2 and 3 from the N-terminal regions
of the protein, 161-162 is between segment 5 and 6; the
region 65-73 and the C-terminal "tail" of bacteriorhodopsin
should be on the opposite membrane surfaces. In order to
confirm this supposition we analyzed chymotrypsin and papain
effects on the vesicles obtained from the cells of Halobacterium halobium according to Blaurock et al. (6). Over
70% of the vesicles have the original orientation of the
membrane, i.e. similar to that in the cells. 90% of the
vesicles were sealed, and the treatment with proteolytic
enzymes had no effect on their integrity. The rates of
cleavage of the bond 71-72 with chymotrypsin on the vesicles
and membranes under the same conditions and splitting of the
17 C-terminal amino acids with papain on the same preparations allow the conclusion that the bond 71-72 and the C-
terminal region of bacteriorhodopsin are located on the
opposite membrane surfaces (the C-terminal on the cytoplasmic
surface; bond 71-72 on the outer surface). Membrane aggregation in 30 mM NaCl, 30 mM $MgSO_4$, 10 mM Tris HCl, pH 8.0 can
explain the fact that the rates of cleavage of the bond 71-72
with α-chymotrypsin in the vesicles and membranes differ with
the rate of hydrolysis of bacteriorhodopsin in the purple
membranes with α-chymotrypsin in 50 mM ammonium bicarbonate
buffer, pH 8.0, being significantly higher.

Analysis of the fragment, formed as a result of proteolysis of bacteriorhodopsin, permitted the localization of
segments of the polypeptide chain accessible to proteases and
apparently disposed on the membrane surface. These are
Glu-Ala-Glu-Ile (3-4), Gly-Leu-Thr-Met-Val-Pro-Phe-Gly (65-
73), Ser-Met (161-162) and Gly-Glu-Ala-Glu-Ala-Pro-Glu-Pro-
Ser-Ala-Gly-Asp-Gly-Ala-Ala-Ala-Thr-Ser (230-247).

These 33 amino acids compose 13% of the bacteriorhodopsin protein chain. Earlier Englander (7) showed that approximately 25% of the peptide bonds in the membrane are easily accessible to water. Thus, only a part of the bacteriorhodopsin molecule in contact with the aqueous phase, is accessible to proteolytic enzymes.

This study localized the sites of the polypeptide chain accessible to protease action and suggested a model of the arrangement of bacteriorhodopsin in the purple membrane (Fig. 1).

The new aspect of this model is that the Lys residue responsible for the binding of chromophore is located on the second α-helical segment and disposed closer to the membrane cytoplasmic surface.

It is known that retinal is bound to ε-amino group of Lys 41 via a protonated aldimine bond (1). Recently it was shown that the reduction of aldimine in bacteriorhodopsin in the light and in the dark leads to products containing the ε-N-retinyl-lysine at different sites of the polypeptide chain (8). Treatment of purple membranes in the light with NaBH$_4$, followed by cyanogen bromide cleavage of retinyl-bacterioopsin and separation of resultant peptides showed that retinal is attached to Lys 215 (9). This conclusion was confirmed by isolating the ε-N-retinyl derivative of H-Ala-Lys-OH from the pronase digest of the fragment 72-247.

Chymotrypsin-treated purple membranes contain functionally active bacteriorhodopsin cleaved into two fragments (1-71) and (72-247) (4). The aldimine groupings in the preparation can be reduced with NaBH$_4$ not only in the light but also in the dark (8,9). In the first case retinyl residues are located mainly at Lys 215 and in the second case - at

Lys 41.

The data suggest that N-N migration of retinal is likely to be a component of the photochemical and/or transport cycle of bacteriorhodopsin (10).

Elucidation of the migration process of retinal and the hypothesis about the migration in transport mechanism of bacteriorhodopsin are of great interest and can shed light on the determination of its functioning.

REFERENCES

1. Ovchinnikov, Yu.A., Abdulaev, N.G., Feigina, M.Yu., Kiselev, A.V. and Lobanov, N.A. (1979) FEBS Lett. 100, 219-224.
2. Gerber, G.E., Gray, C.P., Wildenauer, D. and Khorana, G.H. (1977) Proc. Natl. Acad. Sci. USA 74, 5426-5430.
3. Grinkevich, V.A., Arzamazova, N.M., Potapenko, N.A., Grinkevich, K.H., Kravchenko, Z.B., Feigina, M.Yu. and Aldanova, N.A. (1979) Bioorg. Khim. 5, 1757-1774.
4. Abdulaev, N.G., Feigina, M.Yu., Kiselev, A.V., Ovchinnikov, Yu.A., Drachev, L.A., Kaulen, A.D., Khitrina, L.V. and Skulachev, V.P. (1978) FEBS Lett. 90, 190-194.
5. Henderson, R. and Unwin, P.N.T. (1975) Nature 257, 28-31.
6. Blaurock, A.E., Stoeckenius, W., Oesterhelt, D. and Scherphef, G. (1976) J. Cell Biol. 71, 1-22.
7. Englander, S.W. and Englander, I.I. (1977) Nature 265, 658-659.
8. Ovchinnikov, Yu.A., Abdulaev, N.G., Tsetlin, V.I., Kiselev, A.V. and Zakis, V.I. (1980) Biooorg. Khim. 6, 1427-1429.
9. Shkrob, A.M., Rodionov, A.V. and Ovchinnikov, Yu.A. (1981) Bioorgan. Khim., in press.
10. Ovchinnikov, Yu.A., Abdulaev, N.G., Shkrob, A.M. and Tsetlin, V.I. (1981) FEBS Lett., in press.

THE LIGHT DRIVEN SODIUM PUMP OF HALOBACTERIUM HALOBIUM: ITS DISCOVERY AND SPECULATIONS ABOUT ITS BIOENERGETIC ROLE IN THE CELL

Russell E. MacDonald

Department of Biochemistry, Molecular and Cell Biology, Cornell University, Ithaca, NY 14853

When whole cells of Halobacterium halobium are illuminated anaerobically a complicated pattern of ion fluxes occurs which is accompanied by ATP synthesis (1). Until a few years ago it was assumed that these ion fluxes were dependent primarily on the operation of the proton pump, bacteriorhodopsin (bR). Illumination activates the bacteriorhodopsin photocycle, causing a rapid efflux of protons and forming an electrochemical proton gradient. Protons were proposed to return through an F_1ATPase, driving the synthesis of ATP (2), and an electrogenic Na^+/H^+-antiporter driving the efflux of sodium (3). Potassium uptake was proposed to occur by simple electrophoretic permeability (Fig. 1A).

An abundance of evidence suggested that bacteriorhodopsin was the only photopigment present and therefore must account for all of these fluxes (1). Even the observations of Kanner and Racker (4) that membrane vesicles derived from these cells were composed of two classes, one which pumped protons in the same direction as in whole cells, and a second class in which the proton flux was reversed, did not elicit much concern. They could be explained by simply postulating that in some vesicles the

V. P. Skulachev and Peter C. Hinkle (eds.), Chemiosmotic Proton Circuits in Biological Membranes
in honor of Peter Mitchell   ISBN 0-201-07398-6

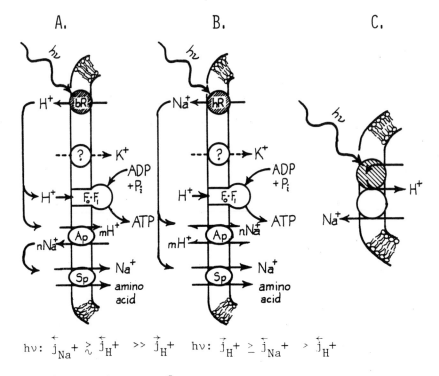

$$h\nu: \quad \overset{\leftarrow}{j}_{Na}{}^+ \overset{>}{\sim} \vec{j}_H{}^+ \quad >> \quad \vec{j}_H{}^+ \qquad h\nu: \quad \vec{j}_H{}^+ \geq \overset{\leftarrow}{j}_{Na}{}^+ \quad > \quad \vec{j}_H{}^+$$

Ap = antiporter; Sp = symporter; m ≥ n

Fig. 1.   Ion fluxes generated in response to illumination
of H. halobium vesicles.
A.   The ion fluxes are those assumed to occur on
illumination of vesicles (and cells) in which hR
is absent, and are thus those that would occur in
direct response to H^+ efflux via bR.   B.   The ion
fluxes are those assumed to occur on illumination
of vesicles (and cells) in which bR is absent, and
are thus those that would occur in direct response
to Na^+ efflux via hR.   In addition H^+ efflux must
also be driven by respiration and anaerobically
by reversal of the ATPase (not shown).   Anaerobically in H. halobium R_1, bR and hR are both present
(21) and may generate complicated patterns of ion
fluxes depending on the internal and external
sodium concentration and pH.   Ion fluxes in R_1mR and
ET15 are simpler and may be quite similar to those
shown in B. K^+ influx probably occurs on a uniporter (5), but it does not appear to be involved

directly in the fluxes shown. C. The ion fluxes resulting from a photopigment tightly associated with a Na^+/H^+ exchange protein. Protons are circulated and Na^+ is ejected on illumination as a tightly coupled secondary event (after Mitchell, 6).

membrane was oriented inside-out. Such an explanation had ample support from other membrane vesicle preparations in which the membrane was known to be reversed because of the availability of the ATPase to externally added ATP, e.g. sub-mitochondrial particles (7), or the "everted" membrane vesicles derived from E. coli (8).

The observations of Matsuno-Yagi and Mukohata (9) on a mutant strain (R_1mR) of H. halobium which was deficient in bacteriorhodopsin made it more difficult to ignore the "reversed" proton fluxes. In this strain illumination caused only alkalinization of the medium in contrast to the transient alkalinization followed by acidification commonly observed in the parent (R_1) strain. They showed that the mechanism responsible for this proton uptake was different from bacteriorhodopsin in several ways: (1) it was destroyed by heating for 5 min at 70°C; (2) it was resistant to bleaching in the presence of hydroxylamine; (3) it had an action spectrum for maximum proton uptake between 580nm and 660nm rather than at 570nm as found for the bR containing parent R_1 strain. However, they noted that illumination of these cells caused an increased ATP synthesis just as did illumination of the R_1 strain leading them to suggest that "bacteriorhodopsin in a special environment" was responsible for these changes.

At about the same time, Janos Lanyi and I decided to look more carefully at the "slowly sedimenting" class of membrane vesicles with an apparently reversed proton flux that Kanner and Racker had described (4). We were able to repeat their observations that illumination caused proton uptake, and that this uptake was stimulated by proton specific ionophores such as FCCP or 1799, and abolished by nigericin. Except for the stimulation by the proton iono-phores, the results obtained with this class of vesicles were similar to what had been observed with bR reconsti-tuted liposomes (10). The suggestion of Kanner and Racker that these were inside-out vesicles similar to the liposomes was appealing although not entirely satisfactory for two reasons: (1) the model did not explain how an uncoupler such as 1799 could stimulate proton uptake if the primary light driven response was the release of protons to the vesicle interior by bR. Kanner and Racker offered the explanation that since these vesicle populations were heterogeneous, the uncoupler inhibited net proton efflux in the class with bR in the outside-out orientation while not affecting the class with the reversed orientation. In fact, when they used 0.5mM 1799, all proton fluxes were abolished. However, we found that concentrations of 1799 as low as $0.5\mu M$ were sufficient to stimulate proton uptake in these vesicles while it required 10-times this amount to appreciably reduce proton efflux in outside-out vesicles. (2) The model did not account for our additional observa-tion that valinomycin abolished proton uptake, even allow-ing the possibility that the vesicles were heterogeneous and that valinomycin increased efflux of H^+ by the outside-out vesicles (11).

However, I became interested in examining them further as a possible way of studying the mechanism of light driven ATP synthesis in these organisms. Results from experiments designed to study ATP synthesis were discouraging. Neither ATP synthesis nor hydrolysis could be observed when ADP or ATP were added directly to the vesicles. When ATP was placed inside the vesicles, rapid hydrolysis occurred with or without illumination. Illumination inhibited hydrolysis somewhat but ATP synthesis could not be detected even after addition of ADP, P_i and $MgSO_4$ to the inside of the vesicles. Similar results were obtained on addition of ATP or ADP and P_i to outside-out vesicles prepared from the same strain of H. halobium.

If these vesicles were inside-out and accumulated H^+ on illumination, this should cause the Na^+/H^+-antiporter to bring Na^+ into these "inside-out" vesicles. Again, the predicted result was not obtained: even after prolonged illumination, no uptake of $^{22}Na^+$ could be detected in vesicles previously depleted of sodium. Yet in these depleted vesicles amino acid uptake was shown to be driven by a sodium gradient (high outside). Uptake also occurred when the sodium concentration on either side of the membrane was initially equal if the vesicles were illuminated. No uptake occurred at low (<100mM) sodium concentrations as is also true for outside-out vesicles (11). From these results I could only conclude that light must induce a membrane potential (negative inside) which drives electrogenic Na^+-amino acid symport. This was readily confirmed by following the uptake of ^3H-TPMP$^+$ which showed that on illumination a membrane potential in the order of -150mV to -180mV is formed. It was obvious that Na^+ must be circulating in illuminated vesicles, otherwise amino acid uptake could not occur. Although it was still possible to argue that these observations could be explained by the

presence of a mixed population of inside-out vesicles
(hereafter arbitrarily called M vesicles) and outside-out
vesicles (called L vesicles), we began to have doubts.

It seemed evident to me that either our techniques for
measuring ion fluxes were very inexact, or our idea that M
vesicles were inside-out was wrong. Perhaps we were refusing
to see the obvious! Indeed the results could also be
explained if light rather than causing proton efflux/influx,
caused the movement of some other ion as the primary event.

Therefore we proposed, as a working hypothesis, that M
vesicles contain a "light driven sodium pump" which on
illumination causes sodium efflux directly (Fig. 1B). In
contrast, in L vesicles which contain mainly the bacteriorhodopsin H^+ pump and a Na^+/H^+-antiporter, Na^+ efflux is a
secondary response driven by protonmotive force (3) (Fig.
1A). Thus, in M vesicles light causes the primary electrogenic efflux of Na^+, and H^+ enters the vesicles as a secondary response to the membrane potential created by sodium
efflux. This passive entry of protons is stimulated by
proton ionophores like 1799 and abolished by valinomycin
which abolishes membrane potential in the presence of K^+.
To our surprise this model was consistent with all of our
data to that point, but it remained to be shown that the
primary ion flux responsible for the membrane potential was
that of Na^+ and not K^+ or Cl^- or some trace ion such as
Mg^{++} or Ca^{++}.

The chance observation that vesicles prepared in 3 M
CsCl did not respond to illumination at all, unless Na^+ was
added, strongly supported our initial idea that the ion
responsible was sodium. Later we were able to show that
the same was true for vesicles suspended in KCl but this

required special precautions to get rid of traces of
sodium ions in the KCl solutions (12). The possible
contribution of other ion fluxes still has not been rigor-
ously ruled out except by our inability to detect them.

It now remained for us to convince others that this
model was tenable. My colleague Janos Lanyi, was somewhat
skeptical to say the least when Ed Lindley and I presented
him with our evidence. Yet he made the very useful suggestion that it might be more convincing to our case if our
studies were carried out in a strain such as the red mutant
(R_1mR) which had been described by Matsuno-Yagi and Mukohata.

This turned out to be a very useful suggestion. Membrane vesicles prepared from this strain, like the whole
cells, did not cause any detectable acidification of the
medium when illuminated, even in the presence of valinomycin, which "activated" proton efflux in most preparations
of M vesicles. Instead, they showed pronounced H^+ uptake
and in this and in all other respects were similar to M
vesicles. When they were illuminated either in the presence
or absence of 1799, a membrane potential was formed and the
vesicle interior was acidified. Both R_1mR and M vesicles,
when pre-loaded with various concentrations of $^{22}Na^+$, lost
$^{22}Na^+$ much more rapidly when illuminated than in the dark.
This efflux was not inhibited by 1799 or by valinomycin.
Yet similar experiments in L vesicles showed that light
stimulated sodium efflux was abolished by these ionophores.
Later (13) we were able to show that proton uptake in M
vesicles and R_1mR vesicles had an action spectrum similar
to that reported for R_1mR cells and distinct from the
action spectrum for proton efflux in L vesicles. We were
now convinced that the fluxes taking place in M vesicles

were not an artifact due to heterogeneity of the vesicle
preparation. Thus we concluded that the "bacteriorhodopsin
like pigment" noted by Matsuno-Yagi and Mukohata was very
similar to, if not identical with, the photopigment responsible for the sodium efflux in M vesicles and R_1mR vesicles.

In the Fall of 1978, one of my graduate students,
Richard Greene, went to Lanyi's laboratory to try to convince
him that we had indeed discovered a light driven sodium
pump in this organism. Together they were able to repeat
our experiments and to extend them in several ways. Most
importantly, they showed clearly that sodium efflux was independent of proton motive force and thus that it could not
proceed via a Na^+/H^+-antiporter coupled to pmf (14). Ed
Lindley and I undertook the task of convincing Ef Racker
that his model to explain ion fluxes in these vesicles
needed some revision. We were able to show that, even at
low concentrations, the ionophores used were able to dissipate pmf, and further that we could reproduce all the
changes he and Kanner had seen in M vesicles, in R_1mR
vesicles, which were almost devoid of bR. Thus we all
finally concurred that a second light-driven mechanism for
extrusion of Na^+ must be present in addition to Na^+/H^+
antiporter. It seemed most likely that this second mechanism was entirely separate from bacteriorhodopsin, but at
that time the evidence was not conclusive.

We presented our findings at the Biophysical Society
meetings in Febraury, 1979 (15) and in detail later that
year (12,14,16).

Yet several difficulties remained, not the least being
the role of this new pump in the cell and whether it could
not be more simply explained by "bacteriorhodopsin in a

special environment" as suggested by Matsuno-Yagi and
Mukohata. This latter problem was eliminated by the
availability of a new mutant, (ET15), isolated by Jürgen
Weber, which lacked bacteriorhodopsin entirely, although it
still ejected Na$^{|}$ on illumination and took up protons.
Weber generously made his mutant available to us and we
were able to show that vesicles of this strain showed the
same ion fluxes on illumination as M or R_1mR vesicles.
Lanyi and Weber (17) obtained unequivocal spectroscopic
evidence that a pigment was present in these cells which
required retinal for function and which had an absorption
maximum at 588nm to 590nm in agreement with the action
spectrum reported for proton uptake (9,13,14). This pigment,
later named halorhodopsin (hR) by Mukohata (18), has a
molar extinction coefficient of ca. 48,000, compared to
63,000 for bR and differs from bR in a number of other
ways: dark adaptation is not observed, it has a pH dependent
absorption spectrum in the visible region, and is destroyed
by heating. Weber and Bogomolni (19), using flash spectroscopy, further showed that the new photopigment undergoes a
photocycle similar to that for bR but quite distinct both
in the spectral properties and stability of the intermediates
in the cycle.

   Thus, it is now clear that the "inside-out" class of
vesicles reported by Kanner and Racker are not inside-out
at all, but rather are outside-out and contain a predominant
new pigment, halorhodopsin, which is responsible for the
ion fluxes observed, bearing out once again Racker's
aphorism, "Troubles are Good for You" (7).

   But puzzling and important questions remain. How is
it that proton uptake occurs in M vesicles which also con-

tain large quantities of bacteriorhodopsin that should
create a large proton efflux on illumination? Is the bR
inactive, or is it randomly oriented so that the net H^+
flux is zero? Since a number of treatments (heat, detergents,
aging and high K^+) which destroy or greatly inhibit halorhodopsin also cause a large increase in H^+ efflux, while
valinomycin which abolishes membrane potential (in the
presence of K^+) does not induce any proton uptake, we
assume that bR is mostly in an inactive form, at least in M
vesicles. However we lack definitive proof for this
assumption.

What is the role of halorhodopsin in the energy
economy of the cell? Certainly in the absence of bR it
enables the cells to eject Na^+ and to synthesize ATP as a
result of the electrochemical ion gradient created as shown
by Matsuno-Yagi and Mukohata (9) and Mukohata and Kaji
(21). But why is hR always present in strains with large
amounts of bR which can generate even larger electrochemical proton gradients? The final answer to this question
is not yet known, but several observations may shed some
light and permit some interesting speculations.

(1) No strains of H. halobium have yet been isolated
which contain bR and lack hR, although strains lacking both
pigments or lacking bR are found both in nature and in
laboratory cultures. (2) The membrane potential generated
by the illumination of vesicles which contain only hR is in
the order of -180mV under appropriate conditions, and forms
immediately. This is true also in vesicles (L vesicles)
which contain active bR and eject protons. Yet in intact
R_1 cells the initial pH response is the uptake of protons.
Lanyi and MacDonald (3) and Hartmann and Oesterhelt (20)

have argued that this is due to the electrogenic return of
protons via the Na^+/H^+-antiporter while Stoeckenius et al.
(1) attribute this uptake to ATP synthesis. (3) In cells
light stimulates the immediate synthesis of ATP (2), thus
proton entry to drive ATP synthesis and Na^+ efflux via the
antiporter would result in acidification of the cell interior. (4) Although on illumination halorhodopsin generates
a large enough membrane potential to drive ATP synthesis,
it does not cause a large enough sodium efflux to remove
protons via the antiporter operating in reverse or to
account for the net sodium efflux observed in whole cells
or in M vesicles containing bR. (5) Illumination of bR,
however, can bring about the rapid efflux of protons from
the cell and create a pH gradient that can drive the
Na^+/H^+-antiporter and thus the rapid efflux of Na^+.

If hR is mainly involved in generating an electric
potential which can drive ATP synthesis, then it should be
possible to show this in the various classes of membrane
vesicles we have studied. Another of my graduate students,
Robert Clark, has been able to study the effects of these
ion fluxes on ATP levels in membrane vesicles prepared from
R_1, R_1mR, and ET15 cells.

In R_1 vesicles ATP synthesis is comparable to that
synthesized anaerobically in whole cells on illumination,
and the light induced ATP level is stable. Addition of
nigericin diminishes the amount of synthesis as expected
from the magnitude of the pH gradient but does not eliminate
it. In R_1mR vesicles ATP synthesis is transient unless a
proton exchanger such as nigericin is present to prevent
excessive acidification of the vesicle interior. (Detailed
studies show that this strain is not entirely lacking in

bR.) In ET15 vesicles which do lack bR entirely and are
unlikely to respire under the conditions used, little ATP
synthesis can be detected unless nigericin is present. In
both of the latter vesicle preparations, ATP incorporated
by osmotic shock is rapidly hydrolyzed, indicating that
active ATPase is present. Mukohata[1] has found similar
stabilization of light induced ATP synthesis in whole cells
of R_1mR by the addition of the Cl^-/OH exchanger, triphenyl-
tin chloride. Vesicle preparations also synthesize ATP if
an ascorbate-TMPD system is used to stimulate electron
transfer through the cytochromes.

We speculate that the major role of hR is to create an
electrochemical sodium gradient in light under aerobic
conditions. This enhances the ability of the cells lacking
bR to synthesize ATP and to augment the electrochemical
proton gradient created by respiration to drive the Na^+/H^+-
antiporter and thus to cause the rapid efflux of Na^+.
Sodium efflux in bR deficient strains would otherwise be
limited by the low internal pH which would result from
proton entry, and may shut off or even reverse the antiporter.
Bacteriorhodopsin is required to permit the cells to grow
in low oxygen tensions when respiration is limited and H^+
efflux is insufficient to maintain internal cell pH. Of
course neither photopigment is absolutely necessary, as
evidenced by the ability of these cells to grow in the dark
under laboratory conditions.

A final problem which must be addressed is the mechanism
whereby hR causes the electrogenic movement of Na^+ across

---

1. private communication

the membrane. All attempts to isolate and reconstitute the pump have failed so we again are left to speculation. Two models seem plausible at present: (1) hR functions very much like bR, the Na^+ replacing H^+ in the sequence of events resulting from the absorption of light energy. Unfortunately this model is not very helpful since so little is known about the molecular mechanism of H^+ extrusion. (2) The second model is based on the suggestion of Peter Mitchell (6) that coupled mechanisms of energy transfer may exist in which there is a net movement of only one species across the membrane barrier. Thus if hR, a bR like pigment, is tightly coupled to a second polypeptide with Na^+/H^+-exchange properties, on illumination, a proton would be released from the photopigment to the Na^+/H^+-exchange protein in such a way that a Na^+ was released to the bulk phase external to the membrane and the H^+ to the internal bulk phase. In the second half of the cycle the proton would be taken up again by the photopigment and a sodium ion from the internal bulk phase of the membrane and the cycle would be repeated. This would result in the net electrogenic efflux of Na^+ but would cause no net proton flux (Fig. 1C).

Evolutionarily, the halobacteria are thought to be members of a very primitive group called Archaebacteria (which are mainly anaerobes). In a relatively alkaline medium light would cause sodium efflux and development of a membrane potential. The passive proton entry in response to the $\Delta\tilde{\mu}_{Na}^+$ would cause relatively mild acidification of the cell (e.g. from pH 8.5 to pH 6), but if the external medium were more acid the same electrochemical sodium gradient would require a mechanism for direct proton ejection if the cell were to survive. If model 2 (above) is correct, this need not have required the development of an entirely new photopigment; only the dissociation of hR from the Na^+/H^+ exchange protein and modification which would allow release of the proton to the exterior aqueous phase of the membrane. This does not explain why bR is produced in such excess; . . . could it be that the cell has no effective control mechanism for hR synthesis? Yet, if synthesized in excess, hR could quickly cause the cell interior to become acid enough to kill the cell if it were illuminated anaerobically or even aerobically. In place of an adequate control mechanism, it instead synthesizes an excess of the proton pump, bacteriorhodopsin, which is stored in the membrane. If the pH of the medium becomes too low or if excess hR is synthesized, the bR will be activated (either by internal or external pH) and prevent the internal pH from remaining low, while at the same time assuring the continued net efflux of sodium, maintenance of an electrochemical proton gradient and synthesis of ATP.

REFERENCES

1. Stoeckenius, W., Lozier, R.H., and Bogomolni, R.A. (1979) Biochim. Biophys. Acta 505, 215-278.
2. Bogomolni, R.A., Baker, R.A., Lozier, R.H. and Stoeckenius, W. (1976) Biochim. Biophys. Acta 440, 68-88.
3. Lanyi, J.K. and MacDonald, R.E. (1976) Biochemistry 15, 4608-4614.
4. Kanner, B. and Racker, E. (1975) Biochem. Biophys. Res. Commun. 64, 1054-1061.
5. Wagner, G., Hartmann, R. and Oesterhelt, D. (1978). Eur. J. Biochem. 89, 169-179.
6. Mitchell, P. (1979) Eur. J. Biochem. 95, 1-20.
7. Racker, E. (1976) A new look at mechanisms in bio-energetics. Academic Press, New York.
8. Rosen, B. (1979) Bacterial Transport. Marcel Dekker, New York.

9. Matsuno-Yagi, A. and Mukohata, Y. (1977) Biochem. Bio-
    phys. Res. Commun. 78, 237-243.
10. Racker, E. and Stoeckenius, W. (1974) J. Biol. Chem.
    249, 662-63.
11. MacDonald, R.E. and Lanyi, J.K. (1975) Biochemistry 14,
    2882-2889.
12. Lindley, E.V. and MacDonald, R.E. (1979) Biochem.
    Biophys. Res. Commun. 88, 491-499.
13. Greene, R.V., MacDonald, R.E. and Perreault, G.J. (1980)
    J. Biol. Chem. 255, 3245-3247.
14. Greene, R.V. and Lanyi, J.K. (1979) J. Biol. Chem.
    365, 10986-10994.
15. MacDonald, R.E., Lanyi, J.K., Greene, R.V. and Lindley,
    E.V. (1979) Biophys. J. 25, 205a.
16. MacDonald, R.E., Greene, R.V., Clark, R.D., and Lindley,
    E.V. (1979) J. Biol. Chem. 254, 11831-11838.
17. Lanyi, J.K. and Weber, H.J. (1980) J. Biol. Chem. 255,
    243-250.
18. Mukohata, Y., Matsuno-Yagi, A. and Kaji, Y. (1980) in
    Saline Environment (Morishita, H. and Masui, M., eds.)
    pp. 31-37., Univ. of Tokyo Press, Tokyo.
19. Weber, H.J. and Bogomolni, R.A. (1981) Photochem.
    Photobiol. 33, 601-608.
20. Hartmann, R. and Oesterhelt, D. (1977) Eur. J. Biochem.
    77, 325-335.
21. Mukohata, Y. and Kaji, Y. (1981) Arch. Biochem. Bio-
    phys. 206, 72-76.

THE ELECTROGENIC PROTON PUMP IN NEUROSPORA CRASSA[1]

Clifford L. Slayman and Carolyn W. Slayman

Departments of Physiology and Human Genetics
Yale School of Medicine
New Haven, CT   06510

During the past decade, it has become clear that transport through fungal plasma membranes takes place by what
might be called generalized chemiosmotic mechanisms (1,2).
The primary transport process is an ATP-driven electrogenic
proton pump, which--at least in the case of the mycelial
ascomycete, Neurospora--can extrude acid at 1-2 moles/liter
cytoplasm every hour (3) while consuming 20-40% of the total
metabolic energy turnover (4). The resulting inwardly directed proton gradient then acts by means of proton-substrate
symport systems, to bring amino acids, sugars, and other
organic nutrients into the cells (5,6,7); and the electric
potential itself drives in cations (8) and may drive out
anions. Plasma membrane-bound ATPases have been identified
with the primary proton pump in several species of Candida,
in Rhodotorula gracilis, Saccharomyces cerevisiae, Schizo-
saccharomyces pombe, and in Neurospora crassa (9), and have

---

[1]Supported by NIH Grants GM-15858 and GM-15761, and NSF
Grant PCM77-25199.

V. P. Skulachev and Peter C. Hinkle (eds.), Chemiosmotic Proton Circuits in Biological Membranes
in honor of Peter Mitchell   ISBN 0-201-07398-6

been purified to homogeneity from the latter two organisms
(10,11). It is Neurospora, however, that has proven unique
in lending itself both to biochemical characterization of
the H^+ pump and to direct electrophysiological studies of
the corresponding electrogenic transport process.

BIOCHEMISTRY OF THE ATPase

Preparing a clean plasma membrane fraction in which to
study the fungal transport ATPase has been greatly complicated by the difficulty of breaking the polysaccharide cell
wall without breaking mitochondria, whose fragments become
ubiquitous membrane contaminants. Initially, that problem
was bypassed in Neurospora by use of a wall-less strain,
whose plasma membrane could be stabilized with concanavalin
A (12,13), allowing it to be collected by low speed centrifugation following hypotonic lysis. Later, Bowman et al.
developed a more efficient procedure using chitinase proto-
plasts of wild-type Neurospora which had not been treated
with concanavalin A (11). These were lysed under gentle
conditions, keeping most organelles intact, so that clean
plasma-membrane vesicles could be separated by differential
centrifugation alone. The ATPase activity of such membranes
is 3.5–8.0 µmoles ATP split/min·mg protein; and the ATPase
accounts for 5–10% of total membrane protein (Fig.1A; Ref.
10).

The enzyme has been solubilized from the membrane with
0.6% deoxycholate in the presence of 45% glycerol (11), and
purified by centrifugation through a glycerol gradient.
This procedure recovers about 30% of the total starting
ATPase with specific activities of 50–98 µmoles/min·mg

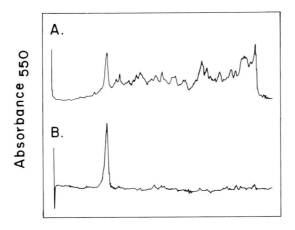

Fig. 1.   Densitometer tracings of SDS-polyacrylamide gels
          stained with Coomassie blue.
          A: Plasma membranes, 19.7 µg protein; B: Purified
          membrane ATPase, 1.2 µg protein.

protein. Upon SDS-polyacrylamide gel electrophoresis, the
purified enzyme shows a single major band of M_r = 104,000
(Fig. 1B). Thus, with respect to size and the requirement
for detergent extraction, the Neurospora plasma membrane
ATPase (and those of other fungi as well (9)) closely resembles the [Ca^{++}]-ATPase of sarcoplasmic reticulum and the
large subunit of the [Na$^+$,K$^+$]-ATPase in most animal cell
plasma membranes. It is an integral membrane protein of
relatively simple structure, and differs profoundly from the
F_0F_1-type ATPases which carry out reversible proton pumping
in energy-conserving membranes.

   The inhibitor sensitivity of the Neurospora plasma
membrane ATPase (14) also distinguishes it clearly from the
F_0F_1-ATPases. Oligomycin, venturicidin, and azide have
essentially no effects on the enzyme at the highest concentrations which are practical to test. However, both diethylstilbestrol and vanadate, which do not block mitochondrial ATPase, are powerful inhibitors of the plasma

membrane ATPase, with $[I]_{0.5}$ values equal to 10 μM and 1
μM, respectively. Dicyclohexylcarbodiimide (DCCD) also
blocks the Neurospora ATPase, but reacts with the major
polypeptide (M_r = 104,000; M.R. Sussman, experiments in
progress) rather than with any low molecular weight proteolipids (as in F_0F_1-ATPases).

As might be expected from its vanadate sensitivity, the
enzyme forms an acyl phosphate intermediate in the course of
catalyzing ATP hydrolysis. The major polypeptide (M_r =
104,000) is labelled from $[^{32}P]$-ATP at concentrations which
approach the physiologic $K_{1/2}$ for both proton transport (ca.
2 mM; Ref. 4) and ATPase activity (16; R.J. Brooker & C.W.
Slayman, experiments in progress). Using perchloric acid as
a reaction stop, in combination with pulsed and/or sustained
$[^{32}P]$-ATP, Scarborough (16) was able to show that phosphorylation approaches a maximal level within 2 sec., and undergoes rapid turnover upon addition of excess nonradioactive
ATP. Similar results have been described for the S. pombe
enzyme (17). Thus, in its reaction mechanism as well as in
its subunit structure, the fungal plasma-membrane ATPase
resembles the $[Na^+,K^+]$-ATPase, the $[Ca^{++}]$-ATPase, and the
$[H^+,K^+]$-ATPase of animal cells.

ELECTRICAL PROPERTIES OF THE PROTON PUMP IN INTACT CELLS

There is now abundant evidence that the fungal plasma-
membrane ATPase functions physiologically as a proton pump
whose most easily observed electrical expression (in Neurospora) is its contribution of about 175 mV to the normal
resting membrane potential ($\Delta\psi$; Ref. 18). A high rate of
metabolic turnover, coupled with obligatory aerobic habits

leaves the organism vulnerable to sudden respiratory block-
ade, as (for example) by cyanide. And such treatment results in simultaneous decay of intracellular ATP and membrane potential, with a half-time of about 7 sec at 25°
(Ref. 4). Such experiments have been refined and elaborated
to yield an enzyme-like kinetic relationship between membrane potential and $[ATP]_i$:

$$\Delta\psi = -7 + \frac{-311 \cdot [ATP]_i}{2 + [ATP]_i} \cdot \qquad (1)$$

It was this finding which first predicted the $K_{1/2}$ of 2 mM
ATP, which was referred to above. Since the reaction product for an ion pump is not membrane potential per se, but
transmembrane current flow, the above quantitative relationship contains a hidden parameter, membrane resistance, which
must be presumed constant for a simple interpretation of the
result.

But the existence of electric current as a bona fide
reaction product opens the enzyme behavior to a third
dimension of kinetic analysis, in which membrane potential
--rather than substrate concentration--is treated as the
driving variable. In order to see how electrical parameters
can enter into the overall behavior of ion pumps, it is
helpful to have an explicit kinetic model, such as that in
Fig. 2. The form of this model, simplified to two states of
the "carrier", has been chosen because steady-state electrical data give direct information only about those states
which are charged and cross the membrane; all other states
and reaction steps can be lumped together into the apparent
reaction constants κ_{oi} and κ_{io} (19). A quantitative treatment of the model, using a symmetric Eyring barrier to

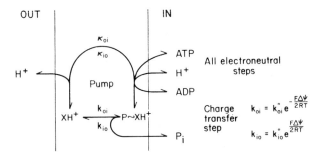

Fig. 2.   Simplified two-state carrier model for an electrogenic proton pump.

introduce dependence on $\Delta\psi$, makes it possible to dissect the
behavior of the pump out of the electrical behavior of the
total membrane.

The procedure has been used to analyze effects of three
different depolarizing agents: cyanide, vanadate, and
butyrate (Fig. 3). While depolarization is expected for
both cyanide (ATP withdrawal) and vanadate (interference
with ATP binding), the effect of butyrate, which increases
$[H^+]_i$, is paradoxical. Indeed, detailed electrical kinetic
experiments (20), carried out by means of a rapid voltage-
clamp sweep between -300 and 0 mV membrane potential, reveal
that butyrate actually does increase current flow through
the pump, while both cyanide and vanadate inhibit that
current. Net depolarization by butyrate, therefore, must
result from a second action, which has been identified as a
large increase in membrane leakage permeability.

More important, however, is the fact that in all three
cases the same lumped reaction step is affected: the carrier reloading step (κ_{oi}) in Fig. 2. Cyanide and vanadate
both reduce κ_{oi}, while butyrate increases it, the magnitude
of change being roughly proportional to the change in short-
circuit current ($\Delta\psi=0$) seen in Fig. 3. Since the cytoplasmic

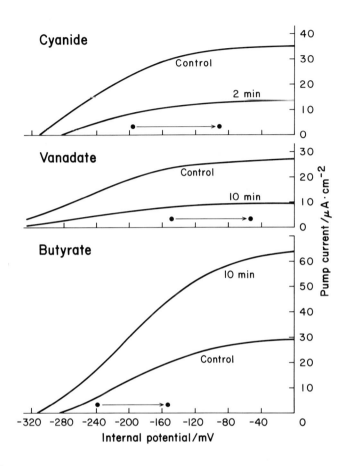

Fig. 3.   Current-voltage curves for the plasma membrane
          proton pump of Neurospora. Before (control) and
          during treatment with three different depolarizing
          agents. Dots and arrows along the abscissa in-
          dicate the amount of depolarization produced.

concentrations of ATP and H$^+$ both enter into κ_{oi}, the calculated changes of κ_{oi} are consistent with the known actions
of all three agents.

RECENT EXPERIMENTS WITH MEMBRANE VESICLES

Most arguments linking the membrane ATPase of Neuro-spora with actual transport of protons have been indirect (13,21), and it was not until stable, functional vesicles of the Neurospora plasma membrane were prepared (22) that the association between H^+ flow, ATP hydrolysis, and membrane electrogenesis could be shown directly.

Vesicles prepared either by the concanavalin A technique or the chitinase protoplast technique are functionally inverted, pumping protons inward to generate pH gradients (ΔpH) up to 2 units, as measured by accumulation of $[^{14}C]$-imidazole or by fluorescence quenching of fluorescein-labelled dextran (22), quinacrine, or acridine orange (23). pH gradients of this magnitude depend on the presence of permeant anions such as SCN^-, NO_3^-, or Cl^-. When only trace amounts of these ions are present, membrane potentials (Δψ) up to 100 mV (vesicle interior positive) can be estimated from the distribution of $[^{14}C]$-SCN^- (22,23). Both ΔpH and Δψ are dissipated by ATPase inhibitors or general proton ionophores.

Experiments are presently underway to convert the vesicles into flat bilayers, so that the electrical properties of the vesicle membranes can be assessed directly and compared with those of the intact cells.

REFERENCES

1. Slayman, C.L. (1974) in Membrane Transport in Plants, (U. Zimmermann and J. Dainty, eds.) pp. 107-119, Springer-Verlag.
2. Slayman, C.W. and Slayman, C.L. (1975) in Molecular Aspects of Membrane Phenomena (H.R. Kaback, et al., eds.) pp. 233-248, Springer-Verlag.

3. Slayman, C.L. and Gradmann, D. (1975) Biophys. J. 15, 968-971.
4. Slayman, C.L., Long, W.S. and Lu, C.Y.-H. (1973) J. Membr. Biol. 14, 305-338.
5. Eddy, A.A. (1978) Curr. Top. Membr. Transp. 10, 279-360.
6. Slayman, C.L. and Slayman, C.W. (1974) Proc. Nat. Acad. Sci. USA 71, 1935-1939.
7. Reichert, U., Schmidt, R. and Foret, M. (1975) FEBS Lett. 52, 100-102.
8. Slayman, C.L. (1977) in Water Relations in Membrane Transport in Plants and Animals. (A.M. Jungreis, et al., eds.) pp. 69-86, Academic Press.
9. Goffeau, A.L. and Slayman, C.W. (1981) Biochim. Biophys. Acta, in press.
10. Dufour, J.-P. and Goffeau, A. (1978) J. Biol. Chem. 253, 7026-7032.
11. Bowman, B.J., Blasco, F., and Slayman, C.W. (1981) J. Biol. Chem., submitted.
12. Scarborough, G.A. (1976) Proc. Nat. Acad. Sci. USA 73, 1485-1488.
13. Bowman, B.J. and Slayman, C.W. (1977) J. Biol. Chem. 252, 3357-3363.
14. Bowman, B.J., Mainzer, S.E., Allen, K.E. and Slayman, C.W. (1978) Biochim. Biophys. Acta 512, 13-28.
15. Kuroda, H., Warncke, J., Sanders, D., Hansen, U.-P., Allen, K.E. and Bowman, B.J. (1980) in Plant Membrane Transport: Current Conceptual Issues, (R.M. Spanswick et al., eds.) pp. 507-508, Elsevier.
16. Dame, J.B. and Scarborough, G.A. (1980) Biochem. 19, 2931-2937.
17. Amory, A., Foury, F. and Goffeau, A. (1980) J. Biol. Chem. 255, 9353-9357.
18. Slayman, C.L. (1965) J. Gen. Physiol. 49, 93-116.
19. Hansen, U.-P., Gradmann, D., Sanders, D. and Slayman, C.L. (1981) J. Membr. Biol., in press.
20. Sanders, D., Hansen, U.-P. and Slayman, C.L. (1981) Proc. Nat. Acad. Sci. USA, in press.
21. Slayman, C.L. (1970) Amer. Zool. 10, 377-392.
22. Scarborough, G.A. (1980) Biochem. 19, 2925-2931.
23. Perlin, D.S. and Slayman, C.W. (1981) Fed. Proc. 40, 1784, item 1404.

H^+ TRANSPORT IN STOMACH

G. Sachs

Laboratory of Membrane Biology
University of Alabama in Birmingham
University Station
Birmingham, AL   35294

The enormous influence that Peter Mitchell has had on transport research in the two decades that have passed since publication of the chemiosmotic hypothesis (1) includes gastric secretion. At the time that he was a lecturer in Zoology at Edinburgh, I remember, as would many other students his ability to rapidly understand a lecture on almost any topic and to ask the most penetrating questions. I am not sure whether my memory is playing tricks, but I seem to remember a seminar he gave where he postulated that gastric acid secretion depended on the splitting of water by a vectorial ATPase. Considering that this was the late fifties, the prevailing concept at the time was that gastric acid secretion depended on a redox pump separating H^+ and electrons (2). Connecting the 2 schemes would lead to chemiosmosis in the mitochondrial membrane.

[1]Supported by NIH grant AM-28459, and NSF grant PCM 78-09208 and PCM 80-08625.

V. P. Skulachev and Peter C. Hinkle (eds.), Chemiosmotic Proton Circuits in Biological Membranes in honor of Peter Mitchell   ISBN 0-201-07398-6

As it has turned out, gastric acid secretion as carried out across the secretory canaliculus of the parietal cell seems to depend on an ATPase, with no intervention of a redox system.

A.   ISOLATED CELL SYSTEMS. The development of methods for measuring acid secretion by isolated cell systems from mammalian gastric mucosa depended on the use of weak base trapping methods which in turn had been developed for the study of pH gradients in a variety of vesicular systems. The weak base chosen, aminopyrine, has a pK_a of 5 (3). Accumulation of this base then depends on the development, by the parietal cell, of acid compartments of a pH less than this. A cell to medium ratio of 500 in a rabbit gastric gland preparation, with a compartment volume of about 10% represents an actual ratio of 5000 reflecting a pH in the acid compartment of 1.3 which is close to the expected pH of 0.8. The boundary of this low pH compartment is the secretory canaliculus of the parietal cell, as shown by the accumulation of the fluorescent weak base, acridine orange (4).

A simplification of this isolated cell model was achieved by disruption of the cellular plasma membrane, with maintenance of the integrity of the canaliculus membrane (5, 6). This allowed the demonstration that added ATP was able to generate pH gradients at the acid secretory site in the intact cell, in spite of mitochondrial inhibition by CN^- or N_3^-. Mitochondrial redox systems were therefore unlikely to participate directly in H^+ secretion. Using digitonin and oligomycin, ATP was also able to restore aminopyrine accumulation to control levels in the absence of O_2. This last result (FIGURE 1) excludes any redox contribution to the acid gradient (6).

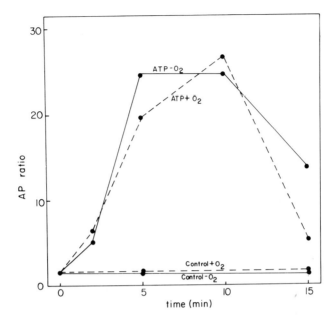

Fig. 1.   The restoration of acid secretion by ATP with
          oligomycin and anoxia (from Malinowska, et al).

It is well known that parietal cell acid secretion
depends on the presence of K[+] (7). It was found that in
gastric glands removal of medium K[+] inhibited aminopyrine
accumulation, as expected (8). However, the additional removal of Na[+] allowed reaccumulation of aminopyrine (9). This
result demonstrates that intracellular Na[+] is inhibitory to
acid secretion. The probable explanation is that Na[+] is an
inhibitory cationic ligand at the cytosolic face of the
ATPase.

A model developed from studies of gastric vesicles is
that the gastric ATPase acts as an electroneutral H[+] for K[+]
exchanger, the K[+] having to have access to the luminal face
of the enzyme (10). It is also known that, as for Na[+], K[+]
binding to the cytosolic face of the enzyme is able to inhibit phosphorylation (11). In the intact system, as in

gastric vesicles, K^+ must leave the parietal cell cytoplasm and enter the canaliculus lumen for reabsorption by the ATPase. The level of K^+ required for half maximal activation of breakdown of E-P at neutral pH is in the range of 200 μM (11). As acidification proceeds, higher K^+ levels are required. To measure the affinity of K^+ for H^+ secretion in the intact parietal cell, it was essential, in Na^+ free conditions, to be able to vary cytosolic K^+ over a wide range. This was achieved by amphotericin treatment of the gastric glands and in unstimulated glands the $K_{0.5}$ was 18 mM, and this fell to 12 mM in stimulated glands (FIGURE 2) (12). This finding was interpreted as showing that activation of secretion required activation of a KCl permeation pathway or establishment of access of KCl pathway to the luminal face of the gastric ATPase. Studies therefore on the intact cell, suggest that the K^+ activated ATPase (13) is the enzyme responsible for parietal cell acid secretion. The KCl necessary for secretion is supplied by an electroneutral diffusion pathway in parallel to the enzyme since protonophores do not inhibit secretion due to ATP in permeable gastric glands (6). The interaction between the KCl pathway and the enzyme is the probable means whereby the parietal cell is activated (14). Vesicles have been isolated from secreting tissue which exhibit a high KCl permeability (15). Evidence is therefore accumulating for an antiport pump/symport leak model for parietal cell acid secretion (10). Why this rather special system should have developed in the parietal cell is not clear. However, the ΔpH of 7 units developed by the pump almost requires an electroneutral pump and electroneutral KCl pathway. For example, at 160 mM H^+ concentration there is no known ionophore that would be K^+ rather than H^+ selective.

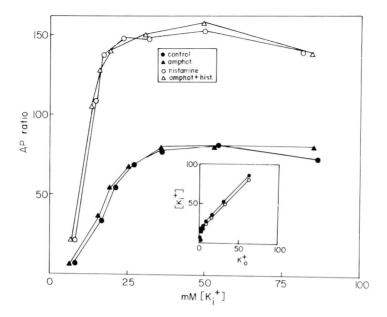

Fig. 2. Acid secretion as a function of cell K$^+$ in Na$^+$ free
medium following treatment with amphotericin (from
Koelz, et al).

Two possibilities are visualized for the location of the KCl
pathway. Firstly, that there are physically distinct membranes, one containing the ATPase, the other the KCl symport
pathway which interact and secondly that the KCl pathway is
part of the ATPase complex and is activated by the cAMP and
Ca^{++} second messenger signals.

B.   ISOLATED ENZYME VESICLES. Considerable progress has
been made since the initial description of the enzyme and
its transport of H$^+$ (13, 16).

With the addition of ATP and KCl simultaneously to vesicles isolated from the parietal cell there is little, if any,
uptake of H$^+$ into the vesicle lumen. Since the vesicles are
inside out with respect to the membrane orientation in the
intact cell, this would be the expected direction of H$^+$ transport. If, however, valinomycin is added, so that penetration

of valinomycin-K^+ along with Cl^- can occur, uptake of H^+ is
seen with a maximal pH gradient developing in about 5-10
minutes. This can be explained by a requirement for K^+ in
the vesicle interior. This is established by preequilibration
of the vesicles with KCl prior to ATP addition. Under these
circumstances, H^+ uptake rises progressively as the internal
KCl concentration rises. At equilibrium with 150 mM KCl, the
addition of ATP results in the uptake, within about 45 seconds
of 100 nmole H^+ per μl vesicle space, based on measurement of
the extravesicular pH change. On the other hand, measurement
of changes of intravesicular pH, using a variety of weak base
probes, shows uptake of 1 nmole H^+ per μl vesicle volume at
high ATP concentrations (17). The difference must be accounted
for by buffering. Since all the uptake depends on intravesicular K^+ and is reversed by ionophores, it is likely that the
buffering is on the luminal side of the pump barrier. If
most of the buffering is due to protein and given a MWt of
the ATPase of 300,000 then about 60 nmoles H^+ are bound per
mole pump protein. Alternatively aminosugars or phospholipids
such as PS, PI could account for much of the buffering capacity.

The final ΔpH of 3 or 4 units that is reached by the KCl
equilibrated vesicles is not due to lack of intravesicular K^+.
Thus, even if internal K^+ is increased to 200 mM or more, the Δ
pH is not increased. Hence, at about pH 3 in these vesicles
a leak of HCl occurs which overcomes pump capacity. This
leak appears to be related to carboxyl groups since treatment
with low concentrations of DCCD reduces leak of H^+ (18). One
could speculate that the H^+ leak was due to an artefact of
preparation, in that the vesicles are derived from normally
tubular structures, or that, upon loss of the activation
system, which involves addition of a KCl symport pathway,

the H$^+$ leak appears.

From the above, the gastric ATPase functions as an H$^+$:K$^+$
exchange pump. Measurement of development of potentials
during pump activity show the absence of either negative or
positive potentials unless induced by protonophore or valinomycin dependent diffusion potentials. Hence, in vesicles, as
in the parietal cell, the pump is electroneutral (17).

The entry of KCl, although slow in these vesicles, is
also by electroneutral cotransport. Thus, entry of KCl is
faster in the majority of vesicles then entry of K$_2$SO$_4$ or
KSCN (19). Recently large vesicles have been prepared from
secreting rabbit mucosa which show a high KCl permeability
(15).

The discussion of pump transport would be incomplete
without some reference to stoichiometry. In the absence of
any data suggesting that the free energy of ATP hydrolysis
in the parietal cell cytoplasm is about 16 K cal per mol, a
ΔpH of 6.6 units and a ΔpK$^+$ of 1 unit requires that the
stoichiometry does not exceed 1 mol H$^+$ per ATP hydrolyzed.
Although Forte claims that this is indeed the stoichiometry
achieved, there is in those data, no correction for scalar
ATP hydrolysis (33). In our hands, at zero K$^+$ gradient
conditions, or with outward K$^+$ gradients, over a range of
ATP concentrations, the stoichiometry is 2 or even more
(FIGURE 3). Whereas this stoichiometry is compatible with
the ΔpH achieved in the vesicles, it is not compatible with
the gradient capacity of the parietal cell proton pump.
Various errors must be considered in stoichiometry measurements. Not all the vesicles may be functional resulting in
scalar ATP hydrolysis. This would lead to an underestimate
of the stoichiometry. Binding of H$^+$, the Bohr proton effect,
would lead to an overestimate of stoichiometry. A significant

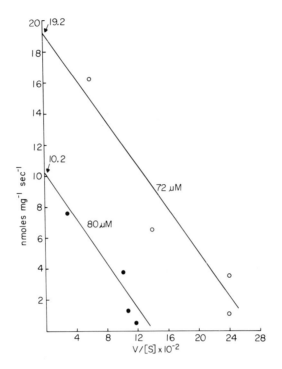

Fig. 3. Stoichiometry of H^+ to ATP at K^+ equilibrium (from Rabon).

contribution of Bohr protons is made unlikely by the absolute

internal K^+ requirement and the inhibition of all pH changes

by ionophores such as gramicidin or nigericin.

Since the stoichiometry of the ATPase in permeable cells

should be 1 H^+ per ATP hydrolyzed, the finding that the ratio

is significantly higher in ATPase vesicles implies that either

this is a variable stoichiometry pump or that in the vesicle

some alteration of structure has occurred so that an invalid

transport reaction is taking place. Variable stoichiometry

pump concepts are not fashionable, especially when related to

pumps that act via covalently liganded phosphate. Thus, for

example, the Ca^{++}-ATPase seems to have a fixed stoichiometry

of 2, and 3 Na^+ are exchanged for $2K^+$ by the $Na^+ + K^+$ ATPase.

However, it is possible to visualize a variable H^+/ATP stoi-

chiometry without problems of premature reversal.

For example, assume two protonable groups with a pK$_a$ of
7 present on the enzyme. Activation by ATP shifts the pK$_a$ of
one of these to 4, the other to 1. At our initial pH of 6 or
7, both groups will readily deprotonate, bind K$^+$ and 2 H$^+$
will be exchanged for 2 K$^+$. As the luminal pH falls, the
high pK$_a$ group will not dissociate and 1 H$^+$ will exchange
for 1 K$^+$. Thus, the stoichiometry will change from 2 to 1.
Moreover, if both groups must protonate on the luminal surface
for pump reversal, no reversal will be seen until the luminal
pH reaches 1. At low luminal pH, if the proton does not
dissociate from the high pK group evidently there is little
expenditure of energy involving this group, and at high pH
energy expenditure is less than a fixed stoichiometry in
initiation of a proton gradient.

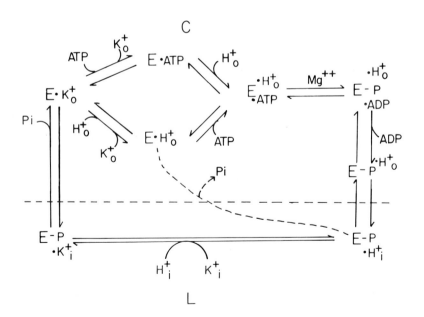

Fig. 4. Reaction pathway of gastric ATPase (from Stewart, et al).

C.   REACTION PATHWAY OF THE ATPase. Analysis of the reaction
pathway of the ATPase has involved both steady state measurements and transient kinetic data (11, 20, 21). FIGURE 4
summarizes our current concept of the reaction steps involved.
The formation of EP in the presence of cytosolic K^+ requires
the initial displacement of bound K^+ by ATP or cytosolic H^+.
In terms of conformation, there is an $E.K^+_{out}$ form of the
enzyme. Binding of ATP to the enzyme induces yet another
conformation of unphosphorylated enzyme, evidenced by more
rapid phosphorylation by added Mg^{++}, protection against
tryptic hydrolysis (22) and changes in CD spectrum (23).
Binding of Mg^{++} results in formation of EP. EP exists in
two forms, an ADP sensitive configuration as shown by the
presence of an ATP-ADP exchange reaction and a form whose
hydrolysis is accelerated by luminal K^+.

The exchange reaction is accelerated by K^+, and the
optimal ratio of ADP to ATP is 2:1. The first finding can
be explained by the rapid conversion of the EP forms and in
the absence of K^+ little of the ADP sensitive EP form is
present. K^+ accelerates the breakdown and rephosphorylation
cycle. One explanation for the 2:1 ratio of nucleotides is
that there are 2 nucleotide binding sites per enzyme.

These partial reaction kinetics are reflected in the
overall ATPase kinetics, in that K^+ shows a biphasic effect
on ATPase activity, luminal K^+ accelerating and cytosolic K^+
inhibiting the enzyme. They also explain the sidedness of
the effects of K^+ on transport.

Apart from these results there is a mounting body of
evidence that the enzyme functions as a dimer of the catalytic
site. There are two apparent K_m values for ATP both in terms
of ATPase and E-P formation. It seems there are TNP-ATP

binding sites of different affinities (24). UV irradiation
inhibits ATPase activity more rapidly than the pNPPase partial
reaction (18).

There are 2 vanadate inhibitory states, of high and low
affinity. In terms of molecular weight vanadate inhibition
in the high affinity state indicates a minimum molecular weight
of 300,000 daltons. Electron irradiation also shows a similar
MWt for ATPase and pNPPase activity. The enzyme is therefore
oligomeric (25).

The purest preparation available to date shows that the
ATPase occurs in vesicles 90% of whose protein content is
accounted for by a group of 100,000 MWt peptides. These peptides are not homogeneous, based on isoelectric focusing or
tryptic digestion. Maximal E-P levels, based on Lowry protein
determinations are about 1.5 or 2 nmole per mg protein, depending on ATP concentration. If we assume that all the protein
is active enzyme of 300,000 MWt then at maximal EP there is
less than one phosphorylation site per mol enzyme. The lower
level, however, is only 0.5 mole per mole enzyme. Various
explanations can be offered. The obvious one is that only
50% of the protein is active enzyme and the rest is either
non-enzyme peptide or inactive. Another explanation is that
only 1/2 of EP is acid stable. This would be a different
model from those currently in vogue for Na$^+$K$^+$ ATPase, whose
dimeric catalytic subunits appear to participate in the reaction. No precise information is available as to the nature
of the peptides comprising the H$^+$+K$^+$ ATPase. Partial tryptic
digestion data give some preliminary clues (22). Of the
100,000 MWt group of peptides, trypsin readily digests 2/3 of
the protein, leaving relatively intact, at 100,000 MWt, a
strongly PAS positive peptide. In the presence of ATP where
the catalytic activity is protected, E-P formation at the

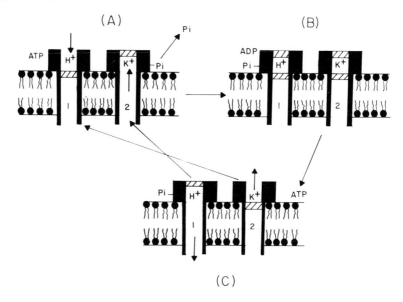

Fig. 5. Model of dimer for $H^+ : K^+$ exchange by gastric ATPase.

100,000 region of the SDS gel is maintained but 1/3 of the
protein continues to be hydrolyzed to initially 2 lower molecular weight forms, with only slight changes in ATPase activity.
Accordingly one third of the protein is the catalytic subunit
of the enzyme, and two thirds may not be involved in catalysis
per se. It is clear that the ability to isolate and reconstitute enzyme from subunits is essential for further progress
in this area.

D.   CATALYSIS-TRANSPORT COUPLING. Since a functional dimer
for the gastric ATPase is a distinct possibility, a model for
transport by this enzyme is presented in FIGURE 5 (21). Basically, this is a push-pull dimer hypothesis, with 2 gates on
either side of the cation binding sites, which are visualized
as present in the hydrophilic segment of the catalytic subunit. As visualized there are 3 states of the dimer A, B
and C. In state A monomer 1 binds ATP and cytosolic K^+.
Conversion to state B involves closing of both gates, with

monomer 1 phosphorylated and monomer 2 with K^+ bound and
occluded. Conversion to state C opens 2 gates, in monomer
1, releasing H^+ luminally and in monomer 2 K^+ cytosolically,
with ATP binding. Conversion back to state A interconverts
the 2 monomers. Thus both subunits participate in catalysis
and transport. The scheme shows only half site phosphorylation
and this is more consistent with E-P formation by the H^++K^+
ATPase than what has recently been described for the Na^++K^+
ATPase (26). The binding of Pi may be the gate mechanism for
the cytosolic face of the enzyme and the affinity changes for
H^+ and K^+ determines the gating on the luminal face of the
pump.

     This model specifies neither ligand binding sites, not
the nature of the gating mechanism. Site specific reagents
have shown the presence of amino groups at the ATP binding
site (27) as well as the involvement of SH groups (28). Histidine reactive ligands have indicated a role for this residue
(29) and DCCD and EEDQ have defined carboxyl groups in the
enzyme reaction. The latter reagent has shown that one of
the reactive carboxyl groups may be required for the binding
of luminal K^+ (30). This approach does not however give much
insight as to the motion of ligand sites during catalysis.

     It would seem probable, that whether a covalent interme-
diate is formed or not, that all ATP driven pumps have a similar mechanism. The hydrophobic membrane segment is likely to
have appropriate cation selectivity, although it may not be
absolute, simply allowing translocation of the necessary
cations, H^+ in the case of neurospora or F_1 ATPases, Ca^{++} and
H^+ or K^+ in the case of Ca^{++}-ATPase, Na^+ and K^+ in the instance
of the Na^++K^+ ATPase and H^+ and K^+ in gastric ATPase. The
forward transport mode depends absolutely on binding of the

initial cationic ligand to an appropriate number of binding
sites. This allows the transfer of phosphate from ATP to its
electrovalent or covalent binding site. This traps the ligand
in a pocket on the enzyme and the other side of the pocket
opens, with a decrease in ligand affinity. Loss of the ligand
with or without replacement with another cation depending on
whether the pump is a uniport or antiport type, determines
loss of bound phosphate with closure of the pocket which opens
at the appropriate side of the enzyme with the rebinding of
ATP.

The gastric ATPase poses a special problem, in that there
is almost a 7 log change in affinity for H^+. Whether this
occurs in a single step or not is not known. Returning to the
problem of variable stoichiometry, a 2 stage model using a
single ATP cycle may be suggested. Since there appears to
be 2 ATP sites, a possibility is that the high affinity site
on one catalytic subunit shifts the pK_a from 7 to 4 on one
site. Binding of ATP to the other subunit, while causing the
same alteration on its monomer, may by interaction cause a
further lowering of the pK_a of the proton site on the other
subunit (FIGURE 6).

The group that finally donates a proton to the medium at
pH 0.8 is a mystery. Whether a carboxyl group or phosphate
group, the pK must be changed from about 3 to its final value
by a change in environment, perhaps by approach of $R-NH_3^+$
residues which would stabilize the anionic form.

A point of interest is that HVO_4^{2-} inhibits the ATP with
high affinity, reducing activity by about 50%, inhibition with
low affinity then inhibits the rest of enzyme activity. In
permeable gastric glands, HVO_4^{2-} inhibition occurs also across
4 decades of concentration. Nevertheless in gastric vesicles,
binding with high affinity totally inhibits transport and E-P.

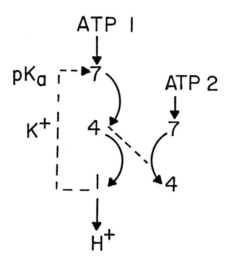

Fig. 6. 2 stage model for high pH gradients achieved by gastric ATPase.

Thus the low affinity state for $HVO_4{}^{2-}$, although playing a measurable role in transport in permeable glands, is not evident, except for ATPase activity, in isolated vesicles (31). E. BIOLOGICAL ROLE OF ATPase. The gastric H$^+$+K$^+$ ATPase may play 2 roles in cation translocation. In the stomach, acidification is its major role. Nevertheless in Na$^+$ free conditions, reabsorption of K$^+$ across the luminal surface of the parietal cell has been detected perhaps due to activity of this pump. A monoclonal antibody which reacts with the glycoprotein component of the gastric membranes, has been shown to cross react with cells in the colonic epithelium and also the renal cortical collecting duct (32). A role in K$^+$ reabsorption in the former tissue, and in the same process or acidification in the latter may be suggested.

REFERENCES

1. Mitchell, P. (1961) Nature, 191, 144-148.
2. Lundh, E.J. (1978) J. Exp. Zool. 51, 265-278.
3. Berglindh, T., Obrink, K.J. (1976) Acta Physiol. Scand. 96, 150.
4. Dibona, D.R., Ito, S., Berglindh, T., and Sachs, G. (1979) Proc. Nat. Acad. Sci. U.S.A. 76, 6689-6693.
5. Berglindh, T., Dibona, D.R., Pace, C.S. and Sachs, G. (1980) J. Cell. Biol. 85, 293-401.
6. Malinowska, D., Koelz, H.R. and Sachs, G. (1981) Proc. Nat. Acad. Sci. U.S.A., submitted.
7. Harris, J.B., Franks, H., and Edelman, I.S. (1958) Am. J. Physiol. 195, 499-504.
8. Berglindh, T. (1978) Acta Physiol. Scand. Spec. Suppl. 55-68.
9. Berglindh, T., Helander, H.F. and Sachs, G. (1979) Scand. J. Gastro. Suppl. 55, 7-14.
10. Sachs, G., Chang, H., Rabon, E., Schackmann, R., Lewin, M. and Saccomani, G. (1976) J. Biol. Chem. 251, 7690-7698.
11. Wallmark, B., Stewart, H.B., Rabon, E., Saccomani, G. and Sachs, G. (1980) J. Biol. CHem. 255, 5313-5319.
12. Koelz, H.R., Sachs, G., and Berglindh, T. (1981) Am. J. Physiol., in press.
13. Ganser, A.L., and Forte, J.G. (1973) Biochim. Biophys. Acta 307, 169-180.
14. Sachs, G., Rabon, E., Helander, H.F., Ito, S., Dibona, D.R., Saccomani, G. and Berglindh, T. (1979) in Hormone Receptors (G. Rosselin et al., eds.) pp. 327-336, Elsevier North Holland Publishing Co.
15. Wolosin, J.M. and Forte, J.G. (1981) Biophys. J. 33, 219a.

16.   Lee, J., Simpson, E. and Scholes, P. (1974) Biochem.
      Biophys. Res. Comm. 60, 825-832.

17.   Rabon, E., Chang, H., and Sachs, G. (1978) Biochemistry
      17, 3345-3353.

18.   Chang, H., Saccomani, G., Rabon, E., Schackmann, R. and
      Sachs, G. (1977) Biochim. Biophys. Acta 464, 313-327.

19.   Rabon, E., Takeguchi, N. and Sachs, G. (1980) J. Membr.
      Biol. 53, 109-117.

20.   Wallmark, B., and Mardh, S. (1979) J. Biol. Chem. 259,
      11899-11902.

21.   Stewart, H.B., Wallmark, B., and Sachs, G. (1981) J.
      Biol. Chem. 256, 2682-2690.

22.   Saccomani, G., Dailey, D.W. and Sachs, G. (1979) J. Biol.
      Chem. 254, 2821-2827.

23.   Saccomani, G., Chang, H.H., Spisni, A., Helander, H.,
      Spitzer, H.L. and Sachs, G. (1979) J. Supramol. Struct.
      11, 429-444.

24.   Saccomani, G. and Sartor, G. unpublished observations.

25.   Saccomani, G., Sachs, G., Cupoletti, J. and Jung, C.Y.
      (1981) J. Biol. Chem. submitted.

26.   Peters, N.H.M., Swarts, H.G.P., Depont, J.J.H.H.M.,
      Stekkores, F.M.A.H.S. and Bonting, S.L. (1981) Nature
      290, 332-339.

27.   Schrijen, J.S., Luyben, W.A.M.H., Depont, J.J.H.H.M.
      and Bonting, S.L. (1981) Biochim. Biophys. Acta 597,
      331-344.

28.   Schrijen, J.J., Luyben, W.A.M.H., Depont, J.J.H.M.,
      Bonting, S.L. Biochim. Biophys. Acta 640, 473-486.

29.   Saccomani, G., Barcellona, M.L., Spisni, A., and Sachs,
      G. (1981) Biophys. J. 33, 295a.

30. Saccomani, G., Barcellona, M.L. and Sachs, G. (1981) J. Biol. Chem. submitted.

31. Faller, L.D., Malinowska, D., and Rabon, E. unpublished observations.

32. Smolka, A.J.M., unpublished observations.

33. Reenstra, W., Lee, H.C. and Forte, J.G. (1980) in Hydrogen Ion Transport in Epithelia, (I.Schulz et al, eds) pp. 155-164, Elsevier North Holland Publishing Co.

THE CHROMAFFIN GRANULE: PROTON-CYCLING IN THE SLOW LANE[1]

David Njus, Michael Zallakian, and Jane Knoth

Department of Biological Sciences, Wayne State University,
Detroit MI 48202

Peter Mitchell's chemiosmotic theory rationalizes an
astonishing number of diverse phenomena (1). In this host of
energy-coupling systems, the proton cycle in chromaffin granules is distinguished by its simplicity and its slowness.
Chromaffin granules have a single mission - to store catecholamine in the adrenal medulla for secretion in times of
stress. To maintain an internal catecholamine concentration
of 0.55 M, the granules are equipped with a proton-translocating ATPase and a monoamine/H^+ antiporter (2,3). This
system must maintain a large catecholamine concentration
gradient, but, in contrast to other proton-translocating
systems, it does not actively transduce energy. In fact,
chromaffin granules pump protons and consume proton motive
force with unusual sluggishness. The uncoupled ATPase activity is only 0.2 μmol/min·mg membrane protein (4,5) compared
with 6 μmol/min·mg in inhibitor-depleted submitochondrial

[1]Supported by the National Science Foundation (BNS-7904752)
and the Michigan Heart Association.

V. P. Skulachev and Peter C. Hinkle (eds.), Chemiosmotic Proton Circuits in Biological Membranes
in honor of Peter Mitchell   ISBN 0-201-07398-6

particles (6). The V_{max} for (-) norepinephrine transport is about 7.7 nmol/min·mg membrane protein (7) compared with ∿100 nmol/min·mg for lactose transport in E. coli membrane vesicles (8).

This leisurely pace confers a number of technical advantages since it permits measurements that require some time to make. Thus, proton translocation in chromaffin granules can be followed conveniently by isotope distribution techniques (9-11) and even by ^{31}P-NMR (9,12,13). The slowness is also a theoretical advantage. Because transmembrane currents are smaller, various energy stores should be more nearly in equilibrium. Perhaps partly for that reason, measured catecholamine gradients correlate very well (14,15) with measured pH gradients (ΔpH) and membrane potentials (Δψ). Thus, the chromaffin granule permits some unique studies of energy coupling.

Other recent reviews have discussed the composition (16) and molecular organization (17) of chromaffin granules. Here we will focus on the proton-translocating ATPase and on the transport powered by it.

ATPASE FUNCTION

The chromaffin-granule ATPase requires Mg^{2+} and hydrolyzes extragranular but not intragranular ATP. The observation of ATP-dependent, uncoupler-sensitive ANS fluorescence enhancement first led Bashford et al. (18) to suspect that the ATPase translocates protons. It has since been clearly established that the ATPase generates membrane potentials (inside positive) and pH gradients (inside acid). ATP-dependent Δψ has been measured using the lipid-soluble anion SCN^- and the

optical probes bis (3-phenyl-5-oxoisoxazol-4-yl) pentamethine
oxonol and 3,3'-dipropyl-2,2'-thiadicarbocyanine (10,19-22).
The creation of pH gradients has been observed using the weak
base methylamine, the fluorescent indicator 9-aminoacridine,
and ^{31}P-NMR (9,10,12,13,21,22).

The intragranular resting pH is about 5.7 (9,12,13,23).
In the presence of a permeant anion, ATP causes an acidification of 0.4 to 0.5 pH units. The copermeant anion (Cl^- or I^-)
is required to obtain significant internal pH changes because
the granule matrix is strongly buffered. A large proton
concentration must be transported to overcome the buffering
effect, and these protons must be electrically neutralized by
the permeant anion (9). The resting chromaffin-granule
membrane potential is approximately equal to the H^+ equilibrium potential (24). At pH 6.9, this is about -70 mV.
Adding ATP (in the absence of permeant anions) changes the
membrane potential to approximately +50 mV (10). Similar
ATP-dependent ΔpH and $\Delta\psi$ are observed in ghosts, chromaffin
granules that have been lysed and resealed (11,14,15,21).

Roisin et al. (25) have shown that the ATPase is reversible. ATP is synthesized if a K^+ diffusion potential and
pH gradient are imposed across the membrane. The only estimate of the stoichiometry of the ATPase is that of Njus et al.
(12): between 2 and 4 H^+ translocated per ATP.

ATPASE STRUCTURE

Dichloromethane-solubilized ATPase has been highly
purified (4). Although the granules have relatively little
ATPase activity compared to mitochondria, the specific activity of purified chromaffin-granule ATPase (15 μmol/min·mg of

protein) is close to that of the mitochondrial F_1 ATPase (4).
This implies that the ATPase is more sparsely distributed in
chromaffin-granule membranes and, in fact, Winkler and Westhead (17) calculate that there may be as few as 10 ATPase
molecules per granule.

The chromaffin-granule ATPase has also been solubilized
using Lubrol PX (26), Nonidet P-42 (27), methylene chloride
(28) and sodium cholate (5,29). The cholate-solubilized
ATPase can be reconstituted into lipid vesicles and is more
active if reconstituted with chromaffin-granule lipids rather
than with soybean lipids (5,29). The reconstituted activity
is inhibited by N,N'-dicyclohexylcarbodiimide and stimulated
by the uncouplers S-13 and CCCP. Thus, the reconstituted
enzyme seems to be a functional proton pump.

Since chromaffin granules are commonly prepared from
bovine adrenal medullae, it is interesting to compare the
granule ATPase with the mitochondrial ATPase from bovine
heart. The molecular weight of solubilized chromaffin-granule
ATPase is approximately 400,000 (28) compared with 395,000
for beef heart mitochondrial F_1-ATPase (30). The three
largest subunits of the two enzymes have identical molecular
weights (51,000, 50,000 and 28,000) as revealed by SDS gel
electrophoresis (4). Moreover, partial proteolytic digestion
of beef heart and chromaffin-granule ATPase subunits produces
very similar peptides (4). Finally, immunological tests
indicate that the bovine chromaffin-granule ATPase is structurally similar to the bovine heart mitochondrial ATPase (4).

The chromaffin granule and mitochondrial ATPases are
similarly inhibited by quercetin, N,N'-dicyclohexylcarbodi-
imide, the alkyl tins, 4-chloro-7-dinitrobenzofurazan and
silicotungstate (4,28,31,32). Unlike mitochondrial ATPase,

chromaffin-granule ATPase is not inhibited by oligomycin, aurovertin or efrapeptin although solubilization increases its sensitivity to the latter two compounds (4,28). Urea and silicotungstate inhibit the chromaffin-granule ATPase activity but they do not cause removal of the F_1 portion as they do in mitochondria (31). Thus, although the chromaffin-granule and mitochondrial ATPases are similar, they are not identical.

PROTON-LINKED TRANSPORT

In addition to 0.55 M catecholamine, chromaffin granules contain 120 mM ATP and 22 mM ascorbate (3,16). The proton motive force generated by the chromaffin-granule ATPase drives catecholamine uptake and may also be involved in the transport of ATP and ascorbate (Figure 1).

Chromaffin-granule ghosts take up catecholamine in response to either $\Delta\psi$ or ΔpH or both acting together (11, 14, 15). Since it is driven by ΔpH (interior acid), amine uptake must be coupled to H^+ efflux (or OH^- influx). Since $\Delta\psi$ (interior positive) drives uptake, two or more H^+ must be exchanged for each catecholamine cation. Assuming that this antiport or exchange diffusion has a stoichiometry of n H^+ per catecholamine cation, the equilibrium catecholamine gradient is

$$\frac{[RNH_3^+]_{in}}{[RNH_3^+]_{out}} = \left\{ \frac{[H^+]_{in}}{[H^+]_{out}} \right\}^n e^{(n-1)F\Delta\psi/RT}$$

The dependence of catecholamine gradients on both $\Delta\psi$ and ΔpH indicate an exchange stoichiometry of 2 H^+/amine cation (14, 15).

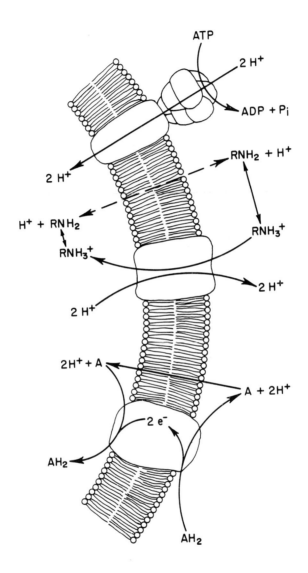

Fig. 1   Possible proton-linked transport systems in the chromaffin-granule membrane. AH_2 = ascorbate; RNH_3^+ = monoamine

Monoamine transport appears to be mediated by a translocator since it is saturable and inhibited by reserpine (7).
The translocator carries serotonin as well as the catecholamines epinephrine, norepinephrine and dopamine. It has been
solubilized using sodium cholate and successfully reconstituted into soybean lipid vesicles (33). The reconstituted
translocator mediates ΔpH-dependent, reserpine-sensitive
serotonin accumulation.

Catecholamines can apparently deprotonate and enter
liposomes electroneutrally (34). In chromaffin granules, this
unmediated reserpine-insensitive catecholamine flux is normally negligible compared to active transport. However, at high
catecholamine concentrations, active transport saturates and
this passive uptake becomes significant (35). Passive uptake
of the less polar analogues tyramine and octopamine is significant even at low concentrations; rapid passive permeability
may account for the poor active transport of these compounds.

ATP uptake may also be coupled to the proton pump.
Aberer et al. (36) reported that chromaffin granules take up
ATP and that uptake is inhibited by uncouplers and atractylo-
side. They speculate that the positive internal potential
could provide the driving force for uptake of the negatively
charged ATP. Net uptake of adenine nucleotides has not yet
been clearly demonstrated, however.

Very little is known about ascorbate accumulation.
Ingebretsen et al. (37) estimated that ascorbate is four times
more concentrated in the granules than in the cytoplasm.
Tirrell and Westhead (38) reported that dehydroascorbate but
not ascorbate enters the granules. They suggested that the
granules could trap and accumulate ascorbate simply by having
an efficient mechanism for reducing internal dehydroascorbate.

372   DAVID NJUS et al.

Although a reduction mechanism has not been reported, we
speculate that intragranular ascorbate might be reduced by
extragranular ascorbate. The reduction potential of ascorbate is pH-dependent, being ∿50 mV higher at pH 5.5 than at
pH 7.0. Consequently, the pH gradient should drive electrons
from external to intragranular ascorbate. The membrane potential (interior positive) will also promote this electron
transfer. This mechanism is a novel way of using the transmembrane proton gradient to drive dehydroascorbate reduction
and ascorbate accumulation. In this connection, it is noteworthy that the granule membranes contain a cytochrome b-561
with a reduction potential of +140 mV (39) compared to the
ascorbate reduction potential of +58 (outside) to +110
(inside). The cytochrome could be responsible for transferring electrons from external to internal ascorbate.

CONCLUSION

Chromaffin granules are a popular model for other neurosecretory vesicles. Consequently, it is not surprising that
other vesicles also appear capable of proton-linked transport.
ATP-dependent, uncoupler-sensitive norepinephrine transport
occurs in synaptic vesicles from rat brain (40). ΔpH-depen-
dent, reserpine-sensitive serotonin uptake occurs in platelet
storage organelles (41). Proton-linked transport may not be
limited to monoamine storage vesicles. Acetylcholine uptake
into vesicles in an adrenal tumor cell line (PC12) is inhibited by uncouplers (42). Even in neurosecretory vesicles
which store peptide hormones in the bovine neurohypophysis,
ATP-dependent uncoupler-sensitive membrane potential changes
have been observed (43). Thus, studies of proton movements

in chromaffin granules, inspired by work on traditional energy-coupling systems, are in turn contributing to the understanding of a new class of proton-cycling vesicles.

REFERENCES

1. Mitchell, P. (1979) Science 206, 1148-1159.
2. Njus, D. and Radda, G.K. (1978) Biochim. Biophys. Acta 463, 219-244.
3. Njus, D., Knoth, J. and Zallakian, M. (1981) in Current Topics in Bioenergetics, Vol. 11 (D.R. Sanadi, ed.), Academic Press, New York, in press.
4. Apps, D.K. and Schatz, G. (1979) Eur. J. Biochem. 100, 411-419.
5. Buckland, R.M., Radda, G.K. and Wakefield, L.M. (1979) FEBS Lett. 103, 323-327.
6. Ferguson, S.J., Harris, D.A. and Radda, G.K. (1977) Biochem. J. 162, 351-357.
7. Phillips, J.H. (1974) Biochem. J. 144, 319-325.
8. Kaczorowski, G.J., Robertson, D.E. and Kaback, H.R. (1979) Biochemistry 18, 3697-3704.
9. Casey, R.P., Njus, D., Radda, G.K. and Sehr, P.A. (1977) Biochemistry 16, 972-977.
10. Holz, R.W. (1978) Proc. Natl. Acad. Sci. USA 75, 5190-5194.
11. Johnson, R.G., Pfister, D., Carty, S.E. and Scarpa, A. (1979) J. Biol. Chem. 254, 10963-10972.
12. Njus, D., Sehr, P.A., Radda, G.K., Ritchie, G.A. and Seeley, P.J. (1978) Biochemistry 17, 4337-4343.
13. Pollard, H.B., Shindo, H., Creutz, C.E., Pazoles, C.J. and Cohen, J.S. (1979) J. Biol. Chem. 254, 1170-1177.
14. Knoth, J., Handloser, K. and Njus, D. (1980) Biochemistry 19, 2938-2942.
15. Phillips, J.H. and Apps, D.K. (1980) Biochem. J. 192, 273-278.
16. Winkler, H. (1976) Neuroscience 1, 65-80.
17. Winkler, H. and Westhead, E.W. (1980) Neuroscience 5, 1803-1823.
18. Bashford, C.L., Radda, G.K. and Ritchie, G.A. (1975) FEBS Lett. 50, 21-24.
19. Scherman, D. and Henry, J.P. (1980) Biochim. Biophys. Acta 599, 150-166.

20. Ogawa, M. and Inouye, A. (1979) Jap. J. Physiol. 29, 309-325.
21. Salama, G., Johnson, R.G. and Scarpa, A. (1980) J. Gen. Physiol. 75, 109-140.
22. Pollard, H.B., Zinder, O., Hoffman, P.G. and Nikodejevic, O. (1976) J. Biol. Chem. 251, 4544-4550.
23. Johnson, R.G. and Scarpa, A. (1976) J. Biol. Chem. 251, 2189-2191.
24. Holz, R.W. (1979) J. Biol. Chem. 254, 6703-6709.
25. Roisin, M.P., Scherman, D. and Henry, J.P. (1980) FEBS Lett. 115, 143-147.
26. Trifaro, J.M. and Warner, M. (1972) Mol. Pharmacol. 8, 159-169.
27. Apps, D.K. and Reid, G.A. (1977) Biochem. J. 167, 297-300.
28. Apps, D.K. and Glover, L.A. (1978) FEBS Lett. 85, 254-258.
29. Giraudat, J., Roisin, M.P. and Henry, J.P. (1980) Biochemistry 19, 4499-4505.
30. Yoshida, M., Sone, N., Hirata, H., Kagawa, Y. and Ui, N. (1979) J. Biol. Chem. 254, 9525-9533.
31. Apps, D.K., Pryde, J.G., Sutton, R. and Phillips, J.H. (1980) Biochem. J. 190, 273-282.
32. Bashford, C.L., Casey, R.P., Radda, G.K. and Ritchie, G.A. (1976) Neuroscience 1, 399-412.
33. Maron, R., Fishkes, H., Kanner, B.I. and Schuldiner, S. (1979) Biochemistry 18, 4781-4785.
34. Nichols, J.W. and Deamer, D.W. (1976) Biochim. Biophys. Acta 455, 269-271.
35. Drake, R.A.L., Harvey, S.A.K., Njus, D. and Radda, G.K. (1979) Neuroscience 4, 853-861.
36. Aberer, W., Kostron, H., Huber, E. and Winkler, H. (1978) Biochem. J. 172, 353-360.
37. Ingebretsen, O.C., Terland, O. and Flatmark, T. (1980) Biochim. Biophys. Acta 628, 182-189.
38. Tirrell, J.G. and Westhead, E.W. (1979) Neuroscience 4, 181-186.
39. Flatmark, T. and Terland, O. (1971) Biochim. Biophys. Acta 253, 487-491.
40. Toll, L. and Howard, B.D. (1978) Biochemistry 17, 2517-2523.
41. Rudnick, G., Fishkes, H., Nelson, P.J. and Schuldiner, S. (1980) J. Biol. Chem. 255, 3638-3641.
42. Toll, L. and Howard, B.D. (1980) J. Biol. Chem. 255, 1787-1789.
43. Russell, J.T. and Holz, R.W. (1981) J. Biol. Chem., in press.

$\Delta \bar{\mu}_{H^+}$ Consumers

CONCEPTS AND EXPERIMENTS IN BIOENERGETICS[1]

Efraim Racker

Section of Biochemistry, Molecular and Cell Biology
Division of Biological Sciences
Cornell University, Ithaca, New York 14853

In dedicating this article to my gentle and fierce

friend, Peter Mitchell, I would like to begin by giving

tribute to his conceptual contributions (1,2) which have

revolutionized our thinking as well as our experimental

approaches. He has forced us to move from the chaos of en-

zymes floating in solution to the construction of organized

compartments in the form of liposomes.

I have chosen this interplay of ideas and experiments

as the major theme of this article. Let us first look at

the past.

------

[1] Supported by NIH grant CA-08964, CA-14454, NSF grant
BMS 7517887, and ACS grant BC-156.

V. P. Skulachev and Peter C. Hinkle (eds.), Chemiosmotic Proton Circuits in Biological Membranes
in honor of Peter Mitchell   ISBN 0-201-07398-6

In the first four decades of this century glycolysis dominated the thinking of biochemists who studied ATP generation. The demonstration of the cytochrome chain by Keilin was a monumental contribution (3). But it was a simple experiment by Engelhardt (4), showing a link between respiration and phosphorylation in nucleated red blood cells, that led to a new concept of oxidative phosphorylation. But it remained a vague concept until Kalckar demonstrated the process of oxidation-linked phosphorylation in a cell-free system (5) that did not glycolyze. Quantitative measurements by Kalckar (5), Belitser and Tsibakova (6) and Ochoa (7) raised a new question and required a new concept: how can consumption of one oxygen give rise to 3 ATP?

Lipmann's classical paper in 1941 (8) brought the problem into sharper focus and introduced thermodynamic thinking to the area. The field of bioenergetics was born. Lehninger (9) identified NADH as the substrate of oxidative phosphorylation and thereby eliminated speculations centering around intermediates of the Krebs cycle as participants. Now, electron transport was the key word. Experiments during the fifties and early sixties from the laboratories of Chance, Ernster, Green, Hatefi, Hunter, Lehninger, and Slater focused on electron transport and characterized the four respiratory segments involved in oxidative phosphorylation as well as the transhydrogenase reaction. The high P:O ratio was no longer a mystery but the mechanism of ATP formation was. Conceptual contributions by Mildred Cohn (10) and Paul Boyer (11) combined with brilliantly executed experiments set limits to free-lance speculations, but the domination of glycolysis was still apparent in the formulation of the chemical hypothesis of oxidative phosphorylation by Slater in 1953 (12).

Based again on a simple experiment which showed that dinitrophenol stimulates the ATPase activity of minced rat muscle, Henry Lardy conceived the idea (13) that the ATPase activity is an expression of a reversal of oxidative phosphorylation. This was a stimulus for the isolation of a soluble ATPase (14) which was shown to be identical with F_1, the coupling factor of oxidative phosphorylation (15). But there was a curious experimental discrepancy: In contrast to the mitochondrial ATPase (16) the soluble enzyme was insensitive to oligomycin. Indeed, this feature caused doubts in many minds with respect to the significance of the soluble ATPase. But it was responsible for the formulation of two concepts. The first was that the membrane can alter the properties of an enzyme attached to it. This concept of allotopy was soon validated experimentally (17). When the purified enzyme was attached to depleted membranes, it became sensitive to oligomycin and it was no longer cold-labile. The second concept was that "troubles are good for you" (18). It gave us the courage to disect the membrane into its components using the troublesome oligomycin-insensitive F_1 assaying for factors that were responsible for imparting oligomycin-sensitivity to the ATPase. In 1966 (19) the oligomycin-sensitive complex was isolated, characterized, and shown to contain multiple "coupling factors."

In 1961 (1) Mitchell proposed that the mitochondrial ATPase is a reversible proton pump which utilizes the electrochemical proton gradient generated by the respiratory chain to generate ATP from ADP and P_i. In 1966 Jagendorf and Uribe (20) demonstrated that during a transition from an acid to an alkaline pH, chloroplasts form ATP in the dark. It took us ten years after Mitchell's first formulation of the chemiosmotic hypothesis to demonstrate the incorporation of the ATPase complex into artificial liposomes and its function as a proton pump (21). Shortly thereafter reconstitution of oxidative phosphorylation with cytochrome oxidase (22) and other complexes (cf 18) followed. None of these experiments eliminated the possibility of a direct interaction between the respiratory chain and the ATPase complex and variants of of the chemical hypothesis persisted in the literature.

The reconstitution of the mitochondrial ATPase with bacteriorhodopsin and the demonstration of light-dependent ATP formation (23) swung the pendulum toward the chemiosmotic hypothesis. It was no longer possible to talk about a high-
energy intermediate of the respiratory chain. There was no
oxidoreduction involved in the light-driven proton pump of
bacteriorhodopsin.

This brief and incomplete historical sketch makes one
point: Experiments without ideas are impotent; ideas without
experiments are sterile. There are no immaculate conceptions
in biological sciences.

So much about the past. There is little controversy
nowadays about the function of the respiratory chain as the
generator of an electrochemical proton gradient and about
the role of the ATPase complex as a reversible proton pump
which utilizes this gradient to generate ATP. There is plenty
of controversy and speculation about the mechanism of this
energy transformation. Once again new concepts are needed
to guide us at the bench and more experiments are needed to
set limits to speculations.

The first question that needs to be answered is whether
there is a phosphorylated intermediate during ATP formation
by the H^+ pump analogous to the aspartyl phosphate intermediate of the Na^+K^+ and Ca^{2+} pumps.

The present evidence and fashion is against the existence
of a phosphorylated intermediate in the proton pump. However,
the experiments that have created the fashion are mainly
negative in character: repeated failures to obtain evidence
in favor of such chemical intermediates. How long can one
hunt for a ghost? Experiments with isotopes are also consistent with the viewpoint that a covalent intermediate does not
exist in oxidative photophosphorylation. Imaginative experiments by Wimmer and Rose (24) have been designed to differ-
entiate between a reversible hydrolysis mechanism (25) and
an in-line displacement exchange mechanism (26) of oxidative
phosphorylation. With ^{18}O in the β γ bridge of ATP these
investigators measured in light-activated chloroplasts β γ
bridge to β non-bridge ^{18}O scrambling as well as the rate of
^{18}O loss from non-bridge oxygen from the γ phosphoryl group
of ATP (which they call $\gamma^{18}O$ washout). A rate of scrambling
lower than that of exchange "would militate against the formation of a phosphorylated intermediate" (24). These experiments of Wimmer and Rose are consistent with the reversible
ATP hydrolysis mechanism and inconsistent with an in-line
oxonium ion displacement. However, the authors emphasize
the ambiguities of these experiments. They did not eliminate
the possibility of a phosphorylated intermediate. A stereio-
chemical approach to the mechanism of the ATPase reaction was

taken by Webb et al. (27) in which γ-S-ATP was hydrolyzed in

[^{17}O] enriched water in the presence of mitochondrial ATPase.

The configuration of the hydrolysis product showed that in-

version of the γ-phosphorus atom has taken place, suggesting

that no phosphoenzyme intermediate had been formed. This

mechanism is similar to that catalyzed by many kinases in

which inversion takes place (28) and is in contrast to the

two-step mechanism (e.g. via a phosphoenzyme intermediate)

which takes place with retention of configuration.   The data

of Webb et al. (27) are rather convincing but have been per-

formed with soluble ATPase (F_1).   The hydrolysis catalyzed

by this enzyme may not be representative of the reactions

that take place during ATP synthesis.   We must remember the

case of glyceraldehyde-3-phosphate dehydrogenase which cata-

lyzes hydrolysis of acylphosphates even when the active site

is blocked by a sulfhydryl reagent (cf 29, p. 33). Similarly,

it seems quite possible that the hydrolysis of ATP by F_1,

which is far more rapid than the rate of ATP synthesis, rep-

resents an illicit entry of water and an abortive reaction

mechanism.

The impressive fact remains that other ion pump enzymes

that are capable of ATP formation driven by an ion gradient

have a phosphoenzyme intermediate. Why should the proton

pump be so different? The repeated failures to detect a

phosphoenzyme could be blamed on a greater lability of the intermediate because of the unavoidable presence of protons. In an analogous situation the E_2-P intermediate of the Ca^{2+} pump ATPase is exquisitely sensitive to Ca^{2+} which in the absence of ADP causes rapid hydrolysis (30). Perhaps the strongest argument against the phosphoenzyme intermediate is the fact that our birthday celebrity does not believe in it.

At the present time there are basically three hypotheses of the mechanism of ATP generation by the proton pump. The first one by Peter Mitchell is a direct mechanism proposing an interaction of the proton flux with P_i at the active site of F_1, the energy transformer of the ATPase complex. This activation of P_i is accompanied by a concerted attack by ADP resulting in ATP formation. There is no direct evidence either for or against this hypothesis and no change in this state of affairs is in sight. In contrast to previous formulations of Mitchell which were pregnant with experimental approaches, this has not born experimental fruits.

Indirect mechanisms involving conformational changes of the enzyme have been more fruitful. They center on two basic ideas. Boyer (31) and Slater (32) and Kozlov and Skulachev (33) invoke changes in nucleotide binding, while I have proposed (34,35) that the binding energy of Mg^{2+} to to the protein is the driving force of ATP formation.

The most interesting departure from the conventional viewpoint is that the major energy-requiring step is not the formation of the anhydride bond of ATP but the dissociation of bound ATP or Mg^{2+} from the enzyme. Slater's formulation (32) was mainly based on the fact that isolated F_1 preparations from mitochondria and chloroplasts contain firmly-bound ATP that exchanges when F_1 is attached to the membrane with external nucleotides during electron flow. However, it is now generally agreed (36) that the rate of dissociation of this bound ATP is too slow to be compatible with the overall rate of oxidative- or photo-phosphorylation. Boyer's proposition was largely based on the important observation that the intermediate $P_i \rightleftharpoons H_2^{18}O$ exchange took place even in the presence of uncouplers of oxidative phosphorylation. This observation is also quite compatible with the formulation of the Mg^{2+} cycle hypothesis which I would like to discuss in greater detail, particularly because it has not received much attention since it was formulated (34).

I would like to recapitulate briefly how the idea of the Mg cycle mechanism for oxidative phosphorylation came about and to emphasize that it was not based on any experiment with ATP-generating proton pumps. For many years I have felt that for the study of the mechanism of ATP-driven ion translocation and its reversal, the Ca^{2+} pump of sarcoplasmic reticulum and the Na$^+$K$^+$ pump may be more suitable than the ATP-driven proton pumps. Firstly, they have a chemically defined phosphorylated intermediate. Secondly, they are structurally much simpler. They have one major α subunit which contains the active site and which forms the phosphorylated intermediate. The roles of other subunits such as the β subunit of the Na$^+$K$^+$ ATPase and the proteolipids that are present in purified preparations of both Na$^+$K$^+$ and Ca^{2+} ATPase have still eluded definition. The similarities between the Ca^{2+} and Na$^+$K$^+$ ATPase are striking, but there are differences as well. For example, the 53,000 dalton glycoprotein of the Na$^+$ is extraordinarily tightly associated with the α subunit, while in the case of the Ca^{2+} ATPase the 53,000 dalton glycoprotein is readily removed during purification (37) and does not seem to be required for the reconstitution of an efficient Ca^{2+} pump (38). A proteolipid preparation when added to the Ca^{2+} ATPase during reconstitution increased the efficiency of pumping (39). On the other hand, a preparation free of proteolipids (40) catalyzes the transport of Ca^{2+} (41) but the efficiency ratio (Ca^{2+} transported/ATP hydrolyzed) is low (below 1). Vesicles reconstituted with preparations of Ca^{2+} ATPase which contain the proteolipids, give efficiency ratios approaching 2.

Although we do not have an entirely clear picture of the components of the physiological pump, it appears that the subunits associated with the α subunit play a regulatory rather than an essential role in the mechanism. The α subunit of the Ca^{2+} ATPase is by itself capable of functioning as an ATP-driven Ca^{2+} pump (41).

In contrast with this simplicity is the complexity of the ATP-driven proton pump (42) with a minimum of 10 subunits (α, β, γ, δ, ε, of F_1, F_6, OSCP, F_2, proteolipid and 28,000 dalton polypeptide). In view of this it is quite possible that Mitchell will prove to be right in his proposition that the basic mechanism of the proton pump is different from that of the Ca^{2+} and Na^+ pump. On the other hand, the complexity of the proton pump may have evolved during evolution from a much simpler structure for very good reasons. Why is it that the energy transformer of the proton pump is outside of the membrane but in the case of the Ca^{2+} and Na^+-K^+ pumps the transformer is embedded in the membrane? Perhaps the first ATP-generating proton pump was also intra-membranous and utilized an available electrochemical proton gradient supplied by sulfuric acid in the environment. Only later, when cells learned to generate their own proton gradients by cleavage of water or by oxidation of substrates, did it occur to the cell to push the enzyme out of the

membrane and to either increase its effectiveness as a
scavenger of ADP and P_i or to remove it from the influence
of surface charges on the membrane. This required an increased complexity: the formation of a stalk as a proton
pipeline (δ subunit) and its secure anchorage in the membrane.
In the case of the mitochondrial membrane, two protein attachment factors (F_6 and OSCP) were designed to serve this purpose. But does this necessarily mean that the basic mechanism needs to be different?

In any case, we studied the mechanism of ATP generation
by the Ca^{2+} ATPase of sarcoplasmic reticulum and observed
that a solubilized purified enzyme, without the aid of a
gradient in the absence of a compartment, can generate close
to one ATP per enzyme molecule (30). The experimental conditions to achieve this were rather stringent and required
two steps. The enzyme incubated with only Mg^{2+} and P_i
yielded $E_2 - P$. Similar first-step experiments have been
performed previously in many laboratories with both Ca^{2+}
and Na^+K^+ ATPase (cf 18). We then showed (30) that when
ADP and Ca^{2+} were added simultaniously in a second step,
ATP was formed. If Ca^{2+} was added alone or if Ca^{2+} was
present during the first step, $E_2 - P$ was hydrolyzed and no
ATP was formed. This experiment on the net formation of
ATP in the absence of an ion gradient has been confirmed

in the laboratories of Hasselbach, deMeis and Berman. ATP

formation from P_i and ADP without ion gradient was also ob-

served with the Na^+K^+ ATPase (43). Key features of these

experiments are: a) in contrast to the reversal of the pump

action which leads to ATP formation on dissipation of a Ca^{2+}

gradient, there is no Ca^{2+} gradient required with the solu-

bilized enzyme. b) the formation of $E_2 - P$ takes place with-

out addition of nucleotides and in the absence of Ca^{2+}. In

fact, as mentioned above, traces of Ca^{2+} lead to hydrolysis

of $E_2 - P$. Even hydrophobically-bound Ca^{2+}, which can only

be removed by the use of ionophores in the presence of EGTA

(44), was responsible for some losses in the level of $E_2 - P$

attainable when the enzyme was incubated with Mg^{2+} and P_i.

A better understanding of the first step of $E_2 - P$ formation

emerged from calorimetric studies with both Na^+K^+ ATPase (45)

and Ca^{2+} ATPase (46). Large heat changes were observed when

the enzymes were allowed to interact with either Mg^{2+} or P_i,

but when both were added under conditions of $E_2 - P$ formation,

less heat was liberated than on addition of Mg^{2+} alone (45).

These findings suggested that major conformational changes

take place in the proteins on interaction with their ligands.

Since the only requirement for $E_2 - P$ formation is the addi-

tion of Mg^{2+} and P_i, we proposed (45) that the energy of

ligand binding is the driving force for ATP formation. An

extension of this basic idea to membrane-associated ion trans-location was formulated (34,35) with the following features shown in Fig. 1:   The energy of Mg^{2+} binding, perhaps in conjunction with P_i binding, is the driving force for the formation of a high energy enzyme phosphate intermediate. This could be an anhydride between an aspartic residue of the protein and phosphate as was shown in the case of the Ca^{2+} and Na^+K^+ ATPase (cf 35 for historical review), or a non-covalent intermediate capable of transfer to ADP as pictured in Fig. 1 in the case of the proton pump.   The ex-periments with solubilized Ca^{2+} ATPase revealed that ATP for-mation can be achieved almost stoichiometrically with $E_2 - P$ (30).   Of course, this is a single event.   In order to gen-erate ATP continuously an additional mechanism must be in-voked.   Such a mechanism is shown in Fig. 1.   By opening and closing of the channel the site at which Mg^{2+} is bound be-comes intermittently exposed to an ion gradient (Ca^{2+} in the case of the Ca^{2+} pump when it generates ATP, or H^+ in the case of the H^+ pump).   This ion gradient is the force that pushes Mg^{2+} from its site while the ion traverses from one side of the membrane to the other.   The opening and closing of the channel is visualized to be a function of the state of phosphorylation.   When ATP is formed the channel closes again (see Fig. 1) and now Mg^{2+} can return to its site and renew the cyclic process of ATP formation.

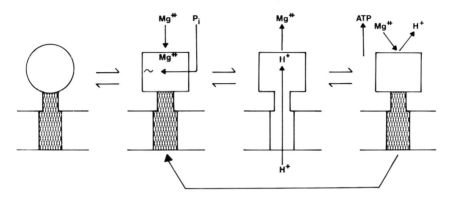

Fig. 1. <u>Proposed mechanism for the operation of the
        proton pump</u>.

    This hypothesis has stimulated us to conduct many experi-

ments on the two major aspects of the formulation: the cyclic

movement of Mg^{2+} and the cyclic opening and closing of the

channel. A competition between Mg^{2+} and the transport ion

should be demonstrable. This has been done in (unpublished)

experiments with the Ca^{2+} and H^+ ATPases. We observed confor-

mational changes in the ATPase protein on addition of Mg^{2+},

e.g. by demonstrating exposure of accessible groups (45).

We have attempted (without success) to measure the cyclic

attachment of Mg^{2+} to the Ca^{2+} ATPase. These failures were

not entirely unforeseen in view of the high K_d value of 3 mM

for Mg^{2+}. The second feature of the hypothesis induced us

to search for a natural membrane component that, like

oligomycin, is capable of closing the channel. An excellent
candidate for such a function was found in the 28,000 dalton
protein which inhibits ATP hydrolysis catalyzed by phospho-
lipid-depleted preparation of the ATPase complex (42).

But progress has been slow. We need some new concepts,
ideas on how the membrane can breathe, how the channels can
be opened and closed. As we focus on this problem, we see
a widening horizon. How do other channels operate? How
does acetylcholine open its receptor and what closes it when
desensitization sets in? How do toxins, veratridine, or the
membrane potential dictate the accessibility and passage of
ions through the channel?

How about it Peter? Can you once again steer us to
some new, exciting adventures?

REFERENCES

1. Mitchell, P. (1961) Nature (London) 191, 144-148.
2. Mitchell, P. (1966) *Chemiosmotic coupling in oxidative
   photosynthetic phosphorylation*. Bodmin, England, Glynn
   Research Ltd.
3. Keilin, D. (1925) Proc. Roy. Soc. B98, 312-339.
4. Engelhardt, V.A. (1932) Biochem. Z. 251, 343-368.
5. Kalckar, H.M. (1937) Enzymologia 2, 47-52.
6. Belitser, V.A. and Tsibakova, E.T. (1939) Biokhimiya 4
   516-535.
7. Ochoa, S. (1943) J. Biol. Chem. 151, 493-505.
8. Lipmann, F. (1941) Adv. Enzymol. 1, 99-162.
9. Lehninger, A.L. (1955) Harvey Lect. 49, 176-215.
10. Cohn, M., Drysdale, G.R. (1955) J. Biol. Chem. 216, 831-
    846.
11. Boyer, P.D. (1958) Proc. Int. Symp. Enzyme Chem.,Maruzen,
    Tokyo, pp. 301-307.

12. Slater, E. (1953) Nature (London) 172, 975-978.
13. Lardy, H.A., Elvehjem, C.A. (1945) Ann. Rev. Biochem. 14, 1-30.
14. Pullman, M.E., Penefsky, H.S., Datta, A. and Racker, E. (1960) J. Biol. Chem. 235, 3322-3329.
15. Penefsky, H.S., Pullman, M.E., Datta, A. and Racker, E. (1960) J. Biol. Chem. 235, 3330-3336.
16. Lardy, H.A., Johnson, D., and McMurray, W.C. (1958) Arch. Biochem. Biophys. 78, 587-597.
17. Racker, E. (1963) Biochem. Biophys. Res. Commun. 10, 435-439.
18. Racker, E. (1976) *A new look at mechanisms in bioenergetics.* Academic Press, New York.
19. Kagawa, Y. and Racker, E. (1966) J. Biol. Chem. 241, 2461-2482.
20. Jagendorf, A. and Uribe, E. (1966) Proc. Natl. Acad. Sci. USA 55, 170-177.
21. Kagawa, Y. and Racker, E. (1971) J. Biol. Chem. 246, 5477-5487.
22. Racker, E. and Kandrach, A. (1971) J. Biol. Chem. 246, 7069-7071.
23. Racker, E. and Stoeckenius, W. (1974) J. Biol. Chem. 249, 662-663.
24. Wimmer, M.J. and Rose, I.A. (1977) J. Biol. Chem. 252, 6769-6775.
25. Shavit, N., Skye, G.E. and Boyer, P.D. (1967) J. Biol. Chem. 242, 5125-5130.
26. Korman, E.F. and McLick, J. (1972) J. Bioenerg. 3, 147-158.
27. Webb, M.R., Grubmeyer, C., Penefsky, H.S. and Trentham, D.R. (1980) J. Biol. Chem. 255, 11637-11639.
28. Knowles, J.R. (1980) Ann. Rev. Biochem. 49, 877-919.
29. Racker, E. (1965) *Mechanisms in bioenergetics.* Academic Press, New York.
30. Knowles, A.F. and Racker, E. (1975) J. Biol. Chem. 250, 1949-1951.
31. Boyer, P.D. (1977) Ann. Rev. Biochem. 46, 957-966.
32. Slater, E.C. (1977) Ann. Rev. Biochem. 46, 1015-1026.
33. Kozlov, I.A. and Skulachev, V.P. (1977) Biochim. Biophys. Acta 463, 29-89.
34. Racker, E. (1977) Ann. Rev. Biochem. 46, 1006-1014.
35. Racker, E. (1977) in Calcium binding proteins and calcium function (R.H. Wasserman et al., eds.) Elsevier North-Holland, pp. 155-163.
36. McCarty, R.E. (1979) Trends Biochem. Sci. 4, 18-30.
37. MacLennan, D.H. (1970) J. Biol. Chem. 245, 4508-4518.
38. Racker, E. (1972) J. Biol. Chem. 247, 8198-8200.
39. Racker, E. and Eytan, E. (1975) J. Biol. Chem. 250, 7533-7534.

40. Green, N.M. (1975) in Calcium transport in contraction and secretion (E. Carafoli, et al., eds) North-Holland, Amsterdam, pp. 339-348.
41. Knowles, A., Zimniak, P., Alfonzo, M., Zimniak, A. and Racker, E. (1980) J. Membrane Biol. 55, 233-239
42. Alfonzo, M. and Racker, E. (1979) Canadian J. Biochem. 57, 1351-1358.
43. Taniguchi, K. and Post, R.L. (1974) J. Biol. Chem. 250, 3010-3018.
44. Pick, U. and Racker, E. (1979) Biochemistry 18, 108-113.
45. Kuriki, Y., Halsey, J., Biltonen, R. and Racker, E. (1976) Biochemistry 15, 4956-4961.
46. Epstein, M., Kuriki, Y., Biltonen, R. and Racker, E. (1980) Biochemistry 19, 5564-5568.

ON THE MECHANISM OF H$^+$-ATP SYNTHASE[1]

Paul D. Boyer

Department of Chemistry and Molecular Biology Institute
University of California, Los Angeles, California 90024

INTRODUCTION

One objective of this essay is to consider some aspects of the evidence that contributes to our present understanding of how ATP is made in oxidative phosphorylation and photophosphorylation. Attention is directed to the important types of experimental findings and what they tell us. It seems likely that ATP synthesis occurs essentially by a reversal of hydrolysis, with energy driving the process by changes in the nature and strength of binding of reactants at the catalytic site. A second objective is to correlate mechanistic evidence with Mitchell's splendid contributions leading to the recognition that electrochemical proton gradients across coupling membranes--the protonmotive force--can be reversibly coupled to

[1] Supported by NIH grant GM 11094, NSF grant PCM 75-18884 and DOE contract DE-AMO3-765F00034.

V. P. Skulachev and Peter C. Hinkle (eds.), Chemiosmotic Proton Circuits in Biological Membranes in honor of Peter Mitchell
ISBN 0-201-07398-6

electron transport and to ATP cleavage (1).

HOW PRESENT CONCEPTS DEVELOPED

Only a limited amount of the vast literature in the field actually contributes to an understanding of how ATP is made. No one key finding has provided compelling insight. Our present understanding has come from the accumulation of findings that when sifted and examined are found to be consistent with energy-linked binding changes having a primary role, and with the reaction of ADP and P_i to give ATP and HOH at the catalytic site occurring largely or wholly independent of energy input.

The time-honored approach of finding what components are necessary and what intermediates may participate in a process has set important limitations, and served to eliminate many possibilities. ATP synthesis occurs on coupling membranes in which enzyme complexes for electron transport and for ATP formation are imbedded. Most importantly, ATP synthesis appears to use the same catalytic sites or loci that catalyze ATP hydrolysis, whether on the membrane or in the isolated and purified ATPase. The search for covalent intermediates has led to the probability that none exist, a result with profound mechanistic implication. The application of isotope exchange probes and the development of techniques for detecting and for measuring turnover of bound reactants has led to the recognition of the role of energy-linked binding changes. These various approaches to mechanism developed independently from the recognition of the importance of electrochemical proton gradients in energy transmission.

The realization that the energy for ATP formation can be provided by proton translocation across a coupling membrane provided a salient explanation for earlier evidence that ATP

formation and cleavage could occur without requiring concomitant oxidation-reduction. But, as noted by Mitchell,(2) proton translocation could be coupled to ATP synthesis by a variety of indirect mechanisms, including participation of non-
phosphorylated covalent intermediates or energy-linked conformational changes in proteins of the ATP synthase complex.
Recognition of the importance of proton translocation did not
point the way to how energy is used in the ATP synthase complex.
However, the role of proton translocation did raise the possibility as suggested by Mitchell, of a direct involvement of
the protons in the formation of the covalent structure of ATP
(3). More important was the necessity that any mechanism proposed for ATP synthesis had to be able to account for coupling
to proton translocation across the membrane. A synthesis of
ATP driven by energy-linked conformational changes provides a
logical basis for how ATP formation may be coupled to proton
translocation. Recognition of and experimental evidence for
this coupling mechanism removed a considerable reluctance to
accept the proposed role for proton translocation.

    If the field had developed without Peter Mitchell, it is
possible that the growing understanding of the role of energy-
linked conformational changes, the experimental separation of
phosphorylations from oxidations, and the lack of detected
intermediates would have led to a prediction of coupling by
energy-linked proton translocation. Mitchell let us avoid
this slower pathway to the understanding of the transmission
of energy from oxidations to phosphorylation.

SYNTHESIS AS A REVERSAL OF HYDROLYSIS

    The view is becoming increasingly adopted that net ATP
synthesis coupled to energy use occurs essentially through an

energy-linked reversal of hydrolysis. The simplest possibility
is that during either synthesis or hydrolysis the same catalytic sites or loci on the ATP synthase complex are used for
the binding of the ATP, ADP and P_i. However, some steps in
the reaction sequence that occur in hydrolysis by the isolated
ATPase must be changed when the membrane-bound complex functions
in the synthase mode. What these changes may be is considered
briefly later. Some of the reasons for regarding synthesis as
a reversal of hydrolysis are given here.

That a communal enzyme and likely a communal pathway is
used for synthesis or hydrolysis has gained support from the
myriad of fractionation, inhibition and mutant studies showing
that an ATPase complex isolatable from competent membranes is
essential for electron transport-linked phosphorylation by
mitochondria, chloroplasts and microorganisms. This ATPase is
the only ATP binding protein found on coupling membranes, other
than the nucleotide translocase of mitochondria, in amounts
reasonable for participation in ATP synthesis. The amounts of
bound catalytic intermediates demonstrated with chloroplast
thylakoid membranes and likely participating with other membranes, is accounted for by the amounts of the ATPase present.

Chemical characterizations of ATP formation also point to
synthesis as a simple elimination of water from P_i to form ATP.
No cofactors or covalent phosphorylated or nonphosphorylated
intermediates have been found. In ATP formation, an oxygen
from P_i is lost to water and in cleavage of ATP a water oxygen
appears in P_i. Further, the cleavage with the isolated ATPase
occurs with inversion of configuration around the P atom, consistent with a single displacement on the P by an attacking
water oxygen (4).

Although the participation of one catalytic site on the
β-subunit for both synthesis and hydrolysis seems attractive,

there is some uncertainty about this at present. This uncertainty arises principally from differing inhibitions that have
been observed. Most active site inhibitors have been studied
only with the isolated ATPase, and the behavior of inhibited
or modified ATPase when present on membranes has received only
limited attention. One example is the provocative observation
of Vallejos et al. (5), that during modification of arginine
residues in chromatophores ADP but not ATP can protect against
inactivation of synthesis capacity, but that ATP and not ADP
protects against inactivation of ATPase. The authors suggest
that portions of the catalytic sites involved may be different.
Similarly, a striking result comes from the careful studies of
Steinmeier and Wang (6), who demonstrated that ATPase inhibited
by reaction with NBD-Cl when reconstituted onto depleted membranes allows energy-linked synthesis to occur. Ferguson and
Radda (7) showed that the tyrosine residue that is modified by
NBD-Cl is very likely not at the catalytic site for hydrolysis.
Apparently the catalytic sites are available for synthesis.

The phenomenon could be related to the interesting observations from Vinogradov's laboratory (8) that preincubation of
submitochondrial particles with low concentrations of ADP, and
in absence of added ATP, results in inhibition of the initial
rate of ATPase without effecting the capacity for oxidative
phosphorylation. It is tempting to consider that this ADP
inhibition, the NBD-Cl inhibition and the action of ATPase
inhibitor protein are all reflections of a control mechanism
whose function is to conserve ATP when ATP/ADP ratios and
energy supply are unfavorable.

Irrespective of whether identical, closely identical or
even separate sites are involved in synthesis and hydrolysis,
the evidence remains that the first covalent bond formed by

either P_i or ADP is that in ATP itself, and it is thus useful to regard the energy-linked synthesis as occurring by reversal of a hydrolytic sequence. Steps in this sequence that might be modified by energy input are considered in the next section.

CHANGES THAT OCCUR UPON ENERGIZATION

Evidence now appears convincing that the phosphate oxygen exchanges of oxidative and photophosphorylation result from reversible formation of ATP from ADP and P_i at the catalytic site. The deductions about mechanism that follow if energy-linked ATP synthesis and oxygen exchanges result from such a reversal of hydrolysis by the H^+-ATP synthase are powerful and simple. They can be illustrated by considering a minimal reaction scheme and the changes in rates that must be brought about by energization.

The three minimal required steps as depicted in Eq. 1 are

$$E + ADP + P_i \underset{k_2}{\overset{k_1}{\rightleftharpoons}} E{:}^{ADP}_{P_i} \underset{k_4}{\overset{k_3}{\rightleftharpoons}} \overset{HOH}{\underset{HOH}{}} E{\cdot}ATP \underset{k_6}{\overset{k_5}{\rightleftharpoons}} E + ATP \tag{1}$$

a competent binding of ADP and P_i, conversion to ATP with formation of water, and release of ATP. Any or all of the three steps could be modified by energy input. For example, Mitchell has commented that the proton gradient may promote binding of P_i (3) and Slater has suggested that energy may cause release of tightly bound ATP (9).

Without energization, the overall equilibrium for ATP formation, to the nearest power of 10, may be taken as 10^{-6}. Thus for equilibrium with 1 mM P_i and 1 mM ADP only 10^{-12}M

$$K_{eq} = 10^{-6} = \frac{[ATP]}{[ADP][P_i]} = \frac{[10^{-12}]}{[10^{-3}][10^{-3}]}$$

ATP would be present. With the energization provided by oxidative phosphorylation, the concentration of ATP attainable in
a dynamic steady state and in apparent equilibrium ($\sim K_{eq}$) with
1 mM P_i and 1 mM ADP is about 10 mM ATP or

$$\sim K_{eq} = \frac{[10^{-2}]}{[10^{-3}][10^{-3}]} = 10^4 \quad .$$

Thus, the energization change of K_{eq} to $\sim K_{eq}$ is equivalent to
about 10 orders or magnitude, or a ΔG for ATP synthesis of
about 13.5 kcal/mole.

What is important for our purpose is that for the minimal
sequence of Eq. 1 for the following holds:

$$K_{eq} = \frac{k_2\ k_4\ k_6}{k_1\ k_3\ k_5} , \text{ and } \sim K_{eq} = \sim \frac{(k_2\ k_4\ k_6)}{(k_1\ k_3\ k_5)}$$

where the $\sim$ and the parentheses mean that energization must
change one or more of the six rate constants to give an overall change of apparent equilibrium by a factor of 10^{10}. The
question is thus which rate constants are changed by energization? Does energization change rate constants for covalent
bond formation or for reactant binding? A clear answer is
provided by the oxygen exchange measurements.

Measurement of the extent of oxygen exchange and the distribution of oxygen-labeled species formed from highly labeled
reactants allows deductions about how bound P_i or bound ATP
partition between release or exchange. Appreciable oxygen
exchange will accompany ATP hydrolysis only if $k_3 \cong$ or $> k_2$,
that is, if the rate of formation of ATP from P_i at the

catalytic site is about the same as the rate of release of P_i.
A striking characteristic of the oxygen exchanges is that with
deenergized submitochondrial particles at all ATP concentrations or with purified ATPase at low ATP concentration, oxygen
exchanges show that rapid reversal of hydrolysis of ATP at the
catalytic site still occurs. This is incompatible with energization changing k_3 or k_4; that is driving the covalent bond
forming step. Reasons for this incompatibility are given in
the following paragraphs.

   If energization were to drive covalent bond formation,
this could be done by promoting the water formation step
governed by k_3, or the reverse step which is governed by k_4.
The requirement of a large change in k_4 for coupled ATP synthesis, with k_1 and k_2 remaining the same, would mean that
with deenergized submitochondrial particles or with isolated
ATPase a rapid and reversible formation of bound ATP from
medium P_i and ADP should still be occurring. Energization by
decreasing k_4 would allow build up of E·ATP and ATP release.
But such a sequence would demand an ability of deenergized
submitochondrial particles or isolated ATPase to catalyze a
rapid $P_i \rightleftharpoons$ HOH exchange with only P_i and ADP present. This
is contrary to experimental fact. Also, because ATP hydrolysis
can be rapid in deenergized systems, and $P_i \rightleftharpoons$ ATP exchange can
be rapid during net ATP synthesis, k_4 must be relatively large
with or without energization.

   If energization changed k_3 to a $\sim k_3$ by a factor of 10^{10},
or even by much less, then the probability of oxygen exchange
during ATP hydrolysis by deenergized systems would be near
zero. Considerable medium $P_i \rightleftharpoons$ HOH exchange accompanies ATP
synthesis, with characteristics showing that k_2 and k_3 do not
differ by more than an order of magnitude. A similar result

applies to ATP hydrolysis with both energized and deenergized submitochondrial particles. I conclude that rate constants governing covalent bond formation remain largely or wholly unchanged upon energization.

The continuation of oxygen exchanges in deenergized systems is readily accommodated by energization affecting the binding of reactants. The binding change mechanism for ATP synthesis is based on various experimental findings showing that energization promotes the binding of P_i and ADP in a mode competent for ATP formation and the release of tightly bound ATP. In terms of Eq. 1 this could theoretically be by an increase in k_1 and k_5 or by a decrease in k_2 and k_6. Because the $P_i \rightleftharpoons$ ATP exchange is rapid when energized submitochondrial particles drive ATP synthesis to a quasi-equilibrium, k_2 and k_6 must remain relatively large. For this reason, and because experiments show lack of competent P_i binding and of ATP release upon deenergization, the major changes appear to be in k_1 and k_5. In terms of the minimal system given by Eq. 1, the apparent equilibrium attainable with energization is as follows:

$$\sim K_{eq} = \frac{k_2 \; k_4 \; k_6}{\sim k_1 \; k_3 \sim k_5} \quad .$$

Although present evidence is consistent with changes only in k_1 and k_5 upon energization, much additional measurement is essential to find whether modifications in other rate constants may also occur.

Two different ways may be suggested as to how energization can change a k_1 and k_5 to a $\sim k_1$ and $\sim k_5$; that is, to change each such that $\sim k_1 \sim k_5$ is some 10 orders of magnitude greater than $k_1 k_5$, as is necessary to account for the overall change in apparent equilibrium constant.

One way may be that energization in some manner deforms or modifies the groups or surfaces participating in reactant binding in a manner to effect the necessary changes. This would mean that the structure of the catalytic site, the binding groups and restrictions are different from those involved in deenergized cleavage. Stated another way, some enzyme conformations or arrangements participate that do not exist during catalysis by the isolated ATPase.

A second possibility is that the isolated ATPase has the capacity for and indeed undergoes the same conformational and active site changes as shown by the ATP synthase complex during net and reversible ATP synthesis. Essentially, the rates of transition between conformations, and thus the equilibria involved, would be changed by energization. For example, tightly bound ATP dissociates very slowly from the isolated ATPase or deenergized membranes, but slow dissociation undoubtedly occurs and a conformation that allows dissociation must be attainable. With energization, attaining this conformation may be favored.

APPLICATION TO A MORE COMPLEX SEQUENCE

The minimal sequence shown by Eq. 1 is useful for consideration of the principal parts of the overall reaction cycle that may be modified by energy input. The actual reaction steps for ATP synthesis are demonstrably more complex, but the simple considerations developed above are applicable to more complex sequences. Essentially, in order to achieve net ATP formation, energy input must modify rate constants if energy-linked synthesis occurs by use of catalytic sites that also can participate in ATP cleavage when there is no linkage to an energy-requiring reaction, such as proton translocation.

As a working basis, my laboratory group is currently
assessing a mechanism as depicted in our previous publica-
tions (e.g. 10). In this mechanism one energy-linked conformational event promotes both competent ADP and P_i binding and
ATP release for two identical catalytic sites that alternate
in function. The key step may be depicted as follows:

$$\begin{array}{c} ADP \\ P_i \end{array} : E < ATP \xleftrightarrow{\quad\overset{\sim}{\nwarrow}\quad} \begin{array}{c} ADP > \\ P_i > \end{array} E \cdot ATP$$

The complete sequence includes branch pathways for reactant
binding or release and covalent interconversion. Although the
scheme appears complex, at higher substrate only 6 different
enzyme species exist with interconversion governed by 8 rate
constants. We are at present, by various techniques, attempting to further appraise if the scheme is valid and to devise
approaches that will give values for the rate constants and
effects of energization on rates. With the purified ATPase
the same scheme appears to apply, with addition of the possi-
bility of a relatively slow dissociation, $E\begin{smallmatrix}<ADP \\ <P_i\end{smallmatrix} \longrightarrow E + ADP +$
P_i, without ATP binding at the alternate site. Such a model
appears to adequately account for biphasic velocity vs. substrate curves for the beef heart F_1-ATPase and for modulations
of oxygen exchange by ATP concentration.

CONCLUSION

It is a pleasure and privilege to make a contribution to
a volume honoring Peter Mitchell. His theoretical vision and
experimental aptitude led the field to the recognition of the
importance of energy-linked proton translocation in electron
transport-coupled phosphorylations and in active transport.
A coupling of proton translocation to various processes through
energy-linked conformation changes affecting binding of

reactants or of transported substances provides a very appealing general way that nature may use Mitchell's protonmotive
force.

REFERENCES

1. Mitchell, P. (1979) Science 206, 1148-1159.
2. Mitchell, P. (1966) Research Report No. 66/1, Glynn Res.
    Ltd., Bodmin, Cornwall, pp. 192.
3. Mitchell, P. (1974) FEBS Letters 43, 189-194.
4. Webb, M. R., Grubmeyer, C., Penefsky, H. S. and Trentham,
    D. R. (1980) J. Biol. Chem. 255, 11637-11639.
5. Vallejos, R. H., Lescano, W. I. M., Lucero, H. A. (1978)
    Arch. Biochem. Biophys. 190, 578-597.
6. Steinmeier, R. C. and Wang, J. H. (1979) Biochemistry 18,
    11-18.
7. Ferguson, S. J., Lloyd, W. J., Lyons, M. H., Radda, G. K.,
    (1975) Eur. J. Biochem. 54, 117-126.
8. Minkov, I. B., Vasilyeva, E. A., Fitin, A. F., Vinogradov,
    A. D. (1980) Biochem. Int'l. 1, 478-485.
9. Slater, E. C. (1977) Ann. Rev. Biochem. 46, 1015-1026.
10. Rosen, G., Greeser, M., Vinkler, C. and Boyer, P.D.
    (1979) J. Biol. Chem. 254, 10654-10661.

HOW DOES MEMBRANE POTENTIAL DRIVE ATP SYNTHESIS?

Igor A. Kozlov

Isotope Department, A.N. Belozersky Laboratory of
Molecular Biology and Bioorganic Chemistry,
Moscow State University, Moscow 117234, U.S.S.R.

INTRODUCTION. Mitchell's chemiosmotic theory (1,2) may be considered to have been indisputably proved (see reviews 3-6). However, how the difference in the electrochemical potentials of H^+-ions on the mitochondrial membrane ($\Delta\bar{\mu}_{H^+}$) bring about the ATP synthesis reaction remains a mystery. Like any other enzyme reaction, ATP synthesis occurs in at least three stages: 1) the binding of the reaction substrates (ADP and P_i) to the active site of mitochondrial H^+-ATPase; 2) the catalytic step of the reaction (the formation of ATP from ADP and P_i in the active site of ATPase); and 3) the release of ATP from the active site into the solution.

To elucidate the mechanism of the transformation of the energy $\Delta\bar{\mu}_{H^+} \rightleftharpoons$ ATP, two questions must be answered consecutively: which stage of the ATP-synthetase reaction is affected by membrane potential? And how does the membrane potential shift the equilibrium of the given stage in the reaction in a favorable direction? In my opinion, the first of these problems can already be regarded as solved. The data allow us to conclude that the membrane potential lowers the affinity of the active site of ATPase to ATP, thereby allowing the release of the ATP from the active site into the matrix. These data are discussed in the first section of this paper.

V. P. Skulachev and Peter C. Hinkle (eds.), Chemiosmotic Proton Circuits in Biological Membranes
in honor of Peter Mitchell   ISBN 0-201-07398-6

The second problem - what is the mechanism of $\Delta\bar{\mu}_H^+$-depen-
dent ATP release from the active site of mitochondrial
ATPase? - has still not been solved. Some hypotheses on this
subject are discussed in the second part of the paper.

IDENTIFICATION OF THE ENERGY-DEPENDENT STAGE IN THE ATP
SYNTHESIS REACTION. ATP hydrolysis is accompanied by the
release of a large amount of energy [the hydrolysis equilibrium constant K_H' is approximately equal to $10^5 M$ (7)]. It
was quite natural to suppose that in membrane-linked phosphorylation the energy of $\Delta\bar{\mu}_H^+$ is expended on ATP formation
in the active site of ATPase.

The most elegant scheme of this type was proposed by
Mitchell (8). Mitchell suggested that H^+ ions could be
pumped into the ATPase active site located on the matrix side
of the mitochondrial membrane, when $\Delta\bar{\mu}_H^+$ is generated across
the membrane. Such acidification of the active site leads to
a shift of the ATPase reaction equilibrium towards ATP synthesis. Mitchell's idea explains how ATP synthesis is
supplied with energy when $\Delta\bar{\mu}_H^+$ across the membrane is in the
form of $\Delta\psi$ as well as in the form of ΔpH. This makes the
idea of H^+ ions being pumped to the active site very attractive. However, the notion that ATP synthesis in the active
site requires energy, is now highly problematic. The results
obtained in our group testify to the fact that in the absence
of any external source of energy ($\Delta\bar{\mu}_H^+ = 0$) the equilibrium
of the ATPase reaction in the active site is greatly shifted
towards ATP synthesis compared with equilibrium of ATP
hydrolysis in water.

The idea that energy released in the electron transport

chain is expended not at the catalytic site, but at the stage
of ATP release from the ATPase active site, was first put
forward by Boyer et al. (9-11). Similar ideas were discussed
in our group on the basis of the chemiosmotic theory.
According to our views (12,13), ATP synthesis in the ATPase
active site occurs without any input of energy, and $\Delta\bar{\mu}_{H}+$
across the membrane is expended by ATP release into the
matrix.

The concept of energy-dependent ATP release from the
ATPase active site has been supported by iostope exchange
experiments, carried out by Boyer's group (14-16). Those
isotope exchange reactions (ATP-$^{32}P_i$ and ATP-$H_2^{18}O$), which
include the stage of ATP release, are inhibited by uncouplers
and, therefore, depend on $\Delta\bar{\mu}_{H}+$. On the other hand, $P_i-H_2^{18}O$
intermediate isotope exchange is not sensitive to uncouplers.
At low ATP concentrations this exchange reaction was even
catalyzed by isolated F_1 (soluble mitochondrial ATPase) (16).
The intermediate $P_i-H_2^{18}O$ exchange probably reflects the
reversibility of ATP hydrolysis in the ATPase active site.
The occurrence of this exchange also testifies to the fact
that the rate of ADP phosphorylation in the active site is
higher than the rate of ADP and P_i release into the solution.

Thus, the results obtained by Choate et al. (16) proved
that ADP phosphorylation in the ATPase active site could
occur at a high rate in the absence of membrane potential,
i.e. ATP synthesis in the active site of ATPase is possible
from a kinetic point of view without the participation of
$\Delta\bar{\mu}_{H}+$.

The studies carried out in our group (17,18) allowed us
to estimate the value of the equilibrium constant of ATP
hydrolysis in the ATPase active site. Fig. 1 shows the

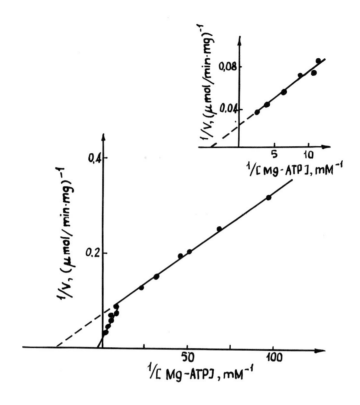

<u>Fig. 1</u>. Dependence of the rate of the F_1-ATPase reaction on the substrate concentration (18). The insert shows an enlarged fragment of the same curve. The ATPase activity was measured in an ATP-regenerating system.

dependence of the rate of ATP hydrolysis by isolated F_1 on the substrate concentrations (Lineweaver-Burke plot). The kinetics of the ATPase reaction do not obey the Michaelis-Menten equation. Similar data were obtained by Schuster et al. (19) and Takeshige et al. (20). According to Fig. 1, the scheme of the ATPase reaction could be described as follows:

$$F_1 + ATP \xrightarrow[k_{-1}]{k_{+1}} [F_1 \cdot ATP] \xrightarrow{K_H} [ADP \cdot F_1 \cdot P_i] \xrightarrow{k_2} F_1 + ADP + P_i$$

$$\Bigg\updownarrow ATP$$

$$\begin{bmatrix} ADP \cdot F_1 \cdot P_i \\ ATP \end{bmatrix} \xrightarrow{k_3} F_1 + ADP + P_i + ATP$$

The ^{18}O isotope exchange studies (16) show that at low
ATP concentrations ADP and P_i release from the ATPase active
site is a rate-limiting step in the ATPase reaction. At high
substrate concentrations ATPase binds the second ATP molecule. This leads to an increase in the ADP and P_i release
rate ($k_3 > k_2$). At high substrate concentrations the rate of
ADP and P_i release begin to be greater than that of ADP
phosphorylation in the active site and, as a result, the
intermediate ^{18}O isotope exchange is not observed (16). The
binding of the second ATP molecule also leads to a decrease
in the affinity of the active site to the substrate (at high
substrate concentrations $K_{m(app)}$ of the ATPase reaction
increases: Fig. 1). Thus, both of the changes in the kinetics
of ATP hydrolysis at high substrate concentrations (the
increase in the rate and the increase in the $K_{m(app)}$) can be
explained by a lowering of the affinity of the factor F_1
active site to ATP and ADP as a result of the second ATP
molecule binding to the enzyme.

For further analysis of the kinetic scheme of the ATPase
reaction we used the non-hydrolyzable ATP analog, AMPPNP. It
appeared that AMPPNP release from the ATPase active site
occurs at a very low rate (17,18) (see also 21,22). k_{-1}
determined from the rate of the reactivation of F_1-ATPase
preincubated with AMPPNP is equal to $2 \times 10^{-2} min^{-1}$ (18).
Thus, the ATP binding to the ATPase active site is almost
irreversible. In this case, at low substrate concentrations

(when no binding of the second ATP molecule occurs) k_{+1} = $k_{cat}/K_{m(app)}$. From the data in Fig. 1 we have k_{cat} = 5 x $10^3 min^{-1}$, $K_{m(app}$ = 0.03 mM and k_{+1} = 1.7 x $10^8 M^{-1} min^{-1}$. Consequently, the constant of ATP dissociation from the ATPase active site K_{ATP} = k_{-1}/k_{+1} is approximately equal to 10^{-10}M. K_{ADP} determined from the data on the competitive inhibition of the ATPase reaction is equal to 0.15 - 0.5 mM (23-25). According to Ting and Wang (26,27) K_{Pi} for the free inorganic phosphate binding to the active site of F_1-ATPase is equal to 1.1 - 1.3 mM. From the energy balance equation we have K_H = $K_{ATP} \cdot K'_H \cdot_{ADP} \cdot K_{Pi}$ where K'_H equal to 10^5M (7) is the constant for the equilibrium of the ATP hydrolysis in water. Thus, K_H = 10 - 100, i.e. the equilibrium in the active site of F_1-ATPase, compared with that in the aqueous solution, is greatly shifted towards ATP synthesis.

A similar conclusion may be drawn from the following in-dependent consideration. As noted above, at low ATP con-centrations the rate of ADP phosphorylation in the active site of ATPase is greater than the ADP and P_i release rate (16). Considering that the release of ADP and P_i is the rate-limiting step of the ATPase reaction (16) and taking into account the data on the ATPase reaction rate (Fig. 1), it may be concluded that the ratio of ATP synthesis in the active site is more than 10^3 turnovers per min. On the other hand, the maximum rate of ATP hydrolysis, like that of any other hydrolase reactions should not exceed 10^5 turnovers per min (the given value is the limit for the substrate protona-tion rate at the active site of the enzyme by a proton-donating group during acid-base catalysis). The ratio of the maximum possible rate of ATP hydrolysis in the active site to the minimum rate of ATP synthesis results in a value of K_H of no more than 100.

As noted above, when the second ATP molecule is bound to factor F_1, the rate of ADP and P_i released from the active site began to be greater than the rate of ATP synthesis in the active site. Since in the active site the ATP synthesis rate differs little from the ATP hydrolysis rate it seems very likely that at high substrate concentrations the ATP hydrolysis in the active site is a rate-limiting step in the ATPase reaction.

The value obtained for K_H confirms the correctness of Boyer's idea that ATP could be formed in the active site without the participation of external sources of energy. Consequently, energy is needed for the release of the synthesized ATP from the active site into the solution. This conclusion has also been confirmed by our experiments (17) on energy-dependent AMPPNP release from the active site of submitochondrial particle ATPase. The ATPase activity measured in uncoupler-treated submitochondrial particles, which have been preincubated with AMPPNP is very low for several minutes and then increases spontaneously (Fig. 2, lower curve). Without the AMPPNP pretreatment the rate of the ATPase reaction is high and constant from the beginning of the assay. In Fig. 3 (curve 1) AMPPNP-pretreated particles were added to a mixture containing succinate. After 20 sec the uncoupler CCCP was added. One can see that in this case ATP hydrolysis is fast and linear; but, if CCCP is added to the reaction mixture before the particles (curve 2), the ATPase is again slower initially, but then accelerates.

These experiments show that the energization of the membrane leads to a sharp increase in the rate of ATP analog release from the active site. The results obtained confirm

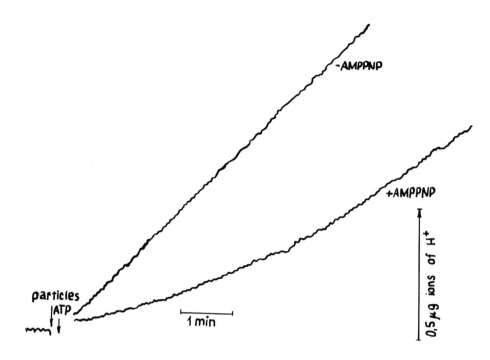

<u>Fig. 2</u>. The spontaneous reactivation of submitochondrial particles preincubated with AMPPNP (17). Particles (80 mg protein/ml) were preincubated for 5 min at 20°C in a solution of 0.25 M sucrose, 10 mM HEPES (pH 7.5) and 0.1 mM MgSO$_4$ with or without 0.1 mM AMPPNP. Then 0.2 ml of this mixture was added to an 8 ml solution of 0.25 M sucrose, 2 mM Tris-HCl (pH 8.3) and 2 mM carbonylcyanide-p-chlormethyoxyphenyl hydrazone (CCCP). The ATPase reaction was initiated by addition of 2 mM Mg-ATP. The reaction was measured at 15°C.

the conclusion that the energy of $\Delta\bar{\mu}_H+$ is expended at the stage of ATP release from the ATPase active site.

HOW DOES $\Delta\bar{\mu}_H+$ FACILITATE THE REMOVAL OF ATP FROM THE ATPase ACTIVE SITE? Two mechanisms are proposed for $\Delta\bar{\mu}_H+$-dependent ATP release from the ATPase active site. According to Boyer (9), $\Delta\bar{\mu}_H+$-supported H$^+$-ion transfer along the H$^+$-conducting

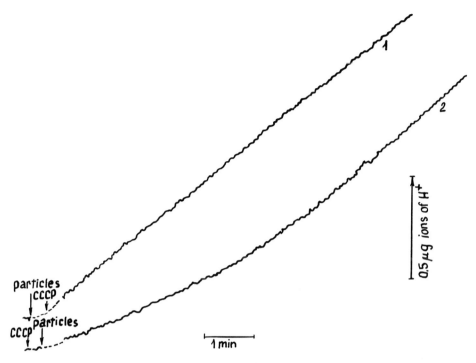

Fig. 3. The effect of energization of the membrane on the
rate of the ATPase reactivation for submitochondrial particles preincubated with AMPPNP (17). Conditions as in Fig.
2, but 10 mM succinate was added to the mixture for measuring
ATPase activity.

pathway is accompanied by conformational rearrangements in

the membrane section of the ATPase complex (F_o). The con-

formational energy accumulated in F_o is transferred to F_1-

ATPase in such a way that the affinity of the ATPase active

site to ATP is sharply decreased.

Another kind of mechanism of $\Delta\bar{\mu}_H+$-supported ATP release

has been proposed by us (12,13). This mechanism is based on

Mitchell's idea on the possible participation of ATP, ADP and

P_i in proton translocation (28,29). According to our scheme, the membrane potential lowers the affinity of the ATPase active site to ATP without changing its affinity to ATP and P_i owing to the fact that ATP is less electro-negative than $ADP + P_i$. In actual fact, at neutral or alkaline pH values ATP has four negative charges. ADP and P_i at neutral pH values have five negative charges in totum. At alkaline pH values or in the complex with positively charged ligands these compounds could even exist in the form of ADP^{3-} and PO_4^{3-}, i.e. all in all they could have six negative charges. If we assume that ADP^{3-} and PO_4^{3-} (or HPO_4^{2-}) bind with six (or five) positively charged protein ligands of F_1-ATPase [such ligands could be atoms of a metal (30), lysine residue (27) and/or arginine residue (31)], then the total charge of the complex will be equal to zero. A complex of the same ligands with ATP^{4-} formed from ADP^{3-} and PO_4^{3-} (or HPO_4^{2-}) with a comsumption of $2H^+$, which has entered the active site along the H^+-conducting pathway from the outer mitochondrial space, will be charged positively. If the ATPase active site is now separated from the matrix by the hydrophobic barrier (electro-isolating layer of the membrane), the positively charged complex of ATP with the ligands will be translocated to the matrix down the $\Delta\bar{\mu}_{H^+}$-gradient.

When ΔpH instead of $\Delta\psi$ is the driving force of the membrane-linked phosphorylation, the translocating of the positively charged complex of ATP with ligands from the active site of ATPase to the matrix will be carried out down the local electric field. This local electric field could be created in the membrane as a result of protonation through the H^+-conducting pathway of certain groups in the region of the active site and the dissociation of H^+-ions from other

groups facing the matrix. The latter mechanism may also work
if the H^+-conducting pathway crosses the hydrophobic barrier
of the membrane and the active site is located on the matrix
side of the membrane. In this case, the H^+-ions being pumped
into the active site area [as is supposed in Mitchell's
scheme (8)] will decrease the affinity of the active site to
the positively charged complex of ATP with ligands. Here
again the generation of $\Delta\bar\mu_H{}^+$ on the membrane will result in
the lowering of the affinity of the ATPase active site to
ATP.

The experiments supporting the proposed mechanism of
$\Delta\bar\mu_H{}^+$-dependent ATP release from the ATPase active site (substrate translocating concept) are described in other articles
(see reviews 12, 13, 32). Here I should like to dwell on
just one aspect of this concept. The location of the ATPase
active site in direct contact with the H^+-conducting pathway
presupposes the existence of a special isolating barrier
between the active site and the matrix. Without such a
barrier H^+-ions will enter the matrix from the H^+-conducting
pathway through the active site, and this results in uncoupling. The existence of an isolating barrier between the
matrix and the active site means that a special mechanism for
substrate translocation should function. In our opinion,
ADP, ATP, and P_i enter the active site by a relay mechanism
(12,13,32). In this relay transfer mechanism the non-catalytic nucleotide binding site(s) takes part. It is quite
possible that the very need for such a relay transfer mechanism
is the main reason for the complicated subunit structure of
ATPase and in particular for the existence of the noncata-
lytic nucleotide binding sites on the α-subunits of F_1-
ATPase (33,34).

CONCLUSION. The research of the last few years has shown that the ATP synthesis in the H^+-ATPase active site may occur spontaneously (without external sources of energy). While this ATP is in the active site, it is not a "high energy compound". To convert the ATP synthesized in the active site into a "high energy compound", the energy of $\Delta\bar{\mu}_{H^+}$ is required. $\Delta\bar{\mu}_{H^+}$ induces ATP release from the active site of H^+-ATPase into the matrix.

The precise mechanism of $\Delta\bar{\mu}_{H^+}$-dependent ATP release is still unknown. It seems, however, quite probable that the difference in charges between the substrates (ADP and P_i) and the product (ATP) of the ATP synthesis reaction is a factor that plays an important part in the mechanism of transformation of energy $\Delta\bar{\mu}_{H^+} \longleftrightarrow$ ATP on the membrane.

ACKNOWLEDGEMENTS. I would like to thank Professor V.P. Skulachev, Dr. V.B. Chernyak, Dr. Ya. M. Milgrom, add Dr. Ye. N. Volfson for discussion of the paper, and my wife Glenys for preparation of the paper.

REFERENCES

1. Mitchell, P. (1961) Nature 191, 144-148.
2. Mitchell, P. (1966) Chemiosmotic Coupling in Oxidative and Photosynthetic Phosphorylation. Bodmin, Glynn Res.
3. Skulachev, V.P. (1974) in Biochem. Soc. Spec. Suppl., Vol. 4, pp. 175-184, Great Britain.
4. Skulachev, V.P. (1977) FEBS Lett. 74, 1-9.
5. Mitchell, P. (1979) Science 206, 1149-1159.
6. Skulachev, V.P. (1980) in Soviet Scientific Reviews. Biology (V.P. Skulachev, ed), Vol. 1, pp. 239-312, Overseas Publ. Association, Amsterdam.
7. Rosing, J., Slater, E.C. (1972) Biochim. Biophys. Acta 267, 275-290.
8. Mitchell, P. (1972) J. Bioenergetics 3, 5-24.
9. Boyer, P.D. (1975) FEBS Lett. 58, 1-6.

10. Boyer, P.D., Cross, R.L. and Momsen, W. (1973) Proc. Natl. Acad. Sci. USA 70, 2837-2839.
11. Cross, R.L. and Boyer, P.D. (1975) Biochemistry 14, 392-398.
12. Kozlov, I.A. (1975) Bioorg. Khimiya (U.S.S.R.) 1, 1545-1569.
13. Kozlov, I.A. and Skulachev, V.P. (1977) Biochim. Biophys. Acta 463, 29-89.
14. Smith, D.J. and Boyer, P.D. (1978) Proc. Natl. Acad. Sci. USA 73, 4314-4318.
15. Kayalar, C., Rosing, J. and Boyer, P.D. (1977) J. Biol. Chem. 252, 2486-2491.
16. Choate, G.L., Hutton, R.L. and Boyer, P.D. (1979) J. Biol. Chem. 254, 286-290.
17. Chernyak, B.V. and Kozlov, I.A. (1979) FEBS Lett. 104, 215-219.
18. Chernyak, B.V., Chernyak, V. Ya., Gladysheva, T.B. and Kozlov, I.A. (1981) Biochim. Biophys. Acta 635, 552-570.
19. Schuster, S.M., Ebel, A.E. and Lardy, H.A. (1975) J. Biol. Chem. 250, 7848-7853.
20. Takeshige, K., Hess, B., Bohm, M. and Limmer-Telschow, H. (1976) Hoppe-Seylers Z. Physiol. Chem. 357, 1605-1622.
21. Philo, R.D. and Selwyn, M.J. (1974) Biochem. J. 143, 745-749.
22. Harris, D.A., Dall-Larsen, T. and Klungsøyr, L. (1981) Biochim. Biophys. Acta 635, 412-428.
23. Kozlov, I.A. and Kononenko, V.A. (1975) Bioorg. Khimiya (U.S.S.R.) 1, 489-493.
24. Wielders, J.P.M., Slater, E.C. and Muller, J.L.M. (1980) Biochim. Biophys. Acta 589, 231-240.
25. Rovery, O.H., Muller, J.L.M. and Slater, E.C. (1980) Biochim. Biophys. Acta 589, 241-255.
26. Ting, L.P. and Wang, J.H. (1980) J. Bioenerg. Biomembranes 120, 79-93.
27. Ting, L.P. and Wang, J.H. (1980) Biochemistry 19, 5665-5670.
28. Mitchell, P. (1974) FEBS Lett. 53, 267-274.
29. Mitchell, P. and Moyle, J. (1974) in Biochem. Soc. Spec. Suppl., Vol. 4, pp. 91-111, Great Britain.
30. Senior, A.E. (1979) J. Biol. Chem. 254, 11319-11322.
31. Markus, F., Shuster, S.M. and Lardy, H.A. (1976) J. Biol. Chem. 251, 1775-1780.
32. Kozlov, I.A. and Skulachev, V.P. (1981) in Current Topics in Membranes and Transport (C.L. Slayman, ed) Vol. 16, Academic Press, New York.

33. Kozlov, I.A. and Milgrom, Ya. M. (1980) Eur. J. Biochem.
    106, 457-462.
34. Kozlov, I.A., Milgrom, Ya. M. and Tsybovsky, I.S.
    (1980) Biochem. J. 192, 483-488.

H^+-ATP SYNTHETASE FROM A THERMOPHILIC BACTERIUM

Yasuo Kagawa

Department of Biochemistry, Jichi Medical School,
Minamikawachi-machi, Tochigi-ken, Japan 329-04

INTRODUCTION. Mitchell's chemiosmotic theory is a paradigm that is now generally accepted after decades of controversy (1). The original proposal of a proton motive ATPase (2) was most conclusively tested after $F_o \cdot F_1$ was extracted from mitochondria and shown to be composed of an ATPase moiety (F_1) and membrane moiety (F_o) (3). Crude $F_o \cdot F_1$ preparations reconstituted into liposomes were shown to translocate H^+ upon ATP hydrolysis (4,5) and to synthesize ATP in the presence of bacteriorhodopsin and crude electron transport components (6,7). The earlier demonstration of ATP synthesis by acid base treatment of chloroplasts was also an important step in establishing the role of protons in energy coupling (8). However, these experiments could not prove that the proton motive ATPase is identical to $F_o \cdot F_1$. In the first place, the preparations contained other proteins that could have transferred energy to $F_o \cdot F_1$. Secondly, impaired oxidative phosphoylation of a crude biomembrane could be restored by the addition of not only a component of $F_o \cdot F_1$ (a coupling factor), but also by other substances such as albumin and small amounts of oligomycin which probably strengthen the membrane structure (7). These objections were overcome with pure stable thermophilic $F_1 \cdot F_o$ ($TF_o \cdot F_1$).

V. P. Skulachev and Peter C. Hinkle (eds.), Chemiosmotic Proton Circuits in Biological Membranes
in honor of Peter Mitchell   ISBN 0-201-07398-6

421

When reconstituted into liposmes $TF_o \cdot F_1$ catalyzed net ATP-synthesis driven by artifically imposed ion gradients (9) or an external electric field (10).

The studies on the molecular mechanism of H^+-translocation, and dissocation into subunits have also been furthered by use of pure, stable and reconstitutable $TF_o \cdot F_1$ since mesophilic $F_o \cdot F_1$'s are unstable, especially after solubilization and dissociation into subunits. The principles of energy transduction established with $TF_o \cdot F_1$ are applicable to all other $F_o \cdot F_1$'s (11), particularly since there is considerable homology in the amino acid sequences in some of the $F_o \cdot F_1$ subunits from mitochondria, chloroplasts and bacterial membranes including those of thermophilic bacteria (12,13). The similarity in the 5 subunits of F_1's from these membranes (14,15,16) is also well established.

SUBUNITS OF $TF_o \cdot F_1$ AND THEIR RECONSTITUTION - TF_o (90,000 daltons) reconstituted into liposomes allows passive leakage of protons down the proton gradient (17,18). When stoichiometric amounts of TF_1 (390,000 daltons, 1 mol TF_1/1 mol TF_o) were adsorbed on TF_o in liposomes, passive leakage of H^+ was completely blocked (18). This complete H^+-gating effect of TF_1 is explained either by the unidirectional arrangement of TF_o (100% of the F_1-binding protein is exposed on the outer surface)or by rectifying activity of TF_o, which allows unidirectional proton flux. When ATP was added to reconstituted $TF_o \cdot F_1$ liposomes, active H^+-transport was observed. All five subunits of TF_1 were required for reconstitution of this activity (19-21) namely: α (54,600 daltons), β (51,000), γ (30,200), δ (21,000) and ε (16,000) (22). However, the complex of γ, δ and ε subunits was sufficient for blocking passive H^+-leakage through TF_o (23). It is uncertain whether the $\gamma\delta\varepsilon$ subunit complex per se is the H^+-gate or whether the complex induces conformational change in TF_o that blocks H^+-leakage.

The α and β subunits both bind AT(D)P. The γ subunit is required to organize the α and β subunits to form an $\alpha\beta\gamma$ complex which has strong ATPase activity. The δ and ε subunits are both required to connect the $\alpha\beta\gamma$ complex to the F_1-binding protein of TF_o. In recent experiments, the formation of an $\alpha\beta$ complex (24) and $\alpha\gamma$ complex were confirmed, but not a $\beta\gamma$ complex (18).

The isolated subunits of E. coli F_1 (EF_1) have also been reconstituted under mild conditions (25). We have also combined TF_1 subunits ($T\alpha$, $T\beta$ and $T\gamma$) with EF_1 subunits ($E\alpha$, $E\beta$ and $E\gamma$). ATPase activity was reconstituted in the following combinations: $E\alpha T\beta E\gamma$, $E\alpha E\beta T\gamma$ and $T\alpha T\beta E\gamma$ (16), suggesting that subunits of different origns have similar roles. $T\beta$ could complement defective $E\beta$, and the Ca-ATPase activity of mutated EF_1 from unc Dll ($E\beta$ mutation) was converted into Mg-ATPase. $T\alpha T\beta E\gamma$ was similar to TF_1 in its activation with Na_2SO_3, methanol and detergents, but other combinations showed properties similar to EF_1. Like EF_1 [^{3}H]-acetyl-TF_1 is not heat stable, and its activity was reconstituted only when the α subunit was replaced by $T\alpha$.

TF_o contains only 3 subunits (26), and similar subunits were found in E. coli F_o (27). They are DCCD-binding protein (7,300 daltons), F_1-binding protein (13,500 daltons) and OSCP-like protein (19,000). The DCCD-binding proteins from all F_o's tested are highly hydrophobic, and show the

following homologous sequence: -Ala^{35}-Arg-Gln-Pro-Glu-Leu-
Arg^{41}-hydrophobic residues-Glu^{56}-Ala- , where DCCD is bound
to Glu^{56} (12). The DCCD-binding protein of TF$_o$ has no Lys;
acetylation of Lys of TF$_o$ caused specific modification of
F$_1$-binding protein (26). The OSCP-like protein was easily
removed with alkali, but its function is still not clear.

PATHWAY OF PROTONS THROUGH TF$_o$ - F$_o$·F$_1$ is characterized by
its ability to translocate H$^+$, so, if the pathway of H$^+$
through F$_o$·F$_1$ is traced, its molecular mechanism may be
elucidated. Morphological (29) and reconstitutional studies
(6,22) show that the direction of H$^+$-flux during ATP-synthesis is from the F$_o$ side to F$_1$, and that it is reversed
during ATPase driven H$^+$-transport.

TF$_o$ is not a hole or mobile carrier, but an H$^+$-carrying
channel.

       TF$_o$ is too large to be a mobile H$^+$ carrier. It is also
unlikely to be a simple hole through which H$^+$ flows because
the rate of H$^+$ translocation through TF$_o$ obeys saturation
kinetics with K$_m$ values of 0.095 μM, indicating the presence
of H$^+$ binding site(s). The pH-velocity profile of H$^+$-
translocation through TF$_o$ indicates passage of H$^+$ or H$_3$O$^+$,
but not OH$^-$. The H$^+$-flux obeys Ohm's law (17), and the V$_{max}$
is only 74 H$^+$/sec·mol TF$_o$ at a Δ$\bar{\mu}_{H^+}$ of 94 mV at 25°C (18).
       The H$^+$ may jump from Tyr^{69} to Glu^{56} and Arg^{14} and/or
Arg^{36} of the DCCD-binding protein of TF$_o$, because iodination
(lowering the pKa) of Tyr^{69} increased the K$_m$ for H$^+$-trans-
location to 0.71 μM (18), and chemical modification of Glu^{56}
with DCCD or that or Arg$^{41/36}$ with phenylglyoxal completely
blocked H$^+$-translocation (28). It is interesting that DCCD-

sensitive H^+-translocating activity was also detected in cytochrome oxidase (30), and a possible H^+ reacting Glu of Tβ was specifically labeled with DCCD (13). The pKa value of these DCCD reactive carboxyl groups is in the neutral range because of its hydrophobic environment.

Migration of H^+ carrying residues in TF_o

Compared with the extremely rapid rate of protonation-deprotonation of free NH- or COOH- groups in a protein (24), the rate of H^+-flux through TF_o and $TF_o \cdot F_1$ is very slow (18). Thus, a simple H^+-jump mechanism through a network of H^+-bonds in TF_o is improbable. In fact, it is difficult to construct a net of H^+-bonds through DCCD-binding protein across the lipid bilayer, because the regions between Tyr^{69} and Glu^{56}, and Arg^{41} are all composed of hydrophobic residues (12). Moreover, nuclear magnetic resonance spectroscopy of the DCCD-binding protein of TF_o revealed no hydrogen bonding around Tyr^{69}, and free movements of C-2/6 and C-3/5 of the residue in organic solvents (360 MHz) (31).

Thus conformational changes of the DCCD-binding protein may cause the slow migration of H^+-carrying residues to adjacent residues. A model for membrane transport through α-helical protein pores assumes a travelling wave carrying H^+ (32). The α-helix content of TF_o was increased by its reconstitution into liposomes (26), and that of the DCCD binding protein was 37.2% (no β-sheets) in chloroform-methanol (31). For control of the rate of conformation change of TF_o, liposomes composed of thermophilic phospholipid (transition temperature, 21-23°C) were used. There was a break in the Arrhenius plot of the H^+-translocation rate at 22°C. There may be many pliable and flexible sequences in the DCCD-binding protein, which allow the migration of Tyr^{69}, Glu^{56} and Arg residues. For example, the glycyl residues (from Gly^{13} to Gly^{24}) at every second position allow for a large range of dihedral angles at the $C\alpha$ atoms in the very hydrophobic region.

PATHWAY OF NUCLEOTIDES IN TF_1

An allosteric and catalytic site in TF_1

Only when the structure of the enzyme-transition complex of the $ATP-TF_o \cdot F_1$ complex during proton driven ATP synthesis is visualized will the molecular mechanism of energy transduction be solved. The nucleotide binding subunits of TF_1 are the α and β subunits (14,21). Complete inactivation of TF_1 by labelling a Glu in the β subunit with $[^{14}C]$-DCCD did not affect tight ADP binding at the α subunit (13). At low concentrations, ADP selectively bound to the α subunit in TF_1, while at high concentrations it bound to both the α and β subunit. The β subunit bound all the substrates of TF_1, including GTP and ITP, while CTP, which is not a substrate, bound only to the α subunit (21). These data suggest that the α subunit has an allosteric site and the β subunit has a catalytic site, although the two binding sites may act cooperatively.

Functioning residues in the catalytic domain

Chemical modification of TF_1 and its subunits may reveal their functioning residues, because of the stability of TF_1 against nonspecific denaturation and its characteristic amino acid composition. When one of the tyrosyl, carboxyl or arginyl residues in the AT(D)P binding domain of the β

subunit of TF$_1$ was chemically modified, its ATPase activity
was lost (13,34).

The presence of Tyr in the vicinity of bound adenine
nuclotide in the β subunit was deduced from the negative
elipticity at 275 nm observed by circular dichroic spectrometry (21). The Tyr might act as a general base in the
hydrolytic reaction. In fact, the following sequence of
the β subunit in intact mitochondrial F$_1$ was found (35): -
Ile-Met-Asp-Pro-Asn-Ile-Val-Gly-Ser-Glu-His-Tyr*-Asp-Val-
Ala-Arg- where Tyr* is the O-[^{14}C]-sulfonylated derivative
of Tyr. The same reagent, p-fluorosulfonylbenzoyl-5'-
adenosine, reacted with the β subunit of TF$_1$. Another
tyrosine modifier, 7-chloro-4-nitrobenzo-2-oxa-1,3-diazole
(NBD-Cl), which completely inhibited the ATPase activity of
TF$_1$ even when only one of the β subunits per F$_1$ had reacted.
However, this tyrosyl residue is different from the Tyr*
described above, and modification with NBD-Cl did not
affect the reaction of [^{14}C]-DCCD with Glu in the following
sequence of the β subunit of TF$_1$ (13): -Ala-Gly-Val-Gly-
Glu*-Arg-, where Glu* represents the N-γ-glutamyl derivative
of dicylohexyl-[^{14}C] urea. In contrast to other residues
in the nucleotide binding domains of TF$_1$ which are protected
against chemical labelling with AT(D)P (34), this Glu*
formation was accelerated (k increased 8-fold) by the
addition of ADP (13). Another carboxyl residue was esterfied
with Woodward's reagent K, and the inactivation of ATPase
activity of TF$_1$ was protected by the addition of AT(D)P or
IT(D)P, but not CTP (34).

Arginyl residues surrounding phosphate groups of bound
nucleotides were found in adenylate kinase by X-ray crystallography (36). Similarly, 4 moles of [^{14}C] phenylglyoxal,

incorporated into one mole of TF_1, completely inactivated
its ATPase activity, and AT(D)P prevented the modification
of one Arg per mole (34). It is interesting that in the
mitochondrial β subunit, the amino acid sequence around
Glu* was identical to that of Tβ but the other Glu** was
labelled with [^{14}C]-DCCD (37): -Ala-Gly-Val-Gly-Glu*-Arg-
Thr-Arg-Glu-Gly-Asn-His-Leu-Tyr-Glu**-Met-. The underlined
homology suggests the importance of this segment in the
catalytic domain. Glu* and Glu** may cooperate when both
are close in the domain, and DCCD may label only one of the
two in a "charge relay system".

Nucleotides do not affect the helix nor β-sheets but the
higher structure of TF_1. There are many hypothesis on the
conformational change associated with nucleotide binding to
F_1 during ATP synthesis (38,39). In fact, ^{3}H-incorporation
into F_1 was observed during photophosphorylation (40).

The conformation of the isolated subunits has been
studied in TF_1 (20). The α helix and β sheet contents of
the α subunit were 31% and 19%, respectively, and those of
the β subunit were 34% and 23%. The infrared absorption
spectrum of the α subunit showed an amide I peak at 1648
cm^{-1}, while that of the β subunit showed a sharper amide I
peak at 1640 cm^{-1}, because the β subunit has larger amounts
of antiparallel β sheet structure than the α subunit.

The binding of AT(D)P to TF_1, did not change the
contents of α helix and β sheet, which are the stable
backbones of the proteins. In order to examine the conformational change in the more flexible portion of the subunits,
the kinetics of ^{1}H-^{2}H exchange of peptide NH-groups was
measured with a computerized Fourier transform infrared

spectrometer at 1550 cm^{-1} (24). The relaxation spectra of exchange in the subunits clearly showed that both subunits were stabilized by the addition of nucleotides (24).

Crystallographic analyses of TF_1 by computerized image reconstruction revealed that individual molecules appear hexagonal, whereas their outline was not as smooth in AMPPNP-TF_1 as in the N_3-TF_1 (41,42). The pseudo 6-fold and 2-fold symmetry becomes conspicuous and six separable peaks of density could be observed. On binding of ATP, the space group of chloroplast F_1 crystals also changed from C_{222} to P_{422} (43).

There are several examples of conformational changes induced by nucleotides, without a change in the contents of α helix and β sheets. X-ray crystallography of adenylate kinase (36) and several dehydrogenases (44) revealed a phosphoryl binding loop between the first β sheet strand of a Rossmann fold and the following α helix. The major difference between the free and nucleotide bound conformations is in the movement of this phosphoryl binding loop. There are several similarities between these nucleotide binding proteins and the α and β subunits: the bound nucleotides are in extended (anti) form (21), and adenine base is fixed with tyrosyl residues (21).

ATP synthesis in $TF_o \cdot F_1$ without net H$^+$-flux. Net ATP synthesis directly driven by $\Delta\bar{\mu}_H{}^+$ in vesicles containing $F_o \cdot F_1$ is sensitive to DCCD or oligomycin (9,45,46). In experiments with external electric pulses imposed on $TF_o \cdot F_1$ to analyze this process with good time resolution (10), it was found that DCCD did not interfere with net ATP synthesis if the diameter of the particles was as large as that of mitochondria and a sufficient membrane potential was established (47). The amount of ATP synthesized was 0.05 nmoles/mg protein/pulse, for a rectangular pulse of 680 V/cm. With repeated pulses, the velocity of ATP synthesis was 1.83 nmoles/sec/mg (47) which was comparable to that of $\Delta\bar{\mu}_{H^+}$ driven ATP synthesis in mitochondria (0.5 nmole/sec/mg) (45) and submitochondrial particles (0.2 nmoles/sec/mg) (46). A pulse duration of only 0.1 msec still supported ATP synthesis, which was DCCD insensitive but sensitive to aurovertin and dinitrophenol (10^{-4}M)

If the conformation of $F_o \cdot F_1$ changed, the energy of conformational change could synthesize ATP through a change in binding energy of ADP, ATP and P_i (48).

FUTURE STUDIES - Three lines of research have been started to elucidate the enzyme-transition state complex of $TF_o \cdot F_1$ under the $\Delta\bar{\mu}_{H^+}$ (49). a) Direct electrical analysis, such as impalement of $TF_o \cdot F_1$ macroliposomes with microelectrodes, and application of an electric field to the $TF_o \cdot F_1$ system. b) Crystallographic analysis of TF_1 and the subunits, their three-dimensional structure in the presence of heavy metals and several ligands. c) Genetic analysis of the $TF_o \cdot F_1$ gene (unc operon) to establish the amino acid sequence of the whole enzyme subunits. Thermostable plasmids and thermophilic gene products and their mutants will be useful in these studies.

REFERENCES

1. Mitchell, P. (1979) Science 206, 1148–1159.
2. Mitchell, P. (1961) Nature (London) 191, 144–148.
3. Kagawa, Y. and Racker, E. (1966) J. Biol. Chem. 241, 2467–2474.
4. Kagawa, Y. and Racker, E. (1971) J. Biol. Chem. 246, 5477–5487.
5. Kagawa, Y. (1972) Biochim. Biophys. Acta 265, 297–338.
6. Racker, E. and Stoeckenius, W. (1974) J. Biol. Chem. 249, 662–663.
7. Racker, E. (1976) A New Look at Mechanism in Bio-energetics, Academic Press, New York.
8. Jagendorf, A.T. and Uribe, E. (1966) Proc. Natl. Acad. Sci. U.S.A. 55, 170–177.
9. Sone, N., Yoshida, M., Hirata, H. and Kagawa, Y. (1977) J. Biol. Chem. 252, 2956–2960.
10. Rögner, M., Ohno, K., Hamamoto, T., Sone, N. and Kagawa, Y. (1979) Biochem. Biophys. Res. Commun. 91, 362–367.
11. Kagawa, Y. (1980) J. Membrane Biol. 55, 1–8.
12. Sebald, W., Hoppe, J. and Wachter, E. (1979) In "Functions and Molecular Aspects of Biomembrane Transport" (Quagliariello, E., Palmieri, F., Papa, S. and Klingenberg, M., eds.), Elsevier, Amsterdam, pp. 63–74.
13. Yoshida, M., Poster, J.W., Allison, W.S., and Esch, F.S. (1981) J. Biol. Chem. 256, 148–153.
14. Kagawa, Y., Sone, N., Hirata, H. and Yoshida, M. (1979) J. Bioenerg. Biomembr. 11, 39–78.
15. Apps, D.K. and Schatz, G. (1979) Europ. J. Biochem. 100, 411–419.
16. Futai, M., Kanazawa, H., Takeda, K. and Kagawa, Y. (1980) Biochem. Biophys. Res. Commun. 96, 227–234.
17. Okamoto, H., Sone, N., Hirata, H., Yoshida, M. and Kagawa, Y. (1977) J. Biol. Chem. 252, 6125–6131.
18. Sone, N., Hamamoto, T. and Kagawa, Y. (1981) J. Biol. Chem. 256, in press.
19. Yoshida, M., Sone, N., Hirata, H. and Kagawa, Y. (1977) J. Biol. Chem. 252, 3480–3485.
20. Yoshida, M., Sone, N., Hirata, H., Kagawa, Y. and Ui, N. (1979) J. Biol. Chem. 254, 9525–9535.
21. Ohta, S., Tsuboi, M., Oshima, T., Yoshida, M. and Kagawa, Y. (1980) J. Biochem. (Tokyo) 87, 1609–1617.
22. Kagawa, Y. (1979) Biochim. Biophys. Acta 505, 45–93.

23. Yoshida, M., Okamoto, H., Sone, N., Hirata, H. and Kagawa, Y. (1977) Proc. Natl. Acad. Sci. U.S.A. 74, 936-940.
24. Ohta, S., Tsuboi, M., Yoshida, M. and Kagawa, Y. (1980) Biochemistry 19, 2160-2165.
25. Dunn, S.D. and Futai, M. (1980) J. Biol. Chem. 255, 113-118.
26. Kagawa, Y., Sone, N., Hirata, H., Yoshida, M. and Okamoto, H. (1976) J. Biochem. (Tokyo) 80, 141-151.
27. Fillingame, R.H. (1980) Ann. Rev. Biochem. 49, 1079-1113.
28. Sone, N., Ikeba, K. and Kagawa, Y. (1979) FEBS Lett. 97, 61-64.
29. Kagawa, Y. and Racker, E. (1966) J. Biol. Chem. 241, 2475-2482.
30. Casey, R.P., Thelen, M. and Azzi, A. (1980) J. Biol. Chem. 255, 3994-4000.
31. Kagawa, Y. (1980) unpublished.
32. Dunker, A.K. and Marvin, D.A. (1978) J. Theor. Biol. 72, 9-16.
33. Kozlov, I.A. and Milgrom, Y.M. (1980) Europ. J. Biochem. 106, 451-462.
34. Arana, J.L., Yoshida, M., Kagawa, Y. and Vallejos, R.H. (1980) Biochim. Biophys. Acta 593, 11-16.
35. Esch, F. and Allison, W.S. (1978) J. Biol. Chem. 253, 6100-6106.
36. Pai, E.F., Sachsenheimer, W., Schrimer, R.H. and Schltz, G.E. (1977) J. Mol. Biol. 114, 37-45.
37. Yoshida, M., Allison, W.S. and Esch, F.S. (1981) Fed. Proc., in press.
38. Harris, D.A. (1977) Biochim. Biophys. Acta 463, 245-273.
39. Boyer, P.D., Chance, B., Ernster, L., Mitchell, P. Racker, E. and Slater, E.C. (1977) Ann. Rev. Biochem. 46, 955-1026.
40. Ryrie, I.J. and Jagendorf, A.T. (1972) J. Biol. Chem. 247, 4453-4459.
41. Wakabayashi, T., Kubota, M., Yoshida, M. and Kagawa, Y. J. Mol. Biol. 117, 515-519.
42. Wakabayashi, T. (1978) In "Diffraction Studies of Biomembranes and Muscles and Synchrotron Radiation" (Mitsui, T., ed.) Proc. 4th Internatl. Symp. Div. Biophys., Taniguchi Foundation, Tokyo, pp. 315-339.
43. Kuhlmeyer, J. and Paradies, H.H. (1980) Eur. J. Cell Biol. 22, 277-287.

44. Schulz, G.E. and Schirmer, R.H. (1978) Principles of
    Protein Structure, Springer-Verlag, Heidelberg.
45. Reid, R.A., Moyle, J. and Mitchell, P. (1966) Nature
    212, 257-258.
46. Thayer, W.S. and Hinkle, P.C. (1975) J. Biol. Chem.
    250, 5330-5335.
47. Hamamoto, T., Ohno, K. and Kagawa, Y. (1981) in
    preparation.
48. Jencks, W.P. (1980) Adv. Enzymol. 51, 75-106.
49. Kagawa, Y., Sone, N., Hamamoto, T., Futai, M. Ohta, S.
    and Wakabayashi, T. (1981) In "International Cell
    Biology 1980-1981" (Schweiger, H.G., ed.), Springer-
    Verlag, Berlin, pp 719-727.

SUBUNIT FUNCTIONS IN THE F_1 ATPase OF ESCHERICHIA COLI[1]

Stanley D. Dunn and Leon A. Heppel

Section of Biochemistry, Molecular and Cell Biology
Cornell University
Ithaca, NY 14853

INTRODUCTION. The proton-translocating ATPase is found in similar form in the membranes of bacteria, mitochondria and chloroplasts. This complex enzyme couples the synthesis and hydrolysis of ATP to the movement of protons across the membrane as proposed by Mitchell (1,2). Bacteria which are growing aerobically generate a protonmotive force by respiration and use the ATPase complex to produce ATP in the process of oxidative phosphorylation. Bacteria which are growing in the absence of any terminal electron acceptor use the ATPase as a proton pump, hydrolyzing glycolytic ATP to generate the protonmotive force which is needed for active transport and other energy-requiring functions.

The ATPase complex consists of two portions, F_o[2],

---

[1] Supported by NIH Grant AM-11789 and NSF Grant 78-11796.

[2] Abbreviations used are: F_o, that portion of the proton-translocating ATPase which is integral to the membrane; F_1, that portion of the proton-translocating ATPase which is peripheral to the membrane; ECF_1, E. coli F_1; MF_1, mitochondrial F_1; CF_1, chloroplast F_1; TF_1, the F_1 of a thermophilic bacterium PS3; DCCD, dicyclohexylcarbodiimide; NBD chloride, 4-chloro-7-nitro-2-oxa-1,3-diazole; NAP_4-ADP, 3'-0-(4-[N-(4-azido-2-nitrophenyl)amino]butyryl)ADP.

V. P. Skulachev and Peter C. Hinkle (eds.), Chemiosmotic Proton Circuits in Biological Membranes
in honor of Peter Mitchell   ISBN 0-201-07398-6

which is embedded in the membrane, and F_1, which is peripheral. It is believed that Escherichia coli F_o consists of 3 polypeptide chains which function as a proton-specific channel (3). The F_1 portion of the complex contains the catalytic site for ATP synthesis and hydrolysis; its 5 subunits are designated α, β, γ, δ and ϵ in order of decreasing molecular weight.

The F_1 of E. coli, ECF_1, is found on the inner surface of the plasma membrane of whole cells. Disruption of bacteria by passage through a French pressure cell produces inverted membrane vesicles with ECF_1 on the outside. Electron microscopic examination of negatively stained vesicles reveals ECF_1 as knobs with a diameter of 100 $\overset{o}{A}$ which appear to project from the membrane via a stalk (4). This morphology is similar to that of F_1 in submitochondrial particles and thylakoid membranes.

We have approached the question of subunit function in ECF_1 by isolating the subunits, studying their properties, and combining them to reconstitute activity. In this paper we will review the current knowledge of subunit structure and function in ECF_1. We have quoted some work from other laboratories, but a comprehensive summary of the literature is not possible in this short communication.

THE ECF_1 COMPLEX. ECF_1 is released from inverted membrane vesicles by incubating them in low ionic strength buffer which contains no Mg^{2+}. The resulting depleted membranes are much more permeable to protons because of the proton-conducting activity of F_o (3), which is no longer blocked by ECF_1. The released ECF_1 behaves as a normal soluble protein and can be purified by conventional methods (5-7). Isolated ECF$_1$ has coupling factor activity, which means that addition of ECF$_1$ to depleted membrane vesicles restores energy transducing activities, such as oxidative phosphorylation and energy-dependent pyridine nucleotide transhydrogenase.

The molecular weight of ECF$_1$ has been determined by several techniques. Most give values of 350,000 to 380,000. The tendency of ECF$_1$ to dissociate into smaller subunit complexes is probably responsible for some lower values which have been reported (see ref. 8 for a review of molecular weight determinations). Such dissociation is prevented, or greatly reduced, by inclusion of 10% glycerol in the buffer (9). As for most F$_1$'s (10,11), the tendency of ECF$_1$ to dissociate is enhanced by high salt concentrations and low temperatures. These properties can be exploited in obtaining gentle methods of dissociation for purposes of subunit isolation.

The molecular weights of the ECF$_1$ subunits are: α, 57,500; β, 52,000; γ, 31,000; δ, 18,500; ε, 15,000. Most workers who study bacterial F$_1$'s favor a subunit stoichiometry of $\alpha_3\beta_3\gamma\delta\epsilon$. While some investigators of mitochondrial F$_1$ (MF$_1$) and chloroplast F$_1$(CF$_1$) share this view, others prefer $\alpha_2\beta_2\gamma_2\delta_{1-2}\epsilon_{1-2}$ (see refs. 8 and 12 for discussions of subunit stoichiometry). Figure 1 shows a proposed model for the subunit structure of ECF$_1$ (13).

For purposes of this review, we will divide ECF$_1$ into the major subunits (α, β, and γ) and the minor subunits (δ and ε). This division is based on criteria of structure, function and reconstitution. The major subunits combine to produce a complex with ATPase activity. Both association and dissocation of this complex in vitro are slow processes.

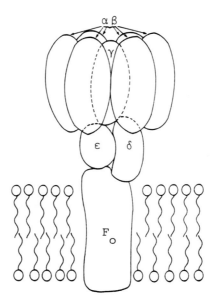

Fig. 1   A model for the subunit structure of ECF$_1$ (13).
F_O is shown without detail, as little is known
about the subunit arrangement and interactions
within this portion.

In contrast, the δ and ε subunits bind rapidly and reversibly
to this catalytic complex.

ISOLATION OF ECF$_1$ SUBUNITS. Each of the subunits of ECF$_1$
has been obtained in a pure, nondenatured state. When the
subunits are mixed under the proper conditions, coupling
factor activity is reconstituted (14).

Two methods for isolating the major subunits of ECF$_1$
have been developed (14,15). Here is a brief description of
the method we commonly use (14). ECF$_1$ which lacks the δ
subunit (7) is dialyzed overnight against buffer at pH 6.0
containing 1$\underline{M}$ NaCl and 250 m$\underline{M}$ NaNO$_3$, then frozen at -80°C.

This causes dissociation of the complex and loss of ATPase activity. Storage of the protein at -80°C for at least one day improves the yield of subunits. The solution is then thawed, diluted with an equal volume of low ionic strength buffer, and applied to a column of hydroxyapatite at pH 8.0. The α and β subunits are eluted from this column with 30 m$\underline{M}$ sodium phosphate, then resolved on a column of DEAE-Sepharose which is developed with a gradient of NaCl. The γ and ε subunits are eluted from the hydroxyapatite with a gradient of sodium phosphate in 3$\underline{M}$ urea. ε elutes with the urea front and γ elutes as a sharp peak at about 90 m$\underline{M}$ phosphate. Inclusion of urea in this step is essential because it dissociates ε from γ. In the absence of urea these subunits coelute.

The δ and ε subunits are obtained by the procedure developed by Smith and Sternweis (16). The larger subunits are denatured by 50% pyridine, then δ and ε are resolved on a column of Sephadex G-75. ε obtained by either the pyridine method or the hydroxyapatite method has identical properties.

Methods for isolating the subunits of MF$_1$ and CF$_1$ in nondenatured form have yet to be developed. However, the subunits of TF$_1$, the F$_1$ of the thermophilic bacterium PS3, have been isolated and TF$_1$ coupling factor activity has been reconstituted from the subunits (17). The extreme stability of TF$_1$ necessitates the use of strongly denaturing conditions (6M guanidine hydrochloride during complex dissociation and 8M urea during subunit separation). This requires that the subunits refold properly after isolation. In contrast, ECF$_1$ is dissociated by relatively mild conditions, and the large subunits appear to maintain their nondenatured conformations during isolation. The ECF_1 methods are therefore better models for future attempts to isolate the subunits of MF_1 and CF_1.

THE MAJOR SUBUNITS. The isolated α subunit exists as a monomer up to concentrations of about 0.6-1.0 mg/ml in dilute Tris-HCl buffer at pH 8.0, 4°C. At higher concentration aggregation is seen in sedimentation velocity experiments, and precipitation sometimes occurs. Higher temperatures and higher salt concentrations enhance the tendency of α to aggregate.

Isolated α binds one ATP or ADP with K_D's of 0.1 and 0.9 μM, respectively (14). Occupation of the site by ATP causes α to undergo a large conformational change, which has been observed as a 14% increase in both the diffusion coefficient measured by inelastic light scattering (18) and the sedimentation coefficient measured by moving boundary velocity sedimentation (19). Release of ATP from the α-ATP complex is unusually slow. We have measured a first order dissociation rate constant of 0.21 per minute at 22°C (19).

The properties of this nucleotide binding site on α suggest that it corresponds to the "tight" binding sites of ECF_1 (20) rather than to the catalytic site. However, the extent to which these properties are changed when α is incorporated into the catalytic complex is not known.

The isolated β subunit remains in solution to concentrations of several mg per ml, and is the easiest of the large subunits to handle. At 20°C, however, β tends to form soluble aggregates which are stable enough to be detected by nondenaturing polyacrylamide gel electrophoresis and by

velocity sedimentation (S. Dunn, unpublished observations).
At 4°C, β is mostly monomeric, but some dimer is present.

Isolated β binds aurovertin (14), an inhibitor of the
ATPase activity of most bacterial and mitochondrial F_1's.
The K_D of this interaction is 4 µM. Aurovertin binds to the
β subunit of MF_1 also (21,22), suggesting a functional correlation of the β subunits of ECF_1 and MF_1. This correlation could not be assumed, because the subunits are named
simply according to their mobilities on SDS-polyacrylamide
gels. One could easily imagine an inversion of molecular
weight between the α and β subunits of bacterial and mitochondrial coupling factors.

Recently, Lunardi and coworkers (23) have labeled
isolated β with a photoactivatable ADP analog, NAP_4-ADP, indicating the presence of an adenine nucleotide binding site.
It seems likely that this site has a lower affinity than the
site on α, as we have had difficulty detecting it by equilibrium methods. This site on β is probably the best candidate for the active site of ATP synthesis and hydrolysis.

The γ subunit is the most difficult of the subunits
to handle. We find that salts, such as .2M NaCl or ammonium
sulfate, are required to keep the subunit in solution at 4°,
and that 10% glycerol should be included to prevent precipitation upon freezing and thawing. Under these conditions γ
remains monomeric at concentrations lower than 0.1 mg per
ml. Aggregation occurs at higher concentrations.

THE $\alpha_3\beta_3\gamma$ CATALYTIC COMPLEX. In some multisubunit enzymes,
such as E. coli aspartate transcarbamylase, regulatory subunits modulate the activity of catalytic subunits. In
others, such as the mitochondrial pyruvate dehydrogenase

complex, the different polypeptides catalyze sequential steps of the overall reaction. ECF_1 does not appear to fit into either of these types, however, as no catalytic activity has been detected in any of the isolated subunits.

The ATPase site is within the $\alpha_3\beta_3\gamma$ complex. This has been shown by removal of δ and ϵ (and most of γ) by proteolysis (6) and by the specific removal of ϵ (24) from enzyme which already lacked δ. In each case, ATPase activity was retained.

In addition, ATPase activity is reconstituted from mixtures of the α, β and γ subunits by dialysis against buffer at pH 6.0 containing Mg^{2+} and ATP (14,15). We have never detected the reconstitution of significant ATPase activity if any of these subunits is omitted. The minor subunits, δ and ϵ, are not required.

The β subunits of F_1's are labeled, with concomitant loss of ATPase activity, by a number of protein modifying reagents and adenine nucleotide affinity labels, suggesting that β contains the active site. The following results obtained with ECF_1 have come from Vignais and coworkers. Incubation of ECF_1 with dicyclohexylcarbodiimide (DCCD) under slightly acidic conditions causes inactivation of ATPase activity. This inactivation is accompanied by the incorporation of 1 mol of DCCD per mol of ECF_1. The label is found on the β subunit (25). Similar results were obtained when ECF_1 was treated with NBD chloride (26). On the other hand, some evidence suggests that labeling of the nucleotide binding site of α also causes inactivation of ATPase activity. Both α and β were labeled when ECF_1 was illuminated in the presence of NAP_4-ADP, a photoaffinity label (23). Inactivation was correlated with the incorporation of 2 mol of

NAP$_4$-ADP per mol of ECF$_1$, although α was preferentially labeled at low concentrations of the probe.

Other evidence also indicates that the α and γ subunits play important roles. For example, the mutant strain AN120 has been shown, by in vitro subunit complementation studies, to produce a defective α subunit (27,28). The mutant ECF$_1$ appears to be normal in structure, stability, and ability to bind adenine nucleotides (29), yet lacks the ability to hydrolyze or synthesize ATP. Regarding γ, the "α$_3$β$_3$" ATPase obtained by tryptic digestion of ECF$_1$ (6) retains a fragment of γ and is inhibited by anti-γ antiserum (30). The requirement for this fragment of γ in maintaining ATPase activity may reflect a purely structural role, but it is also possible that γ contributes essential catalytic residues. In summary, while β is most strongly implicated in catalysis by current evidence, each of the major subunits plays an important, though not yet fully understood, role.

THE MINOR SUBUNITS. The δ and ε subunits bind rapidly, reversibly, and independently to the catalytic complex α$_3$β$_3$γ (24,31). A single copy of each of these minor subunits must be present for the ATPase to bind to F$_o$ in depleted membrane vesicles (24,32). This result suggests that δ and ε may form the stalk which connects ECF$_1$ to F$_o$. Definitive evidence that these subunits occupy this position in ECF$_1$F$_o$ has yet to be obtained, however.

Recently we have presented evidence indicating that the binding of δ to ECF$_1$ is eliminated by the proteolytic removal of short peptides from the NH$_2$-terminus of the α subunits of the complex (33). Treatment of ECF_1 with any of a variety of proteases causes the loss of coupling factor activity with a concomitant slight increase in the mobility of α on SDS-polyacrylamide gel electrophoresis. Other changes in the polypeptide pattern are also seen, but these changes vary from one protease to another. Sequence analysis of the NH_2-terminal region of the α subunits isolated from ECF_1 which had been treated with trypsin or chymotrypsin indicated that trypsin removed 15 residues and chymotrypsin removed 19 residues. The single tryptophan residue of α was COOH-terminal in these altered α subunits as well as in normal α. ATPase complexes which were reconstituted by mixing normal β and γ with either of these modified forms of α were unable to bind the δ subunit, as determined by sucrose gradient centrifugation. These results indicate that the NH_2-terminal portion of α is involved in binding the δ subunit. The possibility that direct binding interactions are involved is further suggested by the finding of Bragg and Hou (34) that dithiobis(succinimidyl propionate) crosslinks the α and δ subunits of ECF_1.

The ε subunit is a partial noncompetitive inhibitor of the ATPase activity of isolated ECF_1. Kinetic analysis indicates a K_i in the range of 3-10 n$\underline{M}$ and maximal inhibition of 70-90% (31). The inhibition of ECF_1 by added ε, when an endogenous ε subunit was already present, was confusing initially. The following picture has emerged from the studies of Laget, Smith and Sternweis (24,31,35). There appears to be a single ε binding site on $\alpha_3\beta_3\gamma$ and endogenous ε is inhibitory provided it remains bound. The K_D of this site is equal to the measured K_i. As the ECF_1 concentration in the customary ATPase assay is low (0.3 to 0.6 n$\underline{M}$)

relative to the K_D, most of the endogenous ε dissociates
from the enzyme, which then exhibits high ATPase activity.
Added ε binds to the available sites, inhibiting the enzyme.
Inhibition of ATPase activity by endogenous ε can be demonstrated by doing the assay at much higher ECF_1 concentration
(35). Under these conditions, anti-ε serum markedly activates the ATPase.

The membrane-bound ECF_1F_o is highly active as an
ATPase even though it contains ε. Sternweis and Smith (31)
demonstrated that allowing ε-inhibited ECF_1 to bind to
depleted membranes actually restores full ATPase activity to
the complex. One could suggest that the binding of ECF_1 to
F_o alters either the conformation of ε or the interaction of
ε with the catalytic subunits.

Excess ε has no significant effect on the ATPase
activity, or ATP-dependent energy coupling properties of
membrane-bound enzyme (31). Thus, the properties of ε are
quite different from those of the mitochondrial ATPase inhibitor protein (36,37) which inhibits both ATPase activity
and ATP-dependent energy coupling in submitochondrial particles.

The results described above cast doubt on the earlier
suggestion that ε plays a regulatory role (16). It is still
possible, however, that ε mediates the regulation of the
complex by an unidentified molecule. Sternweis (13) found
that anti-ε serum inhibited ATPase activity and ATP-dependent energy transduction in membrane vesicles without causing
release of ECF_1. Perhaps, it was suggested, the antibody
mimics the effects of a natural inhibitor which causes ε to
assume an inhibitory interaction with the catalytic complex.
Another theory is that the inhibition of soluble ATPase by ε

is a mechanism for preventing any free ECF_1, perhaps that which has just been assembled from newly synthesized subunits, from uselessly hydrolyzing cellular ATP (31).

Bragg and Hou (34) have shown that treatment of ECF_1 with dithiobis(succinimidyl propionate) crosslinks γ and ε. We have found that the isolated γ subunit binds ε with high affinity (38). This interaction was shown in three ways: 1) ε, which contains no tryptophan, quenches the tryptophan fluorescence of γ; 2) a $\gamma\varepsilon$ complex can be isolated by gel filtration of a mixture of γ and ε, and 3) γ specifically protects ECF_1 from inhibition by ε. The data indicate a 1:1 stoichiometry and a K_D in the range of 3 n$\underline{M}$. No interaction of ε with α or β was detected. It seems safe to say, therefore, that γ contains the site at which ε binds to ECF_1.

OUTLOOK. We have focused this review on the usefulness of subunit isolation and reconstitution as a tool in studying the structure-function relationships of the E. coli coupling factor. The amenability of E. coli to genetic analysis and the recent development of methods for isolating ECF_1F_o (39) are two other factors which make this bacterium an attractive system for further investigations of the mechanism of oxidative phosphorylation.

The following areas of research will probably be pursued intensively during the next few years: 1) Subunit stoichiometry and arrangement in ECF_1F_o; 2) Subunit function; 3) The sequence of the unc operon, which encodes all of the known ECF_1F_o polypeptides; and 4) Physiological control of ECF_1F_o synthesis and function.

REFERENCES

1. Mitchell, P. (1961) Nature (London) 191, 144-148.
2. Mitchell, P. (1966) Biol. Rev. 41, 445-502.
3. Negrin, R.S., Foster, D.L., and Fillingame, R.H. (1980)
    J. Biol. Chem. 255, 5643-5648.
4. Hinkle, P.C., and McCarty, R.E. (1978) Sci. Am. 238,
    104-123.
5. Bragg, P.D., and Hou, C. (1972) FEBS Lett. 28, 309-
    312.
6. Nelson, N., Kanner, B.I., and Gutnick, D.L. (1974)
    Proc. Natl. Acad. Sci. USA 71, 2720-2724.
7. Futai, M., Sternweis, P.C., and Heppel, L.A. (1974)
    Proc. Natl. Acad. Sci. USA 71, 2725-2729.
8. Fillingame, R.H. (1981) Curr. Top. Bioenerg. 11, in
    press.
9. Laget, P.P. (1978) Arch. Biochem. Biophys. 189, 122-
    131.
10. Penefsky, H.S., and Warner, R.C. (1965) J. Biol. Chem.
    240, 4694-4702.
11. Lien, S., Berzborn, R.J., and Racker, E. (1972) J.
    Biol. Chem. 247, 3520-3524.
12. Senior, A.E. (1979) in Membrane Proteins in Energy
    Transduction (R.A. Capaldi, ed.) pp. 233-278, Marcel
    Dekker, New York.
13. Sternweis, P.C. (1978) Ph.D. Thesis, Cornell University,
    Ithaca, N.Y.
14. Dunn, S.D., and Futai, M. (1980) J. Biol. Chem. 255,
    113-118.
15. Futai, M. (1977) Biochem. Biophys. Res. Commun. 79,
    1231-1237.
16. Smith, J.B., and Sternweis, P.C. (1977) Biochemistry
    16, 306-311.
17. Yoshida, M., Sone, N., Hirata, H., and Kagawa, Y. (1977)
    J. Biol. Chem. 252, 3480-3485.
18. Paradies, H.H. (1980) FEBS Lett. 120, 289-292.
19. Dunn, S.D. (1980) J. Biol. Chem. 255, 11857-11860.
20. Maeda, M., Kobayashi, H., Futai, M., and Anraku, Y.
    (1976) Biochem. Biophys. Res. Commun. 70, 228-234.
21. Verschoor, G.J., van der Sluis, P.R., and Slater, E.C.
    (1977) Biochim. Biophys. Acta 462, 438-449.
22. Douglas, M.G., Koh, Y., Dockter, M.E., and Schatz, G.
    (1977) J. Biol. Chem. 252, 8333-8335.
23. Lunardi, J., Satre, M., and Vignais, P.V. (1981) Bio-
    chemistry 20, 473-480.
24. Sternweis, P.C. (1978) J. Biol. Chem. 253, 3123-3128.

25. Satre, M., Lunardi, J., Pougeois, R., and Vignais, P.V. (1979) Biochemistry 18, 3134-3140.
26. Lunardi, J., Satre, M., Bof, M., and Vignais, P.V. (1979) Biochemistry 18, 5310-5316.
27. Dunn, S.D. (1978) Biochem. Biophys. Res. Commun. 82, 596-602.
28. Kanazawa, H., Saito, S., and Futai, M. (1978) J. Biochem. (Tokyo) 84, 1513-1517.
29. Bragg, P.D., and Hou, C. (1977) Arch. Biochem. Biophys. 178, 486-494.
30. Smith, J.B., and Wilkowski, C. (1978) Fed. Proc. 37, Abstr. 1385.
31. Sternweis, P.C., and Smith, J.B. (1980) Biochemistry 19, 526-531.
32. Sternweis, P.C., and Smith, J.B. (1977) Biochemistry 16, 4020-4025.
33. Dunn, S.D., Heppel, L.A., and Fullmer, C.S. (1980) J. Biol. Chem. 255, 6891-6896.
34. Bragg, P.D., and Hou, C. (1976) Biochem. Biophys. Res. Commun. 72, 1042-1048.
35. Laget, P.P., and Smith, J.B. (1979) Arch. Biochem. Biophys. 197, 83-89.
36. Pullman, M.E., and Monroy, G.C. (1963) J. Biol. Chem. 238, 3762-3769.
37. Ernster, L., Carlsson, C., Hundal, T., and Nordenbrand, K. (1979) Methods Enzymol. 55, 399-407.
38. Dunn, S.D. (1980) Fed. Proc. 39, Abstr. 1962
39. Foster, D.L., and Fillingame, R.H. (1979) J. Biol. Chem. 254, 8230-8236.

AN ESSENTIAL CARBOXYL GROUP FOR H$^+$ CONDUCTION

IN THE PROTEOLIPID SUBUNIT OF THE ATP SYNTHASE

Jürgen Hoppe and Walter Sebald

Gesellschaft für Biotechnologische Forschung mbH..
Mascheroder Weg 1, D-3300 Braunschweig-Stöckheim,
Federal Republik of Germany

Membrane bound ATP-synthases isolated from various organisms show common structural and functional properties [1-4]. They are composed of a membrane associated part F_1, which bears the ATPase activity and the membrane integrated part F_0, catalyzing H$^+$-conduction across the membrane. Both parts are necessary for energy transduction. A functional F_0 part has been isolated from the thermophilic bacterium PS-3 and from E. coli [5-8]. A minimum subunit composition of two different subunits was found in PS-3. In E.coli three different subunits were identified [6-8]. The major constituent of the F_0 part is a protein of about 8000d which most likely exists as a hexamer [9]. This protein is extractable with chloroform/methanol or with butanol and thus is referred to as a proteolipid. Beechey and cow. [10] discovered that dicyclohexylcarbodiimide (DCCD) inhibited the ATPase activity in beef heart mitochondria. The hydro-phobic carbodiimide was found to be covalently bound to a proteolipid which was later identified as a subunit of the ATP synthase [1-4]. The proteolipid subunit appeared to be

V. P. Skulachev and Peter C. Hinkle (eds.), Chemiosmotic Proton Circuits in Biological Membranes
in honor of Peter Mitchell   ISBN 0-201-07398-6

the target of several hydrophobic antibiotics e.g. oligomycin. But oligomycin only inhibited the activity of ATP synthases from mitochondria and some photosynthetic bacteria,
as e.g. <u>Rhodospirillum rubrum</u> [11,13]. Oligomycin could be
coupled to the proteolipid using [^{3}H]borohydrid as a reducing reagent [14]. Both inhibitors, DCCD and oligomycin,
seem to compete for the same binding site at the proteolipid
as the presence of oligomycin reduces the binding of DCCD
[15].

In recent years numerous proteolipid subunits from
various organisms have been sequenced [16-21]. Amino acid
substitutions which lead to inhibitor resistancy or to a
nonfunctional enzyme have been determined [16,19-22]. This
article will therefore concentrate on the description of the
primary structure of this protein, especially on the identification of an invariant carboxyl residue which seems to be
intimately involved in protonconductance.

General properties

The proteolipids can be generally purified by extraction with chloroform/methanol and subsequent chromatography
on carboxymethyl-cellulose in chloroform/methanol [16-22].
All the sequences were determined by automated solid phase
Edman degradation [16-22]. The proteins contain 72 - 82
amino acid residues which number is in agreement with the
molecular weights determined on SDS-Gels. They are extremely hydrophobic containing only 16 - 25% polar residues
which explain their solubility in organic solvents. Polar
residues are clustered at the N-terminus and in the middle
of the protein (residues 40 - 50 using the numbering of the
<u>Neurospora crassa</u> sequence). Long hydrophobic stretches of
about 25 amino acid residues are found both in the N-terminal as well as in the C-terminal part of the sequence.

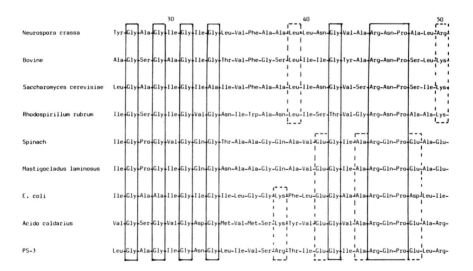

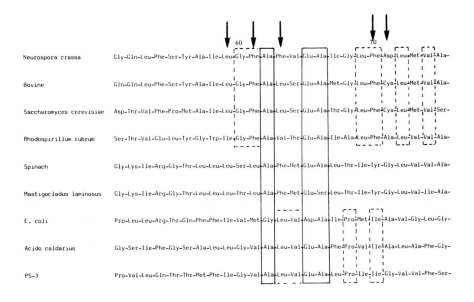

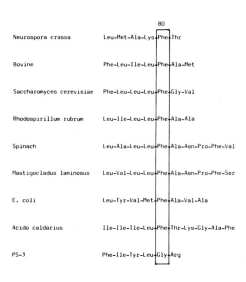

Fig. 1 <u>Amino acid sequence of the proteolipid subunit of various ATP synthases.</u>
Solid lines indicate conserved amino acid residues in all organisms, dashed lines amino acids specific for a group of organisms. Arrows indicate where mutations occurred leading to oligomycin resistance.

In the most thoroughly investigated membrane protein, the
bacteriorhodopsin from <u>Halobacterium halobium</u>, stretches of
25 hydrophobic amino acid residues are found to traverse
the lipid bilayer in an α-helical conformation [23].

A comparison of the sequences of these homologous
proteins revealed the numerous conserved amino acid residues. These residues might be indispensable for the function or the maintainance of certain structure of the protein. Extensive homologies among the sequences of the proteolipid subunit were found. In the middle of the N-terminal
hydrophobic stretch (residues 27 - 33) four glycine resi-
dues are conserved. Gly_{42}, arg_{45}, asn/gln_{46}, pro_{47} localized
in the hydrophilic segment were also found to be invariant.
In this segment the single conserved basic amino acid residue (arg_{45}) occurs. The only invariant acidic amino acid
residue is observed in the middle of the C-terminal hydrophobic stretch (position 65). With one exception (aspartic
acid in <u>E. coli</u>), this amino acid is a glutamic acid. This
acidic residue is flanked by two conserved alanyl residues
(position 62 and 66). At the C-terminus (position 80) a conserved phenylalanine was found.

Oligomycin binding

According to their homologies clearly two groups of
proteolipids are found. One containing the mitochondrial
proteins plus the <u>Rhodospirillum rubrum</u> protein, the other
containing the bacterial proteins (<u>E. coli</u>, <u>acido caldarius</u>,
PS-3). The chloroplast and the cyanobacterial proteins seem
to be more related to the bacterial ones. Interestingly,
ATP synthases from the first group show oligomycin sensitivity. Oligomycin is possibly bound via a Schiff base to
the proteolipid and a lysine residue should be the attachment site [14]. The only conserved lysine residue amongst

this group is lys_{14} favouring this group for the interaction
with oligomycin. But chemical proof is still lacking that
oligomycin binds exclusively in all four organisms to this
conserved lysine residue. Other amino acid residues likely
to be involved in oligomycin binding were detected by the
analysis of inhibitor resistant mutants [22]. The mutations
were found to be clustered around the invariant acidic
amino acid residue 65 located in highly conserved regions
(positions 59 - 63, positions 70-71). Two phenylalanine residues in the ATP synthase proteolipid are unique for the
oligomycin sensitive organisms (61 and 70). These residues
either are effected by the mutation or the mutation maps
close to this residue. It is thus most likely that oligomycin
binds to this segment in the amino acid sequence.

DCCD binding

DCCD binds covalently to the proteolipid subunit. The
use of $[^{14}C]DCCD$ allowed the identification of the target
amino acid [16-21]. In all analyzed proteolipids the covalently bound ^{14}C-labelled inhibitor could be traced back to
a single fragment produced by CNBr and/or N-bromosuccinimide
cleavage [16-21]. Automated solid-phase Edman degradation
of the modified fragment lead to the liberation of bound
radioactivity during one degradation step only. In all organisms the invariant acid amino acid residue 65 was exclusively labelled adding further evidence for the importance
of this residue. Interestingly, labelling of only a part of
the proteolipid oligomer with DCCD completely abolishes the
enzymatic activity of the ATP synthase [9,15,17] indicating
that the proteolipid monomers act in cooperative fashion.

DCCD resistant mutants from E. coli have been isolated.
Two classes according to their decreased sensitivity towards

DCCD were identified [20]. In both classes the isoleucine
residue 32 is substituted, which is located in a highly
conserved region of the polypeptide. Class one contains a
valine residue at this position leading to a moderate resistancy while class two is strongly resistant. Here a threonine is found instead of the isoleucine. Interestingly, also
in oligomycin resistant mutants the amino acid exchange was
found in a conserved part of the protein.

Fig. 2 Amino acid substitution in mutant proteolipid sub-
       units from E. coli.

       The numbering according to the sequence of the Neu-
       rospora crassa protein is used (see Fig. 1).

       Dicyclohexylcarbodiimide resistant mutants

                                   32
       Wild type   -Ala-Ile-Gly-Ile-Gly-Ile-Leu-Gly-
       Class one mutants   -Ala-Ile-Gly-Val-Gly-Ile-Leu-Gly-
       Class two mutants   -Ala-Ile-Gly-Thr-Gly-Ile-Leu-Gly-

       Mutants leading to a deficient F_0 part

                                   65
       Wild type   -Gly-Leu-Val-Asp-Ala-Ile-Pro-Met-
       DG 7/1   -Gly-Leu-Val-Gly-Ala-Ile-Pro-Met-
       DG 18/3   -Gly-Leu-Val-Asn-Ala-Ile-Pro-Met-

Mutants with defective F_0

       It was shown above that the invariant acidic amino
acid 65 can be covalently modified by DCCD. But covalent
modification or just noncovalent binding could induce allosteric conformational changements leading to a nonactive
ATP synthase complex. Mutants defective in H^+ conduction
were selected for nonbinding of DCCD and analyzed for amino

acid exchanges in the proteolipid subunit. Two mutants with
an altered proteolipid subunit were detected. Mutant DG 7/1
contains a glycine instead the aspartic acid [19]. Diploid
strains containg both wild type and mutant alleles were analyzed for H^+ conduction [24]. A strong negative complementation was found indicating that the mutant protein could
substitute the wild type one. Thus, most likely the mutant
protein exhibits the same conformation in vivo than the wild
type protein. In mutant 18/3 an asparagine is found instead
of the aspartic acid. This is the smallest possible "modification" since just the charge is abolished. This result demonstrates that a chargeable group in the proteolipid is
essential for H^+ conduction. All experimental evidence suggests that this group is located in the middle of the lipid
bilayer. Firstly, it occurs in the middle of a hydrophobic
stretch in the amino acid sequence; secondly, only hydrophobic carbodiimide can interact with this residue [15,25].

Conclusion

There is strong evidence that a oligomeric proteolipid
subunit of ATP synthase is intimately involved in H^+ conduction. In some reconstitution experiments with artificial liposomes and the isolated protein H^+ conductivity could be
measured [26-28]. But this activity amounted only a few
percents of the specific activity of an intact F_0 part [28]
and it is thus questionable if the proteolipid alone constitutes the protonchannel. Other subunits might be required
for full expression of the proton conductance which either
are directly involved in the catalytic mechanism or are
needed to maintain a specific conformation of the proteolipid
(stablilization of the oligomer).

Two models for protonconduction through the membrane
exist. The first model includes a chain of hydrogen

bonds provided by polar amino acid residues or by water lining the interior of a hydrophilic pore [29,30]. The second model developed by Boyer [31] suggests the migration of a negatively charged amino acid chain. This residue should move in the protonated form into one direction and move back in the ionic form. If the proteolipid alone constitutes the proton channel, it appears to be difficult to construct a network of hydrogen bonds with the four invariant residues found in this molecule. This would favour the model of protontranslocation by migration of a charged group.

REFERENCES

1. Sone, N., Yoshida, M., Hirata, H. and Kagawa, Y. (1975) J. Biol. Chem. 250, 7917-7923.
2. Friedl, P., Friedl, C. and Schairer, H.U. (1979) Eur. J. Biochem. 100, 175-180.
3. Pick, U. and Racker, E. (1979) J. Biol. Chem. 254, 2793-2799.
4. Foster, D.L. and Fillingame, R.H. (1979) J. Biol. Chem. 254, 8230-8236.
5. Sone, N., Yoshida, M., Hirata, H. and Kagawa, Y. (1978) Proc. Natl. Acad. Sci. U.S.A. 75, 4219-4223.
6. Negrin, R.S., Foster, D.L. and Fillingame, R.H. (1980) J. Biol. Chem. 255, 5643-5648.
7. Schneider, E. and Altendorf, K. (1980) FEBS Lett. 116, 173-176.
8. Friedl, P. and Schairer, H.U. (1981) FEBS Lett. in press.
9. Sebald, W., Graf, T., Lukins, H.B. (1979) Eur. J. Biochem. 93, 587-599.
10. Beechey, A.M. (1966) Biochem. Biophys. Res. Commun. 23, 75-80.
11. Lardy, H.A., Johnsen, D. and Murray, W.C. (1958) Arch. Biochem. Biophys. 78, 587-597.
12. Glehn, M., Norrestam, R., Kierkegaard, P., Marun, L. and Ernster, L. (1972) FEBS Lett. 20, 267-269.
13. Schneider, E., Schwuléra, U., Müller, H.W. and Dose, K. (1978) FEBS Lett. 87, 257-260.
14. Enns, R.K. and Criddle, R.S. (1977) Arch. Biochem. Biophys. 182, 587-600.
15. Kiehl, R. and Hatefi, Y. (1980) Biochemistry 19, 541-548.

16. Sebald, W., Hoppe, J. and Wachter, E. (1979) in Functional and Molecular Aspects of Biomembrane Transport (E. Quagliariello et al. eds) pp. 63-74. Elsevier/North-Holland Biomedical Press.
17. Hoppe, J. and Sebald, W. (1980) Eur. J. Biochem. 107, 57-65.
18. Sebald, W., Machleidt, W. and Wachter, E. (1980) Proc. Natl. Acad. Sci. U.S.A. 77, 785-789.
19. Hoppe, J., Schairer, H.U. and Sebald, W. (1980) FEBS Lett. 109, 107-111.
20. Hoppe, J., Schairer, H.U. and Sebald, W. (1980) Eur. J. Biochem. 112, 17-24.
21. Sebald, W. and Wachter, E. (1980) FEBS Lett. 122, 307-311.
22. Sebald, W., Wachter, E. and Tzagoloff, A. (1979) Eur. J. Biochem. 100, 599-607.
23. Engelman, D.M., Henderson, R. McLachlan, A.D. and Wallace, B.A. (1980) Proc. Natl. Acad. Sci. U.S.A. 77, 2023-2027.
24. Friedl, P., Friedl, C. and Schairer, H.U. (1980) FEBS Lett. 119, 254-256.
25. Cattel, K.J., Lindop, C.R., Knight, I.G., and Beechey, R.B. (1971) Biochem. J. 125, 169-177.
26. Criddle, R.S., Packer, L. and Shieh, P. (1977) Proc. Natl. Acad. Sci. U.S.A. 74, 4306-4310.
27. Nelson, N., Eytan, E., Notsani, B., Sigrist, H., Sigrist-Nelson, K. and Gitler, C. (1977) Proc. Natl. Acad. Sci. U.S.A. 74, 2375-2378.
28. Sigrist-Nelson, K. and Azzi, A. (1980) J. Biol. Chem. 255, 10638-10643.
29. Williams, R.J.P. (1978) FEBS Lett. 85, 9-19.
30. Nagle, J.F. and Morowitz, H.-J. (1978) Proc. Natl. Acad. Sci. U.S.A. 75, 298-302.
31. Boyer, P.D. (1980) First european bioenergetics conference , short reports pp. 133-134.

PROTON CONDUCTION BY H^+-ATPase

Sergio Papa and Ferruccio Guerrieri

Institute of Biological Chemistry, Faculty of Medicine
University of Bari, Bari, Italy

The H^+-ATPase of coupling membranes can be resolved into
two multipeptide moieties: the soluble catalytic sector, F_1,
and the membrane sector, F_o. F_1 can mediate H^+ diffusion in
native (1-3) and artificial (4-9) membranes. In the mitochondrial H^+-ATPase there are additional proteins apparently
involved in the binding of F_1 to F_o (the oligomycin-sensi-
tivity-conferring protein and F_{c2} or F_6) and an ATPase inhibitor protein (10). Definite progress has been made in the
elucidation of the protein structure of F_1 and F_o and the
catalytic mechanisms of F_1. This is dealt with elsewhere in
this volume. The way in which F_1 and F_o together catalyze
synthesis of ATP driven by transmembrane $\Delta\mu H^+$ and, in reverse, active H^+ transport at the expense of ATP hydrolysis
is, however, not yet known. In this paper the characteristics
and possible molecular mechanisms of transmembrane H^+ translocation by H^+-ATPase will be reviewed.

REGULATION OF PROTON CONDUCTION BY pH AND TRANSMEMBRANE $\Delta\mu H^+$.
Upon displacement or removal of F_1 from membrane bound H^+-
ATPase, the H^+ conductivity of F_o is unmasked (1-3,11),

V. P. Skulachev and Peter C. Hinkle (eds.), Chemiosmotic Proton Circuits in Biological Membranes
in honor of Peter Mitchell   ISBN 0-201-07398-6

In "inside out" vesicles of the inner membrane prepared by sonication of beef heart mitochondria in the presence of EDTA (ESMP), relaxation of proton gradients formed by respiration exhibits two apparent first order phases, with rate constants of 1 and 0.1 sec^{-1} respectively (3). Both phases are an expression of H^+ conduction by H^+-ATPase as judged from inhibition by N,N'-dicyclohexylcarbodiimide (DCCD) and oligomycin (3). The fast phase ceases when approximately one third of the $\Delta\mu H^+$ is relaxed. Collapse of $\Delta\psi$ did not abolish the biphasic nature of H^+ release; thus, it depends on ΔpH (3). The same pattern of H^+ release is observed in submitochondrial particles devoid of F_1 (USMP) when respiratory $\Delta\mu H^+$ is enhanced to the values observed in ESMP by inhibiting H^+ release with oligomycin (12).

In chloroplasts light-dependent $\Delta\mu H^+$ induces high H^+ conductance in the unmodified H^+-ATPase (13), in the enzyme modified by amidinating (14) and thiol-group blocking agents (15), as well as in F_o after F_1 removal (11).

All this indicates that transmembrane ΔpH, more acidic inside the vesicles, enhances H^+ conductivity of F_o. As part of $\Delta\mu H^+$ decays, the system reverts to low H^+ conductivity. Related to this behavior of F_o in the native membranes is the observation that in liposomes H^+ conductivity of F_o of the thermophilic bacterium PS3 (4,16) and chloroplasts (8) is enhanced at pH below 7 with a pH dependence which indicates involvement of a monoprotic site with pK of 6.8 (4). In the mitochondrial membrane F_o contains one exposed polypeptide at each side of the membrane (17). In "inside out" ESMP, F_o can directly sense, as in thylakoids, intravesicular pH changes. Acidification of this space can induce high H^+ conductivity by causing protonation of critical residue(s) of F_o. The observation that H^+ conduction by PS3-F_o exhibits saturation kinetics with respect to H^+ concentration (16) confirms that proton transfer by ionizable groups represents the rate-limiting step of the process.

CONTROL OF PROTON CONDUCTION BY POLYPEPTIDE INTERACTION. Removal with Sephadex chromatography of the ATPase protein inhibitor from ESMP enhances H^+ conductivity of F_o (3,12,18). The ATPase inhibitor is also removed from submitochondrial particles during respiration-driven $\Delta\mu H^+$-formation (19). When F_1 also is removed (USMP), the decay of $\Delta\mu H^+$ exhibits simple first order kinetics (3,13). Adding back F_1 to depleted vesicles restores the biphasic pattern of H^+ release. Interestingly enough the kinetic constant of the rapid H^+ release phase in Sephadex particles and F_1-reconstituted USMP was higher than that of monophasic H^+ diffusion in USMP (12).

Adenylylimidophosphate (AMP-PNP) and alkyl cations, which inhibit ATP hydrolysis in ESMP or in isolated F_1, also slow down the decay of the aerobic $\Delta\mu H^+$ in ESMP (2,3,12,18). This inhibition has a sigmoidal titration curve, is synergistic with inhibition by oligomycin and disappears when F_1 is removed from ESMP (3). Thus binding of inhibitory ligands to F_1 seems to induce a structural change in the F_o-F_1 complex, which results in a decreased H^+ conductivity and enhanced sensitivity of F_o to inhibition by oligomycin.

Binding of ATP or ADP prevents the enhancement of H^+ conductivity induced in chloroplast H^+-ATPase by high $\Delta\mu H^+$ (13). Independent lines of evidence indicate that in chloroplasts the enhancement of H^+ conductivity by high $\Delta\mu H^+$ is

associated with conformational changes in F_1 and/or modification of its interaction with F_o, which result in the exposure
of free amino-groups (14), maleimide-reactive groups (15,20)
and proton exchanging groups (21).

It seems possible to conclude that the interaction
between F_1 and F_o polypeptides controls H^+ access (during ATP
hydrolysis) and H^+ exit (during ATP synthesis or uncoupled
decay of $\Delta\mu H^+$) at the side of the H^+ channel in F_o in contact
with F_1. In the presence of a large $\Delta\mu H^+$ the F_1-F_o interaction introduces a pathway with high proton conductivity.

AMINOACID RESIDUES INVOLVED IN H^+ CONDUCTION. Use of DCCD,
which reacts with glutamic (or aspartic) acid, led to identification of the role in H^+ conduction of a glutamic residue
(aspartic in E. coli) located in an invariant position (65
according to Neurospora sequence numbering) of a 7000-8000
dalton polypeptide of F_o (22,23). The essential role in H^+
translocation of this residue is also shown by the finding
that its substitution by glycine in E. coli mutants results
in suppression of proton conductivity (24,25).

The inhibition by lipophilic cations of chemical catalysis
by F_1 and proton translocation by H^+-ATPase (2,3,12,18)
indicate that negatively charged groups located in the hydrophobic environment of F_1 play an essential role. Inhibition
of ATP hydrolysis and H^+ conduction in ESMP could also be
produced by an anionic amphiphile like sodium dodecylsulfate.
Furthermore, the inhibition caused by one of the two amphiphiles
was reversed by stoichiometric amounts of the other (12,26).
These observation suggest that ionic interactions between
acidic and basic residues in hydrophobic regions of F_1 and

F_o are involved in H$^+$ translocation.

Studies with amino acid reagents show that proton conduction involves polar residues of F_o other than the DCCD-reactive residue. Sone et al. (16,27) reported that tyrosine nitration with tetranitromethane or arginine modification with phenylglyoxal in F_o of thermophilic bacterium PS3 cause inhibition of H$^+$ conduction in liposomes. Sigrist-Nelson and Azzi (8) found that treatment of the DCCD-binding proteolipid of chloroplast H$^+$-ATPase with tetranitromethane or phenyl-isothiocyanate - since the proteolipid has no cysteine residues the latter substance can only react with free amino groups - resulted in depression of H$^+$ conductivity.

Pansini et al. (12) and Guerrieri and Papa (26,28) have found that treatment of ESMP or USMP with phenylglyoxal or tetranitromethane caused inhibition of H$^+$ conduction. Treatment of ESMP or USMP with butanedione, which is even more specific for arginine than phenylglyoxal, stimulated $\Delta\mu$H$^+$ relaxation. This could be due to specificity of attack of different arginines of F_o or to modification by one of the reagents of residue(s) other than arginine (12,26).

MOLECULAR MECHANISM OF PROTON TRANSLOCATION. The DCCD-binding proteolipid of F_o, like the five polypeptides of F_1, has been strictly preserved during evolution (22). They should thus represent components essential to the basic function of the complex. The α and β subunits of F_1 are responsible for nucleotide binding and chemical catalysis. The DCCD-binding proteolipid functions as a transmembrane proton translocator (5-8). The γ, δ and ε subunits of F_1 and the 15,000 daltons protein of PS3 of F_o (29) or its equivalent in other organisms seem to provide the connection between F_1 and F_o (17,29). These polypeptides may be involved in the $\Delta\mu H^+$-dependent interaction of F_1 with F_o previously described. This interaction, which probably involves salt bridges between acidic residues in F_1 and basic residues in F_o might play a specific role in the coupling of H^+ translocation to chemical catalysis. Elucidation of the protein structure of the F_1-F_o connection subunits should help us understand the gating and coupling function of H^+-ATPase.

The knowledge of the structure of the DCCD-binding proteolipid of F_o and of the residues involved in proton conduction allows speculation about the molecular mechanism of proton conduction by this component. Of the 70-80 residues of the proteolipid, around 80% are apolar. Most of them are clustered in two segments of 20-25 residues, separated by a polar segment of 10-20 residues (22). The proteolipid could be bent on itself (22,23) with the two hydrophobic segments embedded in the membrane and the hydrophilic loop exposed at the surface. The proteolipid probably exists as a hexamer in the membrane (30). The monomers, as well as the hexamer react with DCCD (30) and the carbodiimide-reactive residues appear to be 15 Å from each other (31). In analogy to the arrangement of bacteriorhodopsin in the purple membrane (32), the double hydrophobic segments of the six monomers - probably coiled as α-helices - (32) might extend side by side across the membrane perpendicularly to its plane so as to form a bundle with a central channel where H^+ translocation would take place (Fig. 1). The central polar loop and the polar N-terminus of a single monomer could be exposed at the opposite sides of the membrane. The monomers can be parallel

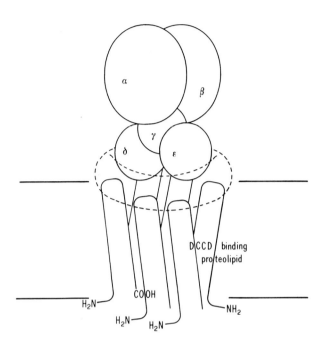

Figure 1. Hypothetical arrangement in the membrane of polypeptides of F_1 and DCCD-binding proteolipid of F_o. Other
membrane subunits are indicated by the dotted line.

or antiparallel.

    In all the proteolipids so far characterized the DCCD-
reactive residue lies in the middle of a hydrophobic sequence,
which could raise the pK of the carboxylic group to the pK of
6.8 observed for H$^+$ conduction by PS3 F_o in liposomes (4).
The six subunits of the hexamer appear to function in a concerted way (22,30).

    The DCCD-binding residue is apparently in close vicinity
of isoleucine-28. In fact subustitution of this isoleucine
in E. coli mutant results in resistance to DCCD (25). Substitution of residues in the vicinity of the DCCD-binding

position in Neurospora and yeast results in oligomycin resistance (22). Since the acidic residue-65 is located in a hydrophobic segment with such a critical configuration, it is difficult to visualize how it could, on its own, pick up H^+ from one water phase and release it to the opposite one. H^+ could, however, be exchanged at the membrane surface by other residues and then be transferred to residue-65. Arginine and tyrosine residues appear, in fact, to participate in H^+ translocation by F_o (8,12,16,27,33). The positions of these residues remain to be identified. It seems, however, significant that only one arginine is present in the DCCD-binding proteolipid of mitochondria, at position 45, and this is also occupied by arginine in the other DCCD-binding proteolipids so far analyzed (22). The tyrosine of the DCCD-binding proteolipid of PS3 is located at position 68 (22). Beef heart and Neurospora mitochondria have one tyrosine residue at position 56. In the DCCD-binding protein of PS3 and chloroplasts tyrosine-56 is replaced by an isofunctional threonine residue (Fig. 2). In E. coli and S. cerevisiae hydroxyl residues are missing at position 56 but a threonine is present at position 55 in the first and at position 52 in the second case (Fig. 2). Furthermore we have found (28) that inhibition of H^+ conduction by tetranitromethane treatment of submitochondrial particles modifies the sensitivity to oligomycin. Thus the hydroxyl residues located in the hydrophobic segments of the proteolipid and the invariant arginine-45 could be involved in H^+ translocation. In the two hydrophobic segments of a monomer there are 3-7 hydroxyl residues in the various species examined (22), 18-42 hydroxyl residues in the hexamer. The monomers could be slightly

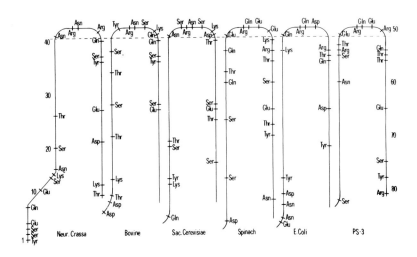

Figure 2. Position of polar residues in the DCCD-binding
proteolipids of H^{+}-ATPase (adapted from ref. 22 and 23).

displaced with respect to each other. It follows that these
residues are numerous enough to be distributed along all of
the proposed channels of the hexamer. It is conceivable that
hydroxyl residues from adjoining chains, joined by hydrogen
bonds (34,35), constitute a continuous network with the
acidic residues-65 in the middle, along which protons can
rapidly move across the membrane from the entry to the exit
mouth of the channel. Motion of residues can cover possible
gaps. It is, however, possible that intercalated between
hydroxyl residues, other polar residues and/or hydrogen-
bonded H$_2$O molecules also participate in H^{+} transfer. The
arginine-45 and other basic residues in the central loop or
in N-terminus could be involved in the access of H^{+} at the
entry mouth and their release from the exit mouth of the

channel. Modification by phenylglyoxal of basic residues at the entry mouth will depress proton conductivity; modification by butanedione of basic residues at the exit mouth will enhance proton conductivity (12,26,28). The basic residues at the mouth of the F_o channel can form salt bridges with acidic residues of the connection polypeptides of F_1. Formation of salt bridges can shift the pK of the residues engaged. Furthermore pK shifts caused by hydro-anhydro bond exchange catalyzed by F_1 could play a role in H^+ pumping (2,12).

REFERENCES

1. Hinkle, P.C. and Horstmann, L.L. (1971) J. Biol. Chem. 246, 6024-6028.
2. Papa, S., Guerrieri, F., Lorusson, M., Pansini, A., Izzo, G., Boffoli, D. and Capuano, F. (1977) BBS Library 14, 127-138.
3. Pansini, A., Guerrieri, F. and Papa, S. (1978) Eur. J. Biochem. 92, 545-551.
4. Okamoto, H., Sone, H., Hirata, H., Yoshida, H. and Kagawa, Y. (1977) J. Biol. Chem. 252, 6125-6131.
5. Nelson, N., Eytan, E., Natsani, B., Sigrist, H., Sigrist-Nelson, K. and Gitler, C. (1977) Proc. Natl. Acad. Sci. USA 74, 936-940.
6. Criddle, R.S., Packer, L. and Shieh, P. (1977) Proc. Natl. Acad. Sci. USA 74, 4306-4310.
7. Celis, H. (1980) Biochem. Biophys. Res. Commun. 92, 26-31.
8. Sigrist-Nelson, K. and Azzi, A. (1980) J. Biol. Chem. 255, 10638-10643.
9. Negrin, R.S., Foster, D.L. and Fillingame, R.H. (1980) J. Biol. Chem. 255, 5643-5648.
10. De Pierre, J.W. and Ernster, L. (1977) Ann. Rev. Biochem. 46, 201-262.
11. Ho, Y. and Wang, J.H. (1979) Biochem. Biophys. Res. Commun. 89, 294-299.
12. Pansini, A., Guerrieri, F. and Papa, S. (1979) In Membrane Bioenergetics (C.P. Lee et al., eds) pp. 413-428, Addison Wesley Publishing Company, Reading, MA USA

13. Portis, A.R., Magnusson, R.P. and McCarty, R.E. (1975)
     Biochim. Biophys. Res. Commun. 6, 877-884.
14. Oliver, D. and Jagendorf, A. (1976) J. Biol. Chem. 251,
     7168-7175.
15. Wagner, R. and Junge, W. (1977) Biochim. Biophys. Acta
     462, 259-272.
16. Sone, N., Hamamoto, T. and Kagawa, Y. (1981) J. Biol.
     Chem. 256, 2873-2877.
17. Ludwig, B., Prochaska, L. and Capaldi, R.A.(1980)
     Biochemistry 19, 1516-1523.
18. Pansini, A., Guerrieri, F. and Papa, S. (1978) in
     Frontiers of Biological Energetics (P.L. Dutton et al.,
     eds.) pp. 359-366, Academic Press, New York.
19. Van De Stadt, R.J., De Boer, B.L. and Van Dam, K. (1973),
     Biochim. Biophys. Acta 292, 338-349.
20. McCarty, R.E. and Fagan, J. (1973) Biochemistry 12,
     1503-1507.
21. Ryrie, I. and Jagendorf, A.T. (1972) J. Biol. Chem. 247,
     4453-4459.
22. Sebald, W., Hoppe, J. and Wachter, E. (1979) in Function
     and Molecular Aspects of Biomembrane Transport (E.
     Quagliariello et al., eds.) pp. 63-74, Elsevier/North
     Holland, Amsterdam, New York.
23. Altendorf, K.H., Hammel, U, Deckers, G., Kiltz, H.H.
     and Schmid, R. (1979) in Function and Molecular Aspects
     of Biomembrane Transport (E. Quagliariello et al.,
     eds.) pp. 53-61, Elsevier/North-Holland, Amsterdam, New
     York.
24. Hoppe, J., Schairer, H.U. and Sebald, W. (1980) FEBS
     Lett. 109, 107-111.
25. Wachter, E., Schmid, R., Deckers, G. and Altendorf,
     K.H. (1980) FEBS Lett. 113, 265-270.
26. Guerrieri, F. and Papa, S. (1980) First European Bio-
     energetics Conference Short Reports, pp. 207-208,
     Patron, Bologna, Italy.
27. Sone, N.I., Ikeba, K. and Kagawa, Y. (1979) FEBS Lett.
     97, 61-64.
28. Guerrieri, F. and Papa, S. (1981) in preparation.
29. Kagawa, Y., Sone, N.I., Hirata, H. and Yoshida, M.(1979)
     J. Bioenerg. Biomembr. 11, 39-78.
30. Sebald, W., Graf, Th. and Lukins, H.B. (1979) Eur. J.
     Biochem. 93, 587-599.
31. Sigrist-Nelson, K. and Azzi, A. (1979) J. Biol. Chem.
     254, 4470-4474.

32.   Engleman, D.M., Henderson, R., McLachlan, A.D. and
      Wallace, B.A. (1980) Proc. Natl. Acad. Sci., USA 77,
      2023-2027.
33.   Wachter, E., Schmid, R., Deckers, G. and Altendorf, K.
      (1980) in First European Bioenergetics Conference Short
      Reports, pp. 175-176, Patron, Bologna, Italy.
34.   Nagle, J.F. and Morowitz, H.J. (1978) Proc. Natl. Acad.
      Sci. USA 75, 298-302.
35.   Dunker, A.K. and Marvin, D.A. (1978) J. Theor. Biol. 72,
      9-16.

PROTON CHANNELS IN ATP-SYNTHETASES

Nathan Nelson

Department of Biology, Technion- Israel
Institute of Technology, Haifa, Israel

A general mechanism which functions in most
living creatures is like a rose in a garden of thorns for
the biological sciences. Mitchell's chemiosmotic hypothesis
(1,2,3,4) is one of very few such roses that have been bloom-
ing magnificiently in the last ten years. Mitchell's hypothesis has been proved to be applicable not only to the study
of energy transduction but also to ion transport across biological membranes. The role of proton grandients in energy
transduction has been emphasized and detailed mechanisms
have been proposed for the build-up of protonmotive force
by electron transport processes and its utilization for ATP
formation. Even though the concept of the formation of electrochemical gradients is general, it is clear now that each
"coupling site" operates with a different mechanism (4,5).
On the other hand the proton-ATPase complex acts as an ATP-
synthetase via similar mechanism in the various energy transducing membranes (5,6,7,8,9). Mitchell has predicted the
function of a reversible proton-ATPase enzyme in energy transducing membranes, and has proposed that the ion selectivity

V. P. Skulachev and Peter C. Hinkle (eds.), Chemiosmotic Proton Circuits in Biological Membranes
in honor of Peter Mitchell   ISBN 0-201-07398-6

of the process should be at the level of the membrane (1,2,3).

The proton-ATPase complex is composed of two sectors (6,7,10): A catalytic sector that is hydrophilic in nature and a membrane sector that is hydrophobic in nature. The function of the catalytic sector is to catalyze the formation of ATP at the expense of energy provided by a flux of protons. The function of the membrane sector is to provide the catalytic sector with a specific flux of protons across the membrane. Racker (5) and his colleagues have shown that resolution and reconstitution studies are the best way to study the mechanisms of these two processes. They showed that upon reconstitution of mitochondrial hydrophobic proteins into phospholipid vesicles a proton leak was created. This proton leak could be blocked by oligomycin or dicyclohexyl-carobodiimide in a fashion resembling that for F_1 depleted mitochondrial membranes. This approach was a landmark in the study of proton conduction across biological membranes.

Proton channels in chloroplast membranes. McCarty and Racker (11) were the first to demonstrate that removal of CF_1 causes a proton leak in chloroplast membranes. A question arose "what is the mechanism of this proton conduction?" A turnover of up to about 10^4 protons per second per CF_0 could be estimated for open CF_0 in chloroplast membranes at pH 6 (12). This turnover qualified the CF_0 as a candidate for a proton channel. However, direct demonstration of a channel mechanism in CF_0 is not available. CF_1 functions as a gate for the proton conduction across CF_0. Therefore, dissociation of a few CF_1 molecules from the membrane might create a proton leak sufficient to uncouple the entire organelle. Upon removal of CF_1 spontaneous inactivation of the proton conduction took place, and it was proposed that this

phenomenon   is   a common property of all the proton channels in proton ATPase complexes (12). This property of the
proton channel might be necessary for maintaining the protonmotive force during biogenesis of the enzyme (12,13) and even
during steady state energy transduction.

Structure and function of the membrane sectors of proton-
ATPase complexes. The TF_o from the thermophylic bacterium
PS-3 was shown to be the simplest membrane sector of all
proton-ATPase complexes (8). Initially it was shown to be
composed of three different polypeptides, and later it was
demonstrated that two subunits were sufficient for its function in ATP-Pi exchange (8). The CF_o of chloroplasts and BF_o
of E. coli are composed of three different subunits (10,12,
13,14). In CF_o the subunits are designated as subunits I
(15 KD), II (12.5 KD) and III (8 KD). Subunit III was
shown to be the DCCD-binding protein (10,12,13). It was
proposed that subunit II prevents the dissociation of subunit
III from its hexamers, and subunit I has been suggested as
the binding site for CF_1 (10,12,13). It seems as if three
subunits are the basic structure of the membrane sector of
the proton-ATPase complexes and the abovementioned three
functions are the minimal requirements for a functional
membrane sector. The mitochondrial F_o is a more complex
structure composed of six or more subunits (5). The common
denominator for all of the membrane sectors is the DCCD-
binding protein that preserved its structure during evolution (15,16).

Reconstitution of channels active in proton production. The
DCCD-binding protein has been isolated from various membranes
containing proton-ATPase complexes (8,10,12). Several

attempts to demonstrate DCCD-sensitive proton conduction
after reconstitution into phospholipid membranes failed (8,
12). In 1977 it was demonstrated that reconstitution of the
chloroplast proteolipid (subunit III of CF_o) into liposomes
prepared from chloroplast lipids yielded DCCD-sensitive proton conduction across the membranes (17). Later it was demonstrated that the proton conduction was correlated with
the amount of proteolipid in the vesicles (18). Sigrist-
Nelson and Azzi (19,20,21) further characterized the system
and clearly demonstrated that a single type of polypeptide
was involved in the proton conduction and that galactolipids
were required for its activity. It was proposed that the
assembly of six copies of that polypeptide is necessary for
the forming of a single channel (12,13,18). Relatively
large amounts of the proteolipid were required for getting
appreciable proton conduction and the amounts of DCCD required for blocking the proton conduction were somewhat higher
than that required for inhibition _in situ_. This apparent
discrepancy can be explained if we assume that in the absence of subunit II of CF_o most of the proteolipid in the
vesicles is in its monomeric form (12,13). Upon assembly of
hexamers of the proteolipid a proton channel is formed. The
hexamer is readily dissociated in the absence of subunit II
and thus, the function of subunit II is to keep the channel
open. DCCD can interact with the monomers but at higher concentration than that required for interaction with the assembled channel. Since the concentration of assembled channels is rather low and they rapidly dissociate, higher concentrations of DCCD are required to inhibit the bulk of the
proton conduction.

The studies with isolated proteolipid from chloroplasts
clearly indicated that active proton channel can be formed

from a single type of polypeptide. However, in order to
avoid accidental leaks in the membrane, mechanistic measures
have been developed to reduce the proton conduction until
the entire proton-ATPase complex is assembled and the proton
channel is properly gated (12,13).

Reconstitution of proteolipid into lipid bilayers. Tzagoloff
and his colleagues (22) studied the proteolipid (subunit 9)
of yeast mitochondria. They made several important observations, one of which was that the proteolipid is soluble in a
chloroform-methanol solution. The proteolipid thus purified
to homogeneity and its chemical properties have been
thoroughly studied (15,16). Criddle et al (23) used the
method of phospholipid impregnated Millipore filters to demonstrate oligmycin-sensitive proton conduction induced by
this preparation. Later on it was reported that K^+ conduction was observed along with the proton conduction (24). It
is doubtful whether the Millipore filter technique is suitable for the reported measurements of proton conduction across
the filters (25). Certainly this method is not suitable for
single channel conduction measurements. In collaboration
with Dr. Hansgeorg Schindler from the Biocenter in Basel,
we studied the yeast mitochondria proteolipid in the lipid
bilayer technique of Montal and Mueller (26). We observed
that the proteolipid isolated with chloroform-methanol
solution exclusively induced a voltage dependent K^+ conduction upon reconstitution into lipid bilayers. Therefore,
the butanol extraction procedure was conducted with yeast
mitochondria in a fashion resembling the one used for the
chloroplast proteolipid (17). The preparation was stored
as a butanolic solution containing the mitochondrial lipids
that are soluble in n-butanol. The purity of this prepara-

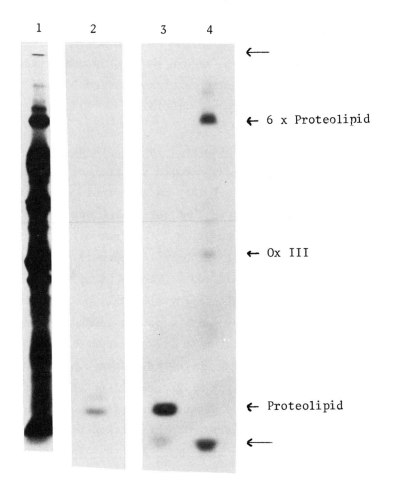

Fig. 1. In vivo and in situ labelling of the proteolipid
with ^{35}S-methionine and [^{14}C]-DCCD.

About two g of yeast spheroplasts were labelled with
about 1 mCi of ^{35}S-methionine in the presence of 100
µg cycloheximide. After 30 min of incubation the
cells were washed once with 100 ml of salt solution
containing 1.2 M sorbitol and mitochondria were prepared. The proteolipid was isolated as previously
described (17). Isolated yeast mitochondria containing about 5 mg of protein in 1 ml of 10 m̊M Tri-
cine (pH 8), were incubated for 30 min at room

temperature with about 20µCi of [14C]-DCCD. A sample
of 10 µl was dissociated with 2% SDS and 2% mercapto-
ethanol. The rest of the membranes were used for the
purification of proteolipid. Lane 1; autoradiography
of gel of membrane sample (containing about 50 µg protein) after labelling with 35S-methionine. Lane 2;
autoradiography of gel containing about 2 µg of 35S-
methionine labelled proteolipid. Lane 3; autoradiography of [14C]- DCCD labelled proteolipid containing about 2 µg protein. Lane 4; autoradiography of
mitochondrial membranes labelled with [14C]-DCCD containing about 50 µg protein.

tion was verified by the extraction of the proteolipid from
cells that were labelled with 35S-methionine. Figure 1
shows that most of the label in the purified preparation
coincides with the position of [14C]-DCCD-labelled proteolipid. This experiment indicates that indeed proteolipid is
the only polypeptide in the mitochondrial membranes which is
soluble in n-butanol. Upon reconstitution of this preparation into a phospholipid bilayer, a proton conduction across
the membrane was observed. The selectivity for protons was
usually greater than a thousandfold over potasium. A detailed study on the effect of pH, imposed electric potential,
specific inhibitors and the degree of cooperativity among
copies of the proteolipid was conducted. The heart of the
matter is depicted in figure 2. The figure shows single
channel conduction resolved by Dr. Schindler with purified
proteolipid reconstituted in a bilayer of ether lipids. The
channels were resolved at about pH 2 and showed single channel conduction of about 20 pS that was only slightly influenced by the imposed voltage. The selectivity of the channels
for protons over potasium was up to 2000 under the experimental conditions. Therefore, the proton channel of the
membrane sector of proton-ATPase has been demonstrated for
the first time and it appears to behave like a bonafide
channel.

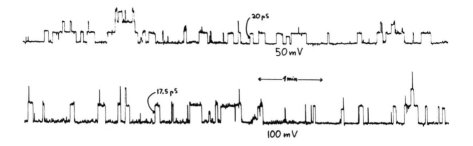

Fig. 2. <u>Single channel conduction of yeast mitochondria</u>
<u>proteolipid.</u>

Yeast mitochondria proteolipid was isolated by the
butanol extraction procedure (17). The preparation
was incorporated into ether lipids and after the
formation of bilayer the electric conduction was
measured at pH 2.2 at the given imposed potentials
(H. Schindler and N. Nelson manuscript in preparation).

<u>The proton channel - a few facts, more imagination.</u> There
are strong indications that the DCCD-binding protein is the
major constituent of the proton channel. Can it function
by itself as a proton channel? Kagawa and his collaborators
(8) reconstituted individual subunits of F_o from thermophylic
bacteria into phospholipid vesicles. They clearly demonstrated that two polypeptides were required to induce proton
conduction in the vesicles and the DCCD-binding protein by
itself failed to do so. The rates of proton conduction
were rather low and the system was influenced by changes at
the phase transition temperature - a characteristic behaviour
of carriers (27). On the other hand with butanol-extracts
from chloroplasts it was demonstrated that the chloroplast
DCCD-binding protein by itself can induce proton conduction
into lipid vesicles providing that chloroplast lipids were
present in the vesicles (17,18,21). Here too the calculated
rates of proton conduction were far too low in comparison

with CF_1-depleted chloroplasts (see 12). In this chapter we
have demonstrated for the first time that the DCCD-binding
protein from yeast mitochondria can form typical proton channels upon reconstitution into lipid bilayers. This observation leaves little doubt that indeed the DCCD-binding protein
from proton-ATPase can form proton channels by itself.

The reconstituted yeast mitochondria proteolipid appeared in the bilayer system as a typical "fast channel".
There are strong indications that in situ the proton channel
is a fast proton conductor (12). If so, why does the proteolipid reconstituted into vesicles induce only slow proton
conduction, and what is the biological significance of this
phenomenon? The key for answering this question lies in the
fact that the DCCD-binding protein (Proteolipid) can act in
proton conduction only in its oligomeric form. There are
several indications that six copies of the DCCD-binding
protein are present in each proton-ATPase complex and it has
been assumed that the assembly of six copies is necessary for
its activity (12,13,17,19,20). It has been proposed that
only a very small fraction of the reconstituted proteolipid
is in its hexameric form in a given time, and this would explain the low proton conductivity of the system (12,13). If
this is the case, it is reasonable to assume that a second
polypeptide in F_o keeps the six copies of proteolipid assembled into an active proton channel (12). Moreover, in the absence of F_1 even the assembled F_o undergoes spontaneous inactivation (12). The biological significance of these
phenomena might be seen as a safeguard mechanism. It has
been suggested that when a few F_1 sectors are accidently removed from the membrane, the open channels are partially inactivated. If by a biological mistake the DCCD-binding
protein is synthesized in larger amounts than the other sub-

units of the ATPase, its assembled hexameric form will be in such a small amount that a significant proton conduction will not take place (13). These two phenomena would prevent uncoupling of the energy transduction in the entire organelle.

It is quite likely that the hexameric form of the proteolipid in proton-ATPase complexes has indeed evolved as a safeguarding mechanism against proton leaks. On the other hand it might be important for the mechanism of proton conduction and the formation of an effective proton filter in the channel. It is possible that only the hexamer can form a continuity of water molecules across the membrane for the formation of a "proton wire". It might be necessary to introduce six residues of aspartic acid or glutamic acid in the middle of the membrane and by so doing to construct the proton filter. Six proline residues in adjacent position might do the job. The large size of the channel and its high selectivity might also be constructed from a narrow hydrophobic barrier constructed of six phenylalanine residues in a hydrophylic environment. Bilayer studies might answer a few quite important questions concerning the mechanism of proton chanelling.

During my initial steps in bioenergetics my main difficulty with the Mitchell's hypothesis was how to handle proton leaks in the membranes. Now, when we start understanding the elegant way by which nature handled this complicated matter, we realize how much vision Dr. Mitchell had in constructing his ingenious hypothesis.

fort1

ORT

REFERENCES.

1. Mitchell, P. (1961) Nature 191, 144-148.
2. Mitchell, P. (1966) "Chemiosmotic Coupling in Oxidative and Photosynthetic Phosphorylation" Glynn Res. Bodmin, Cornwall, England.
3. Mitchell, P. (1968) "Chemiosmotic Coupling in Energy Transduction" Glynn Res. Bodmin, Cornwall, England.
4. Mitchell, P. (1979) in "Membrane Bioenergetics" (C.P. Lee et al., eds.), pp. 361-372. Addison-Wesley, Reading, Massachusetts.
5. Racker, E. (1976) "A New Look at Mechanisms in Bioenergetics." Academic Press, New York.
6. Senior, A.E. (1973) Biochem. Biophys. Acta 301, 249-277.
7. Nelson, N. (1976) Biochem. Biophys. Acta 456, 314-338.
8. Kagawa, Y. (1978) Biochem. Biophys. Acta 505, 45-93.
9. Rott,R. and Nelson,N. (1981) J. Biol. Chem. in press.
10. Nelson,N. (1981) Curr.Top.Bioenerg. in press.
11. McCarty, R.E. and Racker, E. (1966) Brookhaven Symp. Biol. 19, 202-214.
12. Nelson,N.(1980) Ann. N.Y. Acad.Sci. 358, 25-36.
13. Nelson,N., Nelson,H. and Schatz,G. (1980) Proc. Natl. Acad. Sci. U.S.A., 77, 1361-1364.
14. Foster, D.L., Mosher, M.E., Futai, M. and Fillingame, R.H. (1980) J. Biol. Chem. 255, 12037-12041.
15. Sebald,W. and Wachter,E. (1978) in "Mosbacher Colloquium on Energy conservation in Biological Membranes" (G. Schafer and M.Klingelberg, eds.), pp. 228-236. Springer-Verlag, Berlin.
16. Sebald,W. and Wachter,E. (1980) FEBS Lett. 122, 307-311.
17. Nelson, N., Eytan,E., Notsani,B., Sigrist, H., Sigrist-Nelson,K. and Gitler,C. (1977) Proc. Natl. Acad.Sci. U.S.A. 74, 2375-2378.
18. Nelson,N., Eytan,E., and Julian,C. (1977) Proc. Int. Congr. Photosynth., 4th. (1977) pp. 559-570.
19. Sigrist-Nelson, K., Sigrist,H. and Azzi,A. (1978) Eur.J. Biochem. 92, 9-14.
20. Sigrist-Nelson,K. and Azzi,A. (1979) J. Biol. Chem. 254, 4470-4474.
21. Sigrist-Nelson,K. and Azza,A. (1980) J. Biol. Chem. 255, 10638-10643.

22.   Sierra, M.F. and Tzagoloff,A. (1973) Proc. Natl. Acad. Sci. U.S.A. 70, 3155-3159.
23.   Criddle, R.S., Packer, L. and Shien,P. (1977) Proc. Natl. Acad. Sci. U.S.A. 74, 4306-4310.
24.   Criddle, R.S., Johnston,R., Packer, L., Shieh,P.K. and Konishi,T. (1979) in "Cation Flux Across Bio-membranes" Mukohata et al. eds., pp. 399-407, Academic Press, New York.
25.   Moran,A., Tal, E., Eytan,E. and Nelson,N. (1980) FEBS Lett. 110, 62-64.
26.   Montal, M. and Mueller,P. (1972) Proc.Natl. Acad. Sci. U.S.A. 69, 3561-3566.
27.   Okamoto,H., Sone, N., Hirata,H., Yoshida,M. and Kagawa,Y. (1977) J. Biol. Chem. 252, 6125 -6131.

ENERGY-LINKED NICOTINAMIDE NUCLEOTIDE TRANSHYDROGENASE

Jan Rydström[a], C. P. Lee[b] and Lars Ernster[a]

[a]Department of Biochemistry, Arrhenius Laboratory, University of Stockholm, S-106 91 Stockholm, Sweden, and

[b]Department of Biochemistry, Wayne State University, School of Medicine, Detroit, Michigan 48201, U.S.A.

INTRODUCTION

Energy-linked nicotinamide nucleotide transhydrogenase reaction catalyzed by submitochondrial particles was first demonstrated in 1963 (1) and has ever since served as a valuable tool for the study of mitochondrial energy transduction (2). Being the first example of an enzyme capable of utilizing energy derived from the respiratory chain directly, without the participation of the phosphorylating system, the transhydrogenase proved useful for the demonstration of energy-coupling in nonphosphorylating submitochondrial particles (3) and later also in phosphorylation-deficient bacterial mutants (4). Although the chemiosmotic hypothesis had been formulated in 1961 (5), the energy-linked transhydrogenase reaction was interpreted in terms of the "chemical" hypothesis of oxidative phosphorylation (6), involving non-phosphorylated high-energy intermediates on the pathway of energy transfer between the respiratory chain and ATP synthesis (1,2). However, in 1966 Mitchell (7) proposed that transhydrogenase, like other membrane-bound redox catalysts involved in energy conservation, functions as a vectorial proton translocator. Evidence supporting this proposal was obtained by Mitchell and Moyle (8,9) and by Skulachev (10).

V. P. Skulachev and Peter C. Hinkle (eds.), Chemiosmotic Proton Circuits in Biological Membranes
in honor of Peter Mitchell   ISBN 0-201-07398-6

The final proof, however, had to await the isolation and purification of transhydrogenase (11,12) and the reconstitution of proton-translocating transhydrogenase using the purified enzyme and artificial liposomes (11,13). Indeed, the transhydrogenase today appears to represent the best documented case of a redox-coupled proton pump. It constitutes as such a highly appropriate subject of a chapter in this volume dedicated to Peter Mitchell, especially as some of the early studies quoted above (8) involved a first opportunity to personal contact between our laboratories, through a visit of C. P. Lee, then working in Stockholm, to Bodmin (cf. ref. 14).

Nicotinamide nucleotide transhydrogenases, catalyzing the reaction

$$NADH + NADP^+ \rightleftharpoons NAD^+ + NADPH \qquad (1)$$

are of two types (see ref.15 for review). One is an exclusively bacterial enzyme. It is easy to solubilize, is a flavoprotein, and has a single catalytic site for NAD(H) and NADP(H). It is specific for the 4B hydrogen atom of both NADH and NADPH and reacts essentially according to a binary-complex ("ping-pong") mechanism. The other is the mitochondrial transhydrogenase, but it occurs also in certain bacteria. It is firmly membrane-bound, is not a flavoprotein, and has separate catalytic sites for NAD(H) and NADP(H). It is specific for the 4A hydrogen atom of NADH and the 4B hydrogen atom of NADPH, and it reacts according to a short-lived ternary-complex (Theorell-Chance) mechanism. In spite of these differences, the two enzymes have one feature in common: in the absence of specific effectors, the maximal velocities of the reactions catalyzed by both enzymes are much slower in the forward (left-to-right accord-

ing to equation 1) than in the reverse direction. Specific
effectors can enhance the forward reaction, probably by
altering the conformational state of the enzyme. The
$[NADPH]/[NADP^+]$ ratio, 2'-AMP and Ca^{2+} are such effectors
of the bacterial type of enzyme. In the case of the mitochondrial type of enzyme, the situation is more complex.
The forward maximal velocity of this enzyme appears to be
regulated by the prevailing protonmotive force across the
membrane, $\Delta\tilde{\mu}_{H^+}$, which, in turn, is determined by the equilibrium state of the energy-linked transhydrogenase reaction

$$NADH + NADP^+ + nH_c^+ \rightleftharpoons NAD^+ + NADPH + nH_m^+ \qquad (2)$$

(where the subscripts c and m refer to the cytosolic and the
matrix side of the inner mitochondrial membrane, respectively) as well as by other membrane-associated reactions that
influence $\Delta\tilde{\mu}_{H^+}$. In this way, energy has both a kinetic and
a thermodynamic effect on the mitochondrial type of transhydrogenase. In fact, the demonstration of energy-linked
transhydrogenase in 1963 (1) concerned the kinetic effect
of energy on the reaction, and it was only a year later that
the thermodynamic effect, i.e. an actual shift of equilibrium of the transhydrogenase reaction upon energization,
was first shown (16).

In the sections that follow we shall first review
current information concerning the proton-pump activity of
mitochondrial transhydrogenase, and then discuss the kinetic
and thermodynamic aspects of the energy-linked transhydrogenase reaction. Following this, we shall present some recent
data concerning the reaction mechanism of the enzyme. In
the final section we shall consider various proposals regarding the energy-coupling mechanism of transhydrogenase,
in particular its relationship to the mitochondrial ATPase

system. Various aspects of transhydrogenase are treated in
several previous review articles (15,17-20), and the present
"mini-review" is therefore focused on recent developments.

THE PROTON-TRANSLOCATING FUNCTION OF TRANSHYDROGENASE

The first indication for a transhydrogenase-catalyzed
transport of solute protons was obtained by Mitchell (8)
with highly coupled submitochondrial particles. In these
experiments the substrate couple NADPH plus NAD$^+$ was found
to generate proton uptake at a rate of 0.2 protons per NADP$^+$
formed. The opposite direction of the reaction, i.e., with
the substrates NADH plus NADP$^+$, led to proton extrusion.
On the basis of these findings, Mitchell concluded that
transhydrogenase is a transmembrane proton pump. Similar
conclusions were reached by Skulachev and associates (10,
21). Subsequently, on the basis of results obtained with
intact rat liver mitochondria, Mitchell and Moyle (9) suggested that 2 protons were translocated per NADP$^+$ formed. Later
experiments by Rydström (22) indicated that protons indeed
have a direct role in the regulation of the kinetic properties of mitochondrial transhydrogenase through acidification
of selected part(s) of the enzyme which accompanies energization of the submitochondrial particles. However, evidence
for direct transhydrogenase-linked proton translocation,
i.e., without the possible contribution of other mitochondrial proteins, e.g., ATPase, was obtained with a partially
purified and reconstituted transhydrogenase (23) which was
shown to generate a membrane potential in the presence of
NADPH plus NAD$^+$. Subsequently, transhydrogenase purified
to homogeneity (Fig. 1A) was shown to have little or no activity when reconstituted in liposomes, but the activity

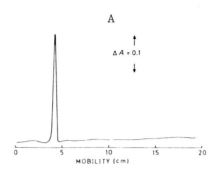

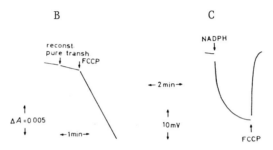

Fig.1. SDS-Polyacrylamide gel electrophoresis of purified transhydrogenase from beef heart (A);
effect of carbonyl cyanide p-trifluoromethoxy-
phenylhydrazone (FCCP) on the activity of transhydrogenase reconstituted in liposomes (B);
generation of a membrane potential by reconstituted transhydrogenase as indicated by the
FCCP-sensitive uptake of tetraphenylboron (C).
From Höjeberg and Rydström (11).

could be restored by disruption of the vesicles or by the

addition of uncouplers of oxidative phosphorylation (Fig.

1B) (11), indicating that the coupled activity is limited

by a pH-gradient and/or a membrane potential. Thus, these

preparations were shown to generate a membrane potential

(Fig. 1C) (11), and a pH-gradient by quenching 9-amino-

-acridine (13) or a derivate of this compound, 9-amino-6-

-chloro-2-methoxy-acridine (24). Protons taken up by the

vesicles were also monitored inside the vesicles by a trapped pH indicator, dextrane-linked fluoroescein (25), as well
as outside the vesicles by a sensitive pH electrode (26).
Using a pH electrode O'Neal and Fisher (26) determined the
number of protons taken up by the vesicles and the simultaneous rate of formation of NADPH; the ratio between these two
parameters came out to be close to 1. In addition to this
evidence, which strongly suggests a proton pump function of
transhydrogenase, there are other lines of indirect evidence
obtained from effects of artificial pH gradients, potassium
ion gradients in the presence of valinomycin (24,25) and
nitrate ions (24). That transhydrogenase probably contains
a proton channel sensitive to N,N'-dicyclocarbodiimide
(DCCD) similar to mitochondrial ATPase (27) and cytochrome
oxidase (28) was earlier observed by Dontsov et al. (21),
who demonstrated that uptake of lipophilic anions catalyzed
by submitochondrial particles in the presence of NADPH plus
NAD^+ is sensitive to DCCD but not to oligomycin. However,
this interesting finding has not been followed up. Also,
interactions between proton-translocating (oligomycin-sensitive) ATPase and transhydrogenase in a reconstituted system has recently been described (24) as will be discussed
later.

KINETIC EFFECTS OF ENERGY ON TRANSHYDROGENASE

Energy-linked changes of the affinities of the mitochondrial transhydrogenase for its substrates were observed
with submitochondrial particles by Rydström et al. (Table 1)
(29). These changes favor binding of NADH and $NADP^+$ and
dissociation of NAD^+ and NADPH, with a simultaneous increase
in maximal activity for the reduction of $NADP^+$ by NADH (29).

Table 1.   Rate constants for the nonenergy-linked and
            energy-linked transhydrogenase reactions.
            From Rydström et al. (29).

Rate constant[a]	NADH → NADP$^+$		NADH > NADP$^+$ (+ succ.)	
	First substrate bound		First substrate bound	
	NADH	NADP$^+$	NADH	NADP$^+$
k_1	1.4	0.3	5.3	10.2
k_2	10.8	10.7	0	0
k_3	0.3	1.4	10.2	5.3
k_4	3.0	2.1	2.1	1.0
k_5	20.6	20.4	166	226
k_6	2.1	3.0	1.0	2.1

[a]The rate constants k_1, k_3, k_4 and k_6 are expressed as μM^{-1} x min^{-1} whereas k_2 and k_5 are expressed as min^{-1}. k_2 and k_5 are the off-rate constants for the first substrate and last product, respectively, and k_1 and k_6 are the on-rate constants for the first substrate and last product, respectively.

Since the presence of energy only decreases the affinities of the enzyme for NAD^+ and NADPH without effect on the maximal activity for reduction of NAD^+ by NADPH, it appears that the former increase in maximal activity is mainly due to the increased dissociation of NAD^+ and NADPH, primarily that of NAD^+. The large energy-linked decrease in K_m for $NADP^+$ in the reduction of $NADP^+$ by NADH may thus be a secondary effect caused by the increased dissociation of NAD^+. A recent reinvestigation of the steady-state kinetics of the purified and reconstituted transhydrogenase reveals that the enzyme most likely follows a random ternary-complex mechanism (30) rather than an ordered mechanism as proposed

earlier (31). However, the interpretations outlined above
are still consistent with a short-lived complex, i.e.,
Theorell-Chance, mechanism.

Hatefi and coworkers (32,33) have recently shown that
submitochondrial particles from beef heart catalyze a reduction of $[^{14}C]$-NADP$^+$ and various NADP$^+$ analogues by NADPH.
These reactions appear to be catalyzed by transhydrogenase
as indicated by their sensitivity to butanedione and trypsin
(32,33). A similar activity with thio-NADP$^+$ as acceptor
catalyzed by isolated transhydrogenase in an antibody-sensit-
ive manner was also observed by Anderson et al. (34). All
of these activities were increased to various extents by
energy; however, the maximal energy-linked activities were
relatively low, about 10-30 % of those found with the natural substrates (32,33). A suggestion that the mechanism for
this type of reaction involves binding of NADPH to the
NAD(H)-site of transhydrogenase (33) is supported by a report (34) that NAD(H)-site specific inhibitors, e.g., ace-
tyldephospho-CoA (cf. 35), are inhibitory. An alternative
possibility involving NAD(H) bound to transhydrogenase is
considered in the section on Reaction mechanism of transhydrogenase of this review.

Energy-linked affinity changes also seem to be of
importance for the effect of certain inhibitors of transhydrogenase, e.g., metal ions (36,37). The energy-linked
transhydrogenase reaction catalyzed by submitochondrial
particles is known to be inhibited by Mg^{2+} to a lesser
extent than the nonenergy-linked reaction (36). In addition,
the effect of Mg^{2+} is pH-dependent with an increasing effect
of the inhibitor with increasing pH (36). Recently, Mg^{2+}
was shown to be a competitive inhibitor with respect to

$NADP^+$(37) and is therefore presumably specific for the catalytic NADP(H) site. The pH dependence of the inhibition was
reinvestigated and a close to competitive relationship between solute protons and the extent of inhibition by Mg^{2+}
was demonstrated (37). Since a lowering of pH has been
shown to partially mimic energization (22), it is possible
that the protons exert their effect through a proton-depend-
ent increase.in the affinity of the enzyme for NADP(H); such
affinity changes have indeed been observed (22). A recent
report by Galante et al. (38) considers the possibility that
the effect of pH is partially related to the extent of protonation of the 2'-phosphate group of $NADP^+$, or of regulatory
group(s) of the enzyme. Other inhibitors, e.g., those with
structures similar to those of the transhydrogenase substrates, have similar effects both in the absence and in the
presence of energy (35). Presumably, the reason is that the
energy-linked affinity changes affect the substrates and
the competing inhibitors equally and thus no significant
energy-linked change in K_i value is seen.

THERMODYNAMIC EFFECTS OF ENERGY ON TRANSHYDROGENASE

         Previous studies on the thermodynamics of the trans-
hydrogenase have established that the apparent equilibrium
is shifted from unity to about 500 upon energization (16).
Although it has repeatedly been pointed out that this value
most probably represents a steady-state (19, see also 39),
recent reports (23,24) have attempted to provide explanations
for the discrepancy between energy input and output of energy in the energy-linked transhydrogenase system calculated
as theoretical expenditure of energy in the form of ATP and
observed recovery of energy as the ratio of NADPH plus NAD^+

by NADP$^+$ plus NADH. A further discussion of this and related questions is therefore warranted. If one considers the
ATPase-transhydrogenase system closed, i.e., without leaks
or competing reactions, the theoretical true equilibrium
constant for the ATP-driven transhydrogenase reaction may be
calculated to be close to 10^5 M (39) (assuming a ΔG^o value
for ATP hydrolysis of 7.3 kcal/mole). However, the latter
value can of course only be obtained at true thermodynamic
equilibrium which is not possible when the reaction is catalyzed by submitochondrial particles or intact mitochondria
(cf. ref. 40). There are several competing reactions, e.g.,
other energy-linked reactions which tend to lower the energy
available for the transhydrogenase. In intact mitochondria
there are also competing dehydrogenase systems that tend to
reoxidize NADPH and rereduce NAD$^+$ (42).

Submitochondrial particles have also been suggested to
contain uncoupled transhydrogenase, which will counteract
increased NADPH plus NAD$^+$ levels (36). Most important,
however, is the fact that when the apparent equilibrium
approaches 500 (calculated on the basis of the nicotinamide
nucleotide levels), the concentrations of the substrates
NADP$^+$ and NADH will approach their K_m values. This means
that the rate of the energy-linked reduction of NADP$^+$ by
NADH will be continuously decreasing, a process that may be
calculated to start already at or before an apparent equilibrium of about 25 (assuming starting concentrations of NADP$^+$
and NADH of 500 µM which are converted to 475 µM of NADPH
and NAD$^+$). At the same time are the K_m values for NADP$^+$
and NADH increased sharply due to competitive product inhibition by NADPH and NAD$^+$. Counteracting reactions catalyzed
by, e.g., uncoupled transhydrogenase, will become increas-

ingly important and a steady state is rapidly obtained.
The concerted action of the factors mentioned above seems to
fully explain the observed maximal value of 500. Moreover,
if the stoichiometry of the energy-linked transhydrogenase
proves to be one $H^+/2e^-$, as indicated by recent measurements
with reconstituted systems (26,34), this may imply that only
one-half or one-third mole of ATP (depending on the assumed
H^+/ATP ratio) is consumed per mole of NADPH formed. In this
case the value of 500 (corresponding to 3.8 kcal/mole) would
be very close to a true equilibrium.

     Considering the above factors, it appears that there
is no need to invoke a possible energy-requiring and "non-
-productive" conformational change of transhydrogenase as
proposed by Hatefi (32,33). Indeed, conformational changes
of transhydrogenase are now considered to be highly likely,
but these are believed to occur as part of the energy transduction process and are thus "productive". The possibility
that reduction of $NADP^+$ by NADPH through binding of NADPH
to the NADH-binding site provides a futile energy-consuming
cycle, appears unlikely under physiological conditions where
both NAD^+ and NADP(H) are present and the affinity of NADH
for the NAD(H)-binding site exceeds that of NADPH for the
same site with a factor of more than 50 fold (cf. ref. 33).
Nevertheless, the observation of this type of interaction
may prove very useful in the elucidation of the detailed
energy-linked steps in energy-linked transhydrogenation.

     The ATP-driven transhydrogenase reaction was recently
reconstituted from purified transhydrogenase and transhydro-
genase-free oligomycin-sensitive ATPase (Complex V) (24).
It was established that an energy-linked change of the
equilibrium was only about 2 fold in this system, as com-

pared to about 500 fold with submitochondrial particles
(16). These results show that coupling between the ATPase
and the transhydrogenase took place in the same vesicle but
also that the incorporation of the two systems occurred to
a large extent in separate vesicles which caused a slow
change in equilibrium due to the counteracting activity of
transhydrogenase in ATPase-free vesicles.

REACTION MECHANISM OF TRANSHYDROGENASE

As indicated previously in this review (see section
Kinetic effects of energy on transhydrogenase), the kinetic
mechanism of the mitochondrial transhydrogenase probably
follows a random type reaction sequence, where the transfer
of the hydride ion during catalysis occurs at the level of
the ternary NADPH-E-NAD$^+$ (or NADP$^+$-E-NADH) complex. The
kinetic data appear to exclude a reduced enzyme intermediate.
This is also consistent with the fact that purified mitochondrial transhydrogenase does not contain flavin (11,12,24)
as a possible reducible prosthetic group, although there are
disulfide and thiol groups that may participate in a hypothetical redox function of the enzyme (42). A likely consequence of the presence of reducible groups involved in
hydride ion transfer is that the reduced transhydrogenase
would exchange this ion in the form of protons with the
surrounding medium, a reaction which clearly has been shown
not to occur (43). Recently, Fisher and coworkers (44)
reported that reconstituted pure mitochondrial transhydrogenase, catalyzing the coupled and slow reduction of acetyl-
pyridine-NAD$^+$ by NADPH, is markedly activated by added small
amounts of NADH; uncoupled transhydrogenase is not affected
by NADH. The initial rate of the NADH-induced reaction is
approximately equal to the maximal uncoupled rate with only

NADPH as reductant. These experiments have been repeated by Enander and Rydström (20) and are shown in Figs. 2A and B. Apparently, the presence of NADH has no effect on the rate of proton translocation induced by acetylpyridine-NAD$^+$ and NADPH (44), and it was therefore proposed (44) that the reduction of acetylpyridine-NAD$^+$ by NADH under these conditions is due to an uncoupled additional reaction catalyzed by transhydrogenase, although the presence of NADPH is necessary for this reaction to occur. Obviously, the effect of NADH may reflect an increased steady-state level of a hypothetical reduced enzyme intermediate under coupled conditions, which would facilitate a reduction of the hydrogen acceptor acetylpyridine-NAD$^+$. Since NADH does not affect proton pumping significantly, it may be inferred that the primary and hypothetical reduction of the transhydrogenase by NADPH could be the partial reaction responsible for proton translocation.

It is conceivable, however, that the reduction of acetylpyridine-NAD$^+$ by NADH in the presence of NADPH may be explained by an alternative mechanism. If the dissociation of NADP$^+$ from the coupled enzyme is slower than that of the other product, acetylpyridine-NADH, then it is possible that added NADH may bind to the NAD(H)-site, reduce the bound NADP$^+$ to NADPH and dissociate from the enzyme. The NADPH thus formed would reduce acetylpyridine-NAD$^+$ etc. The sequence of events would be:

$$\text{NADH} + \text{NADP}^+ \rightleftharpoons \text{NAD}^+ + \text{NADPH} \qquad (1)$$

$$\text{NADPH} + \text{acetylpyridine-NAD}^+ \rightleftharpoons \text{NADP}^+ + \text{acetyl-}$$
$$\text{pyridine-NADH} \qquad (3)$$

_____

$$\text{Sum:} \quad \text{NADH} + \text{acetylpyridine-NAD}^+ \rightleftharpoons \text{NAD}^+ + \text{acetyl-}$$
$$\text{pyridine-NADH} \qquad (4)$$

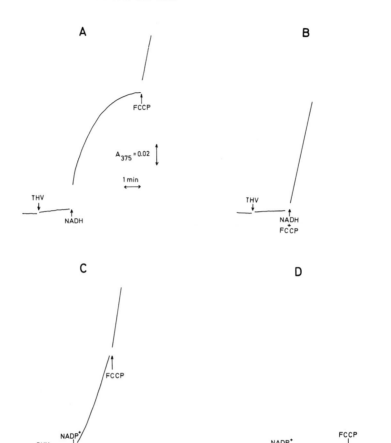

Fig. 2. Reduction of acetylpyridine-NAD$^+$ by NADPH and
NADH catalyzed by isolated and reconstituted
transhydrogenase. Traces A and B: medium contained 80 mM potassium phosphate (pH 6.3),
0.2 mM NADPH and 0.2 mM acetylpyridine-NAD
in a final volume of 1 ml; additions were:
transhydrogenase vesicles (THV, 10 µg protein),
11.5 µM NADH and 1 µM FCCP. Trace C: medium
contained 80 mM potassium phosphate (pH 6.3),
0.2 mM NADH and 0.4 mM acetylpyridine-NAD$^+$ in
a final volume of 0.5 ml; additions were: THV
(20 µg protein), 0.4 mM NADP$^+$ and 1 µM FCCP.
Trace D: conditions were as in C except that
the medium contained 2 mM oxidized glutathione
and 10 µg glutathione reductase. From Enander
and Rydström (30).

It is also important to note that reactions 1 and 3
represent two opposite reactions and that the sum of the two
reactions therefore presents no change in the proton-motive
force in coupled vesicles generated by the reaction preceed-
ing 1. As shown in Figs. 2C and D the above hypothetical
mechanism has in fact been subjected to an experimental test
(30). NADH and acetylpyridine-NAD$^+$ were added to a relatively large amount of reconstituted coupled vesicles; at this
point a very slow reaction took place. When NADP$^+$ was added,
a progressively faster reaction was observed, which eventually reached a constant rate. The concentration of acetylpyridine-NADH formed during the progressive phase corresponded fairly well with about twice the K_m value for NADPH
measured separately (31). Addition of an uncoupler, e.g.,
FCCP, led to a marked stimulation of the reaction (Fig. 2C)
(30), and suggests that reactions 1 and 3 are not equally
affected by a proton-motive force. Tentatively, it is reaction 3 which is rate-limiting for the overall effects of
energy on reaction 4. If oxidized glutathione plus glutathione reductase was added prior to NADP$^+$ the reaction was
strongly inhibited (Fig. 2D) (30) which shows that reduction
of NADP$^+$ to NADPH is a necessary partial reaction in the
reduction of acetylpyridine-NAD$^+$ by NADH. Washout of [^{3}H]
from [4A-^{3}H]-NADH via the transhydrogenase under coupled
or uncoupled conditions was negligible (30). These results
may indeed be interpreted to indicate that, under coupled
conditions, NADH reduces acetylpyridine-NAD$^+$ via NADPH and
not through a reduced enzyme intermediate. Although the bulk
of the reaction appears to be dependent on a saturating
NADPH concentration, the possibility cannot be eliminated
at the present time that NADP$^+$ can undergo a redox cycle

without being released to the medium.

In analogy with the effect of NADH on the reduction of acetylpyridine-NAD$^+$ by NADPH, reduction of thio-NADP$^+$ by NADH, representing the opposite reaction, is also stimulated by NADPH but to a lesser extent (30). As expected, the low rate of reduction of thio-NADP$^+$ by NADPH was markedly stimulated by NAD$^+$ (30). If reduction of thio-NADP$^+$ (or ^{14}C--NADP$^+$) by NADPH is measured directly, i.e., without an intermediate NAD$^+$ reduction, it is therefore of obvious importance to eliminate the possible contribution of bound NAD$^+$ (cf. refs. 32,33).

Thus, there is presently no evidence favoring the role of a reduced enzyme intermediate in the mitochondrial transhydrogenase reaction. On the other hand, it is clear that the transhydrogenase forms tight complexes with NADH and NADP$^+$ in the course of the energy-linked reaction, which may thus be comparable to firmly bound prosthetic groups in e.g. flavoproteins.

ENERGY-COUPLING MECHANISM

Early proposals concerning the mechanism of the energy-linked transhydrogenase reaction were based on the "chemical" hypothesis of oxidative phosphorylation (6) and visualized the involvement of high-energy intermediates of the type I~X, NADH~I, NADP$^+$~I, etc. (1,2). These proposals, however, just as the chemical hypothesis as a whole, had to be abandoned because of lack of experimental evidence. A possible functional relationship between transhydrogenase and the NADH dehydrogenase complex of the respiratory chain, suggested at an early stage (45) but soon challanged (17), was restressed in recent years (46), based on an observed

NADPH oxidase activity of submitochondrial particles. However, these observations found their explanation in the
earlier known (47) ability of NADH dehydrogenase to exhibit
some reactivity with NADPH (48), a feature that appears to
be common to NAD(H)-specific dehydrogenases especially at
slightly acidic pH (49). The recently reported slow reactivity of the NAD(H)-binding site of transhydrogenase
with NADP(H) (32,33) is probably another reflection of this
feature.

Now that it is clear that isolated mitochondrial
transhydrogenase can generate a transmembrane proton gradient in the course of its catalytic reaction (11,13), the
next major question concerns the molecular mechanism by
which this is achieved. That the transhydrogenase does not
function as a "redox loop" in the classical chemiosmotic
sense (7) can be safely concluded on account of the facts
(cf. ref. 50) that the transfer of hydrogen between NAD(H)
and NADP(H) is direct, without interaction with the protons
of water (43); that NAD(H) and NADP(H) react with the enzyme on the same (matrix) side of the membrane (51); that the
two substrates do not cross the membrane (a possibility
considered initially (52-54) but later discarded); and that,
as discussed in the previous section, the enzyme most probably does not contain any endogenous redox groups involved
in catalysis (with the possible exception of firmly-bound
nicotinamide nucleotides). It is therefore now generally
agreed that the coupling between the catalytic event and the
proton translocation in the case of transhydrogenase is
indirect. Current proposals, listed in Fig. 3, visualize
that the protons are carried across the membrane either
entirely by the enzyme protein itself or, at least partly,

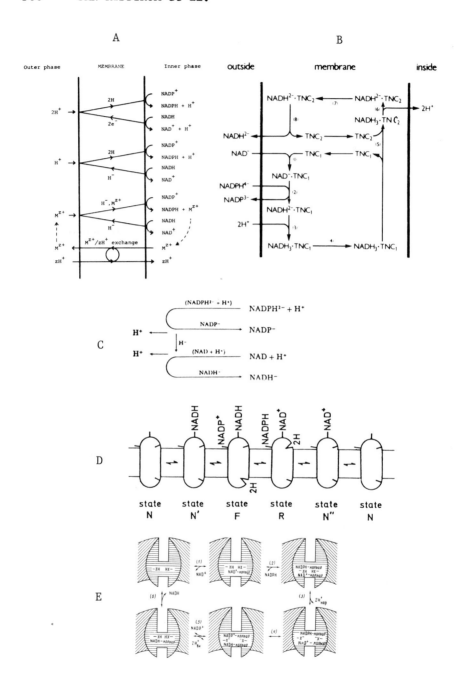

Fig. 3. Proposed mechanisms of proton-translocating
transhydrogenase. A, Mitchell (7); B, Skulachev (10); C, Mitchell (55); D, Rydström (19);
E, Kozlov (56).

by charged groups of the substrates. These alternatives
are similar to those being considered in the case of the
proton-translocating ATPase, where one view favors the
concept of entirely protein-mediated proton translocation
(57), whereas the other stresses the role of substrates as
proton carriers (58).

Certain similarities between mitochondrial transhydrogenase and ATPase have been pointed out in the past (59)
and are further underlined by recent knowledge of the modes
of action of the two enzymes. From the data reviewed earlier in this paper (cf. Table I) it appears to be clear that
what energy, i.e., $\Delta\tilde{\mu}_{H^+}$, is doing thermodynamically to transhydrogenase is to facilitate the binding of NADH and NADP$^+$
and the release of NAD$^+$ and NADPH (29); the actual conversion of the bound substrates to products proceeds without
appreciable requirement of energy. Similarly, it has been
proposed (60,61) that in the case of the ATPase system, the
available $\Delta\tilde{\mu}_{H^+}$ is used primarily for the binding of ADP +
P$_i$ and the release of ATP, while the conversion of bound
ADP + P$_i$ to ATP proceeds without further energy requirement.
It has also been proposed (62) that the ATPase operates by
catalytic cooperativity between identical subunits, where
binding of ADP + P$_i$ to one subunit promotes the release of
ATP from another subunit. This "alternate-site" or "bind-
ing-change" mechanism has received considerable experimental
support in recent years (63). Whether a similar mechanism
holds for transhydrogenase is not known but appears to be
an attractive possibility in view of the dimeric nature of
the enzyme (64). Another striking similarity between the
transhydrogenase and ATPase is the kinetic effect of energy.
Thus, as pointed out in the introduction, $\Delta\tilde{\mu}_{H^+}$ acts as an

effector of the mitochondrial transhydrogenase, enhancing
the maximal velocity of the reaction. Similarly, $\Delta\tilde{\mu}_H+$ can
enhance the mitochondrial ATPase activity (65,66) when the
latter is suppressed by the protein known as the Pullman-
-Monroy ATPase inhibitor (67). Thus, even though the
transhydrogenase and ATPase are widely different in structure, both seem to be regulated by the prevailing $\Delta\tilde{\mu}_H+$.

In recent years there has been growing evidence that
energy transfer between membrane-associated energy-transducing units may take place by localized electrochemical
events along or within the membrane in addition to bulk
proton gradients. The pertinent literature has been reviewed in several recent papers (68-70). One piece of
evidence in favor of this concept relates to the interaction
of transhydrogenase and ATPase. It has been shown (66,71)
that inhibition of the ATPase activity of submitochondrial
particles with increasing amounts of the Pullman-Monroy
inhibitor results in a parallel inhibition of the energy-
-linked transhydrogenase activity (Fig. 4). The ATPase
activity as such was not rate-limiting for the transhydrogenase, as could be ascertained by appropriate controls.
The parallel inhibition of the transhydrogenase activity
rather seemed to be due to the fact that, under the conditions employed, the inhibitor was bound to the ATPase in a
virtually irreversible manner. These findings were interpreted as suggesting that the ATPase and transhydrogenase
interact in a localized fashion, each ATPase being able to
"energize" transhydrogenase only in a limited domain within
the membrane. Similar indications were subsequently obtained (72) with F_1-ATPase-depleted submitochondrial particles in which ATP-driven transhydrogenase activity was restored by the addition of increasing amounts of F_1. Again,

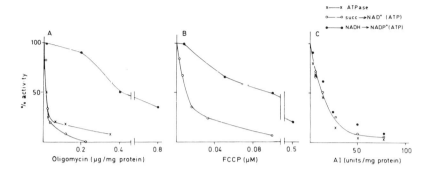

Fig. 4. Effects of oligomycin, FCCP and ATPase inhibi-
        tor (AI) on ATP-dependent activities of AI-
        -depleted Mg^{++}-ATP particles. From Ernster
        et al. (71).

the reappearance of ATP-driven transhydrogenase paralleled
that of reconstituted (oligomycin-sensitive) ATPase activity,
in spite of the fact that the total reconstituted ATPase
activity at any point along the titration curve was in
large excess of that of the ATP-driven transhydrogenase.
In addition, the reconstitution of the latter activity paralleled the appearance of ATP-induced ANS response (72),
which may be used as an indicator of localized charge-sepa-
ration in the membrane (73). The possibility of a localized
interaction between ATPase and transhydrogenase has recently
also been stressed by Anderson et al. (34) based on the observation that the ATP-driven transhydrogenase reaction is
particularly sensitive to antibodies against purified transhydrogenase. Just as in the case of the proton-translocating
activity of transhydrogenase, the final proof of a localized
interaction between transhydrogenase and ATPase will have to
await the demonstration of such an interaction in a reconstituted system consisting of the purified enzymes and arti-

ficial liposomes. Studies with such a system have recently been initiated (24) and will hopefully provide information in the near future concerning this principally important problem in membrane bioenergetics.

The authors' studies quoted in this paper have been supported by the Swedish Natural Science Research Council and the Swedish Cancer Society.

REFERENCES

1. Danielson, L. and Ernster, L. (1963) Biochem.Z. <u>338</u>, 188-205.
2. Lee, C.P. and Ernster, L. (1966) in <u>Regulation of Metabolic Processes in Mitochondria</u> (J.M. Tager et al., eds.) BBA Library, Vol. 7, pp. 218-234, Elsevier Publishing Comp., Amsterdam and London.
3. Lee, C.P., Azzone, G.F. and Ernster, L. (1964) Nature <u>201</u>, 152-155.
4. Cox, G.B. and Gibson, F. (1974) Biochim. Biophys. Acta <u>346</u>, 1-25.
5. Mitchell, P. (1961) Nature <u>191</u>, 144-148.
6. Slater, E.C. (1953) Nature <u>172</u>, 975-978.
7. Mitchell, P. (1966) Chemiosmotic Coupling in Oxidative and Photosynthetic Phosphorylation, Glynn Research, Bodmin.
8. Mitchell, P. and Moyle, J. (1965) Nature <u>208</u>, 1205-1206.
9. Mitchell, P. and Moyle, J. (1973) Biochem. J. 132, 571-585.
10. Skulachev, V.P. (1970) FEBS Lett. <u>11</u>, 301-308.
11. Höjeberg, B. and Rydström, J. (1977) Biochem. Biophys. Res. Commun. 78, 1183-1190.
12. Anderson, W.M. and Fisher, R.R. (1978) Arch. Biochem. Biophys. 187, 180-190.
13. Earle, S.R., Anderson, W.M. and Fisher, R.R. (1978) FEBS Lett. 91, 21-24.
14. Mitchell, P. and Moyle, J. (1966) in <u>Biochemistry of Mitochondria</u> (E.C. Slater et al., eds.) pp. 53-74, Academic Press, London and New York.
15. Rydström, J., Hoek, J.B. and Ernster, L. (1976) The Enzymes <u>13</u>, 51-88.
16. Lee, C.P. and Ernster, L. (1964) Biochim. Biophys. Acta <u>81</u>, 187-190.
17. Lee, C.P. and Ernster, L. (1964) Ann. Rev. Biochem. <u>33</u>, 729-788.
18. Lee, C.P. and Ernster, L. (1967) Methods Enzymol. <u>10</u>, 738-744.
19. Rydström, J. (1977) Biochim. Biophys. Acta 463, 155-184.
20. Rydström, J. (1981) in <u>Mitochondria and Microsomes</u> (C.P. Lee et al., eds.) pp. 317-335. Addison-Wesley, Reading, Mass.
21. Dontsov, A.E., Grinius, L.L., Jasaitis, A.A., Severina, I.I. and Skulachev, V.P. (1972) J. Bioenerg. <u>3</u>, 277-303.
22. Rydström, J. (1974) Eur. J. Biochem. 45, 67-76.
23. Rydström, J., Kanner, N. and Racker, E. (1975) Biochem. Biophys. Res. Commun. <u>67</u>, 831-839.

24. Rydström, J. (1979) J. Biol. Chem. <u>254</u>, 8611-8619.
25. Earle, S.R. and Fisher, R.R. (1980) Biochemistry <u>19</u>, 561-569.
26. Earle, S.R. and Fisher, R.R. (1980) J. Biol. Chem. <u>255</u>, 827-830.
27. Beechey, R.B., Roberton, A.M., Holloway, C.T. and Knight, J.G. (1967) Biochemistry <u>6</u>, 3867-3879.
28. Casey, R.P., Thelen, M. and Azzi, A. (1980) J. Biol. Chem. <u>255</u>, 3994-4000.
29. Rydström, J., Teixeira da Cruz, A. and Ernster, L. (1971) Eur. J. Biochem. <u>23</u>, 212-219.
30. Enander, K. and Rydström, J. (1981) submitted for publication.
31. Teixeira da Cruz, A., Rydström, J. and Ernster, L. (1971) Eur. J. Biochem. <u>23</u>, 203-211.
32. Hatefi, Y., Phelps, D.C. and Galante, Y.M. (1980) J. Biol. Chem. <u>255</u>, 9526-9529.
33. Phelps, D.C., Galante, Y.M. and Hatefi, Y. (1930) J. Biol. Chem. <u>255</u>, 9647-9652.
34. Anderson, W.M., Fowler, W.T., Pennington, R.M., Fisher, R.R.)1981) J. Biol. Chem. <u>256</u>, 1888-1895.
35. Rydström, J. (1972) Eur. J. Biochem. <u>31</u>, 496-504.
36. Rydström, J., Teixeira da Cruz, A. and Ernster, L. (1970) Eur. J. Biochem. <u>17</u>, 56-62.
37. O'Neal, S.G., Earle, S.R. and Fisher, R.R. (1980) Biochim. Biophys. Acta <u>589</u>, 217-230.
38. Galante, Y.M., Lee, Y. and Hatefi, Y. (1980) J. Biol. Chem. <u>255</u>, 9641-9646.
39. Rydström, J. (1972) Mitochondrial Nicotinamide Nucleotide Transhydrogenase. Kinetics and Functional Relationship to the Energy-conserving System of the Respiratory Chain. Thesis, University of Stockholm.
40. Klingenberg, M. and Slenczka, W. (1959) Biochem. Z. <u>331</u>, 486-517.
41. Hoek, J.B., Ernster, L., de Haan, E.J. and Tager, J.M. (1974) Biochim. Biophys. Acta <u>333</u>, 546-559.
42. Earle, S.R., O'Neal, S.G. and Fisher, R.R. (1978) Biochemistry <u>17</u>, 4683-4690.
43. Lee, C.P., Simard-Duquesne, N., Ernster, L. and Hoberman, M.D. (1965) Biochim. Biophys. Acta <u>105</u>, 397-409.
44. Earle, S.R., Wu, L. and Fisher, R.R. (1980) 7th Annual Meeting American Society of Biological Chemists (FASEB), abstr. nr. 543.
45. Hommes, F.A. and Estabrook, R.W. (1963) Biochem. Biophys. Res. Commun. <u>11</u>, 1-6.
46. Djavadi-Ohaniance, L. and Hatefi, Y. (1975) J. Biol. Chem. <u>250</u>, 9397-9403.

47. Rossi, C., Cremona, T., Machinist, M. and Singer, T.P. (1965) J. Biol. Chem. 240, 2634–2643.
48. Rydström, J., Montelius, J., Bäckström, D. and Ernster, L. (1978) Biochim. Biophys. Acta 501, 370–380.
49. Navazio, F., Ernster, B.B. and Ernster, L. (1957) Biochim. Biophys. Acta 26, 416–421.
50. Ernster, L. (1975) Plenary Lecture, 9th FEBS Meeting. FEBS Symp. 35, 257–285.
51. DePierre, J.W. and Ernster, L. (1977) Ann. Rev. Biochem. 46, 201–262.
52. Klingenberg, M. (1963) in Energy-Linked Functions of Mitochondria (B. Chance, ed.) pp. 121–142, Academic Press, New York.
53. Papa, S. and Francavilla, A. (1967) in Mitochondrial Structure and Compartmentation (E. Quagliariello et al., eds.) pp. 363–372, Adriatica Editrice, Bari.
54. Tager, J.M., Groot, G.S.P., Roos, D., Papa, S. and Quagliariello, E. (1969) in The Energy Level and Metabolic Control in Mitochondria (S. Papa et al., eds.) pp. 453–462, Adriatica Editrice, Bari.
55. Mitchell, P. (1972) J. Bioenerg. 3, 5–24.
56. Kozlov, I.A. (1979) Biokhimiya 44, 1731–1737.
57. Boyer, P.D. (1981) in Mitochondria and Microsomes (C.P. Lee et al., eds.) pp. 407–426. Addison-Wesley, Reading, Mass.
58. Mitchell, P. (1981) in Mitochondria and Microsomes (C.P. Lee et al., eds.) pp. 427–457. Addison-Wesley, Reading, Mass.
59. Ernster, L., Lee, C.P. and Torndal, U.B. (1969) in The Energy Level and Metabolic Control in Mitochondria (S. Papa et al., eds.) pp. 439–451. Adriatica Editrice, Bari.
60. Boyer, P.D. (1974) BBA Library 13, 289–301.
61. Slater, E.C. (1974) BBA Library 13, 1–20.
62. Kayalar, C., Rosing, J. and Boyer, P.D. (1977) J. Biol. Chem. 252, 2486–2491.
63. Boyer, P.D. (1979) in Membrane Bioenergetics (C.P. Lee et al., eds.) pp. 461–479, Addison-Wesley, Reading, Mass.
64. Anderson, W.M. and Fisher, R.R. (1981) Biochim. Biophys. Acta 635, 194–199.
65. Van de Stadt, R.J., De Boer, B.L. and van Dam, K. (1973) Biochim. Biophys. Acta 292, 338–349.
66. Ernster, L., Juntti, K. and Asami, K. (1973) J. Bioenerg. 4, 149–159.
67. Pullman, M.E. and Monroy, G.C. (1963) J. Biol. Chem. 238, 3762–3769.
68. Ernster, L. (1977) Ann. Rev. Biochem. 46, 981–995.

69. Lee, C.P. and Storey, B.T. (1981) in <u>Mitochondria and Microsomes</u> (C.P. Lee et al., eds.) pp. 121-153. Addison--Wesley, Reading, Mass.
70. Conover, T.E. and Azzone, G.F. (1981) in <u>Mitochondria and Microsomes</u> (C.P. Lee et al., eds.) pp. 481-518. Addison-Wesley, Reading, Mass.
71. Ernster, L., Asami, K., Juntti, K., Coleman, J. and Nordenbrand, K. (1977) in <u>Structure of Biological Membranes</u> (Abrahamsson, S. and Pascher, I., eds.) pp. 135-156. Plenum, New York.
72. Nordenbrand, K., Hundal, T., Carlsson, C., Sandri, G. and Ernster, L. (1977) in <u>Bioenergetics of Membranes</u> (L. Packer et al., eds.) pp. 435-446. Elsevier/North Holland, Amsterdam.
73. Nordenbrand, K. and Ernster, L. (1971) Eur. J. Biochem. <u>18</u>, 258-273.

BACTERIAL SYMPORTERS: SURVEY AND MECHANISM

Ian C. West

Department of Biochemistry,
University of Newcastle upon Tyne, NE1 7RU, U.K.

INTRODUCTION

There have been several recent reviews covering
many aspects of bacterial symport processes (1-5). This
essay, dedicated to Peter Mitchell, attempts therefore to
do something slightly different.   In the first part it
focuses on Peter Mitchell's contribution to this area of
biology and aims to reveal the fruits of Mitchell's
distinctive mental and experimental approach.   In the
second part it indicates a possible mechanism, attempting
again to follow Mitchell in applying both imagination and
intuition.

THE FORMULATION OF H^+-SYMPORT HYPOTHESIS AND ITS
APPLICATION TO BACTERIA

At the Biochemical Society Symposium in 1962
Mitchell formulated the suggestion that the active
accumulation of β-galactosides by Escherichia coli is
driven by a cyclic flow of protons (6). According to this

V. P. Skulachev and Peter C. Hinkle (eds.), Chemiosmotic Proton Circuits in Biological Membranes
in honor of Peter Mitchell   ISBN 0-201-07398-6

Scheme (Fig.1) protons were driven out of the cell by
respiration and their return into the cell, by being
coupled to the inflow of β-galactoside, contributed the
free-energy necessary for active accumulation of
galactoside.   Where did this idea come from?

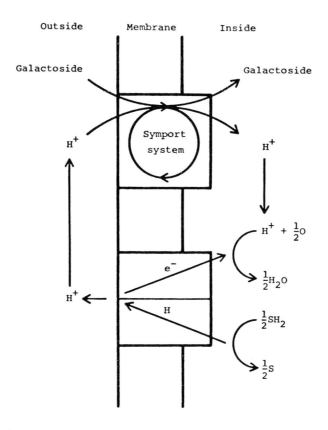

Fig.1   Scheme showing H^+-galactoside symport coupled to
respiration (from Mitchell (6) with permission).

A clear stage in the development of this concept was
the analysis by Mitchell and Moyle of the exchange of
phosphate with phosphate or arsenate across the plasma

membrane of Staphylococcus aureus (7).   So long as the
cells were unable to respire the net inflow or outflow of
phosphate was extremely slow, but the rate of unidirectional
influx was rapid (1.4 n mole min^{-1} (mg dry wt.)$^{-1}$). Mitchell
distinguished two mechanisms, both of which would lead to
a tightly coupled exchange:

(a)   Ussing's mechanism, whereby the carrier cannot
reorientate unladen because, in the presence of saturating
substrate on both sides of the membrane, it is so
promptly loaded;

(b)   A mechanism whereby the carrier cannot reorientate
unladen even in the absence of saturating substrate.

The absence of net leakage into low concentrations
of phosphate indicated the latter mechanism.   Mitchell
suggested that a covalent complex between ion and carrier
could account for a slow rate of unloading which, in turn,
could explain the absence of net flow.   However, that
has remained as an hypothesis and only one of several ways
in which the experimental observations could be explained.
No further work on this system has been published (to my
knowledge) but one substantial benefit arose from this
work of Mitchell and Moyle on S. aureus: it provided
Mitchell with a striking illustration of the tightness
with which two fluxes could be coupled (in this case
anti-coupled).

Mitchell's formulation of H^+-symport was, of course,
preceded by the very clear formulation by Crane and others
(See review by Crane (8)) of Na^+-symport and considerable
data supporting the suggestion that glucose is actively
transported across the intestinal brush-border by
Na^+-glucose symport.

At the same symposium in Prague in 1960, at which Crane presented his Na^+-glucose symport model, another key paper was presented, that by Horecker and colleagues. Mitchell ascribes (6) to Horecker et al.(9) the demonstration that dinitrophenol causes the rapid release of accumulated β-galactoside from Escherichia coli. Horecker et al. seem to have been largely concerned in that paper with their own very similar results on the effect of dinitrophenol on galactose release, but it does not really matter whether it was Horecker and galactose release or Kepes and β-galactoside release (10). The important point is that at that time Mitchell was in a unique position to interpret these observations, for he alone appreciated the role of dinitrophenol in catalysing the passage of H^+ ions through the non-polar region of bacterial and mitochondria membranes (11) and knew that bacterial respiration causes the outward pumping of H^+ ions across the bacterial membrane (12). What these results with dinitrophenol showed to Mitchell was that, if you collapse the electrochemical potential gradient of protons, accumulated galactose and galactosides are released into the medium.

There is no need to labour the point here that a system such as that shown in Fig.1 could work. If the proton motive force were in equilibrium with ATP synthesis by means of a reversible ATPase, as was clearly implicit already in Mitchell's thinking in 1961 (13), and if the stoichiometry of H^+/ATP were 2 and the ΔG of ATP hydrolysis in the region 60 kJ mol^{-1}, then an accumulation ratio ($[galactoside]_{in}/[galactoside]_{out}$) of approaching 10^4 should be possible. Such a flow of protons would provide ample free-energy. Observed accumulation ratios with

TABLE I

Organism	Type of metabolism	Class I Substrates accumulated in respiring vesicles so probably carried by H⁺-symport	Class II Substrates carried by primary active transport	Class III Substrates for PEP-linked group translocation
Escherichia coli	Facultative aerobe	lactose, G-6-P, glucuronate,gluconate, lactate, pyruvate deoxycytidine, Pro, Gly, Ala, Ser, Thr, Glu, Asp, Phe, Tyr, Trp Lys, His, Leu, Ile, Val, Cys, arabinose, galactose,xylose (?)	Glygly, Gln, Met, Arg, ornithine, ribose, K^+(Kdp) Lys, His, Leu, Ile, Val, Cys, arabinose, galactose, xylose(?)	glucose, fructose, hexitols.
Azotobacter vinelandii	Strict aerobe	glucose		
Arthrobacter pyridinolis	Strict aerobe	glucose, fructose, rhamnose, various amino acids		fructose, rhamnose.
Staphylococcus aureus	Facultative anaerobe	all 20 amino acids		glucose, fructose, lactose, galactose, hexitols.

See refs (15) and (16) for sources

galactosides were less than that, though ratios of up to 10^4 were observed with galactose at very low levels of that sugar.   The probable reason for that has emerged only in the last year or two: galactose has a second transport system which operates at very low external concentrations, which is not a proton symport, but which may be a primary active transport system driven by phosphoryl transfer (14).

THE SCOPE OF H^+-SYMPORT IN BACTERIAL TRANSPORT PROCESSES

Kaback and colleagues (see (17) for review) showed that resealed membrane vesicles prepared by osmotic lysis of lysozyme-treated E. coli ML308-225 would accumulate a number of amino acids as well as β-galactosides and some anions (see Table I) if provided with a respirable substrate.   The importance of Kaback's vesicle preparation was that these membrane vesicles were largely empty of the usual cytoplasmic contents of the cell, including soluble enzymes and metabolites such as ATP. However, the membrane bound respiratory chain was clearly intact, at least for certain substrates such as D-lactate. To those equipped with the concept of the proton-translocating respiratory chain, Kaback's results at once suggested that all the compounds accumulated by his vesicle preparations (Table I) are substrates for proton-symport reactions.   The only obvious alternative explanations would be uniport of undissociated acid (e.g. $CH_3.CO.COOH$) or of a positively charged substrate (e.g. Lys^+, K^+), Na^+-substrate symport or $H_2PO_4^-$/substrate antiport (in conjunction with an H^+/Na^+ antiport or a H^+-$H_2PO_4^-$ symport respectively) (Mitchell (18)).

Regarding E. coli, Na$^+$-symport has been described for
melibiose and glutamate but not for other substrates and
there has been no report of a phosphate-linked antiport
(19).

Also listed in Table I are results with other bacterial
species and substrates known to be carried by the two other
main transport systems.   The questions which arise are,
why, in E. coli, are 16 amino acids carried by proton
symport, 4 apparently carried by a primary active
transport system requiring ATP or a derivative, 6 carried
by both type of system, and why are glucose, galactose
and lactose carried by a phosphoenolpyruvate-linked group
translocation system in some organisms and by H$^+$-symport
in others?   The only answers that can be offered at
present, and they are very tentative, are as follows:
(1) Obligate aerobes presumably generate a proton-motive
force (by respiration) as a primary and dependable source
of usable "energy" and they tend to rely on H$^+$-symport to
a greater extent than facultative and anaerobic organisms
(1).   Thus, even glucose is carried by proton-symport
in A. vinelandii (Table I).
(2) Glucose seems to be a preferred substrate for
facultative and anaerobic organisms, and is normally
metabolized by the Embden-Meyerhof-Parnas pathway to
phosphoenolpyruvate (PEP) and pyruvate.   In such organisms
glucose is taken up by the PEP-linked group translocation
system with the generation of glucose-6-phosphate.
Apparently, this does not apply to heterofermentative
organisms that use the phosphoketolase or the anaerobic
Entner-Doudorff pathways for the very good reason that
insufficient PEP is generated (20). Considering lactose

and galactose uptake among the facultative anaerobes, it would seem that S. aureus is marginally more anaerobic than E. coli, or marginally less dependent on the proton cycle.   This correlates with the absence of a constitutive respiratory chain in an aerobically grown S. aureus (21). (3)   While Δp-driven active transport is thermodynamically efficient for moderate substrate levels (10^{-5} - 10^{-3}M) it does not have sufficient concentrating power for very low ($<10^{-6}$M) substrate levels.   On the other hand, the primary active transport systems driven by hydrolysis of ATP (or a derivative) would be wasteful of free-energy at moderate substrate levels but would be able to achieve correspondingly higher concentration ratios (14).   Certainly, these systems are characterized by a very high affinity for substrate.   Could it be then that methionine is only seen by E. coli in very low concentrations?

In Halobacteria and in some marine bacteria several symports appear to operate with Na^+ instead of H^+, and in enterobacteria glutamate and melibiose are obligatorily or facultatively coupled to Na^+ inflow (5).   In the sea and the colon there is, of course, plenty Na^+ (circa 0.47M and 0.12M respectively) but the primary source of energy for osmotic coupling is presumably still the proton, and not the Na^+ ion.   So why is Na^+ preferred in these cases? Could it be simply an accident of evolution?   In Halobacterium halobium on the other hand, there has been a recent report of a light-driven primary sodium pump (22), distinct from and in addition to the well known light-driven proton pump, bacteriorhodopsin.

MECHANISM

Peter Mitchell has repeatedly shown a strong
preference for the most direct sort of coupling mechanism.
He sees this as a starting point, not just for his own
thinking but for the evolution of this sort of energy-
coupling device.   He sees symport, for example, as
arising from the conservation of momentum of the driving
particles as they bump into the driven particles in the
interstices of the symport protein, much as air is
driven down the nozzle of a water-pump.   Thus:

> '..."energy coupling" is attributed to the
> transmission   of "thrusts" along interacting
> trains of chemical particles'(23).

> 'According to the rationale of vectorial
> metabolism and chemiosmotic coupling that I
> have endeavoured to foster, non-radiative
> thermodynamic energy transduction can occur
> only by means of the diffusion of trains or
> groups of material particles that move (with
> conserved impulse and momentum) under the
> influence of forces transmitted by local
> electrical and chemical interactions between
> them.' (18).

> '... the group-translocation pathway represents
> the field of action of a real through-space
> force (Greek:osmos = push) corresponding to the
> chemical group-potential gradient.' (24).

Of course, Mitchell recognizes that in many cases the
'thrusts' must be transmitted by the protein macromolecule
which is the transport catalyst.   Thus in antiport, where
the movement of A is coupled to the movement of B in the
opposite direction, the transfer of momentum cannot be
direct.   But A can be seen as setting up a gradient of
carrier concentration, which could convey B back across
the membrane by the same type of osmotic thrust.

Alternatively, the carrier could be seen as providing
levers and 'articulations, as in a macroscopic mechanical
engine' (23), so that the thrust of A may be transmitted
to B along a vector which is tangential, or at any other
angle, to the vector of the thrust of A.

What type of experiment does this view encourage?
Apart from its intellectual appeal as offering an almost
tangible model of "energy", it certainly has served to
emphasize the fact that there must be a movement in space
of the driving particle, though that is obvious anyway
from the thermodynamic argument that the energy in the
potential gradient of A can only be obtained if that
gradient is consumed. (25)

Most other workers have taken a more kinetic viewpoint. It seems possible that the momentum required for
the passage of solute particles across the membrane could
be easily enough obtained from the normal thermal kinetic
energy of the molecules in the medium. On the other hand,
the rate of transport of B may be expected to depend on
the concentrations of the two substrates A and B and on the
transition probabilities between two or more spatial or
conformational states. So the asymmetry or vectorial
nature of the transport of B could, on this view, depend
upon an asymmetry in the concentrations of A or in the rate
of certain transitions in an orientated electric field.
The more that is learnt of membrane transport proteins
the less likely does it seem that a large movement of any
charged group, other than the free substrate (H^+-ion), occurs
in the direction of the field. Interest therefore focusses
on H^+ concentrations and the manner in which they may be
modified by what Peter Mitchell has called "proton wells",

"hydroxyl wells" and "proton traps" (26).

Winkler and Wilson (27) drew attention to a dramatic change in the apparent K_m for galactoside efflux (K_m^{eff}) caused by metabolism such that a low apparent K_m^{eff} in resting cells is converted to a high apparent K_m^{eff} in metabolizing cells. The apparent K_m^{ent} was not altered. Kaback's group (28) reported that in membrane vesicles the apparent K_m^{ent} for lactose entry is raised 100-fold by the abolition of Δp. The observations of Overath's group (29) are presumably related: it was found that the apparent K_m^{ent} for active transport of lactose into vesicles was 100 times lower than the gross dissociation constant (K_D) for passive binding. However, for another substrate, thiodigalactoside, the two constants were identical, even though that substrate can be actively transported to high concentration gradient.

Unfortunately, K_m cannot be viewed simply as an affinity of carrier for substrate, because even in the most simple-minded model for symport K_m is a complex function of many individual rate-constants (30). Indeed, even the gross K_D is a complex function (30). Moreover, when dealing with a symport process it is clear that the kinetic analysis should be based on two-substrate kinetics. Reported K_m values are only "apparent K_m" values, i.e. values at a non-zero and non-saturating concentration of the second substrate, the H^+-ion. General kinetic models are highly complex, but there seems to be no grounds for any of the simplifying assumptions so often encountered, such as equal rate constants for inward and outward transitions, equal rate constants on both sides of the membrane and the assumption that binding steps are fast

compared with conformational transitions. My own preliminary
calculations indicate that the deprotonation on the inside
of the cells is one of the slower steps in the influx cycle
quite independently of any product inhibition that may
occur due to internal protons (31).

One of the most complete models for proton symport
is that worked out by Komor and colleagues for glucose
uptake by Chlorella which is of particular interest in that
the membrane concerned is the plasma membrane of a
eukaryotic plant. (Reviewed in ref.19). Komor has found
that changing the pH simply titrates the carrier between a
high-affinity form at acidic pH which operates proton-
symport and a low-affinity form at alkaline pH which
catalyses glucose uniport. The "proton well" concept
is invoked as an electric field affects the apparent pK_A
of this titration.

The other H^+-symport that has contributed to our
general understanding is the lactose carrier of E. coli.
Our own work (30) suggests that all the previously reported
effects of Δp on the kinetic behaviour can be explained in
terms of two-substrate kinetics, i.e. in terms of altered
H^+ concentrations on the inside or the outside of the
membrane, though recourse must again be made to Peter
Mitchell's proton wells. The demonstration by Wilson and
colleagues (32, 33) that accumulation can be driven solely
by an electric field is most important in this connection.
Questions that are raised by these models include the
following:

1.   Is substrate binding random or ordered? Kaczorowski
& Kaback (31) have presented tentative evidence for an
ordered binding, proton first. Our own data rule out the

alternative ordered sequence (30).

2.   Which group binds the proton?   I have recently
suggested that the active-site cysteine, Cys 148,
(K. Beyreuther: private communication) is itself involved
on the grounds that its pK_A is in the right range, and that
its reactivity is greatly modified in two mutants which
have lost the ability to accumulate though not to carry
galactoside (34).

3.   What are the individual rate constants of the various
partial reactions involved in substrate binding,
reorientation or conformational change, and substrate
release?   Much ingenious work needs to be done in this
area.

There have been several reports suggesting that the
existence of a membrane potential (inside negative) can
strikingly modify the behaviour of symport carriers (35, 36)
but, as these interesting effects could just as easily
modify the operation of an electroneutral carrier, it
is worth bearing in mind that they may not concern the
active-transport mechanism, but may be regulatory features.

REFERENCES

1.   West, I. C. (1974) Biochem. Soc. Trans. 2, 800 - 803

2.   Hamilton, W. A. (1975) Adv. Microbiol Physiol. 12,
     1 - 53.

3.   Simoni, R. D. & Postma, P. W. (1975) Annu. Rev. Biochem.
     44, 523 - 554.

4.   Harold, F. M. (1977) Current Topics in Bioenergetics
     (Sanadi, D. R., ed.), Vol.6, pp.83 - 149,
     Academic Press, London.

5.   Rosen, B. P. & Kashket, E. R. (1978) in Bacterial
     Transport (Rosen, B. P., ed.), pp.559 - 620,
     Marcel Dekker, Basel.

6.   Mitchell, P. (1963) Biochem. Soc. Symp. 22, 142 - 168.

7.   Mitchell, P. (1954) Soc. Exp. Biol. Symp. 8, 254-261.

8.   Crane, R. K. (Rev. Physiol. Biochem. Pharmacol.)
     78, 99 - 159.

9.   Horecker, B. L., Osborn, M. J., McLellan, W. L.,
     Avigad, G. & Asensio, C (1961) in Membrane Transport
     and Metabolism (Kleinzeller, A. & Kotyk, A. eds.)
     pp.378 - 387, Academic Press, New York.

10. Kepes, A. (1960) Biochim. Biophys. Acta, 40, 70 - 84.

11. Mitchell, P. (1961) Biochem. J. 81, 24p.

12. Mitchell, P. (1962) J. Gen. Microbiol. 29, 25 - 37.

13. Mitchell, P. (1961) Nature 191, 144 - 148.

14. Henderson, P. J. F. (1980) Biochem. Soc. Trans. 8,
     678 - 679.

15. Short, S. A., White, D. C. & Kaback, H. R. (1972)
     J. Biol. Chem. 247, 7452 - 7458.

16. Rosen, B. P. (1978) Bacterial Transport (ed.)
     Marcel Dekker, Basel.

17. Kaback, H. R. (1974) Science 186, 882 - 892.

18. Mitchell, P. (1972) J. Bioenergetics 4, 63-91.

19. West, I. C. (1980) Biochim. Biophys. Acta 604, 91-126.

20. Hays, J. B. (1978) in Bacterial Transport (Rosen, B. P. ed.)
     pp.43 - 102. Marcel Dekker, Basel.

21. Jacobs, N. J. & Conti, S. F. (1965) J. Bacteriol.
     89, 675 - 679.

22. Lindley, E. V. & MacDonald, R. E. (1979) Biochem. Biophys. Res. Commun. 88, 491 - 499.

23. Mitchell, P. (1972) J. Bioenergetics 3, 5 - 24.

24. Mitchell, P. (1979) Eur. J. Biochem. 95, 1 - 20.

25. West, I. C. (1970) Biochem. Biophys. Res. Commun. 41, 655 - 661.

26. Mitchell, P. (1977) Symp. Soc. Gen. Microbiol. 27, 383 - 423.

27. Winkler, H. H. & Wilson, T. H. (1966) J. Biol. Chem. 241, 2200 - 2211.

28. Kaczorowski, G. J., Robertson, D. E. & Kaback, H. R. (1979) Biochemistry 18, 3697 - 3704.

29. Wright, J. K., Teather, R. M. & Overath, P. (1979) in Functional and Molecular Aspects of Biomembrane Transport (Klingenberg, E. M., Palmieri, F. & Quagliariello, E., eds.) pp.239 - 248, Elsevier, Amsterdam.

30. Page, M. G. P. & West, I. C. (1981) Biochem. J. 196, in press.

31. Kaczorowski, G. J. & Kaback, H. R. (1979) Biochemistry 18, 3691 - 3697.

32. Kashket, E. R. & Wilson, T. H. (1972) Biochem. Biophys. Res. Commun. 49, 615 - 620.

33. Flagg, J. L. & Wilson, T. H. (1977) J. Membr. Biol. 31, 233 - 255.

34. West, I. C. (1980) Biochem. Soc. Trans. 6, 706 - 707.

35. Lanyi, J. K. & Silverman, M. P. (1979) J. Biol. Chem. 254, 4750 - 4755.

36. Robertson, D. E., Kaczorowski, G. J., Garcia, M. & Kaback, H. R. (1980) Biochemistry 19, 5692 - 5702.

MECHANISM OF H$^+$/LACTOSE SYMPORT IN ESCHERICHIA COLI

H. R. Kaback

Laboratory of Membrane Biochemistry
Roche Institute of Molecular Biology, Nutley, New Jersey 07110

Although Peter Mitchell's chemiosmotic hypothesis (1-5) is generally associated with oxidative and photophosphorylation, the concept has had an increasingly strong impact on other areas of biology and biochemistry, particularly bacterial active transport. In 1963, it was postulated explicitly (2) that an electrochemical gradient of hydrogen ion ($\Delta\bar{\mu}_{H}+$[1]; interior negative and alkaline) generated by respiration or ATP hydrolysis is the driving force for β-galactoside accumulation in Escherichia coli and that the lac carrier protein translocates substrate with H$^+$, the substrate moving against and the H$^+$ with their respective electrochemical gradients (i.e., symport). Briefly, over the past 10 years, exhaustive studies with intact bacteria and isolated cytoplasmic membrane vesicles have provided virtually unequivocal support for these basic principles with respect to the transport of β-galactosides as well as many other solutes (6-10). Since the energetics of these transport systems have been resolved to a large extent, focus is shifting to a more mechanistic level,

---

[1]Abbreviations: $\Delta\bar{\mu}_{H}+$, electrochemical gradient of H$^+$; $\Delta\Psi$, membrane potential; ΔpH, chemical gradient of H$^+$.

V. P. Skulachev and Peter C. Hinkle (eds.), Chemiosmotic Proton Circuits in Biological Membranes in honor of Peter Mitchell
ISBN 0-201-07398-6

and recent studies (11-14) with the β-galactoside transport
system in E. coli membrane vesicles are beginning to provide
some insight in this regard. It is the purpose of this contribution to review some of these studies.

Before progressing, it is important to point out that
the choice of this transport system for detailed study is
based on a large body of information on the genetics, biochemistry and molecular biology of the system. Although space
limitations preclude detailed discussion of this aspect of the
work, it should be emphasized that since its initial description in 1956 (15), the system has been studied extensively from
many points of view. Genetic evidence indicating that the lac
y gene encodes a product that is responsible for the rapid
influx and efflux of β-galactosides received strong confirmation from differential and double labeling experiments that
identified a specific membrane protein (the lac carrier protein, lac permease or M protein) and demonstrated it to be the
product of the lac y gene, the second of the three structural
genes in the lac operon (16,17). With the advent of genetic
engineering, the lac y gene has been cloned (18) and its product amplified (19) and synthesized in vitro (20). Moreover,
the amino acid sequence of the lac carrier protein has been
deduced from the nucleotide sequence of the gene (21). In
addition, a highly specific photoaffinity label for the lac
carrier has been developed (22), and its use in conjunction
with proteolysis studies has allowed the direct demonstration
that the lac carrier protein spans the membrane[2]. Finally, and
most recently, the lac carrier has been solubilized and reconstituted into proteoliposomes in an active state (23), and the
active protein has been partially purified[3].

---

[2]Goldkorn, T., Rimon, G. and Kaback, H. R., unpublished observations.

MECHANISTIC STUDIES

Efflux is an ordered reaction (11). Carrier-mediated lactose
efflux down a concentration gradient is a first-order process
that is unaffected by protonophores and dependent on ambient
pH, increasing about 3-fold from pH 5.5 to 7.5. In contrast,
experiments performed under identical conditions with equimolar lactose in the external medium demonstrate that exchange
is insensitive to pH and very fast relative to efflux. Symport
of H$^+$ occurs during efflux, resulting in the transient formation of $\Delta\Psi$ (interior negative) as demonstrated by efflux-
dependent, transient accumulation of Rb$^+$ (in the presence of
valinomycin), tetraphenylphosphonium$^+$ or proline and quenching
of the $\Delta\Psi$-sensitive fluorophore 3,3'-dipentyloxacarbocyanine
iodide, all of which are abolished by carbonylcyanide-m-chloro-
phenylhydrazone. Furthermore, the magnitude of the transient
$\Delta\Psi$ generated increases with pH in much the same manner as the
rate of efflux, suggesting tight coupling between lactose and
H$^+$ translocation. Finally, lactose efflux causes uncoupler-
sensitive acidification of the medium[4], providing strong evidence that the electrogenic ion is either H$^+$ or OH$^-$.

Comparison of efflux and exchange rates demonstrates
that exchange is at least 10-times more rapid. Thus, the rate-
determining step for efflux must be associated with a reaction
that corresponds kinetically to the return of the unloaded
carrier to the inner surface of the membrane as this is the
only step in the overall process in which efflux and exchange
differ (Fig. 1). Assuming that loss of H$^+$ and lactose is

[3]Newman, M. J., Wilson, T. H., Foster, D. L. and Kaback, H. R.,
unpublished experiments.

[4]Kaczorowski, G. J. and Kaback, H. R., Unpublished information.

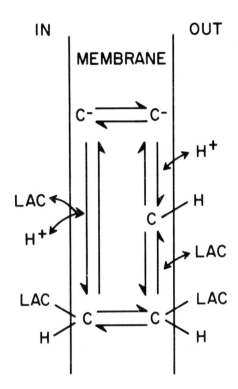

Fig. 1. Schematic representation of reactions involved in
        lactose efflux and exchange. C represents the lac
        carrier protein. Order of substrate binding at the
        inner surface of the membrane is not implied.

required to reinitiate an efflux cycle, external pH might
influence carrier turnover in either of two ways. First,
deprotonation of the carrier might be slow and thereby limit
efflux in a pH-dependent fashion. Although H[+] transfers are
typically fast in soluble enzymes, the process could be altered
by the hydrophobic location of the protein. Second, pH could
alter the equilibrium between the protonated and unprotonated

forms of the carrier (i.e., two conformational states), favoring the unprotonated form at higher pH. Since it is likely that only the deprotonated carrier can recycle, efflux would be partially controlled by external pH, and the rate-limiting step might then involve "movement" of the unloaded carrier. The observed pH dependence of efflux is consistent with either of these suggestions. Conversely, if deprotonation is not obligatory for exchange, H$^+$ would remain bound to the carrier rendering this reaction insensitive to pH (Fig. 1). Given the ordered mechanism shown, in which the carrier releases lactose first followed by loss of H$^+$, deprotonation and/or return of the unloaded carrier might be rate-determining for efflux.

When cells or membrane vesicles are loaded with a substrate, transient uptake of radioactivity is observed, and the process is termed "entrance counterflow" (24). In kinetic terms, the efficiency of the phenomenon is related to the frequency with which the carrier returns to the inner surface of the membrane in the loaded versus the unloaded form (Fig. 1). Counterflow experiments conducted at various pH's reveal that external lactose affects H$^+$ loss from the carrier. When the external lactose concentration is below the apparent K_m of the carrier, counterflow is pH dependent and decreases from pH 5.5 to 7.5, indicating that deprotonation occurs frequently to limit the process. When external lactose is saturating, however, counterflow is unaffected by pH. Moreover, the transient formation of $\Delta\Psi$ observed during lactose efflux is abolished under the latter conditions. These results are consistent with the ordered mechanism for efflux shown in Fig. 1. As efflux is initiated, lactose and H$^+$ bind to the carrier on the inner surface of the membrane. After translocation across the membrane, lactose is released first leaving the protonated carrier. With saturating external substrate, rebinding and influx occur rapidly before deprotonation, and ambient pH has little effect on counterflow. However, when external lactose is subsaturating, rebinding of radioactive substrate is relatively slow, allowing deprotonation and return of the unloaded carrier. As a result, influx of radioactive substrate is diminished (i.e. counterflow is inhibited). Furthermore, as pH is increased, deprotonation and return of the unloaded carrier are enhanced resulting in even less counterflow. The ability of external lactose to inhibit generation of $\Delta\Psi$ during efflux is consistent with this notion. When substrate is present externally at concentrations above the apparent K_m, release of lactose and rebinding of substrate occur before deprotonation and the carrier recycles in the loaded form, thus preventing generation of $\Delta\Psi$.

The unloaded carrier may catalyze movement of negative charge (12). If the rate-limiting step for efflux involves return of the unloaded carrier, conditions that perturb this step should influence the overall rate of efflux without altering the rate of exchange. In order to test these predictions, $\Delta\Psi$'s and ΔpH's were imposed artificially during efflux and exchange with very clearcut results. The rate of efflux is diminished on imposition of $\Delta\Psi$ (interior negative) or ΔpH (interior alkaline) and enhanced when the polarities of the imposed gradients are reversed. The effects are additive, and importantly, the imposed $\Delta\Psi$'s and/or ΔpH's alter the V_{max} of efflux with no significant effect on apparent K_m. Strikingly, moreover, imposition of $\Delta\bar{\mu}_H+$ of either polarity has no effect whatsoever on exchange.

In addition to providing support for the argument that the rate-determining step for efflux involves the return of the unloaded carrier, the findings also have important implications regarding the translocation mechanism. It has been suggested

(25,26) that the unloaded porter catalyzes a reaction involving the translocation of a negative charge, while the loaded porter is neutral, and evidence has been presented that is most easily interpreted in this light (27,28). To a limited extent, the effects of imposed $\Delta\Psi$ and ΔpH on efflux and exchange are also consistent with this hypothesis. Given the observation that lactose translocation under exchange conditions is unaffected by imposition of $\Delta\bar{\mu}_H+$, it seems unlikely that this reaction involves net charge movement. Moreover, since $\Delta\Psi$, in particular, decreases the rate of efflux when the polarity is interior negative and enhances the rate of efflux when interior positive, it seems reasonable to conclude that the unloaded carrier may carry a net negative charge (Fig. 1). If the unloaded carrier were positively charged, the opposite effects would be expected. It should be apparent, however, that these considerations shed little light on the means by which ΔpH alters the rate of efflux, which highlights the importance of determining whether $\Delta\Psi$ and ΔpH affect the same or different steps in the translocation process.

Deuterium solvent isotope effects (12). Given the scheme in Fig. 1, one means by which to further investigate the suggested mechanism is to determine whether carrier turnover exhibits a deuterium solvent isotope effect. If one step in the reaction involves a rate-determining H$^+$ transfer, replacing solvent protium with deuterium might alter the overall reaction rates. Since deprotonation of the carrier is presumed to occur before initiation of another efflux cycle, efflux rates should be decreased in deuterium. Exchange, in contrast, should not be altered if proton loss is not required for this reaction (Fig. 1). At equivalent pH and pD values, efflux rates are diminished 2 to 2.5-fold in deuterated media relative to control rates in protium, while the rate of exchange is identical in deuterium or protium. Furthermore, when counterflow is studied with subsaturating external lactose in deuterated buffer, activity is enhanced. This result is expected from the scheme presented in Fig. 1 because during counterflow under subsaturating conditions, the protonated form of the carrier partitions between two competing pathways: (i) deprotonation and return of the unloaded carrier (i.e., efflux); and (ii) rebinding of substrate and return of the loaded form (i.e., counterflow). Since the deuterated form of the carrier would be favored relative to the protonated form because of an effect on either the rate of deprotonation or on the equilibrium between unloaded and deuterated carrier (i.e., a pK_a effect), the excess deuterated carrier would favor rebinding and influx of substrate, thus enhancing counterflow activity.

$\overline{\Delta\mu}_H+$ Alters the distribution of the lac carrier between two kinetic pathways (14). Under completely deenergized conditions (i.e., facilitated diffusion), the lac transport system exhibits a high apparent K_m for either lactose or β-D-galactopyranosyl 1-thio-β-D-galactopyranoside, and generation of $\overline{\Delta\mu}_H+$ via the respiratory chain results in at least a 100-fold decrease in apparent K_m with little change in V_{max}. Furthermore, a low apparent K_m is observed when $\Delta\Psi$ or ΔpH is dissipated selectively with an appropriate ionophore and when either $\Delta\Psi$ (interior negative) or ΔpH (interior alkaline) is imposed artificially across the membrane. Clearly, therefore, either component of $\overline{\Delta\mu}_H+$ is able to elicit the low apparent K_m characteristic of the energized system. It is also particularly interesting that the $\overline{\Delta\mu}_H+$-induced decrease in apparent K_m is inhibited by diethylpyrocarbonate, a reagent that is relatively specific for histidyl residues at pH 6.0, and by rose bengal

in the presence of light and oxygen, an operation that leads
to photooxidation of histidyl residues (13)[5]. Thus, it seems
likely that a histidine residue(s) in either the lac carrier
itself or another component of the translocation complex plays
an important role in the response of the system to $\Delta\bar{\mu}_H+$.

A detailed series of kinetic experiments were conducted
in which initial rates of lactose transport were studied as a
function of lactose concentration under conditions where ΔpH
and/or $\Delta\Psi$ were varied systematically at pH 5.5 and 7.5. Surprisingly, the results demonstrate that the apparent K_m remains
constant from about -180 mV to -30 mV, while V_{max} varies to the
second power with either component of $\Delta\bar{\mu}_H+$ at both pH's, even
though V_{max} is about 10-fold higher at pH 7.5 over a comparable
range of $\Delta\bar{\mu}_H+$ values. Since a high apparent K_m is observed
under completely deenergized conditions, the findings appear to
be paradoxical; however, studies carried out over an extended
range of lactose concentrations demonstrate that when $\Delta\bar{\mu}_H+$ is
partially dissipated, the system exhibits biphasic kinetics.
One component of the overall process exhibits the kinetic parameters typical of $\Delta\bar{\mu}_H+$-driven active transport (i.e., low apparent K_m; high V_{max}) and the other has the characteristics of
facilitated diffusion (i.e., high apparent K_m; high V_{max}).
Clearly, therefore, in addition to acting thermodynamically as
the driving force for active transport, $\Delta\bar{\mu}_H+$ alters the distribution of the lac carrier between two kinetic states. In this
context, Lanyi (29) has made similar observations with certain
sodium-dependent transport systems and suggested that these
carriers may be oligomeric and possess allosteric properties.
Furthermore, the rates of covalent inactivation of the lac
system by diethylpyrocarbonate (13) and by a variety of malei-
_____
[5]Garcia, M. L., Patel, L., Padan, E. and Kaback, H. R., manuscript in preparation.

mides (30) are enhanced in the presence of $\Delta\bar{\mu}_H{}^+$, implying that there may be a chemical modification in the lac carrier that is the basis for the kinetic alteration.

Since little is known about the molecular mechanism of the lac carrier, it is obviously impossible to provide a completely satisfactory explanation for these phenomena. However, the uniqueness of some of the observations, in particular the second power relationship between $\Delta\bar{\mu}_H{}^+$ and the concentration of the carrier in the low apparent K_m state, call for some attempt at conceptualization. Thus, it is suggested very tentatively and with no firm support that the lac carrier may exist in two forms, monomer and dimer, that the monomer catalyzes facilitated diffusion and the dimer active transport, and finally, that $\Delta\bar{\mu}_H{}^+$ promotes aggregation of monomers to dimers. Although this simplistic notion can account for much of the present data, it is readily apparent that other possibilities exist. For instance, $\Delta\bar{\mu}_H{}^+$ might cause a change in the rate-determining step for transport without a change in the structural state of the carrier. Under conditions of facilitated diffusion, transport might be limited by deprotonation of the carrier on the surface of the membrane while in the presence of $\Delta\bar{\mu}_H{}^+$, a reaction involving return of the unloaded, negatively-charged carrier to the surface might be limiting (cf. above). Since the lac carrier has been reconstituted and is currently being purified in an active state, it might be possible to carry out cross-linking studies under energized and deenergized conditions in order to test the former suggestion. On the other hand, it would be difficult to test the latter suggestion even if the carrier were reconstituted in purified form. In other words, although the data as a whole imply that the lac carrier has oligomeric structure, the monomer-dimer notion should not be taken as a formal hypothesis, but as a potentially testable suggestion.

REFERENCES

1. Mitchell, P. (1961) Nature (London) 191, 144.
2. Mitchell, P. (1963) Biochem. Soc. Symp. 22, 142.
3. Mitchell, P. (1966) "Chemiosmotic Coupling in Oxidative
    and Photosynthetic Phosphorylation", Glynn Research Ltd.,
    Bodmin, England.
4. Mitchell, P. (1968) "Chemiosmotic Coupling and Energy
    Transduction", Glynn Research Ltd., Bodmin, England.
5. Mitchell, P. (1973) J. Bioenerg. 4, 63.
6. Harold, F. M. (1976) Curr. Top. Bioenerg. 6, 83.
7. Kaback, H. R. (1976) J. Cellular Physiol. 89, 575.
8. Konings, W. N. and Boonstra, J. (1977) Curr. Top. in
    Membr. and Transport 9, 177.
9. Lanyi, J. K. (1978) in Energetics and Structure of Halo-
    philic Microorganisms (Caplan, S. R. and Ginzburg, M.,
    eds.) Elsevier/North Holland, Amsterdam, p. 415.
10. Rosen, B. P. and Kashket, E. R. (1978) in Bacterial Trans-
    port (Rosen, B. P., ed.) Marcel Dekker, Inc., NY, p. 559.
11. Kaczorowski, G. J. and Kaback, H. R. (1979) Biochemistry
    18, 3691.
12. Kaczorowski, G. J., Robertson, D. E. and Kaback, H. R.
    (1979) Biochemistry 18, 3697.
13. Padan, E., Patel, L. and Kaback, H. R. (1979) Proc. Natl.
    Acad. Sci. U.S.A. 76, 6221.
14. Robertson, D. E., Kaczorowski, G. J., Garcia, M. L. and
    Kaback, H. R. (1980) Biochemistry 19, 5692.
15. Rickenberg, H. V., Cohen, G. N., Buttin, G. and Monod, J.
    (1956) Ann. Inst. Pasteur 91, 829.
16. Kepes, A. and Cohen, G. N. (1962) in The Bacteria, Vol. IV
    (Gunsalis, I. C. and Stanier, R., eds.) Academic Press, NY
    p. 179.
17. Kennedy, E. P. (1970) in The Lactose Operon (Beckwith,
    J. R. and Zipser, D., eds.) Cold Spring Harbor Labs, Cold
    Spring Harbor, NY, p. 49.
18. Teather, R. M., Müller-Hill, B., Abrutsch, U., Aichele, G.
    and Overath, P. (1978) Mol. Gen. Genet. 159, 293.
19. Overath, P., Teather, R. M., Simoni, R. D., Aichele, G.
    and Wilhelm, U. (1979) Biochemistry 18, 1.
20. Ehring, R., Beyreuther, K., Wright, J. K. and Overath, P.
    (1980) Nature 283, 537.
21. Büchel, D. E., Gronenborn, G. and Müller-Hill, B. (1980)
    Nature 283, 541.
22. Kaczorowski, G. J., LeBlanc, G. and Kaback, H. R. (1980)
    Proc. Natl. Acad. Sci. U.S.A. 77, 6319.
23. Newman, M. J. and Wilson, T. H. (1980) J. Biol. Chem.
    255, 10538.

24. Wong, P.T.S. and Wilson, T. H. (1970) Biochim. Biophys. Acta 196, 336.
25. Schuldiner, S., Kerwar, G. K., Weil, R. and Kaback, H. R. (1975) J. Biol. Chem. 250, 1361.
26. Rottenberg, H. (1976) FEBS Lett. 66, 159.
27. Ramos, S. and Kaback, H. R. (1977) Biochemistry 16, 854.
28. Ramos, S. and Kaback, H. R. (1977) Biochemistry 16, 4271.
29. Lanyi, J. K. (1978) Biochemistry 17, 3011.
30. Cohn, D. E., Kaczorowski, G. J. and Kaback, H. R. (1981) Biochemistry, in press.

ATP AND PROTON-MOTIVE FORCE IN BACTERIAL ION TRANSPORT: VARIATIONS ON A THEME BY MITCHELL.[1]

Franklin M. Harold[*] and Donald L. Heefner

Department of Molecular and Cellular Biology,
National Jewish Hospital and Research Center/
National Asthma Center, Denver, CO 80206, and
*Department of Biochemistry, Biophysics and
Genetics, University of Colorado Medical School
Denver, Colorado 80262.

INTRODUCTION. What makes the chemiosmotic theory so appealing is its capacity to accommodate a wide range of seemingly disparate phenomena within a unified framework. The general proposition is that ion currents across biological membranes are one of the fundamental mechanisms by which living things harness the free energy of metabolism to the performance of useful work. In the prokaryotic context, in which the idea was first explored in depth (1-4), generation of the current is assigned to electrogenic pumps that transport protons outward across the plasma membrane. The current is utilized by an array of biochemical devices, likewise embedded in the plasma membrane, that allow the protons to pass back across the membrane and perform work at the expense of the

---

[1]Supported by NIH grant AI-03568.

V. P. Skulachev and Peter C. Hinkle (eds.), Chemiosmotic Proton Circuits in Biological Membranes
in honor of Peter Mitchell   ISBN 0-201-07398-6

537

538   FRANKLIN M. HAROLD AND DONALD L. HEEFNER

electrochemical free energy of the proton gradient, or protonmotive force. One example of such work is the accumulation of metabolites by bacteria and mitochondria. As Mitchell originally envisaged it, energy coupling to transport is entirely secondary. Cations, particularly potassium, accumulate in the cytoplasm by uniport in response to the electrical potential, interior negative; anions accumulate by symport with protons in response to the pH gradient, interior alkaline; neutral metabolites accumulate by electrogenic symport with protons, responding to the total protonmotive force; and metabolites such as sodium ions are extruded by antiport for protons (3-7). Since 1968, one of the chief objectives of research in this laboratory has been to explore and refine the application of chemiosmotic principles to the transport of ions by bacteria, and particularly by streptococci.

A TRAIL OF RESEARCH. Streptococci are nutritionally exacting organisms, metabolically anaerobes yet tolerant to air. Respiration and oxidative phosphorylation are absent, at least in strain 9790 with which all our work is done; some other streptococci produce cytochromes when grown under suitable conditions (8), but 9790 did not (unpublished observations). The organisms rely entirely on substrate-level phosphorylation for their supply of ATP, specifically on the homolactic fermentation of glucose and on the degradation of arginine to ornithine. This is one of the virtues of streptococci as experimental organisms: we always know where our ATP comes from, and can easily monitor its rate of production. Their other virtue is their susceptibility to a host of ionophores and inhibitors that act at the level of the plasma membrane. It is also convenient that streptococci do not usually form reserve polymers and are therefore energy-depleted within minutes after withdrawal of the substrate.

Early studies (9-12) demonstrated that <u>Streptococcus faecalis</u> 9790 generates a pH gradient and a substantial membrane potential, interior alkaline and negative, as predicted by the chemiosmotic theory; and identified a proton-translocating ATPase as the agency responsible for proton extrusion. Subsequent research, chiefly by T.H. Wilson and P. Maloney (13-15), solidified the identification of a proton-transport ATPase, with a probable stoichiometry of 2H$^+$ expelled per ATP hydrolyzed. The molecular characteristics of the enzyme are well known thanks to the extensive researches of A. Abrams and his associates (16), who first discovered the membrane-bound ATPase of streptococci in 1960. It resembles the ATPases of other bacteria, of mitochondria and of chloroplasts: there is a headpiece composed of five subunits in the ration $\alpha_3\beta_3\gamma\delta\epsilon$, that contains the catalytic site; and a membrane-bound portion, probably consisting of three subunits, that presumably functions as the proton channel (3-7,17). The molecular mechanism of proton extrusion remains elusive, but the presence of an electrogenic proton-translocating ATPase in the plasma membrane proved to be one of the fixed points in a universe in which all else seems inclined to wander.

Like other bacteria, and indeed like virtually all free-living cells, streptococci accumulate potassium ions and expel sodium. In cells growing exponentially, K$^+$ is by far the major intracellular cation; its concentration attains 0.5 M, and may exceed that in the external medium by a factor of 50,000. Sodium, by contrast, is virtually absent: the internal sodium concentration is about one hundredth of the external one. With a membrane potential of up to -150 mV and a pH gradient of one unit or so, it is clear that of the three major cations at least two must be transported actively, against the gradient of electrochemical potential. Our objective, then, is to determine the mechanisms by which K^+ and Na^+ transport are linked to the sole energy source available to streptococci, namely ATP generated by glycolysis and other substrate-level phosphorylation pathways.

A systematic study of this question in 1972 (12,18) generated the following observations and led to the scheme illustrated in Fig. 1a. (i) The electrical potential across the plasma membrane of

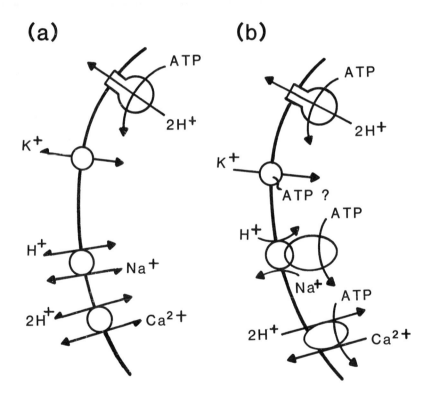

Fig. 1   Cation transport in <u>Streptococcus</u> <u>faecalis</u>, as envisaged in 1972 (a) and in 1981 (b).

glycolyzing cells was abolished by DCCD, a potent inhibitor of the proton-translocating ATPase, and was associated with the extrusion of protons from the cells. (ii) Net uptake of K$^+$ occurred by exchange for either Na$^+$ of H$^+$; it was not much inhibited by valinomycin, but was blocked by proton conductors and was accompanied by expulsion of the lipid-soluble cations DDA$^+$ and TPMP$^+$. We therefore inferred that K$^+$ accumulation is a response to the negative potential produced by the pump, and involves the entry of positive charge. (iii) S. faecalis expelled sodium by exchange for K$^+$, DDA$^+$, TPMP$^+$, Tris and other amines and even by exchange for H$^+$. A subsequent study (19) described net extrusion of Na$^+$ by exchange for Ca^{2+}. The exchange of Na$^+$ for K$^+$ was blocked by DCCD and by proton conductors, evidence that it depends on the generation of a protonmotive force; by contrast, exchange of Na$^+$ for H$^+$ was resistant to DCCD and to proton conductors. Taken together, the data suggested that sodium extrusion is electroneutral and is not obligatorily linked to K$^+$ movements; the simplest hypothesis is antiport of Na$^+$ for H$^+$, as Mitchell had suggested in a personal letter to F.M.H. a year or two before.

These findings listed above were readily accommodated by the traditional chemiosmotic scheme (Fig. 1) that Harold and Papineau invoked (18), but there were two observations that did not fit and implied serious deficiencies. First, transport of both K$^+$ and Na$^+$ in either direction, even homologous exchange of ^{42}K$^+$ for K$^+$ or of ^{22}Na$^+$ for Na$^+$, were seen only in cells provided with a source of metabolic energy; this suggests some role for ATP (or a related metabolite) that had no obvious place in the scheme. Second, the potassium concentration gradient established by glycolyzing cells was substantially greater than that which the membrane potential could support. The methods used to estimate the potential from the distribution of DDA^+ and $TPMP^+$ (12) were crude, yet it seemed that K^+ could not simply accumulate electrophoretically as Fig. 1 implies. The matter was left to rest for a few years, but in 1976 we embarked on a critical re-examination of the roles of ATP and the protonmotive force in the transport of K^+ and of Na^+. It is now clear that the scheme of Fig. 1a is not so much wrong as insufficient; and that scientists were well advised by Whitehead to seek simplicity and then distrust it.

To go beyond the physiological experiments that underpin Fig. 1a it is necessary to work with everted membrane vesicles, in which the site of energy coupling is accessible to experimental manipulation.   Kobayashi et al. (19) described a procedure for preparing such vesicles by use of a French press, and showed that these vesicles take up $^{45}Ca^{2+}$ when incubated with ATP.   The characteristics of Ca^{2+} uptake, however, were quite unexpected. There is solid evidence that everted vesicles from Escherichia coli, Azotobacter and other organisms take up Ca^{2+} by a secondary transport system energized by the protonmotive force, interior positive and acid (20-22). By contrast, $^{45}Ca^{2+}$ uptake by S. faecalis vesicles was resistant to both DCCD and to proton conductors and appeared to be energized by ATP. This conclusion was reinforced by parallel studies with intact cells (19). Calcium-stimulated ATPase activity was not demonstrable at the time, but Dr. M. Solioz (personal communication) has recently succeeded in solubilizing the streptococcal calcium-transport ATPase, and reconstituted it into phospholipid vesicles. It thus seems fairly certain that S. faecalis expels calcium by means of a calcium-ATPase, a mechanism hitherto thought to be confined to eukaryotes. We turned to the study of sodium uptake by everted vesicles with pleasurable anticipation, and little inkling of the complexities that would emerge.

Everted vesicles accumulate ^{22}Na$^+$ very nicely when incubated with ATP, and by a mechanism sensitive to DCCD and to proton
conductors: evidently, sodium transport depends on the protonmotive force, as Fig. 1a requires. But intact cells behaved otherwise: efflux of sodium from the cells, even down the electrochemical potential gradient, was seen only when the cells were able
to generate ATP. Moreover we found that, under certain conditions,
glycolyzing cells can expel Na$^+$ against a concentration gradient of
about 100-fold, even though the proton circulation has been short-
circuited such that there is no measurable pH gradient or membrane
potential. We were forced to conclude (23) that intact cells use
ATP or a related metabolite as the energy source for a primary
sodium pump. The requirement for a protonmotive force under the
conditions used by Harold and Papineau in 1972 was reinterpreted,
to suggest that the sodium pump only operates when the cytoplasmic
pH is alkaline, which in turn depends on proton extrusion.

But what to do about the glaring conflict between the data
from intact cells and those from vesicles? Detailed study of ^{22}Na$^+$
uptake by everted vesicles revealed that under some conditions (high
K$^+$ and pH 8) uptake was, in fact, resistant to ionophores; apparently, vesicles do exhibit at least a degree of ATP-linked sodium
transport.   Might there be two sodium transport systems in S.
faecalis, one linked to ATP and the other to the protonmotive
force? This seems unlikely for many reasons, one of which is the
existence of a mutant (No. 7683, ref. 18) deficient in sodium
transport by both intact cells and vesicles. Besides, to accommodate the data, both systems would have to require ATP. And yet,
there is merit to the notion of two transport systems, because one
can isolate two kinds of revertants. One class (R1) can expel Na$^+$
but is extremely sensitive to inhibition by ionophores, suggesting

that in these revertants the energy source for Na^+ movements is the protonmotive force; the other class (R2) has recovered ATP-driven sodium transport, in both cells and vesicles. We finally decided that coupling of Na^+ movements to ATP and to the proton circulation, respectively, must be alternative modes of a single and rather complex transport system; and that the peculiar characteristics of $^{22}Na^+$ transport in everted vesicles were the result of damage to that system during vesicle preparation (24). Napoleon, had he been faced with the question, would probably have said when in doubt, publish; and so we did.

Our misgivings were resolved just a few months ago when, for reasons to be explained below, it occurred to us that damage to the sodium transport system might be due to endogenous proteases. Everted vesicles prepared in the continuous presence of protease inhibitors (1 mM each of phenylmethylsulfonyl fluoride, p-toluene-sulfonyl fluoride and p-toluenesulfonic acid) behaved just as one would expect if they had an ATP driven sodium pump: uptake was dependent on ATP, was little affected by proton conductors and was stimulated by DCCD. Moreover, protease-protected vesicles exhibit significant and reproducible sodium stimulation of ATPase activity. Two lines of evidence encourage us to believe that protease-protected vesicles contain a distinct sodium-transport ATPase. First, diethylstilbestrol and efrapeptin inhibit the F_1F_0-ATPase of the vesicles, but inhibit neither sodium-stimulated ATPase activity nor $^{22}Na^+$ uptake. Second, the sodium-stimulated activity is present in the parent and in R2 revertants but absent from mutant 7683 and from R1 revertants. The sodium transport system is not identical with that for calcium. Putting together these observations with other still incomplete data, we arrive at the following specula-tive interpretation (Fig. 1b). S. faecalis expels sodium by means of a primary, ATP-driven sodium pump that exchanges Na$^+$ for H$^+$ in an electroneutral manner. The pump is of modular construction, consisting of a Na$^+$/H$^+$ antiporter unit coupled to an ATPase "power pack"; endogenous proteases clip the link, leaving the free antiporter in the membrane to mislead the unwary (Fig. 1b). Mutant 7683 probably has a defect in the antiporter element; revertants recover either the antiporter alone (R1) or a modified holosystem (R2).

It goes without saying that further experimental work is required to put this hypothesis on sound footing; let us here explore some of its implications, experimental as well as conceptual. First, it will be obvious that conclusions about energy coupling to transport should never be based solely on studies with membrane vesicles. The conclusion, that the lac permease of E. coli mediates secondary symport of lactose with protons, is secure thanks to studies with both intact cells and membrane vesicles (25-30). The parallel conclusion, that E. coli expels sodium by secondary antiport for protons (31-36) remains insecure pending critical examination of intact cells to make sure that the secondary porter documented in vesicles is not an artifact. The same doubts arise with regard to many other systems described over the years in membrane vesicles from E. coli, Halobacterium halobium, Mycobacterium phlei and others. Resolution of these doubts will raise another question: why do streptococci use ATP to expel sodium, while other bacteria use the protonmotive force? The answer is probably to be found in the observation (37) that streptococci cannot generate as large a protonmotive force as aerobic organisms do.

Second, our findings call into question Skulachev's hypothesis (38), that the meaning of the universal tendency of cells to accummulate K^+ and expel Na^+ is to be sought in the buffering of the electrochemical potential of protons. The evolutionary origin of the assymmetric distribution of K^+ and Na^+ may well reflect this purpose, but in contemporary streptococci the electrochemical potentials for H^+ and Na^+, at least, appear to be independent of each other.

Finally, the apparent conversion of a pump into a porter by proteolysis can also be considered from another angle. Could it be that the construction, and hence the energy source, of the sodium transport system (Fig. 1b) depends on how the cells are grown? Should this be true we would have an example of what we (Heefner et al., 1980) called, half in jest, a "moped": a transport system which, like the popular macroscopic carrier, can utilize several energy sources alternately or even together. One is tempted to hope that mopeds do not exist, for they would assuredly complicate the analysis of biological transport.

We have thus far said little about potassium uptake, for the simple reason that we do not understand it very well. The process was described in some detail by Bakker and Harold (39), who sharpened the issues posed in 1972 but failed to resolve them. The data indicate that K^+ accumulation depends on the generation of both ATP and the protonmotive force, while $^{42}K^+/K^+$ exchange requires only the former; this conclusion confirms that reached earlier by Rhoads and Epstein (40) for the TrkA system of E. coli. There is also a pathway for K^+ efflux, which likewise requires ATP (or a related metabolite) but is thermodynamically passive. Net accumulation of K^+ can, under favorable circumstances, attain a concentration gradient of some 50,000. If uptake were electrophoretic, this would be in equilibrium with a membrane potential of about -275 mV, far in excess of the measured potential (-140 mV).

We are fairly certain from both published and unpublished data that there is no obligatory coupling between the movements of K$^+$ and of Na$^+$, so that we can consider K$^+$ independently. The experimental results can be accounted for, at least in principle, by two hypotheses. (i) A primary, electrogenic K$^+$ pump, driven by ATP (or a related phosphoryl donor) and regulated by the proton circulation; efflux would require a separate, ATP-dependent pathway. (ii) A secondary porter that is activated by ATP and energized by the proton circulation. To account for the fact that the K$^+$ concentration gradient exceeds the membrane potential, one must either invoke the transport of additional charge, perhaps K$^+$/Na$^+$ or K$^+$/H$^+$ symport; or else the kind of localized proton pathways favored by Kell (41) and before him, by Williams (42).

It is not possible to discriminate between these mechanisms by use of intact cells, so we turned to everted vesicles. To our disappointment, vesicles loaded with ^{86}Rb$^+$ did not expel the isotope when incubated with ATP. Inspired by the observation of Brey et al. (43), that a K$^+$/H$^+$ antiporter in E. coli is extremely sensitive to trypsin, we tried protease inhibitors and that did the trick. Protease-protected vesicles loaded with ^{86}Rb$^+$ exchange radioactivity with external Rb$^+$ with a half-time of about 30 min; upon addition of ATP, exchange is markedly accelerated (t/$_2$ = 2 min). We have yet to convince ourselves that this exchange reflects the K$^+$ transport system, but we live in hope that the problem is, at long last, open to biochemical analysis.

OUTLOOK. Time to pull together the threads of this unfinished enterprise. Our present conception of cation exchanges in S. faecalis is considerably more elaborate than that which sufficed in 1972, but clearly stems from its ancestor by descent with modification. The plasma membrane of S. faecalis contains, not one ion-transport ATPase but at least three: F_1F_0-ATPase, Na^+-ATPase and Ca^{2+}-ATPase. A fourth ATPase, recently solubilized by R. Leimgruber and A. Abrams (personal communication) is in search of a function; a K^+-ATPase has not been detected but may yet turn up. We do not know whether this compex pattern is general among bacteria, or a special feature of streptococci; for the present we favor the latter view, and suspect that a reliance on multiple ion-transport ATPases may be an adaptation to the limited capacity of an F_1F_0-ATPase to pump protons (37). But the distinction between primary, ATP-linked pumps and secondary porters no longer seems as sharp as it once did, and may blur still further should the notion of mopeds prove correct. One feels some sense of loss for the elegant simplicities of ion transport as we saw it a decade ago, but we might have anticipated the outcome: by their very nature, the forces that shape evolution will create architecture that is baroque, if not downright rococo.

REFERENCES

1. Mitchell, P. (1961) Nature 191, 144-148.
2. Mitchell, P. (1962) Biochem. Soc. Symp. 22, 142-168.
3. Mitchell, P. (1966) Biol. Rev. Cambridge Phil. Soc. 41, 445-502.
4. Mitchell, P. (1970) Symp. Soc. Gen. Microbiol. 20, 121-166.
5. Mitchell, P. (1976) Biochem. Soc. Trans. 4, 399-430.
6. Harold, F.M. (1972) Bacteriol. Rev. 36, 172-230.
7. Harold, F.M. (1977) Curr. Top. Bioenerg. 6, 83-149.
8. Ritchey, T.W., and Seeley, H.W., Jr. (1975) J. Gen. Microbiol. 85, 220-228.

9. Harold, F.M., and Baarda, J.R. (1968) J. Bacteriol. 96, 2025-2034.

10. Harold, F.M., Baarda, J.R., Baron, C., and Abrams, A. (1969) J. Biol. Chem. 244, 2261-2268.

11. Harold, F.M., Pavlasova, E., and Baarda, J.R. (1970) Biochim. Biophys. Acta 196, 235-244.

12. Harold, F.M., and Papineau, D. (1972) J. Membrane Biol. 8, 27-44.

13. Maloney, P.C., and Wilson, T.H. (1975) J. Membrane Biol. 25, 285-310.

14. Maloney, P.C. (1977) J. Bacteriol. 132, 564-575.

15. Maloney, P.C. and Schattschneider, S. (1980) FEBS Lett. 110, 3347-340.

16. Abrams, A. (1976) In: The Enzymes of Biological Membranes (A. Martonosi, ed), p 57-73, Plenum Publishing Co., New York.

17. Fillingame, R.H. (1980) Annu. Rev. Biochem. 49, 1079-1113.

18. Harold, F.M., and Papineau, D. (1972) J. Membrane Biol. 8, 45-62.

19. Kobayashi, H., Van Brunt, J., and Harold, F.M. (1978) J. Biol. Chem. 253, 2085-2092.

20. Rosen, B.P., and McClees, J.S. (1974) Proc. Natl. Acad. Sci. U.S.A. 71, 5042-5046.

21. Bhattacharyya, P., and Barnes, E.M. (1976) J. Biol. Chem. 251, 5614-5619.

22. Rosen, B.P. (1981) In: Membrane Transport of Calcium (E. Carafoli, ed). Academic Press, (New York London), in press.

23. Heefner, D.L., and Harold, F.M. (1980) J. Biol. Chem. 255, 11396-11402.

24. Heefner, D.L., Kobayashi, H., and Harold, F.M. (1980) J. Biol. Chem. 255, 11403-11407.

25. West, I.C., and Mitchell, P. (1972) J. Bioenerg. 3, 445-462.

26. Cecchini, G., and Koch, A.L.   (1975)   J. Bacteriol. <u>123</u>, 187-195.

27. Booth, I.R., Mitchell, W.J., and Hamilton, W.A.   (1979) Biochem. J. <u>182</u>, 687-696.

28. Flagg, J.L. and Wilson, T.H.   (1977)   J. Membrane Biol. <u>31</u>, 233-255.

29. Ramos, S., and Kaback, H.R.   (1977)   Biochemistry <u>16</u>, 854-859.

30. West, I.C. (1980) Biochim. Biophys. Acta <u>604</u>, 91-126.

31. Schuldiner, S., and Fishkes, H.   (1978)   Biochemistry <u>17</u>, 706-710.

32. Bhattacharyya, P. and Barnes, E.M.   (1978)   J. Biol. Chem. <u>253</u>, 3848-3851.

33. Beck, J.C., and Rosen, B.P.   (1979)   Arch. Biochem. Biophys. <u>194</u>, 208-214.

34. Niven, D.F. and MacLeod, R.A.   (1978)   J. Bacteriol. <u>134</u>, 737-743.

35. Mandel, K.A., Guffanti, A.A., and Krulwich, T.A.   (1980) J. Biol. Chem. <u>255</u>, 7391-7396.

36. Lanyi, J.K. (1979) Biochim. Biophys. Acta <u>559</u>, 377-398.

37. Kashket, E.R., Blanchard, A.G., and Metzger, W.C.   (1980) J. Bacteriol. <u>143</u>, 128-134.

38. Skulachev, V.P. (1978) FEBS Lett. <u>87</u>, 171-179.

39. Bakker, E.P., and Harold, F.M.   (1980)   J. Biol. Chem. <u>255</u>, 433-440.

40. Rhoads, D.B., and Epstein, W.   (1977)   J. Biol. Chem. <u>252</u>, 1394-1401.

41. Kell, D.B. (1979) Biochim. Biophys. Acta <u>549</u>, 55-99.

42. Williams, R.J.P. (1978) Biochim. Biophys. Acta <u>505</u>, 1-44.

43. Brey, R.M., Rosen, B.P., and Sorensen, E.N.   (1980)   J. Biol. Chem. <u>255</u>, 39-44.

PROTON CURRENT AND DNA TRANSPORT

L. Grinius

Department of Biochemistry and Biophysics
Vilnius University, Vilnius, 232031, U.S.S.R.

INTRODUCTION

Life is impossible without the flow of free energy and information across cell boundaries. The chemiosmotic theory formulated by Mitchell (1-4) described the flow of free energy. According to the theory, power is transmitted by the proton current across the membrane where reversible proton-tranlocating enzymes are located (see 5,6). The transmission of power by proticity requires a membrane that is impermeable to protons. Therefore the ability of nucleic acids to penetrate bacterial and mitochondrial membranes could be rather puzzling. The process of DNA transport across membranes was demonstrated almost forty years ago when Avery and colleagues (7) showed that pneumococci become genetically transformed because of the exogenous DNA uptake. Bacteria are also able to take up isolated phage DNA, the process resulting in the synthesis of new phage particles inside the host cell (8,9). DNA can also be transferred from one intact bacterial cell to another during the sex-conjugation process (10). The uptake of exogenous DNA starts with the adsorption of a donor to the host cell surface. The donor DNA then reaches the cytoplasmic membrane

V. P. Skulachev and Peter C. Hinkle (eds.), Chemiosmotic Proton Circuits in Biological Membranes
in honor of Peter Mitchell   ISBN 0-201-07398-6

of the host and is linearly transported into the cytoplasm.

The aim of this review is to present the basic principles of DNA penetration across biological membranes and construct the simplest working hypothesis that could explain the experimental evidence presently available.

Role of inorganic ions. At neutral pH the DNA molecule is a polyanion because of phosphate group dissociation. Since both respiration and ATP hydrolysis generate an electrical potential across the cytoplasmic membrane ("negative" inside) (see 5,6), to enter the cell DNA should be either transported together with cations or exchanged for anions. There is no evidence available that DNA uptake by bacteria depends on the presence of specific monovalent cations. For example, cells of B. subtilis take up the exogenous DNA equally well in the presence of Na^+, K^+ or Li^+ (11). However, B. subtilis needs Mg^{++} for DNA uptake, but Mg^{++} can be substituted by Ca^{++}, Ba^{++} or Sr^{++}, while such divalent ions as Mn^{++}, Co^{++}, Fe^{++}, Zn^{++}, Cu^{++} or Ni^{++} show little, if any, effect (11).

The process of phage T5 DNA entrance depends specifically on Ca^{++} (12) while for T4 phage the presence of Ca^{++} is not required. The uptake of DNA by both pneumococci (13) and S. pneumoniae (14) also needs Ca^{++} specifically.

Is DNA transported across the membrane together with divalent ions? Some light was cast on this problem by the experiments of Morrison (15) with B. subtilis indicating that only the initiation of DNA transport is sensitive to EDTA. After initiation, DNA transport is resistant to the chelator. These data suggest that divalent ions are required

to initiate but not to continue DNA transport during B.
subtilis genetic transformation.

Pilot-proteins. During phage invasion both nucleic acid and
some phage coat proteins enter the host cell in approximately equimolar amounts and their kinetics of penetration
are similar (see 16). On the basis of these experimental
data Kornberg (17) has formulated a hypothesis implying the
existence of a pilot-protein that leads phage nucleic acid
across the membrane into the cytoplasm. Contrary to this,
phage lambda has no known pilot-protein (see 16). Perhaps
the pilot-protein for phage lambda DNA could be of membrane
origin.

     The growing body of evidence also indicates that pro-
teins are involved in DNA transport during genetic transformation. In the early stages of S. pneumoniae and S.
sanguis transformation, the donor DNA forms a complex with a
protein of 19.5 or 15.5 kilodaltons, respectively (18,19).
Initially the complex formed is located outside the cytoplasmic membrane of S. sanguis and could be released from
the cell under conditions promoting spheroplast formation
(20). The donor DNA-protein complex has been found inside
the S. sanguis cells as well, indicating that the entire
complex is transported across the membrane (20). Despite
the isolation of a similar complex from B. subtilis during
genetic transformation (21), additional experiments are
necessary to prove that the DNA-protein complex penetrates
the membrane.

     A protein bound to either single-stranded or double-
stranded DNA but not to ribonucleic acid has been isolated

by osmotic shock treatment of growing H. influenzae cells
(22). Certain mutant strains of H. influenzae defective in
DNA uptake were found to be deficient in this DNA binding
protein, suggesting the protein participates in DNA transport (22).

No data seem to be available at present on the structure of the nucleoprotein complex formed during the initial
stages of genetic transformation. Nevertheless, it seems
reasonable to extend the idea of pilot-protein to DNA uptake
in bacterial transformation as well. In this case DNA-
binding protein located on the outside surface of the cytoplasmic membrane seems to be the pilot leading DNA through
the membrane.

Rate of DNA transport. DNA transport proceeds with a rate
of at least $3 \cdot 10^3$ base pairs per second during phage T4
infection (16). Thus the rate of DNA transport, 0.3 milliseconds per base pair, is comparable to the rate of electron
transfer along the respiratory chain. According to the
estimation of Brinton (23), the rate of conjugational DNA
transport is about 600 base pairs of DNA per second while
during the genetic transformation of B. subtilis about 55
base pairs of DNA are transferred into the cell per second
(24).

Role of ATP. DNA transport during both phage infection and
genetic transformation can proceed despite the depletion of
intracellular ATP caused by treatment of cells with arsenate
(25,26). Although the arsenate treated cells may have a
low, but sufficient amount of ATP to activate the DNA
transport system, the involvement of ATP as an energy source

seems very unlikely. On the other hand, conjugational DNA
transport is sensitive to arsenate treatment (27). In this
case the role of ATP has not yet been clarified. ATP could
be involved in DNA transport as well as to provide energy
for either the synthesis of F-pili or for DNA unwinding
required for such transport.

Requirement for protonmotive force. A growing body of
evidence indicates that the protonmotive force is involved
in DNA transport across the bacterial membrane. It is well
known that uncouplers of oxidative phosphorylation cause
inhibition of DNA uptake in the early stages of genetic
transformation (see 28). It has been shown recently that
the inhibitory effect of the uncouplers on the transformation of B. subtilis correlates with their effect on the cell
membrane potential (25). The inhibition of B. subtilis
transformation by uncouplers occurs despite the lack of
their effect on ATP levels in the cell (25). Under these
conditions ATP is synthesized by glycolysis. Uncouplers
also inhibit DNA transport during both phage infection
(26,29) and bacterial conjugation (27).

Recently we attempted to reveal the role of the two
components of the protonmotive force, the membrane potential
($\Delta\psi$) and the pH gradient (ΔpH), in DNA transport. To change
the value of $\Delta\psi$, valinomycin, a K^+ ionophore, was used. The
value of ΔpH was changed using nigericin, an ionophore which
exchanges K^+ for H^+. We found that valinomycin caused a
strong inhibition of DNA uptake during B. subtilis transformation whereas nigericin was relatively ineffective (25).
On the other hand, the inhibitory effect of nigericin was
potentiated by valinomycin and vice versa, indicating the

necessity of both $\Delta\psi$ and ΔpH in the DNA uptake during genetic transformation.

A similar pattern of inhibitory effects was found for E. coli invasion by phage T4 (30). The process of phage DNA transport was shown to be sensitive to valinomycin and relatively resistant to nigericin. The data were interpreted as evidence that $\Delta\psi$ is required for phage DNA entrance into the cell. To explain the resistance to nigericin the authors suggested that ΔpH is not involved in phage DNA transport (30). Thus, there is still some uncertainty concerning the role of ΔpH in DNA transport, but it is certain that $\Delta\psi$ is required.

The question arises whether the protonmotive force is required only to initiate phage DNA entrance into the cell or whether it is involved in the overall DNA transport process. To solve this problem the observation of Mekshenkov and Guseinov (32) indicating that the rate of phage T4 DNA entry into E. coli was reduced by lowering the temperature was very useful. This enabled us to start experiments on the requirement of the protonmotive force at different stages of E. coli infection by phage T4 (see 31). A mutant of E. coli (unc A) devoid of F_1 ATPase was used throughout the experiments. The respiratory chain was the sole generator of the protonmotive force in these cells (33). The cell-phage complexes were formed at 10°C and then exposed to cyanide at different stages of the phage DNA entry into the cell (see 31). Phage DNA transport was greatly inhibited by cyanide if the cell-phage complexes were exposed to cyanide during phage DNA entry into the cell. On the other hand, cyanide caused little, if any, effect if added after the completion of DNA entrance. These data lead us to conclude

that the protonmotive force was required for the continuation of the phage DNA entry.

Recently a threshold value of $\Delta\psi$ required for phage DNA
entrance into the cell has been measured in quantitative
studies of the energy supply for phage T4 infection (34).
According to the authors, the decrease of $\Delta\psi$ to -100 mV had
no effect on phage DNA entrance. Below this value a pronounced inhibitory effect was observed. To determine DNA
entry these authors used a defective T4 phage, mutant in
gene 2. On entry the DNA of this phage is rapidly degraded
to acid – soluble material by the cytoplasmic enzyme exonuclease V. However, phage $T42^-$ is able to infect exo-
nuclease V deficient $\underline{E}$. $\underline{coli}$ and thereafter to produce
mutant phage particles. The appearance of acid-soluble DNA
degradation products, after infection of exonuclease V^+
cells by phage $T42^-$, was used as a criterion for DNA entry
into the cytoplasm (30). It is possible, however, that the
degradation of phage DNA upon entrance could create an
additional driving force for DNA transport and that $\Delta\psi$
could be required only to initiate the mutant phage DNA
entry.

Hypothesis. The chemiosmotic theory of energy coupling
provides an excellent conceptual framework to explain the
accumulated evidence and to propose new experimental approaches
to the mechanism of DNA transport. The principle of aniso-
trophic ligand conduction, formulated by Mitchell, enabled
us to suggest (35) the presence of spatially oriented porter
in the membrane that conducts DNA together with protons.
According to this hypothesis, DNA transport is visualized as
a vectorial translocation of chemical groups of this poly-

deoxyribonucleotide across the membrane. The translocation
occurs down the group potential that depends on the value of
the protonmotive force. According to the mechanism proposed, DNA and DNA-binding protein, in Kornberg's terminology
"pilot-protein" (17), form a positively charged complex by
binding protons on the outer surface of the cytoplasmic
membrane. The interaction of the complex with the membrane
results in the formation of a DNA-conducting porter in the
membrane. Owing to protonmotive force the complex moves
across the membrane into the cytoplasm and there liberates
protons. Therefore, both $\Delta\psi$ and ΔpH are required to initiate DNA transport. However, the initiation will depend
only on $\Delta\psi$ if the pilot-protein can only bind protons but
not release them in the cytoplasm.

There is no evidence yet that other proteins except
pilot-protein are transported across the membrane together
with DNA. Pilot-protein is too small to cover the whole DNA
molecule. Therefore the question arises, how does that part
of DNA, which is free from the pilot-protein penetrate the
membrane. One may suggest that to enter the porter the
phosphate groups and nitrogen-containing bases of DNA free
from the pilot-protein bind protons. Then the rise in
energy of the system accompanying the DNA protonation at
physiological pH could be energetically compensated because
of the protonated DNA interaction with the porter. The
compensation effect could also be achieved since one protonated monomeric residue of DNA always leaves the membrane
while another one is forced into it. Thus, the function of
pilot-protein could be to overcome the energetic barrier
upon DNA entrance into DNA-conducting porter and thereafter
to link DNA transport with the proton current (see Fig. 1).

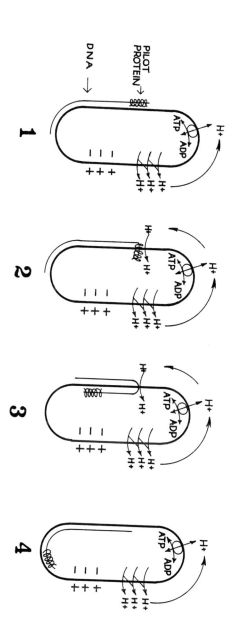

Figure 1. Coupling of DNA Transport to Proton Current.

Unfortunately, little is known about the molecular architecture of the DNA-conducting porter. It seems reasonable that both proteins and phospholipids are involved in the formation of the porter. For example, the E. coli protein coded by the ton B gene was found to be located in the cytoplasmic membrane (36). This protein is required for both phage T4 and ϕ80 to infect E. coli. The membrane also contains the product of pts M gene that is needed for phage lambda DNA entry into the cell (37). Nevertheless, the interaction of these proteins with phage DNA remains to be elucidated.

The experimental results allow some speculation about the physico-chemical features of the DNA-conducting porter. For example, in the case of phage T4 DNA transport the porter must be large enough to permit the entrance of double-stranded DNA, the diameter of which is close to 20 Å. If the porter consisted of an aqueous channel, it could conduct protons across the membrane even in the absence of DNA, which would cause energy dissipation. The experimental data indicate a low permeability of the cytoplasmic membrane to protons thus contradicting such a possibility. However, the adsorption of a few phage T4 particles on E. coli leads to the dissipation of the protomotive force (29,38). It seems reasonable that the deenergization occurs as a result of the interaction of the phage tail with the cytoplasmic membrane. Thus, some proteins of the phage tail presumably increase the membrane permeability to protons. During the cell interaction with a single phage particle the increase in permeability seems to be small because of the lack of an uncoupling effect (29,38). Cell de-energization is also observed upon interaction with phage ghosts, particles lacking

a DNA molecule (39). The effect of ghosts suggests the
formation of an aqueous channel in the membrane but its'
participation in DNA transport seems questionable. The
bonds involved in DNA interaction with the porter are probably of a hydrophobic character. Some energetic difficulties
arise while DNA is transported from aqueous to hydrophobic
environment because some hydrogen bonds between phosphate
groups and water molecules have to be broken for each nucleotide unit entering the hydrophobic phase. These difficulties
will be overcome if protonated DNA within the porter forms
hydrogen bonds with suitable atoms.

There is evidence (40-43) that conversion of double-
stranded DNA to single-stranded fragments is coupled to DNA
uptake by some bacteria. This is often taken as a proof of
the hypothesis formulated by Lacks (40,41), that DNA transport is catalyzed by membrane-bound DNase forming an aqueous
channel. Lacks assumes that to drive DNA transport DNase
clips away one strand of DNA molecule while the remaining
single strand passes through the channel into the cell.
Lacks' hypothesis does not explain the ability of bacteria
to take up single-stranded DNA. The necessity of the protonmotive force for DNA transport also cannot easily fit within
the framework of this hypothesis.

It seems to be more reasonable to account for the role
of DNase as follows. Double-stranded DNA is converted by
DNase to single-stranded fragments, which bind the pilot-
protein and then enter the porter. The specificity of the
DNA-conducting porter seems to be determined by the mode of
the interaction of the pilot-protein with the membrane
components. Thus, the physico-chemical properties of the
pilot-protein and the porter determine whether or not single-

stranded DNA penetrates the membrane. The presence of DNase
seems to be required if the porter conducts double-stranded
DNA. This requirement could be by-passed if either the
porter is rearranged or single-stranded DNA is used instead
of double-stranded. The published experimental evidence
(44-46) fits in quite well with such a point of view.

A possible structure of the DNA-conducting porter is a
DNA-translocase which rotates in the hydrophobic phase of
the membrane. According to V.P. Skulachev (personal communication) the prototype of such a rotating device could be
the molecular engine consuming the proton current to rotate
bacterial flagella. The frequency of flagellar rotation is
about 50 revolutions per second (47). If one base pair of
DNA is translocated across the membrane per revolution of
the translocase, then the enzyme translocating phage T4 DNA
should rotate with a frequency of at least 3000 revolutions
per second, which is probably too rapid to be possible. If
the frequency of rotation is the same as that of the flagellar rotor, the enzyme must translocate 60 base pairs of
phage T4 DNA per revolution.

Data published by several authors (30,33) indicates
that the rate of phage T4 DNA entrance into E. coli is
dependent on temperature. At 10°C, the rate of phage DNA
entry is reduced at least ten-fold. Therefore, according to
the concept of the rotating DNA translocase, one has to
assume that this huge molecule could rotate within the
viscous membrane with a frequency of about 5 revolutions per
second. An alternative to the rotating DNA translocase is a
transmembrane hydrophobic channel where DNA transport
requires minimal changes of conformation of proteins and

phospholipids. Additional experiments are required to make a choice between these alternatives.

ACKNOWLEDGEMENTS. The author is greatly indebted to Prof. V.P. Skulachev and Dr. A.V. Glagolev for valuable discussion and to Mrs. N. Vanagine for correcting the English of this paper.

REFERENCES

1. Mitchell, P. (1963) Biochem. Soc. Symp. 22, 142-168.
2. Mitchell, P. (1972) J. Bioenergetics 3, 5-24.
3. Mitchell, P. (1973) J. Bioenergetics 4, 63-91.
4. Mitchell, P. (1973) in Mechanisms in Bioenergetics (Azzone, G.F., Ernster, L., Papa, S., Quagliariello, E. and Silipardi, N., eds.), pp. 177-201, Academic Press, New York.
5. Haddock, B.A. and Jones, C.W. (1977) Bacteriol. Rev. 41, 47-99.
6. Harold, F.M. (1977) Curr. Top. Bioenerg. 6, 83-149.
7. Avery, O., McLeod, C. and McCarty, M. (1944) J. Exp. Med. 79, 137-158.
8. Guthrie, G.D. and Sinsheimer, R.L. (1963) Biochim. Biophys. Acta 72, 290-297.
9. Mandel, M. and Higa, A. (1970) J. Mol. Biol. 53, 159-162.
10. Lederberg, J. (1956) J. Bacteriol. 71, 497-498.
11. Young, F.E. and Spizizen, J. (1963) J. Bacteriol. 86, 392-400.
12. Lanni, Y.T. (1968) Bacteriol. Rev. 32, 227-242.
13. Seto, H. and Tomasz, A. (1976) J. Bacteriol. 126, 1113-1118.
14. Ronda, C., Lopez, R., Portoles, A. and Garcia, E. (1979) FEMS Microbiol. Lett. 6, 309-312.
15. Morrison, D.A. (1971) J. Bacteriol. 108, 38-44.
16. Goldberg, E.B. (1980) in Receptors and Recognition. Series Virus Receptors (Randall, L. and Phillipson, L., eds.), Chapman and Hall, London.
17. Kornberg, A. (1974) DNA Synthesis, Freeman, San Francisco.

18. Morrison, D.A. and Baker, M.F. (1979) Nature (London)
     282, 215–217.
19. Raina, J.L. and Ravin, A.W. (1980) Biochem. Biophys.
     Res. Commun. 93, 228–234.
20. Raina, J.L., Metzer, E. and Ravin, A.W. (1979) Molec.
     Gen. Genet. 170, 249–259.
21. Pieniazek, D., Piechowska, M. and Venema, G. (1977)
     Molec. Gen. Genet. 156, 251–]61.
22. Sutrina, S.L. and Scocca, J.A. (1979) J. Bacteriol.
     139, 1021–1027.
23. Brinton, C.C. (1965) Trans. N.Y. Acad. Sci. 277,
     1003–1054.
24. Strauss, N. (1965) J. Bacteriol. 89, 288–293.
25. Chaustova, L.P., Grinius, L.L., Griniuviene, B.B.
     Jasaitis, A.A., Kadziauskas, J.P. and Kiausinyte, R.V.
     1980) Eur. J. Biochem. 103, 349–357.
26. Kalaseuskaite, E., Grinius, L., Kadisaite, D. and
     Jasaitis, A. (1980) FEBS Lett. 117, 232–236.
27. Berzinskiene, J.A., Zizaite, L.J., Baronaite, Z.A.
     and Grinius, L.L. (1980) Biokhimiya 45, 1103–1112.
28. Notani, N.K. and Setlow, J. (1974) Progr. Nucleic Acid
     Res. 14, 39–100.
29. Kalaseuskaite, E.V., Armalyte, V.K. and Grinius, L.L.
     (1979) Biokhimiya 44, 221–232.
30. Labedan, B. and Goldberg, E.B. (1979) Proc. Natl.
     Acad. Sci. U.S.A. 76, 4669–4674.
31. Kalasauskaite, E. and Grinius, L. (1979) FEBS Lett.
     99, 287–291.
32. Mekshenkov, M.I. and Guseinov, R.D. (1971) Molekularnaya
     Biologya 5, 445–452.
33. Grinius, L. and Brazenaite, J. (1976) FEBS Lett. 62,
     186–189.
34. Labedan, B., Heller, K.B., Jasaitis, A.A., Wilson,
     T.H. and Goldberg, E.B. (1980) Biochem. Biophys. Res.
     Commun. 93, 625–630.
35. Grinius L. (1980) FEBS Lett. 113, 1–10.
36. Plastow, G.S. and Holland, I.B. (1979) Biochem.
     Biophys. Res. Commun. 90, 1007–1014.
37. Elliot, J. and Arber, W. (1978) Molec. Gen. Gent.
     161, 1–8.
38. Hantke, K. and Braun, V. (1974) Virology 53, 225–236.
39. Duckworth, D.H. (1970) Bacteriol. Rev. 34, 344–363.
40. Lacks, S. (1962) J. Mol. Biol. 5, 119–131.
41. Lacks, S. and Greenberg, B. (1976) J. Mol. Biol. 101,
     255–275.

42. Lacks, S. (1979) J. Bacteriol. <u>138</u>, 404-409.
43. Venema, G. and Canosi, U. (1980) Mol. Gen. Genet. <u>179</u>, 1-11.
44. Postel, E.H. and Goodgal, S.H. (1967) J. Mol. Biol. <u>28</u>, 247-259.
45. Chilton, M.D. and Hall, B.D. (1968) J. Mol. Biol. <u>34</u>, 439-451.
46. Miao, R. and Guild, W.B. (1970) J. Bacteriol. <u>101</u>, 361-364.
47. Weibull, C. (1960) in <u>The Bacteria</u> (Gunsalus, I.C. and Stainer, P.I., eds.), vol. 1, pp. 153-205, Academic Press, New York.

HEAT GENERATION BY MITOCHONDRIA

David Nicholls and Rebecca Locke

Neurochemistry Laboratory, Department of
Psychiatry, Dundee University, Dundee,
Scotland, U.K.

The conventional chemiosmotic proton circuit, Fig. 1, couples respiration tightly with ATP synthesis. In order to utilize mitochondria for heat generation, it is necessary to exploit or circumvent this automatic respiratory control. Examination of chemiosmotic first principles would indicate that this could be accomplished in three ways: first, the respiratory chain can be modified such that electron transfer no longer results in proton translocation; second, proton re-entry into the matrix can be uncoupled from ATP synthesis; third, a dissipative extra-mitochondrial ATPase can be formed to free respiration from the constraints of normal cellular ATP turnover.

Examples of all three possibilities can be demonstrated. A modified respiratory chain was originally suggested as a possible means of thermogenesis in liver mitochondria, a mobile cyt $\underline{c}$ connecting the outer membrane NADH-cyt $\underline{b}_5$ pathway directly to cytochrome oxidase [1]. More recently, Arum Lily mitochondria have been shown to possess a CN-resistant

V. P. Skulachev and Peter C. Hinkle (eds.), Chemiosmotic Proton Circuits in Biological Membranes
in honor of Peter Mitchell   ISBN 0-201-07398-6

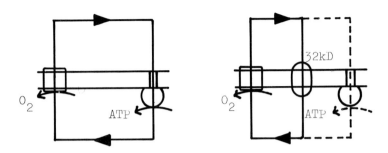

Fig. 1   Conventional proton circuit (a) and modified proton
         circuit of brown fat mitochondria (b).

non-translocating respiratory chain which can generate
sufficient heat to distill off insect-attractant amines [2].
The extra-mitochondrial ATPase mechanism is adopted in
shivering, and by certain insects such as the bumble bee [3]
which dissipate ATP by the parallel activation of fructose-
1,6-bisphosphatase and phosphofructokinase.

        Brown fat adopts the second stratagem [4]. Although
the tissue accounts for at most 1 - 2% of total body mass,
sympathetic nerve stimulation of this tissue can increase its
heat production until it becomes the major source of thermogenesis [5].

        The two questions relevant to bioenergetics are, by
which mechanism is the energy dissipated,and how is the
process regulated? Although the first problem has been solved
the second remains problematical.

        Isolated brown fat mitochondria (BFM) from thermogen-
ically active animals require special incubation conditions
before uncoupler-releasable respiratory control can be seen.

Firstly a purine nucleotide such as ADP, ATP or CDP must be present in the medium and secondly endogenous fatty acids must be removed [4]. With these provisos, the BFM behave conventionally in terms of respiratory control and maintenance of a high $\Delta\mu_H+$, although ATP synthesis is slow due to the relative lack of ATP synthetase [4].

There is compelling evidence that omission of purine nucleotides from the incubation medium activates a specific proton short-circuit present in the inner membrane:

a. Oxygen pulse experiments indicate that nucleotide omission is without effect on proton extrusion by the respiratory chain, but accelerates proton re-entry [6].

b. Non-respiring BFM swell rapidly in KCNS or K-acetate when either valinomycin or nigericin are added, showing that proton permeability is not rate-limiting. Proton permeability becomes limiting when nucleotide is added and now the mitochondria swell only in KCNS plus valinomycin or K-acetate plus nigericin, unless FCCP is present [7].

c. When the membrane proton conductance $(C_m H^+)$ is calculated from parallel measurements of respiration and $\Delta\mu_H+$ it is found that removal of exogenous nucleotide increases the proton conductance from 1 to 10 nmol $H^+.min^{-1}.mg^{-1}.mV^{-1}$ [6]. This high conductance allows a $\Delta\mu_H+$ of only some 80mV to be maintained, with no demonstrable respiratory control [6].

The purine nucleotides bind to a limited number of high affinity binding sites on the outer face of the inner membrane without covalent modification [8]. The nature of these binding sites has been clarified by photoaffinity labelling using an azido derivative of ATP [9]. It was found that the nucleotide interacts with two polypeptides, a 30kD protein which is protected by atractylate (the adenine

nucleotide translocator) and a 32kD protein which is protected
from labelling by GDP and can be therefore identified as the
"short-circuit protein" [9]. Recently the 32kD protein has
been purified from hamster mitochondria [10].

The total amount of 32kD protein present in BFM
correlates well with the thermogenic status of the animal. It
can be increased by cold-adaptation [9,11] and,in agreement
with recent findings that BFM energy dissipation may be
crucial in the control of obesity [12], by over-feeding [13].
In the cold-adapted hamster the 32kD protein can amount to
10% of the inner membraneprotein [9].

BFM show in a particularly clear-cut manner the relat-
ionship between $\Delta\mu_H^+$ and respiration. If C_mH^+ is progressively
increased by either decreasing the nucleotide concentration
or titrating in FCCP, the same response is found: respiration
increases as a linear function of the decrease in $\Delta\mu_H^+$ until
the potential has fallen to about 160mV when no respiratory
control remains [6]. Any further increase in C_mH^+ therefore
produces a decrease in $\Delta\mu_H^+$ with no further increase in
respiration [6]. The relationship between $\Delta\mu_H^+$ and the Gibbs
energy for ATP synthesis has been measured over a range of
potentials [14] and the results indicate that 3 protons are
required for the synthesis and export of one ATP in these
mitochondria.

PHYSIOLOGICAL REGULATION OF THE 32kD PROTEIN

In brown adipocytes it would be advantageous if the
proton conductance of the 32kD protein could be matched to the
thermogenic status of the tissue, since during thermogenesis

a high $C_m H^+$ is necessary to permit uncontrolled respiration, while by contrast a low $C_m H^+$ is required in non-thermogenic conditions to prevent collapse of $\Delta\mu_H+$ under the conditions of decreased substrate supply. The intra-cellular signal which regulates the conductance is as yet ill-defined. Hypothetical candidates may be divided into two types. Self-regulated messengers would be normal intermediates of hormonally-activated lipolysis, such as fatty acids or fatty acyl CoA, whose levels in the cytosol would adjust automatically upon initiation and termination of lipolysis. Independent messengers would not be normal intermediates, but would require some independent regulation; examples of these which have been discussed include a changed cytosolic adenine nucleotide concentration and an increased cytosolic pH.

Although guanine nucleotides are slightly more effective than adenine nucleotides in inhibiting the 32kD protein in vitro [4], the much higher concentration of the latter in the cytosol suggests that they might have the more physiological role in the inhibition of the protein. However, since the 32kD protein has been shown in vitro to have a high affinity for adenine nucleotides [8,14] the millimolar concentrations of adenine nucleotides present in the cytosol would be expected to result in permanent occupation (and hence inhibition) of the protein. One hypothetical means of displacing the nucleotide would be to increase the cytosolic pH, since nucleotide binding to the 32kD protein is very pH sensitive [8]. Chinet et al. [15] have suggested that noradrenaline induced changes in cytosolic pH could be one method of modifying the nucleotide binding and consequently the proton conductance.

An alternative method for displacing nucleotides from

the 32kD protein would be to increase the concentration of
another factor or "anti-nucleotide" which would compete with
the nucleotide for the binding site whilst not itself
inhibiting $C_m H^+$. Cannon et al. [16] have suggested acyl CoA
as such a factor, from the ability of high long-chain acyl
CoA concentrations to reverse the GDP-induced inhibition of
BFM swelling in KCl plus valinomycin. Since Cl^- appears to
permeate by the same nucleotide-sensitive pathway as protons
[4], these authors reasoned that the acyl CoA acted by
displacing nucleotide from the 32kD protein and re-introducing
Cl^- (and by extension proton) permeability. However, while
this self-regulating mechanism is attractive, in this study
the results were obtained with levels of acyl CoA similar to
those known to induce detergent artifacts, and therefore the
physiological relevance of these studies cannot be readily
assessed.

Fatty acids are alternative candidates for the
putative self-regulating cytosolic messenger. At first sight
fatty acids might appear improbable physiological regulators
in view of their apparent non-specificity in mitochondrial
uncoupling, since this can be demonstrated in a variety of
mitochondria. There are however a number of observations,
which taken together suggest that fatty acids themselves are
powerful candidates for the role of physiological self-
regulating messenger. First, freshly prepared BFM have
significant amounts of free fatty acids associated with them
[17]. Even in the presence of purine nucleotides these mitochondria have a proton conductance sufficient to permit
uncontrolled respiration . Removal of these fatty acids, by
albumin or by their oxidation induces respiratory control
[17,18]. Re-addition of very small amounts of fatty acids

induces a thirty-fold greater increase in C_mH^+ per fatty acid bound than in the case of liver mitochondria [17]. Since this can be observed in the absence of CoA or exogenous ATP, the possibility of conversion to fatty acyl CoA under these conditions can be eliminated.

A specific fatty acid induced overriding of respiratory control can readily be demonstrated (Fig. 2). BFM were incubated in a medium designed to approximate, in terms of Mg^{2+}, P_i, ATP and temperature, to the physiological cytosol. The ATP concentration is sufficient to inhibit the 32kD protein, with the result that pyruvate can be oxidized at only 16% of the uncontrolled rate; this then corresponds to the non-thermogenic state of the tissue, the mitochondrial substrate being glycolytic. When a controlled infusion of palmitate is initiated, in order to mimick the effect of hormonally-activated lipolysis, respiration responds immediately by increasing to match the rate of fatty acid supply. Maximal respiration is obtained by the time as little as 5 nmol/mg protein has accumulated in the medium. On terminating the infusion (to mimick the return to non-thermogenic conditions) respiration reverts to the controlled rate with pyruvate as substrate. This respiratory increase is not observed with palmitoyl-carnitine infusion (Fig. 2b) or with palmitate and liver mitochondria (not shown).

With isolated BFM there is therefore clear evidence that fatty acids can selectively modulate the membrane conductance to allow uncontrolled respiration. It remains to be established whether fatty acids themselves, or some derivative, induce the conductance increase, and whether they act at the 32kD protein, or at some independent locus. The

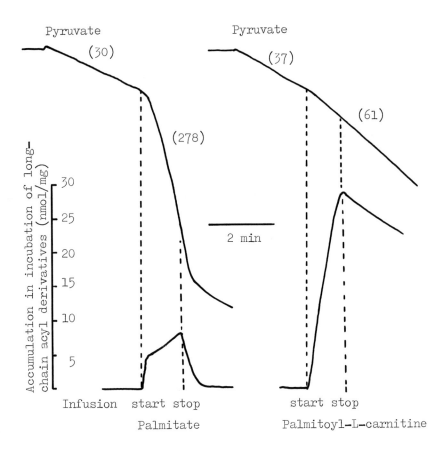

Fig. 2   The respiratory response of hamster BFM to the
infusion of palmitate and palmitoyl-carnitine.
BFM were incubated in the presence of CoA,
carnitine and high (4mM) ATP. Palmitate infusion
reversibly releases respiratory control.

latter would however raise the problem of the role of the
32kD protein. If fatty acids can be shown to modify the 32kD
protein, the mechanism will require investigation, since
fatty acids do not appear to influence nucleotide binding to
the protein [8,17], and do not appear to affect the ability
of nucleotides to inhibit the Cl⁻ permeability of the 32kD

protein [7].

CONCLUSION

Such progress as has been made over the last ten
years towards an understanding of the mechanism of brown
fat thermogenesis would not have been possible without the
framework of the chemiosmotic theory, since without the
concept of the proton circuit all experiments would
continue to be limited to phenomenology. The clarity with
which brown fat mitochondria demonstrate their chemiosmotic
nature provided the impetus for the early conversion of more
than one worker in the field of thermogenesis to the ideas
put forward twenty years ago by Peter Mitchell.

REFERENCES

1. Skulachev, V.P. (1963) Proc. 5th Int. Congr. Biochem.
    (Moscow, 1961) 5, 365-375.
2. Moore, A.L. and Rich, P.R. (1980) Trends Biochem. Sci.
    5, 284-288.
3. Newsholme, E.A. and Crabtree, B. (1976) Biochem. Soc.
    Symp. 41, 61-109.
4. Nicholls, D.G. (1979) Biochim. Biophys. Acta 549, 1-29.
5. Lindberg, O.(1970) Brown Adipose Tissue, Elsevier, New
    York.
6. Nicholls, D.G. (1974) Eur. J. Biochem. 49, 573-583.
7. Nicholls, D.G. and Lindberg, O. (1973) Eur. J. Biochem.
    37, 523-530.
8. Nicholls, D.G. (1976) Eur. J. Biochem. 62, 223-228.
9. Heaton, G.M., Wagenvoord, R.J., Kemp, A. and Nicholls,
    D.G. (1978) Eur. J. Biochem. 82, 515-521.
10. Lin, C.S. and Klingenberg, M. (1980) FEBS Lett. 113,
    299-303.
11. Desautels, M., Zaror-Behrens, G. and Himms-Hagen, J.
    (1978) Can. J. Biochem. 56, 378-390.
12. Rothwell, N.J. and Stock, M.J. (1979) Nature (London)
    281, 31-35.

13. Brooks, S.L., Rothwell, N.J., Stock, M.J., Goodbody, A.E. and Trayhurn, P. (1980) Nature (London) 286, 274-276.
14. Nicholls, D.G. and Bernson, V.S.M. (1977) Eur. J. Biochem. 75, 601-612.
15. Chinet, A., Friedli, C., Seydoux, J. and Girardier, L. (1978) in Effectors of Thermogenesis (Girardier, L. and Seydoux, J. eds.) pp. 25-32, Birkhauser, Basel.
16. Cannon, B., Sundin, U. and Romert, L. (1977) FEBS Lett. 74, 43-46.
17. Heaton, G.M. and Nicholls, D.G. (1976) Eur. J. Biochem. 67, 511-517.
18. Hittelman, K.J., Lindberg, O. and Cannon, B. (1969) Eur. J. Biochem. 11, 183-192.

ACKNOWLEDGEMENT

This work has been supported by grants from the British Science Research Council.

PROTON CIRCUITS OF BACTERIAL FLAGELLA

Alexei N. Glagolev

A.N. Belozersky Laboratory of Molecular Biology and
Bioorganic Chemistry, Moscow State University
Moscow 117234, U.S.S.R.

The organelle of bacterial locomotion appears to be
unique in its main features: the mode of energy supply and
the mechanics of the motion. The immediate source of
energy for motility is, surprisingly, not ATP but $\Delta\bar{\mu}_H^+$; a
flagellum does not propagate waves by beating, but displays
true rotation around its long axis.

Being a left-handed helix (Fig. 1), the flagellum
pushes the cell while rotating counter-clockwise. The
mechanical principle of motion is thus the same as in a
motorboat. Peritrichous flagella form a bundle, rotating
with a speed of 50 rps (1). The cell body rotates 10 times
slower in the opposite direction. Flagella are most pro-
ably driven by a motor (2), i.e. the basal body, which is
embedded in the cell envelope (Fig. 2). The filament is
composed of repeating subunits of a single monopeptide
protein, flagellin (6). The filament is linked to the
basal body by a short hook which is thought to be a joint
in transmitting rotary torque (2).

V. P. Skulachev and Peter C. Hinkle (eds.), Chemiosmotic Proton Circuits in Biological Membranes
in honor of Peter Mitchell   ISBN 0-201-07398-6

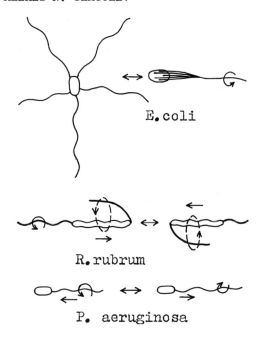

E. coli

R. rubrum

P. aeruginosa

<u>Fig. 1</u>. Different types of flagellation in bacteria.

    First discovered by Abram and colleagues (7), the
basal body was described in detail by De Pamphilis and
Adler (3-5). The basal body of <u>E</u>. <u>coli</u> emerged as a rod
with a set of discs threaded on it and bearing a striking
resemblance to an axis with wheels (Fig. 2). In preparations
with an intact outer membrane the L-disc (from lipopoly-
saccharide) was usually connected to the rod. The P-disc
was assumed to be connected to the peptidoglycan (the
rigid wall) layer, while the S (supramembrane) disc was
never found to be in contact with any layer of the envelope
and was thus believed to be located in the periplasmic
space. The M (membrane) disc was attached to the cytoplasmic
membrane. The conclusion that every disc of the basal body

is located in a definite layer of the cell envelope was
supported by the known dimensions of the envelope layers
and the distances between the discs. The two upper discs
(L and P) were observed to be connected to something resembling a thin film. In a homogenized preparation a disc
would commonly become detached from the rod. A rotational
analysis of an electron micrograph of such a disc has
suggested that it consists of 16 wedge-shaped subunits (4).
In preparations with a broken rod, dyes penetrated to its
center, suggesting that the structure was hollow. In a
gram-positive B. subtilis the basal body lacked the two
connected discs (L and P). It was concluded that the
remaining two discs were homologous to the S and M discs of
gram-negative bacteria. This seems to be unlikely, since
gram-positive bacteria lack periplasmic space, and the S-
disc should thus be located in the rigid cell wall, unlike
the S-disc of E. coli. The composition of the E. coli

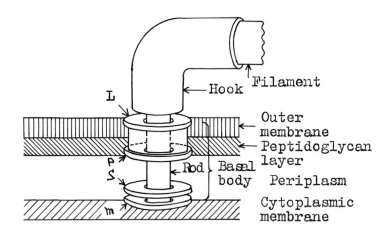

Fig. 2. The structure of the basal body. Based on (3-5).

basal body was determined by Hilmen and Simon (8), who were
able to isolate intact flagella in preparative quantities
from an E. coli multiflagellate mutant. SDS-disc electrophoresis revealed 9 peptide bands, belonging to the basal
body. The molecular weight of the peptides ranged from
9,000 to 60,000. During the procedure the bacterial cells
were prelabeled with ^{35}S and the gels were scanned for
radioactivity. Thus, only peptides containing sulfur amino
acids were resolved; the relative content of each peptide
remains unknown. The identical diameters of all the discs,
the probable subunit structure of the discs (4) and the
tendency of basal bodies to aggregate (3) all suggest that
a major structural protein builds the discs. The eight
circles around the flagella found beneath the outer membrane
of Spirillum serpens are structures that may also be a part
of the locomotive system (9). The circles are concentric,
the largest being 9,000 Å in diameter. The width of the
circle structures is 50 Å. The inner ring encircles the L-
disc of the basal body. All but the inner rings were
destroyed by proteinase digestion. The role of this system
is unknown, but it may serve as a basis for the rotating
flagella.

Flagellar synthesis in enteric bacteria is subject to
glucose catabolite repression and is released in the presence of cyclic-AMP (10). In mot mutants flagella are
morphologically normal, but paralyzed; it is believed that
the mot gene products play a role in the energy transduction
required for basal body rotation (11). The mot A and B
genes were cloned in lambda phage and the synthesis of
their products was directed in a mot E. coli (84,86,79).
The mot A and mot B products appeared to be membrane-bound

peptides 31,000 and 39,000 mol. weight respectively, which
were not a part of the basal body.

THE MECHANISM OF MOTILITY. By analogy with the beating
cilia and flagella of eukaryotes, bacterial motility was
thought to be directed by filament wave propagation. Bacterial flagella are much thinner than the flagella of
eukaryotes, which makes it rather difficult to observe
their motion. Nevertheless, as early as 1909, Reichert was
able to observe flagellar bundles in various motile bacteria
by means of a dark-field condenser using the sun as a light
source (13). The bundles were of helical shape (Fig. 1)
and appeared to rotate (or alternatively to propagate
helical waves). Since then many authors have observed and
described the motion of bacterial flagella (for an interesting history of the subject, see 14).

    These observations did not prevent P. Mitchell from
putting forward a hypothesis of bacterial motility according
to which the flagellum, acting as a giant ionophore, remained stationary, permitting cations to leak into the cytoplasm
down their concentration gradient (15). The resulting
potential difference would then move the cell by a process
that may be considered to be self-electrophoresis. The
model suggested the existence of two vectorial ion transport
processes functioning in the same membrane: a cation pump
and a specific ion channel, which consumed electrochemical
energy and transformed it into mechanical energy. It is
noteworthy that this early model (proposed in 1956) contained
the chief principles of chemiosmotic coupling: an ion pump
and a system for consuming its energy, coupled by the

electrochemical gradient of the ion. This model was re-
vised and extended in 1972, with the redox chain serving as
a proton pump and the flagellum serving as a specific H^+
channel (16). This particular mechanism, proposed by
Mitchell, has not been verified; however, the conversion of
$\Delta\bar{\mu}_{H^+}$ to mechanical work turned out to be correct.

Since Reichert's early study, two alternative models
of flagellar motion have been considered: wave propagation
due to the contraction of the filament, and the rotation of
a rigid helix. Berg and Anderson (2) summarized the extensive indirect evidence in support of the rotary model,
which was finally proven to be correct by the ingeuous
experiments of Silverman and Simon (17). Wild-type E. coli
cells were grown in the presence of glucose; due to catabolite repression the number of flagella was reduced to
approximately one per cell. A suspension of antiflagellin
antibody was placed on a microscope slide, and the antibody
adhered to its surface. Then a bacterial suspension was
added, and the cells became tethered to the glass by their
flagella. The tethered cells rotated rapidly, changing the
direction of rotation periodically. This observation
becomes readily understood if one assumes that at the base
of each flagellum there is a driving force, rotating the
flagellum with respect to the cell body. Then, when the
flagellum is immobilized, the cell rotates. In a free
bacterium the cell body experiences a larger viscous drag,
making the flagella rotate rapidly in a counter-clockwise
direction, while the cell rotates approximately 10 times
slower in the opposite direction, in accordance with
Newton's Law.

In Silverman and Simon's experiments E. coli polyhook mutants also rotated when tethered to the slide surface by an adhered hook antibody. This means that no matter what the mechanism of motion, the filament plays only a passive structural role.

Motility energetics

Many attempts have been made to determine an ATPase activity of flagella or isolated flagellin, but all have failed (18,19). This seemed surprising, since all pre-viously-studied locomotion systems were supported by ATP hydrolysis. Adler and coworkers used F_1-deficient mutants of E. coli to study the ATP requirement of motility (11). E. coli AN120 lacks a functional membrane ATPase, the res-piratory chain being normal. ATP is thus synthesized not in oxidative phosphorylation, but exclusively in substrate-level phosphorylations (glycolysis). The AN120 mutant was highly motile in the presence of oxygen and ceased all move-ment in anaerobic conditions. Since the ATPase was absent, the respiratory chain would not drive ATP synthesis. Exhaustion of cellular ATP to a low level by arsenate treat-ment did not inhibit motility if oxygen and an oxidizable substrate were present. Uncouplers of oxidative phosphoryla-tion immediately arrested movement. Taken together, the results were interpreted as demonstrating the involvement of the "intermediate of oxidative phosphorylation" in driving bacterial motility (11).

Similar results were obtained by Thipayatasana and Valentine in a study of E. coli AN120 motility, using as an assay infection by λ phage, which attacks only rotating filaments. It was found by this test that motility was supported by respiration or NO_3^- reduction and ceased under anaerobic conditions (20). However, it was later demonstrated that DNA transport during phage infection is in itself $\Delta\bar{\mu}_H^+$-dependent as reported in an article by Dr. L. Grinius in this volume. As suggested by V.P. Skulachev, the rotating basal body may serve as a translocase for the transport of phage DNA.

Several authors, analyzing the results of Adler and co-workers, came to the conclusion that motility was actually supported by $\Delta\bar{\mu}_H^+$ (21,22). However, direct evidence was needed.

We studied the energetics of motility on a photosynthetic bacterium R. rubrum (23,24). The results with uncouplers were identical to those of E. coli (11): the introduction of 10^{-6} M CCCP immediately arrested motility. The effectiveness of the uncoupler in inhibiting motility was not dependent on preincubation with oligomycin, an ATPase inhibitor. Given this set of conditions, the uncoupler could not have inhibited motility by lowering the ATP concentration.

To study the role of $\Delta\bar{\mu}_H^+$ in motility, valinomycin in the presence of potassium was added to an illuminated suspension of R. rubrum cells. In the presence of valinomycin K^+ is driven into the cytoplasm by the electric field. As a consequence, $\Delta\psi$ collapses and ΔpH rises to compensate for the decrease in $\Delta\bar{\mu}_H^+$. This compensatory rise in ΔpH is possible only under conditions where a proton pump is operating. Valinomycin has scarcely any effect on motility; neither did a permeant cation TPP^+ at a low concentration. In order to abolish ΔpH the incubation medium was supplemented with a weak permeable acid. Acetate is known to permeate membranes only in the protonated form, and thus it accumulates in the cytoplasm, neutralizing the intracellular alkaline medium. It was found that acetate, as valinomycin, when added alone did not affect motility (23). However, when both valinomycin and acetate were added, motility was completely arrested. This means that either $\Delta\psi$ or ΔpH can support motility; in the absence of both, movement is blocked. As in the case of the uncoupler, the presence of valinomycin, acetate or both did not affect the cellular ATP level (24).

To further test the energy requirements for motility, an artificial proton motive force was imposed across the cell membrane. The proton pumps of R. rubrum cells were blocked with appropriate inhibitors (oligomycin, F^-, antimycin) to arrest motility. In such energy-deprived cells, $\Delta\bar{\mu}_H+$ could be generated in two different ways: a pH shift, resulting in a ΔpH, and K^+ efflux from preloaded cells, resulting in a $\Delta\psi$ (internal negative). In the pH-shift experiments, cells were incubated at pH 9.3 for 5 minutes for the cytoplasmic pH to equilibrate with that of the medium. Then the cells were rapidly transferred to pH 6.1; they became highly motile (Fig. 3a); in 3 min the motility rate gradually decreased to zero, due to the dissipation of ΔpH. The initial value of ΔpH was 3.2, or 192 mV in terms of $\Delta\bar{\mu}_H+$. This value is about the same magnitude as the in vivo $\Delta\bar{\mu}_H+$.

An alkali shift in pH caused a transient lowering of the motility rate in control cells without inhibitors. This effect is evidently due to a decrease in ΔpH and hence in $\Delta\bar{\mu}_H+$. In another experiment, washed cells of R. rubrum in the presence of inhibitors were treated with valinomycin. In this case the outward movement of K^+ down its concentration gradient generated a diffusional potential which was

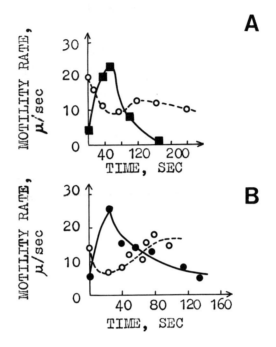

Fig. 3. Energization of R. rubrum motility by an artifical $\Delta\bar{\mu}_H^+$. In (a), deenergized cells were subjected to a base-acid shift at zero time (solid line); control cells without inhibitors (dashed line) were transferred from pH 6.1 to 9.3. (b), valinomycin introduced to deenergized cells at zero time in a K^+-free medium (solid line), or valinomycin added to control cells in the presence of 50 mM K^+ (dashed line).

found to support motility (Fig. 3b). The addition of valinomycin to cells without inhibitors in the presence of K^+ caused a transient decrease in the motility rate that did not fully return to its initial level. The transition in motility rate presumably reflected the decrease in $\Delta\psi$ caused by an inward movement of K^+ and a consequent compensatory increase of ΔpH. In an extensive study of valinomycin

action on the motility of B. subtilis, Shioi and colleagues
found that valinomycin completely inhibited movement if the
external concentration of K^+ was 150 mM or higher at pH 7.0
(25). At lower K^+ concentrations, however, valinomycin did
not inhibit, and if the same cells were starved in a K^+-free
medium to inhibit motility, valinomycin caused transient
motility (25,26). If we assume that valinomycin equilibrates the K^+ gradient (external concentration 150 mM) with
the membrane potential of approximately 120 mV, the final
concentration in the cytoplasm must reach the unrealistic
value of 15 M. The cell may oppose a dangerous increase in
K^+ concentration by a K^+/H^+-antiporter that was predicted by
P. Mitchell (27) and has been recently discovered in E. coli
(28). If this were the case, inhibition of motility by
valinomycin could be explained by a simultaneous decrease in
ΔpH, due to the operation of a K^+/H^+-antiporter. It is
interesting to note that valinomycin had no effect on motility at pH values below 6, due to a large ΔpH under these
conditions (25).

The relationship between the size of the membrane
potential and the rate of motility was elucidated with the
help of artificial lipophilic cations. Their accumulation
is a well-defined probe for $\Delta\psi$ (29). In these experiments
all the proton pumps of R. rubrum except those of the
cyclic electron flow were inhibited. Light-generated $\Delta\psi$ was
followed by the accumulation of TPP^+ present in a concentration of 10^{-6}M, using a phospholipid-saturated millipore
filter as a selective electrode (30). The $\Delta\psi$ was titrated
by increasing amounts of antimycin A, an inhibitor of the
cyclic electron flow. Immediately after the addition of a
given concentration of the inhibitor, a small amount

of the bacteria suspension was removed from the chamber
with the aid of a flat capillary, and motility was measured
(24, Fig. 4). A fair correlation between $\Delta\psi$ and the absolute rate of motility was found. The same relationship was
obtained under a somewhat different set of experimental
conditions:

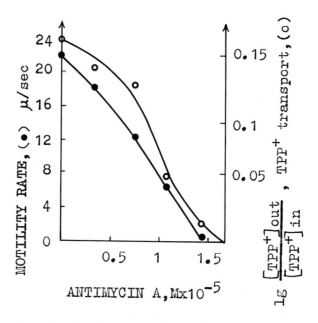

Fig. 4. Correlation between the membrane potential and the
motility rate of R. rubrum. The light-driven $\Delta\psi$ was
titrated by antimycin A in the presence of 10 mM F^-, 5 mM
CN^- and 10 μg/ml oligomycin.

TPA^+ was used instead of TPP^+ and o-phenanthroline instead
of antimycin. Motility was evident even at 10-fold decreased
TPP^+ uptake (Fig. 4). The movement of non-energized cells
upon the imposition of an artificial $\Delta\psi$ or ΔpH, or both, was
also observed with a Streptococcus strain (31). In this
study, a threshold value of $\Delta\bar{\mu}_{H^+} = 60$ mV was necessary to
support translational motility.

The dependence of flagellar angular velocity on the value of $\Delta\bar{\mu}_{H^+}$ was found to be a simple linear relationship: $\Delta\bar{\mu}_{H^+} = K \cdot V$, where K is a constant and V is the speed of rotation (24,32,35). In several studies quantitative data of the relative abilities of $\Delta\psi$ and ΔpH to support flagellar rotation were obtained. An artificial $\Delta\psi$ or ΔpH were found to be equally effective in supporting translational motility of B. subtilis (36). In another study the motility rate of natively energized B. subtilis was measured. B. subtilis appears to be especially convenient in studying the functions of $\Delta\bar{\mu}_{H^+}$ components, since at pH $\leq$ 5.5, $\Delta\bar{\mu}_{H^+} = \Delta pH$ and at pH = 7.5, $\Delta\bar{\mu}_{H^+} = \Delta\psi$ (35). The addition of an uncoupler then makes it possible to vary ΔpH or $\Delta\psi$. By using this approach, it appeared that $\Delta\psi$ was more effective in supporting motility than ΔpH (35). In a study of tethered cells of Streptococcus, the relationships between angular velocity and the magnitude of an artificial $\Delta\psi$ or ΔpH appeared to be somewhat different (32). The speed of cell body rotation showed no threshold dependence on $\Delta\bar{\mu}_{H^+}$. A low $\Delta\bar{\mu}_{H^+}$ threshold of 30 mV was found in a study of B. subtilis motility (33). It is important to mention that ATP synthesis, unlike flagellar rotation, requires a very high threshold $\Delta\bar{\mu}_{H^+}$ value of approximately 180-200 mV (34). Bacteria in search of favorable conditions may thus move when ATP synthesis is arrested. This may explain why bacteria use a $\Delta\bar{\mu}_{H^+}$-linked motor, not an ATP-dependent locomotive system (provided that they indeed had an opportunity to make a decision).

Another interesting feature of the motor is its saturation at a $\Delta\bar{\mu}_{H^+}$ approximately 3.4 of the maximal level (33, 35). Perhaps saturation of the motor speed is not due to any imperfection but, rather, it may have a useful function. To achieve maximum efficiency individual flagella must operate at identical speeds in the flagellar bundle. Minor fluctuations of $\Delta\bar{\mu}_H{}^+$ may variously influence individual flagella, since their basal bodies are placed randomly in the cell membrane. Differences in the rotation speeds of the individual flagella would bring them out of phase and cause damage. Thus it seems reasonable to keep the angular velocity constant in the physiological range of $\Delta\bar{\mu}_H{}^+$, i.e. in the 75–100% interval. This raises an interesting possibility: in monotrichous bacteria flagellar rotation will not saturate at increasing $\Delta\bar{\mu}_H{}^+$ values.

Flagella may rotate equally well in either clockwise (CW) or counterclockwise direction (CCW) (17). Attractants and repellents acting through specific receptors correspondingly suppress or initiate flagellar reversals (3), presumably by changing the concentration of free Ca^{2+} in the cytoplasm (38). Linear movement (CCW rotation) is interrupted by a tumble (CW rotation (39)) if repellent concentration increases. By prolonging runs in favorable directions bacteria migrate up attractant gradients. Although changes in attractants and repellents cause flagella to reverse, it was found that reversals are almost completely suppressed if $\Delta\bar{\mu}_H{}^+$ decreases approximately two-fold (40). The probability of CW rotation occurring increased with an increase in the motility rate and saturated at about the same value of $\Delta\bar{\mu}_H{}^+$. The authors suggested that the chemotactic signal that changes the sense of motor rotation interacts with a $\Delta\bar{\mu}_H{}^+$–consuming step in the mechanism of rotation. This suggestion was supported by the fact that the probability of CW reversal depended on both $\Delta\psi$ and ΔpH. However, decreasing the rotation rate of tethered cells by increasing viscosity had no influence on the probability of reversal. This, with the observation of a weaker dependence of CW rotation on $\Delta\bar{\mu}_{H^+}$ in certain chemotactic mutants (40), may suggest that $\Delta\bar{\mu}_{H^+}$ influences the reversal probably by playing a role in the formation of the chemotaxis signal (Ca^{2+} accumulation). The arrest of CW reversals at 10 $\Delta\bar{\mu}_{H^+}$ levels plays a definite adaptive role, preventing the appearance of left-handed flagella slowly rotating CW (40). In vigorous cells CW rotation brings about a structural transition of the filament: the viscous drag reorients it into a right-handed helix (41). But if a left-handed bundle will start slowly rotating CW, the force will be insufficient to change its structure, and the bundle will jam (42). Perhaps the $\Delta\bar{\mu}_{H^+}$ dependence of the taxis signal is specially adjusted to prevent flagellar bundle damage. In both cases of saturation (the rate of flagellar rotation and the probability of reversals) it seems that the constraints which the complicated mechanics of flagellar bundle operation impose on flagellar rotation are overcome by $\Delta\bar{\mu}_{H^+}$-dependent adjustments.

ENERGETICS OF GLIDING MOTILITY. Many prokaroteic organism do not swim but glide on the surface of solid substances or penetrate viscous media. All gliding organisms, though belonging to different genera, lack external locomotive organelles. Although there is a report that ATP may be the direct source of energy for gliding motility in one case (43), this form of movement is generally driven by $\Delta\bar{\mu}_{H^+}$.

Among gliding organisms spirochetes are perhaps most closely related to flagellated bacteria in respect to the mechanism of motility. Axial fibrils that closely resemble flagella are located between the elastic cell envelope and the plasma membrane. They are composed of a flagellin-like protein and bear basal bodies (44). Berg has theoretically concluded that the rotation of fibrils in the periplasmic space will cause a running wave on the elastic cell envelope, pushing the cell against the substrate (45). It has recently been found that Spirocheta aurantia movement may be supported by respiration in the absence of ATP. Nigericin and valinomycin, causing little change when added separately, completely arrested motility when added together (46). This result is similar to our observation of the $\Delta\psi$ and ΔpH requirements of R. rubrum motility (23).

In Flexibacter polymorphus, a large unicellular heterotrophic bacteria, "endogenous" flagella are not evident, nevertheless, gliding seems to be $\Delta\bar{\mu}_H{}^+$-dependent. It was found that redox chain inhibitors and uncouplers arrest gliding and decrease the ATP level, whereas arsenate, which causes a stronger decrease in ATP, does not inhibit motility (47).

A particularly interesting and complex gliding movement is found in multicellular Cyanobacteria. Linear chains of cells (trichomes) may reach lengths of 3 cm, as in the case of Oscillatoria princeps (48). The directional movement of trichomes on solid surfaces is accompanied by the extrusion of slime. It has been suggested that this is the mechanism of motility. Alternatively, Jarosh suggested that trichomes were wrapped by rotating fibrils (49). Halfen and Castenholz found a layer of fibrils under the outer membrane of Cyanobacteria (48). Freeze-fracture images revealed thin 70 Å-diameter, helical fibrils which were continuous throughout a large number of cells. The discovered structures

closely resembled the fibrils predicted by Jarosh. It was
suggested that the ATP-dependent contraction of the fibrils
would produce a running wave on the surface of the outer
membrane (48). There is little doubt that the fibrils are
involved in motility, since any point on the trichome
surface traces a right-handed helix with a 30° pitch that
coincides with the helix of the individual fibril. In O.
terebriformis fibrils are arranged in a left-handed helix
and the trichome rotates CCW while gliding (48). In studying
the energetics of gliding in Phormidium uncinatum, we found
that uncouplers inhibited movement instantly. After a
minute or two in the dark, with CN^- the trichomes ceased
gliding, as observed in an infrared microscope. Following
incubation of the deenergized trichomes at pH 9.0, the
addition of acid (pH 5.5) fully restored motility (50; Fig.
5a). An artificial $\Delta\psi$ generated by K^+ extrusion in the
presence of valinomycin also supported gliding (Fig. 5b).

A MODEL OF MOTOR ROTATION

The exact mechanism of the motor operation is obscure.
Available knowledge is sufficient to construct schemes, but
insufficient to discriminate between them. Nevertheless,
such models are illustrative and help to build working
hypotheses. The basal body's task is to rotate in the
membrane's plane, while transferring H^+ ions into the cell
across the membrane. A possible mechanism for basal body
rotation is presented in Fig. 6 (24,51). The M-ring, located
in the cytoplasmic membrane, is shown encircled by $-NH_2$
groups. One of these amino groups is accessible to the
upper proton-conducting path. An anionic group (carboxyl,
for example) is fixed to the membrane at the beginning of the

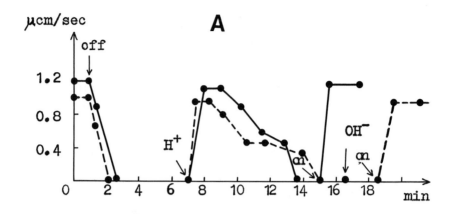

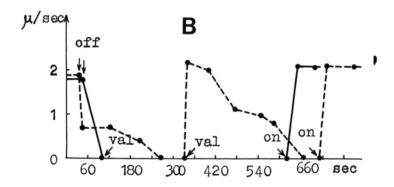

Fig. 5. Gliding of Ph. uncinatum supported by an artifical
$\Delta\bar{\mu}_H{}^+$. In (a), motility was energized by a base-acid
shift. One of the experiments (solid line) was performed
in the presence of 0.1 mM DCCD. In (b), valinomycin was
added to trichomes in K^+ medium (solid line) or in Na^+
medium (dashed line).

lower proton-conducting path. The protonation of $-NH_2$ leads
to electrostatic attraction between the $^+NH_3$ and $-COO^-$ together. The distance between the two proton half-channels
is assumed to be equal to that between the two neighboring
amino groups. Thus, rotation of the $\bar{M}$-ring results in the
next $-NH_2$ being transferred to the upper proton path.

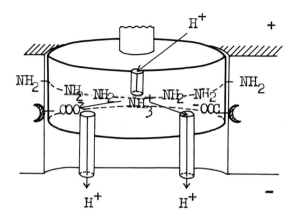

Fig. 6.   A model of basal body rotation.

Protonation of $-COO$ by $-^+NH_3$ results in the extrusion of H^+
into the cytoplasm along the lower path.   The number of H^+
ions translocated per revolution is equal to the number
of $-NH_2$ groups.   Berg has calculated the number of charged
particles needed to rotate the motor, passing down their
electrochemical gradient (52).   If $\Delta\bar{\mu}_{H^+}$ is 200 mV, a tethered
cell's radius 1 μ and its speed of rotation 10 Hz, the
number of protons is approximately 200.   In the above model
(Fig. 6) this would mean that 200 $-NH_2$ groups follow in ∿3
Å steps around the M-disc.   It is significant that among
the 9 peptides of the basal body one is extremely alkali,
having an isoelectric point above 9 (8).   Its positive
charges are most likely exposed at the surface, since DNA
binds to basal bodies in cell lysates and DNAse must be
added during purification (3).   The number of "steps" that
the motor makes was found to be not less than 20 (53) (the
optics set a limit for a higher resolution).   The smooth

unidirectional rotation may indeed result from a statistical
and reversible transport of 1 H^+ at a time if the step is
only 3 Å; however, several H^+ passing the motor simultaneously
would insure the unidrectioness and lower the activation
energy (35). Our model suggests that there may be several
sites of H^+ transport. Since the velocity-load (viscosity)
(54) and velocity $-\Delta\bar{\mu}_{H^+}$ plots (24,32,35) appear to be linear,
we may assume that the H^+/revolution stoichiometry is constant. However, in a monoflagellar P. aeruginosa an increase
in viscosity from 1 to 2 cp increased motility rate by 15%
instead of decreasing it (55). Given a 2-fold viscosity
increase, power must also increase 2-fold, as must stoichiometry, so that there be no decrease in speed. In order to
rule out the unlikely possibility of abnormal speed at ele-
vated viscosity being due to changes in the flagellar structure, it would be necessary to study the dependence of a
tethered P. aeruginosa rotation on viscosity.

When the motor reverses it does so abruptly and for a
reasonable period of time (17). To account for the reversal
it is essential to place a second outer H^+ channel symmetri-
cally to the first (51); the direction of rotation will then
be determined by the alternative opening and closing of the
channels by means of a chemotactic signal. Berg and co-
workers found that an inverse artificial ΔpH or $\Delta\psi$ can also
rotate a tethered Streptococcus cell (32).

According to our scheme, rotation due to a reversed
$\Delta\bar{\mu}_{H^+}$ will simply follow from reversion of the elementary
steps in the process. I must mention that we attempted to
energize motility in Ph. uninatum by a reverse ΔpH (see Fig.
5a), but failed. Perhaps the rotary mechanism of cyanobacteria bears constraints of which Streptococcus is free.

Macnab quite reasonably noted that $\Delta\bar{\mu}_{H}^{+}$ might be changed
into some other form of energy that would, in turn, energize
basal body rotation (56). However, the finding that reverse
$\Delta\bar{\mu}_{H}^{+}$ is also effective rules out this possibility.

Another model of rotation (57) was based on an assumption that H^{+} moves between the S and M rings, forming a
channel on its way. The complexity of the model is increased
by the need for a major conformation change in the structure
of the M-disc that would account for reversibility (see 56
for a discussion).

OUTLOOK. Although no one has yet succeeded in observing the
rotation of the basal body, its unique structure seems to be
the best proof of its function. As it is driven by $\Delta\bar{\mu}_{H}^{+}$
imposed across the cytoplasmic membrane, it is believed that
the M-ring is the principal energy-transforming device (24).
We would also expect that, in cyanobacteria, fibrils lying
between the cell wall and the outer membrane must be connected
to the cytoplasmic membrane and stem from a basal body-like
rotary motor (50). It appears that the evolutionary line of
embedding the locomotive organelle within the cell may have
been followed by the forms that are found in existing species:
common free flagella (E. coli), sheated flagella (V. parahae-
molyticus), flagella sheathed by a cell-wall structure (V.

metchnikovii (58)), periplasmic endoflagella (Spirochaeta)
and fibrils located within the cell envelope (Cyanobacteria)
(as suggested by T.N. Glagoleva). It is interesting to
consider the possibility that $\Delta\bar{\mu}_{H}^{+}$-supported rotary filaments
may be the locomotive organelles of gliding eukaryotes:
diatoms, desmids, red algae and zignematales. Although our

Present knowledge of the mechanims of motility is based on studies of gram-positive and gram-negative bacteria, further progress may perhaps be achieved by investigating the simpler organized cell-wall-free species such as T. acidophilum.

ACKNOWLEDGMENTS. Helpful discussions with Prof. V.P. Skulachev and Dr. M.Yu. Sherman are highly acknowledged.

REFERENCES

1. Weibull, C. (1960) in The Bacteria (J.C. Gunsalus and R.Y. Stainer, eds.), vol. 1,pp. 153-205, Academic Press, New York.
2. Berg, H.C. and Anderson, R.A. (1973) Nature 245, 380-382.
3. De Pamphilis, M.L. and Adler, J. (1971) J. Bacteriol. 105, 376-383.
4. De Pamphilis, M.L. and Adler, J. (1971) J. Bacteriol. 105, 384-395.
5. De Pamphilis, M.L. and Adler, J. (1971) J. Bacteriol. 105, 396-407.
6. Asakura, S. (1970) Adv. Biophys. 1, 99-155.
7. Abram, D., Koffler, H. and Vatter, A.E. (1965) J. Bacteriol. 90, 1337-1354.
8. Hilmen, M. and Simon, M. (1976) Cold Spring Harbor Symp. Book A, pp. 35-45.
9. Coulton, J.W. and Murray, R.E.E. (1977) Biochim. Biophys. Acta 465, 290-310.
10. Dobrogosz, W.J. and Hamilton, P.D. (1971) Biochem. Biophys. Res. Commun. 42, 175-185.
11. Larsen, S.H., Adler, J., Gargus, J.J. and Hogg, R.W. (1974) Proc. Natl. Acad. Sci. USA 71, 1239-1243.
12. Silverman, M., Matsura, P. and Simon, M. (1976) Proc. Natl. Acad. Sci. USA 73, 3126-3130.
13. Reichert, K. (1909) Zentr. Bakteriol. Parasitenk. Infektionskr. Abt. 1, Orig. 51, 14-94.
14. Berg, H.C. (1975) Ann. Rev. Biophys. Bioengeneer 4, 119-136.
15. Mitchell, P. (1956) Proc. Roy. Phys. Soc. (Edinburgh) 25, 32.
16. Mitchell, P. (1972) FEBS Lett. 108, 1-5.

17. Silverman, M. and Simon, M. (1974) Nature 249, 73-74.
18. Barlow, G.H. and Blum, J.J. (1952) Science 116, 787-792.
19. Enomoto, M. (1966) Genet. 54, 715-726.
20. Thipayatasana, P. and Valentine, R.C. (1974) Biochim. Biophys. Acta 347, 464-468.
21. Skulachev, V.P. (1975) Proc. FEBS Meet. 10, 225-238.
22. Liberman, E.A. (1975) Biofizika 20, 1132-1133.
23. Belyakova, T.N., Glagolev, A.N. and Skulachev, V.P. (1976) Biokhim. 41, 1478-1483.
24. Glagolev, A.N. and Skulachev, V.P. (1978) Nature 272, 280-282.
25. Shioi, J., Imae, Y. and Oosawa, F. (1978) J. Bacteriol. 133, 1083-1088.
26. Matsura, S., Shioi, J. and Imae, Y. (1977) FEBS Lett. 82, 187-190.
27. Mitchell, P. (1966) Chemiosmotic Coupling in Oxidative and Photosynthetic Phosphorylation. Bodmin, Glynn Research.
28. Brey, R.N., Rosen, B.B. and Sorensen, E.N. (1980) J. Biol. Chem. 255, 39-44.
29. Grinius, L.L., Jasaitis, A.A., Kadziauskas, Yu.P., Liberman, E.A. and Skulachev, V.P. (1970) Biochim. Biophys. Acta 216, 1-12.
30. Drachev, L.A., Kondrashin, A.A., Samuilov, V.D. and Skulachev, V.P. (1975) FEBS Lett. 50, 219-222.
31. Manson, M.D., Tedesco, P., Berg, H.C., Harold, F.M. and van der Drift, C.A. (1977) Proc. Natl. Acad. Sci. USA 74, 3060-3064.
32. Manson, M.D., Tedesco, P.M. and Berg, H.C. (1980) J. Mol. Biol. 138, 541-561.
33. Shioi, J.-J., Matsura, S. and Imae, Y. (1980) J. Bacteriol. 144, 891-897.
34. Maloney, P.C. and Wilson, T.H. (1974) J. Memb. Biol. 25, 285-310.
35. Khan, S. and Macnab, R.M. (1980) J. Mol. Biol. 138, 599-614.
36. Matsura, S., Shioi, J.-J., Imae, J. and Iida, S. (1979) J. Bacteriol. 140, 28-36.
37. Larsen, S.H., Reader, R.W., Kort, E.N., Tso, W.W. and Adler, J. (1974) Nature 249, 74-77.
38. Ordal, G.W. (1977) Nature 270, 66-67.
39. Khan, S., Macnab, R.M., De Franko, A.L. and Koshland, E.E., Jr. (1978) Proc. Natl. Acad. Sci. USA 75, 4150-4154.

40. Khan, S. and Macnab, R.M. (1980) J. Mol. Biol. 138, 563-598.
41. Macnab, R.M. and Ornston, M.K. (1977) J. Mol. Biol. 122, 1-30.
42. Macnab, R.M. (1977) Proc. Natl. Acad. Sci. USA 74, 221-225.
43. Daniels, M.J., Longland, T.M. and Gilbert, J. (1980) J. Gen. Microbiol. 118, 429-436.
44. Canale-Parola, E. (1978) Ann. Rev. Microbiol. 32, 69-99.
45. Berg. H.C. (1976) J. Theor. Biol. 56, 269-273.
46. Goulbourne, E.A., Jr. and Greenberg, E.P. (1980) J. Bacteriol. 143, 1450-1457.
47. Ridgway, H.F. (1977) J. Bacteriol. 131, 544-556.
48. Halfen, L.N. and Castenholz, R.W. (1970) Nature 225, 1163.
49. Jarosh, R. (1962) in Physiology and Biochemistry of Algae (R. Lewin, ed.) pp. 573-581, New York.
50. Glagoleva, T.N., Glagolev, A.N., Gusev, M.V. and Nikitina, K.A. (1980) FEBS Lett. 117, 49-53.
51. Glagolev, A.N. (1980) J. Theor. Biol. 82, 171-185.
52. Berg, H.C. (1976) Cold Spring Harbor Symp. Book A, pp. 35-45.
53. Berg, H.C. and Turner, L. (1979) Nature 278, 349-351.
54. Schneider, W.R. and Doetsch, R.N. (1974) J. Bacteriol. 117, 696-701.
55. Macnab, R.M. (1979) TIBS, Jan. N 10- N13.
56. Läuger, P. (1977) Nature 268, 360-362.
57. Glauert, A.M., Kerridge, D. and Horne, R.W. (1963) J. Cell Biol. 18, 327-336.
58. Black, F.J., Freundt, E.A., Vinther, O. and Christiansen, C. (1979) J. Bacteriol. 137, 456-460.

UNCOUPLERS OF OXIDATIVE PHOSPHORYLATION[1]

Stuart McLaughlin

Department of Physiology and Biophysics
Health Sciences Center
SUNY, Stony Brook, N.Y. 11794

INTRODUCTION. The first point I would like to make in this
short essay on uncouplers is that the chemiosmotic hypothesis
is great fun to teach to students of the biological sciences.
It is enjoyable not only because it provides a good illustration of the relevance of physics and chemistry to modern biology but also because it is an exciting example of a "paradigm
shift" in the biological sciences (1,2). One is hesitant to
recommend Thomas Kuhn's provocative little book The Structure
of Scientific Revolutions to biology students because all
Kuhn's examples of "paradigm shifts" are drawn from the physical sciences. However, if an intelligent student is armed
with the elements of chemiosmotic theory (3), the concept of
the electrochemical potential and a few facts about ionophores
(4,5) he can experience for himself, at least vicariously,
the pleasure that Peter Mitchell must have felt in attacking
what was established dogma merely two decades ago.

When Mitchell pauses for a philosophical aside in a
review, he prefers to quote Popper rather than Kuhn (6,7). In

---

[1]Supported by NSF grant PCM-7903241

V. P. Skulachev and Peter C. Hinkle (eds.), Chemiosmotic Proton Circuits in Biological Membranes
in honor of Peter Mitchell   ISBN 0-201-07398-6

my opinion Popper's and Kuhn's view of science are not mutually
exclusive and the chemiosmotic hypothesis can serve as a good
illustration of both points of view. Popper's book begins with
the quotation "Hypotheses are nets; only he who casts will
catch" (8). The mesh in Mitchell's net was clearly large and
his catch was undeniably a prize specimen. A feature of
Mitchell's catch that students readily appreciate is that one
need not swallow it whole. One can regard the hypothesis as
exactly that; a working hypothesis to be modified as new experimental results are obtained. More importantly, the chemiosmotic hypothesis can be used to illustrate Popper's view that
a scientific theory must be falsifiable. For example, an important, perhaps essential, feature of the hypothesis is that
electron transport produces a difference in the electrochemical potential of protons ($\Delta\tilde{\mu}_H+$) across the membrane and that
the passive movement of protons down this electrochemical
gradient through the ATPase generates ATP. If the lipids in
the mitochondrial membrane are arranged in the form of a bilayer (9,10) it follows that any weak acid capable of transporting protons across this bilayer by the mechanism illustrated in Fig.1 should, at the appropriate concentration, be able
to uncouple oxidation from phosphorylation. The student can
readily appreciate that the discovery of a single protonophore
that did not act as an uncoupler of oxidative phosphorylation
would falsify this important feature of the hypothesis.

Hanstein and Hatefi appear to have found such a molecule in the form of picrate (11). Picrate does transport
protons across artificial phospholipid bilayer membranes (12),
but it does not uncouple oxidation from phosphorylation in
mitochondria (11). Most weak acid protonophores uncouple
mitochondria and submitochondrial (inside-out) particles with
approximately equal efficacy; picrate uncouples only submito-

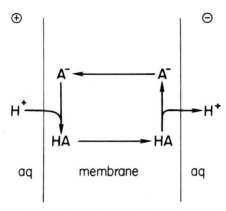

Fig. 1 Diagram illustrating the mechanism by which protono-
        phores such as FCCP (carbonylcyanide p-trifluorometh-
        oxyphenylhydrazone) CCCP (carbonylcyanide m-chlorophe-
        nylhydrazone), and picrate transport protons across
        bilayer membranes. As indicated by the circled posi-
        tive and negative signs, a voltage is assumed to exist
        across the membrane. The rate constants for the heter-
        ogeneous reaction and the transport steps indicated
        by arrows can be determined from electrical relaxation
        experiments using voltage clamp and charge pulse tech-
        niques (13).

chondrial particles (11). Hanstein (14) suggested that this
differential effect of picrate was due to "the nearly complete
inability of picrate to penetrate the inner mitochondrial
membrane" and that all weak acids might exert their uncoupling
effect by binding to a specific site on the inside of the
inner membrane of the mitochondrion.

THE CHEMIOSMOTIC INTERPRETATION OF UNCOUPLER DATA. There is an
alternative interpretation of the results obtained with picrate
and other uncouplers, one that is consistent with the chemiosmotic hypothesis. The membranes of both a mitochondrion and a
submitochondrial particle are closed surfaces; they segregate
the aqueous phase into an inner and an outer compartment. For
most weak acid protonophores the concentrations of the neutral

(HA) form in the inner and outer aqueous phases will be approximately equal in the steady state because the lipid bilayer component of the biological membrane is much more permeable to the HA than to the A^- form. The distribution of the anionic form is governed by the pH of the inner and outer aqueous media in accordance with the Henderson-Hasselbalch relationship. What is exceptional about picrate is its low pK (0.3) and the high, not the low, membrane permeability of the A^- form; it is the A^- rather than the HA form that comes to approximate electrochemical equilibrium. The permeability of a phospholipid bilayer to the A^- and HA forms of the weak acid can be determined from measurements on Mueller-Rudin planar bilayer membranes. At a physiological pH of 7.3 the ratio of the concentrations of the two forms of picrate in the outer aqueous phase is $[A^-]_o/[HA]_o = 10^7$ whereas the ratio of their membrane permeabilities is $P_{A^-}/P_{HA} = 10^{-5}$ (12). Thus, picrate accumulates in submitochondrial particles because of the positive electric potential of the inner aqueous phase. The analysis below demonstrates that the proton flux, and the degree of uncoupling, produced by a given concentration of picrate in the outer solution should be orders of magnitude greater in submitochondrial particles than in mitochondria, as is observed experimentally (11).

The mathematical analysis is simple and applies to the action of picrate and other weak acid protonophores on all topologically closed membranous systems. For a closed system there is no net flux of protonophore across the membrane in the steady state:

$$J^m_{HA} = -J^m_{A^-} \qquad\qquad (1)$$

where J^m denotes a flux through the membrane, inward fluxes positive. The flux of the neutral, HA, form of the weak acid is given by:

$$J^m_{HA} = P_{HA}([HA]_o - [HA]_i) \tag{2}$$

where $[HA]_o$ and $[HA]_i$ are the steady state concentrations of HA in the outer (o) and inner (i) aqueous compartments and P_{HA} is the permeability of the membrane to HA.

The steady state flux of the anionic forms of protonophores such as picrate, FCCP and CCCP through the membrane $(J^m_{A^-})$ is given approximately by the Goldman-Hodgkin-Katz equation (5,12):

$$J^m_{A^-} = P_{A^-} \frac{FV}{RT} \frac{\{[A^-]_o - [A^-]_i \exp(-FV/RT)\}}{1 - \exp(-FV/RT)} \tag{3}$$

where $[A^-]_o$ and $[A^-]_i$ denote the steady state concentrations of the anionic form of the weak acid in the outer and inner aqueous phase and V is the electrostatic potential difference between these phases. The additional relationship required to solve the expressions is the Henderson-Hasselbalch equation:

$$pH_i = pK + \log([A^-]_i/[HA]_i) \tag{4}$$

An analogous equation is valid for the outer aqueous phase.

To solve equations 1-4 numerically, the values of P_{A^-}, P_{HA}, pK, V, pH_i, pH_o and the total concentration of weak acid added to the outer aqueous solution must be specified. The values of P_A- and P_{HA} have been determined experimentally for picrate on artificial bilayer membranes (12). We assume that the membrane potentials are −175 and +175 mV, that the pH values of the inner solutions are 8.3 and 6.3 for mitochondria and submitochondrial particles respectively, and that the pH of the outer solution is 7.3 (12). It follows that 10 μM picrate in the outer aqueous phase should produce a proton flux of $4 \ 10^{-13}$ mol cm^{-2} s^{-1} through the membrane of a submitochondrial particle. This is a sufficient flux to account for the uncoupling effect. On the other hand, the predicted flux of protons through a mitochondrial membrane induced by the same concentration of picrate is only $4 \ 10^{-16}$ mol cm^{-2} s^{-1}, an insufficient flux to induce uncoupling.

The equations above predict that other weak acid protonophores should have approximately equal effects on submitochondrial particles and mitochondria. They do (5).

This chemiosmotic interpretation of the differential effect of picrate can also be applied to biological systems other than mitochondria. Michels and Bakker (15) recently made a detailed and carefully controlled study of the effect of picrate on E. coli and observed that picrate uncoupled energy-linked functions in everted but not in intact membrane systems. Specifically, picrate did not affect the components of $\Delta\tilde{\mu}_H$+ in intact cells, did not stimulate oxygen uptake by the cells and did not abolish its own energy-dependent extrusion by the cells. In everted vesicles picrate inhibited ATP-P_i exchange, decreased the components of $\Delta\tilde{\mu}_H$+ and inhibited its own energy-dependent uptake by the vesicles. Finally, energization of the membrane caused ^{14}C-labelled picrate to be extruded from the intact cell and taken up to a larger extent by the vesicles. These results led Michels and Bakker

to conclude that the mechanism of picrate uncoupling is probably the same in everted bacterial vesicles and in submitochondrial particles and that all the results are consistent
with Mitchell's chemiosmotic hypothesis.

OUTLOOK. There is now good experimental support for the hypo-
thesis that oxidation produces a $\Delta\tilde{\mu}_H{}^+$ and that $\Delta\tilde{\mu}_H{}^+$ couples
oxidation to phosphorylation (3). Furthermore, this feature
of the chemiosmotic hypothesis has withstood all attempts to
falsify it over the past two decades. It is my personal pre-
judice that we should certainly save room on the rubbish heap
of history, alongside phlogiston and the luminiferous ether,
for the elements of the chemiosmotic theory that tomorrow's
experiments will falsify but that we will make faster progress
towards a molecular understanding of today's experiments if
we accept this particular feature of the chemiosmotic hypothesis as a viable paradigm. For example, the kinetic mechanism by which a substituted benzimidazole transports protons
across decane-containing or solvent-free phospholipid bilayer
membranes is now well understood (16). The proton permeability of the bilayer increases quadratically with the concentration of weak acid because the charged permeant species is
a HA_2^- complex formed between the HA and the A^- species.
However, this weak acid acts in a linear manner to uncouple
mitochondria (16). To interpret this result within the framework of the chemiosmotic hypothesis it was speculated that
the intrinsic proteins in the mitochondrial membrane increase
the dielectric constant of the phospholipid bilayer component
of the membrane (16). This, according to the Born equation,
would increase the conductance of the smaller A^- species more
than the conductance of the larger HA_2^- species (17,5). To

illustrate that an increase in the dielectric constant could indeed have such an effect on ion permeation, planar bilayer membranes were formed using chlorodecane rather than decane as a solvent. With these artificial bilayer membranes, the conductance produced by the benzimidazole did increase linearly with the concentration (16).

The suggestion that intrinsic proteins increase the dielectric constant of the bilayer component of the mitochondrial membrane is highly speculative. It should, however, be easy to falsify. The suggestion implies that the permeability of a mitochondrial membrane to all ions must be greater than the permeability of conventional Mueller-Rudin bilayer membrane formed from mitochondrial lipids. The available data are consistent with this suggestion. For example, a typical weak acid protonophore, CCCP, is about two orders of magnitude less effective in transporting protons across planar decane-containing bilayers than across mitochondrial membranes (5). A second test of the suggestion can be made by comparing the permeability of mitochondrial membranes and artificial bilayers to perchlorate and thiocyanate ions (17). Chlorodecane increased the bilayer permeability of these ions by about three orders of magnitude; this value agrees very well with the one obtained using mitochondria (18,19). The biological significance of the enhanced dielectric constant, if it actually exists, is unknown.

ACKNOWLEDGEMENTS. I thank E. Bakker, E. Berry and P. Hinkle for valuable discussions and for making their data available prior to publication.

REFERENCES

1. Kuhn, T.S. (1970) The Structure of Scientific Revolutions, 210 pp. University of Chicago Press.
2. Wade, N. (1977) Science, 197, 143-145.
3. Hinkle, P.C. and McCarty (1978) Sci. Am. 238, 104-123.
4. McLaughlin, S. and Eisenberg, M. (1975) Annu. Rev. Biophys. Bioeng. 4, 335-366.
5. McLaughlin, S. and Dilger, J. (1980) Physiol. Rev. 60, 825-863.
6. Mitchell, P. (1979) Science, 206, 1148-1159.
7. Mitchell, P. (1976) B. Soc. Trans. 4, 399-430.
8. Popper, K.R. (1968) The Logic of Scientific Discovery 480 pp., Hutchinson.
9. Blazyk, J.F. and Steim, J.M. (1972) Biochim. Biophys. Acta, 266, 737-741.
10. Hsia, J.C., Chen, W.L., Long, R.A., Wong, L.T. and Kalow, W. (1972) Proc. Natl. Acad. Sci. USA, 69, 3412-3415.
11. Hanstein, W.C. and Hatefi, Y. (1974) Proc. Natl. Acad. Sci. USA, 71, 288-292.
12. McLaughlin, S., Eisenberg, M., Cohen, F. and Dilger, J. (1978) in Frontiers of Biological Energetics. A. Scarpa, et al., eds.) Vol. 2, pp 1205-1213, Academic Press.
13. Benz, R. and McLaughlin, S. (1981) Biophys. J. 33, 109a.
14. Hanstein, W.G. (1976) Biochim. Biophys. Acta 456,129-148.
15. Michels, M. and Bakker, E.P. (1981) Eur. J. Biochem. Submitted for publication.
16. Dilger, J. and McLaughlin, S. (1979) J. Membrane Biol. 46, 359-384.
17. Dilger, J.P., McLaughlin, S.G.A., McIntosh, T.J. and Simon, S.A. (1979) Science 206, 1196-1198.
18. Berry, E. and Hinkle, P. Personal Communication.
19. Kell, D.B., John, P., Sorgato, M.C. and Ferguson, S.J. (1978) FEBS Lett. 86, 294-298.

FROM BLACK-BOX BIOENERGETICS TO MOLECULAR MECHANICS:

VECTORIAL LIGAND-CONDUCTION MECHANISMS IN BIOCHEMISTRY

Peter Mitchell

Glynn Research Institute, Bodmin, Cornwall, PL30 4AU,
U.K.

INTRODUCTION

When seen retrospectively, the evolution of ideas and
knowledge, like organic evolution, tends to take on a
deceptively logical and inevitable appearance. But, as it
actually happens, the quest for truth through the testing of
imaginary concepts against reality is bound to be an uncertain
and hazardous adventure entailing disappointments as well as
pleasant surprises (1). So, the sharing of the congeniality
of this chemiosmotic celebration with my scientific colleagues
is all the more pleasurable; and I offer some comments on the
general rationale of molecular mechanics, and on specific
vectorial ligand conduction mechanisms in biochemistry, as an
appreciative response to the good chemiosmotic wishes
contained in this book.

V. P. Skulachev and Peter C. Hinkle (eds.), Chemiosmotic Proton Circuits in Biological Membranes
in honor of Peter Mitchell   ISBN 0-201-07398-6

The astonishing success of the 'chemiosmotic
hypothesis' of coupling in oxidative and photosynthetic
phosphorylation, which none of us could possibly have
expected, has produced a tremendous surge of experimental
activity, and has excited the interest of many biochemists in
the mechanism of so-called energetic coupling between protic
osmoenzymes or osmoenzyme systems (such as the cytochrome
system and the reversible $F_O F_1$ ATPase), and protic solute
porters or porter systems, and other protonmotivated devices
(such as the reversible rotatory protic flagellar motor),
which are plugged through the same topologically closed
coupling membrane. There is a strong tendency for such
intense activity and fashionability in a scientific field to
give rise to the establishment of a new speciality that may
become more or less divorced from the mother subject. But, I
would like to do my best to prevent that from happening in the
case of the field of chemiosmotic reactions. The chemiosmotic
concepts of enzyme catalysed group translocation and specific
vectorial ligand conduction were introduced with the object of
helping to explain the general connection between transport
and metabolism in biochemistry; and these concepts were
derived by adding a spatial dimension to Lipmann's classical
biochemical principle of chemical group potential (2,3), and
by adapting other general biochemical principles, as I have
explained previously (see 4). It was only incidentally that
these general vectorial metabolic concepts were used to found
and develop the rather specialised hypothesis of protic
chemiosmotic coupling in oxidative and photosynthetic
phosphorylation, which happened to occupy a central position
in bioenergetics. My main aim was, and still is, not to add
to the specialist parochialisms, but to try to simplify and
improve the generality of biochemical theory, in the hope that

it may make it easier for us to explore and explain experimental biochemical phenomena, and to understand each other's explanations.

Although the 'chemiosmotic hypothesis' has been widely accepted at the physiological (black-box proton pump) level, the concept of vectorial metabolism or direct chemiosmotic reactions —— which provided what I considered to be the biochemically simple (and therefore evolutionarily necessary) basis of the proposed coupling mechanism —— has met with much more resistance (5,6). The consequent proposition that cytochrome oxidase and other osmoenzymes, including the reversible F_OF_1 ATPase, and cytochrome c reductase are equipped with indirectly coupled proton pumping accessories (7-10) has seemed to me to be like a kind of reincarnation of the energy-rich chemical intermediates (4). By contrast, my main thesis is that we should persevere with our attempts to reintroduce the concepts of vectorial (or higher tensorial order) forces, displacements, velocities and momenta into biochemistry (11) by exploiting and developing the notion of specific ligand conduction in a relatively broad physical, chemical and biological context (4).

It is an important and interesting fact that the free energy function of chemical thermodynamics is given by the scalar products of the vectorial forces on the chemical particles and their colinear vectorial displacements during a given thermodynamic process (12,13). The principle of energy conservation, in the form of the first law of thermodynamics, thus enables us to describe the abstract (black-box) energy balance of one reaction against another if the two reactions are stoichiometrically coupled in some unspecified way. However, the abstract scalar free energies obviously contain less information than the spatially deployed vectorial forces

and displacements from which they are derived (14). For that
reason, a spatially more realistic and eventually more
detailed model of a chemical or biochemical reaction may be
obtained by means of (essentially Newtonian) molecular
mechanics, in which one applies not only the principle of
energy conservation but also the principle that the forces of
action and reaction on the ligands involved in a given equilibrium or non-equilibrium process are equal and opposite ——
with the important proviso that one must include centrifugal
statistical mechanical forces due to thermodynamic motion, and
decelerative frictional forces due to imprecision of the
mechanism, as well as static field effect forces (13).
Attempts to use mechanical and engineering analogies to
explain coupling between transport and metabolism in the 1950s
were unsuccessful because the statistical chemical or statistical mechanical forces that play a vital part in systems of
molecular dimensions were overlooked (see Appendix 1.2 in
ref. 4). However, it is noteworthy that molecular mechanical
models can achieve much the same realism as large scale
mechanical devices, provided that care is taken to include the
(statistical) mechanical forces due to thermal agitation, and
the frictional entropy-generating forces due to mechanistic
irregularities (13).

The use of the principle of the balance of dynamic and
static forces in a theory of molecular mechanics makes it
possible to obtain remarkably realistic insights into the
mechanism of (so-called energetic) coupling between one metabolic or transport process and another, because the formation
of primary covalent bonds, or electrovalent or other secondary
interactions, between given ligands may cause a corresponding
coupling between their vectorial (or higher tensorial order)
movements through an appropriately designed substrate-specific

catalytic system (15). Such a catalytic system could, for
example, be a porter, catalysing a purely osmotic antiport
process of the type originally called exchange-diffusion by
Ussing (16); it could be an enzyme like glyceraldehyde-3-
phosphate dehydrogenase, catalysing a phosphorylating redox
reaction, as originally elucidated by Warburg and Christian
(17) and by Racker and Krimsky (18), involving the symfer of
the acyl group of the oxidant with a phosphoryl group, as
phosphoglyceric acid-3-phosphate (13); or it could be an
osmoenzyme like the Na^+/K^+-motive ATPase, catalysing a cation-
translocating ATP hydrolysis, involving the symport of the
cations in electrovalent complexes with the terminal phosphate
group of ATP (see 4). The mechanistic principle of coupling,
by interaction between specific pairs of ligands as they move
along spatially prescribed conduction pathways through the
non-aqueous catalytic domains, and through neighbouring
aqueous or lipid media, could be fundamentally the same in all
cases (4,13). As mentioned twenty years ago (15), one may
accordingly interpret the reciprocal relations of Onsager
(19,20), in the abstract formality of non-equilibrium thermodynamics, as actually representing the reciprocity of bonding
between pairs of ligands (including components of the conformationally mobile ligand-conducting catalysts) involved in the
ligand conduction processes known as metabolism and transport.
To anticipate possible misunderstanding of this simplified
description, in which I have focussed attention on pairs of
ligands, such as the acyl group of glyceric acid-3-phosphate
and the phosphoryl group involved in the phosphorylating
glyceraldehyde-3-phosphate dehydrogenase, let me hasten to
emphasise that there are obviously very complex networks of
forces, involving electrovalent and secondary interactions as
well as covalent bonds in the conformationally articulated

catalytic domains of porters, enzymes and osmoenzymes (13).
But, faced with that very complexity, it is all the more
useful to recognise that forces are conceptually paired in
kinematics (14), and that we can therefore make considerable
progress in our analysis by concentrating attention on
particular pairs of ligands, in selected regions of the
ligand-conduction pathways. Our conceptual model can be made
more detailed and complete as we include an increasing number
of ligand pairs in our analysis. The study of chemiosmotic
reactions has helped to stimulate interest in topologically
realistic molecular mechanisms because the reaction coordinate
(21) of the chemiosmotic process in abstract 6N-dimensional
phase space corresponds to an actual ligand-conducting pathway
that passes through the osmoenzyme in the membrane in real
4-dimensional space-time (11-13).

Attempts have recently been made to adapt the methods
of non-equilibrium thermodynamics to a more mechanistically
real conception of transport and biochemical reactions,
notably by Hill (22,23), Westerhoff and Van Dam (24,25), Walz
(26), Stucki (27), Essig and Caplan (28), Rothschild, Ellias,
Essig and Stanley (29), and Arata and Nishimura (30). This
has been done mainly by choosing the (scalar) thermodynamic
force and flow parameters so that their energetic scalar
products correspond to the scalar products of the vectorial
forces on known chemicals and their colinear displacements in
given devices such as mechanoenzymes, osmoenzymes or porters
(13). Hill has adopted this method very effectively in the
case of muscle contraction (22). It depends fundamentally on
the fact that chemical particles experience real forces
directed down their total chemical potential gradients in
space, the direction and magnitude of the force being given
quantitatively by the total chemical potential gradient

(11-13). It is incidentally unfortunate that the variables that are called forces and flows in the formality of non-equilibrium thermodynamics do not correspond to forces and flows as understood in mechanics. They represent scalar potential energy differences and changes of the quantities of chemicals, respectively —— as in classical chemical thermo-dynamics and kinetics. It is a familiar fact that reaction velocities in chemical kinetics represent scalar rates of chemical change and not velocities in space. The consequent ambiguous use of the words force and velocity in modern bio-energetics is liable to cause confusion of mind as well as simple contextual mistakes.

I suggest that it would now be appropriate to try to develop a more thoroughgoing and self-consistent vectorial molecular mechanical theory of biochemical processes, including both metabolism and transport. Accordingly, we should define the concepts of force and velocity as in mechanics, and we should describe so-called thermodynamic forces and so-called chemical reaction velocities as chemical potential (energy) differences and chemical reaction rates, respectively. Ever since I introduced the term protonmotive force or PMF (by analogy with electromotive force or EMF) in place of protonic potential (energy) difference, I have regretted sacrificing accuracy to attractive analogy. For about the last ten years, I have avoided the use of PMF, except to describe the actual vectorial protonmotive force, and I have described the protonic potential difference as such, or have used the term protonic membrane potential (by analogy with electric membrane potential). It would help to avoid confusion if this convention were generally adopted.

This is not a suitable occasion to attempt a comprehen-sive discussion of the rationale of molecular mechanics; so I

will confine this contribution to some illustrative remarks
about the role of local momentum changes in the forces of
frictional or viscous resistance responsible for microscopic
irreversibility, and about the application of chemiosmotic
molecular mechanical ideas to the cationmotive ATPases.

MOLECULAR MECHANICS OF LIGAND CONDUCTION

In molecular mechanics, we treat the catalytic connec-
tive and transformative ligand-conducting protein molecules
or complexes of vectorial metabolism —— enzymes, catalytic
carriers, porters, and osmoenzymes —— as miniature machines
or engines (12,15). In accordance with the induced fit
concept proposed by Koshland for enzymes (31), we regard the
catalytic protein molecules, or their complexes (such as the
cytochrome system), as having articulated moving parts that
are free to pass through a continuous set of states, corresponding to a configurational cycle, in concert with the
conduction of one or more specific ligands along prescribed
pathways through the system (4,13). In such a statistical
mechanical system, it is important to recognise explicitly
that the working configurational cycle is not prescribed
exactly by the constraints of the field-effect forces in the
system. The working configurational cycle is prescribed only
within certain probabilistic limits corresponding to what we
may regard as the engineering tolerances that natural selection has managed to achieve. The working parts, including
the ligands undergoing conduction, are free to rattle to some
extent within the available tolerances of the molecular
machine, and frictional effects must consequently arise from
decelerative impacts along the lines of designed forward

motion through the working configurational cycle.

There are two aspects of molecular mechanical models that make them appeal particularly to the imagination. First, they make it relatively easy to conceive how the momentum and energy may be transferred from one ligand to another by the (partially) orderly transmission of forces between the ligands within the mechanically articulated ligand-conducting machine, as discussed further in the next section. Second, they enable one to appreciate how frictional effects (arising from a certain degree of disorder) interfere with the transmission of the ligands (and their associated energy) through the ligand-conducting system at the molecular level of dimensions.

MICROSCOPIC REVERSIBILITY. The fact that frictional forces are not intrinsically distinguishable from other conservative forces involved in Newtonian or statistical mechanics at the molecular level of dimensions is commonly stated in the form of the principle of microscopic reversibility (14). However, the principle of microscopic reversibility has also been taken to mean that, in the motion of microscopic particles, there are "no such effects as friction and heating as are observed on a macroscopic scale" (14). The question has therefore been raised: "If all microscopic processes are reversible, how is it that some macroscopic ones are irreversible?" According to Fay (14): "This obvious question plagued scientists for many years, and no mathematically rigorous answer to it has yet been found." In this context, the foundation of the thermo- dynamics of irreversible processes on the principle of micro- scopic reversibility (19,20) must seem paradoxical; and the linear relationship observed between the steady flow velocity and the driving force in biochemical (ligand conduction) systems that are not very close to equilibrium, which has recently been causing some surprise (22-30), would not seem to be susceptible to any explanation at the microscopic level of dimensions. It may therefore be helpful to define a statistical principle of microscopic irreversibility.

MICROSCOPIC IRREVERSIBILITY. Let us define the microscopic irreversibility of a partially orderly molecular mechanism as the probability of loss of the momentum associated with the forward progress of the conduction of a given ligand or representative point in the mechanism, per unit length of the pathway traced by the ligand or point, according to a statistical mechanical formality. Accordingly, let us represent the microscopic irreversibility by a coefficient f, defined as follows:

$$-f = \frac{d(\overline{mv})}{dr}, \tag{1}$$

where $\overline{mv}$ means the total momentum associated with the velocity $\overline{v}$ of the ligand or representative point traversing the pathway r. As a decelerative frictional or viscous force f on the ligand or point is given by

$$f = \frac{d(\overline{mv})}{dt}, \tag{2}$$

provided that f is independent of $\overline{v}$, it follows from (1) that, at a given steady value of $\bar{v}$,

$$-f \;=\; f.\bar{v} \quad . \tag{3}$$

Under a total driving force $\bar{f}$, equal to $-f$, the steady velocity $\bar{v}$ is therefore given by

$$\bar{v} \;=\; \bar{f}/f \quad . \tag{4}$$

Thus, the microscopic irreversibility coefficient f corresponds to a conventional frictional or viscosity coefficient, characteristic of the quantity of entropy produced, or the quantity of free energy converted to thermal energy, per unit progress of the ligand or representative point along the conduction pathway per unit velocity of progress.

  This definition of microscopic irreversibility is, of course, a macroscopic definition in the statistical sense. Nevertheless, it applies to the statistical mechanical space-time behaviour of a partially orderly ligand conduction system at the microscopic or molecular level of dimensions. Incidentally, it indicates very simply why the velocity of steady-state ligand conduction would be expected to be proportional to the driving force $\bar{f}$ in the partially orderly ligand conduction mechanism, provided that f is independent of $\bar{v}$, or provided that the working configurational cycle (and therefore f) is independent of $\bar{v}$.

  In 1940, Kramers (32) obtained a conceptual model of a chemical reaction by comparing it with the Brownian motion of a particle along a reaction coordinate passing through a potential energy barrier in a viscous medium. Under conditions displaced far from equilibrium, and when the system is

highly damped by the viscosity, he obtained the theoretical
result that the reaction rate constant is inversely proportional to the viscosity —— a result described as Kramers' law
(33). It corresponds to Einstein's law relating the diffusion
coefficient inversely to the viscosity of the medium through
which diffusion occurs (34), and to the application of the
Fick diffusion law to chemical group conduction. The microscopic irreversibility of diffusion arises fundamentally from
its partial disorder, and from the consequent annihilation of
the net vector component of the momentum of the particles
along the diffusion pathway, as exemplified by the exceptional
case of superconduction.

MOLECULAR MECHANICAL LUBRICITY. The effective smoothness and
slipperiness of the molecular articulations involved in the
ligand conduction mechanisms catalysed by enzymes, catalytic
carrier proteins, porters, and osmoenzymes —— and also in the
ligand conduction processes catalysed by non-proteins such as
ubiquinone (see 35) —— presumably plays a vital part in keeping down the energetic cost of transmitting chemicals and
energy from one place to another in living organisms. Therefore we may expect that the orderliness and lubricity of the
working configurational or conformational cycles of catalytic
ligand-conducting proteins, and of other components catalysing
vectorial metabolism, may have become highly developed by
natural selection. The tethered lipoate of the α-keto acid
dehydrogenases, described by Reed and Cox (36), provided a
striking but rather specialised example of ways in which
ligand conduction mechanisms may be made relatively orderly.
The electrostatically orientated surface conduction of cytochrome c between cytochrome c oxidase and cytochrome c

reductase, described by Koppenol and colleagues (37), may provide another remarkable example of orderliness in ligand conduction. But I wish to focus attention on more general principles here (4,38).

Molecular mechanical lubrication is presumably achieved in ligand-conducting protein molecules or systems by a dynamically stable structural organisation in which there is not one uniquely stable state of relatively low free energy, but a unique and configurationally contiguous set of interchangeable states of almost equal low free energy, corresponding to the ligand-conducting configurational cycle. The principles governing such dynamic organisation and stability are obviously considerably more complex than those that have been invoked to explain the static organisation and stability of condensed protein and lipid structures by close packing, by charge neutralisation of neighbouring ionisable groups, and by segregation of hydrophobic and hydrophilic moieties. But at least we can say that for motion of the system corresponding to progress along the ligand-conducting cycle, but not otherwise, the interactions between neighbouring groups in the condensed structure must cooperatively give rise to a relatively low and smooth free-energy profile (38).

Gavish (33,39) and Frauenfelder and colleagues (40) have recently cast new light on the complexity of protein dynamics by showing that the conformational mobility of ligand-binding and catalytic proteins may be largely controlled by the viscous resistance of the surrounding medium, and that, under certain conditions, the rate of ligand binding or conduction is inversely proportional to the viscosity of the environment of the protein molecule. Their theoretical objectives are relatively sophisticated and specific, and their emphasis is somewhat different from that adopted here

(33,39,40). But, in the present context, their observations lead to the conclusion that the overall frictional resistance in the process of ligand conduction by catalytic proteins may depend as much on movements of the viscous environment, driven by changes of area or conformation of the outer surface of the molecule during the ligand-conducting configurational cycle, as on potential energy barriers or viscous effects within the catalytic protein molecule itself.

Having had some tentative anticipatory thoughts on this matter, Jennifer Moyle and I found (in unpublished experiments done about five years ago) that the rate of ATP hydrolysis by the F_OF_1 ATPase of rat liver mitochondria in glycerol/water solutions (over the range 0 to 50% glycerol at 25°) is inversely proportional to the viscosity of the medium, and that the rate of transition between the active and inactive states of the enzyme (either way) is inversely proportional to the square of the viscosity of the medium. The latter suggests a requirement for coincidence between two configurational states, both of which are produced with probabilities that are inversely proportional to the viscosity. Our analysis of experimental results described by Caterall and Pedersen (41), likewise showed that the rate of hydrolysis of ATP by the water-soluble F_1 component of the ATPase of rat liver mitochondria in sucrose/water solutions is inversely proportional to the viscosity of the medium.

These interesting observations suggest that most of the frictional resistance and dissipation of free energy in certain ligand conduction reactions may occur, not in the catalytic protein molecule itself, but in the surrounding environment. I therefore suggest that one reason for the evolution of dimeric or polymeric enzymes and osmoenzymes that work by alternating site mechanisms may be that the changes of volume and shape of the monomers can be partially compensatory in the dimer or polymer, so that the frictional losses through environmental viscosity can be mitigated. In that context, it is interesting to speculate that the protonmotive F_0F_1 ATPases might involve a ternary state mechanism working rather like a three cylinder engine (42).

PHOSPHATE-CATION SYMPORT MECHANISM OF CATIONMOTIVE ATPases

Skou's important pioneering work on the Na^+/K^+-motive ATPase in 1957 (43 and see 44) has led to the discovery of a family of cationmotive ATPases that involve aspartyl phosphate as a chemical intermediate in ATP hydrolysis (4,45). This family includes the Na^+/K^+-motive ATPase of animal plasma membranes, the Ca^{2+}-motive ATPase of sarcoplasmic reticula, the H^+/K^+-motive ATPase of gastric mucosae, the H^+-motive ATPase of mould and yeast plasma membranes, the K^+-motive ATPase of bacterial plasma membranes, and probably others (4). It is remarkable that the processes catalysed by these enzymes have not generally been regarded as vectorial metabolic or chemiosmotic reactions. Generally speaking, physiological or physical studies of the inorganic ion transport processes have been pursued in parallel to largely scalar biochemical studies of the intermediary chemical transformations and enzyme conformational transitions that occur during ATP hydrolysis (4,44,45). The comparative lack of liaison between the physiological or physical and biochemical studies may be ascribed partly to the traditional use of black-box energetic concepts to relate scalar chemical transformation to vectorial solute transport, and partly to the fact that the inorganic cations are not generally regarded as proper metabolites,

because they do not readily form stable compounds in aqueous
media.

To commend to the reader the proposition that it may be
useful to try to develop a more thoroughgoing and self-
consistent vectorial molecular mechanical theory of biochemical processes, including both metabolism and transport, it
seems appropriate to outline here a general phosphate-cation
symport principle that might provide the basis for explaining
how the force is transmitted between some ligand involved in
the ligand-conduction process of (reversible) ATP hydrolysis
and the cation(s) conducted through the osmotic barrier region
of the cationmotive ATPase molecule.

The general principle of this proposal has been
outlined from time to time in the past, and it has recently
been discussed in some detail (see 4).

Our point of departure is that, although the coulombic
interaction between an anionic phosphate group and inorganic
cations is relatively weak and dissociable in aqueous media,
because of neutralisation by water dipoles, the interaction
could be very strong in the non-aqueous ligand-conducting
domain of the ATPase molecule, and cation specificity could be
conferred by local ionophoric groups in the ligand-conducting
domains.

In all the cationmotive ATPases that involve an
aspartyl phosphate intermediate, during the overall chemiosmotic reaction, the anionic terminal phosphoryl group of ATP
(or of a competent artificial phosphoryl donor) is known to be
conducted from the aqueous domain at the cytoplasmic side
(which I shall call the near side) into the catalytic domain
of the enzyme, where, at some point in the direction of the
far side, it is accepted by an aspartate group. After a
conformational change in the enzyme, the aspartyl phosphate

intermediate is hydrolysed, and the anionic phosphate group is
conducted back from the direction of the far side to the
aqueous domain at the near side of the enzyme (see references
in 4). Thus, it is evident that if the aspartate group were
to be positioned far enough towards the far side of the enzyme
to permit access of certain cations between the phosphate
group of aspartyl phosphate and the aqueous domain at the far
side of the enzyme, the anionic phosphate group could be used
to carry the cations through the non-aqueous (osmotic barrier)
domain of the enzyme molecule in either direction by a
relatively direct symport mechanism, dependent on electrovalent bonding between the phosphate group and the cations.
Fig. 1 shows a ligand-conduction diagram of the phosphate-
cation symport principle. As mentioned above, cationic specificity could depend on specific ionophoric groups positioned
in such a way as to determine which cations could come into
close apposition with the anionic phosphorus centre in the
ligand-conducting domain. The observed conformational change
between the configurational states (A) of the enzyme involved
in the phosphorylation of the aspartate (when the phosphoryl
group is conducted between ATP in the near aqueous domain and
the aspartate), and the configurational states (B) of the
enzyme involved in the hydrolysis of the aspartyl phosphate
(when the phosphate group is conducted between the aspartate
and inorganic phosphate, P_i, in the near aqueous domain) is
crucial because the two ligand-conduction pathways (marked A
and B in Fig. 1) must be different, so that one pathway is
specific for the conduction of one species of cation with the
phosphate group, and the other pathway is specific for the
conduction of another species of cation, or of no cation, with
the phosphate group, depending on the type of cationmotive
ATPase. For example, I assume that, in the Na^+/K^+-motive

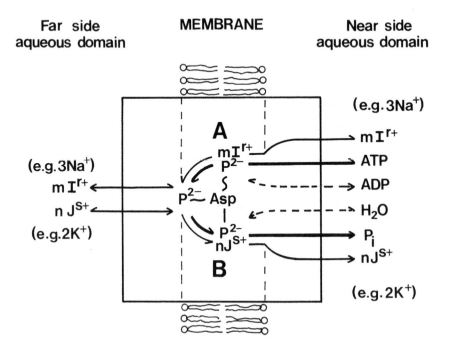

Fig. 1. Ligand-conduction diagram of phosphate-cation symport
         mechanism of cationmotive ATPases. Thick and thin
         lines show phosphoryl-group (or phosphate) and cation
         conduction pathways, respectively. Phosphate-cation
         symport pathways, shown by parallel thick and thin
         lines at A and B, function alternately in different
         conformational states of the enzyme. The conduction
         lines show the space-time connectedness of the
         ligand-conduction pathways diagrammatically. They do
         not show static topology to scale. Asp represents
         the aspartate group that becomes phosphorylated in
         the non-aqueous ligand-conducting catalytic site, and
         P represents phosphoryl or phosphate. The symbols
         $\mathbf{\mathcal{N}}$, $\sim$ and — represent weak, intermediate and strong
         bonds of high, intermediate and low energy,
         respectively.

ATPase, ligand-conduction pathway A is specific for the
symport of $3Na^+$ with the phosphate group, and that ligand-
conduction pathway B is specific for the symport of $2K^+$ with
the phosphate group; whereas, in the protonmotive ATPases[1],
I assume that ligand-conduction pathway A is specific for the
symport of $1H^+$ or $2H^+$ with the phosphate group, but that
ligand-conduction pathway B is specific for the uniport of
the phosphate group. It should, of course, be understood that
the phosphate group is not supposed to move in the conduction
channel independently of other neighbouring groups, but is
supposed to be involved in tightly articulated complexes
including specific ionophoric groups that determine the
cationic specificity of the mechanism. It should be remarked
incidentally, that the cation-phosphate complex undergoing
conduction need not be electrically neutral, and there is no
reason why the phosphate group, carrying a maximum of 2
negative charges, should not form very strong complexes with
cations carrying excess positive charges (e.g. with $3K^+$ or
with $2Ca^{2+}$) in concert with other groups in the non-aqueous
ligand-conduction channels.

EVOLUTIONARY CONSIDERATIONS. The phosphate-cation symport
hypothesis of the mechanism of the cationmotive ATPases outlined above suggests that the various cationmotive ATPases
that have aspartyl phosphate as a chemical intermediate may
all have essentially the same catalytic site structure, and
much the same ligand-conduction mechanism for conducting the
phosphoryl group between ATP, the aspartate group, and

---

[1] The protonmotive ATPases that have aspartyl phosphate as a
chemical intermediate. Not the F_OF_1 ATPases.

inorganic phosphate. The evolution of the family of cationmotive ATPases, each member of which is specific for the
translocation of certain cation species, may have occurred by
modification of ionophoric groups that determine the cationic
specificity of phosphate-cation symport in the ligand-
conduction system of the ATPases. It may be significant, in
the context of this suggestion, that none of the ATPases that
have aspartyl phosphate as a chemical intermediate have yet
been found to translocate anions.

EXPERIMENTAL IMPLICATIONS. The phosphate-cation symport
hypothesis of coupling in cationmotive ATPases appears to be
consistent with the experimental evidence at present
available, as discussed briefly in (4). It provides a
particularly direct and simple explanation of the partial
reactions of cation exchange. For example, in the Na^+/K^+-
motive ATPase, the exchange of Na^+ through the ligand-
conduction system is tightly coupled to the conduction of
phosphoryl groups between the ATP/ADP couple and the aspartate
group, whereas the exchange of K^+ is tightly coupled to the
conduction of phosphoryl groups between the P_i/H_2O couple and
the aspartate group (see 4,44,45). Magnetic resonance studies
by Grisham, Mildvan and colleagues (46-49) suggest that both
Na^+ and K^+ are near the phosphate sites in the Na^+/K^+-motive
ATPase. Space will not permit further discussion of the
available evidence here. But, it should be emphasised that
the most useful function of the phosphate-cation symport
hypothesis may be to pose new experimental questions. For
example, where is the phosphate-accepting aspartate group
situated in the ATPase molecule relative to the non-aqueous
osmotic barrier domain? How mobile is the aspartate group

relative to the non-aqueous ligand-conducting osmotic barrier domain? And, under what conditions, if any, can the phosphate group of the aspartyl phosphate exchange cations with the aqueous medium on the far side of the molecule? In my opinion, the answers to such questions might well help us to satisfy the enquiring mind of the young student who may ask simply, after we have described the excellent agreement of the osmotic and chemical energy balance in the ATPase reaction: "Yes, but how does it actually work?"

ACKNOWLEDGEMENTS

       On this occasion, it is a very special pleasure for me to acknowledge my indebtedness to numerous fellow scientists, living and dead, whose efforts and aspirations I have endeavoured to complement in one way or another. I am particularly grateful to my colleague Jennifer Moyle for stimulating discussion, criticism and support over a period of a third of a century. I thank Robert Harper and Stephanie Key for help in preparing this manuscript. Last, but not least, I thank those individuals and organisations who have provided financial support, especially my brother, C. J. Mitchell, and I salute the Staff and Council of Management of Glynn Research Ltd., whose generous and sympathetic work and attitudes of mind have so far enabled our little research organisation to do some cost-effective and worthwhile research and to survive financially.

REFERENCES

1. Popper, K. R. (1972) Objective Knowledge: An
   Evolutionary Approach, Clarendon Press, Oxford.
2. Lipmann, F. (1941) Adv. Enzymol. 1, 99-162.
3. Lipmann, F. (1946) in Currents in Biochemical Research,
   (D. E. Green, ed.) pp. 137-148, Interscience, New York.
4. Mitchell, P. (1981) in Of Oxygen, Fuels, and Living
   Matter, (G. Semenza, ed.) Part I, pp. 1-160, John Wiley,
   Chichester.
5. Boyer, P. D., Chance, B., Ernster, L., Mitchell, P.,
   Racker, E. and Slater, E. C. (1977) Ann. Rev. Biochem.
   46, 955-1026.
6. DePierre, J. W. and Ernster, L. (1977) Ann. Rev. Biochem.
   46, 201-262.
7. Wikström, M. and Krab, K. (1979) Biochim. Biophys. Acta
   549, 177-222.
8. Wikström, M. and Krab, K. (1980) Curr. Top. Bioenerg. 10,
   51-101.
9. Boyer, P. D. (1979) in Membrane Bioenergetics, (C. P. Lee
   and G. Schatz, eds.) pp. 461-479, Addison-Wesley,
   Reading, Mass.
10. Von Jagow, G. and Sebald, W. (1980) Ann. Rev. Biochem.
    49, 281-314.
11. Mitchell, P. (1962) Biochem. J. 83, 22P-23P.
12. Mitchell, P. (1967) Compr. Biochem. 22, 167-197.
13. Mitchell, P. (1977) Symp. Soc. Gen. Microbiol. 27,
    384-423.
14. Fay, J. A. (1965) Molecular Thermodynamics,
    Addison-Wesley, Reading, Mass.
15. Mitchell, P. (1963) Biochem. Soc. Symp. 22, 142-168.
16. Ussing, H. H. (1947) Nature 160, 262-263.
17. Warburg, O. and Christian, W. (1939) Biochem. Z. 303,
    40-68.
18. Racker, E. and Krimsky, I. (1952) J. Biol. Chem. 198,
    731-743.
19. Onsager, L. (1931) Phys. Rev. 37, 405-426.
20. Onsager, L. (1931) Phys. Rev. 38, 2265-2279.
21. Glasstone, S., Laidler, K. J. and Eyring, H. (1941) The
    Theory of Rate Processes, McGraw-Hill, New York.
22. Hill, T. L. (1977) Free Energy Transduction in Biology,
    Academic Press, New York.
23. Hill, T. L. (1979) Proc. Nat. Acad. Sci. U.S.A. 76,
    2236-2238.
24. Westerhoff, H. V. and Van Dam, K. (1979) Curr. Top.
    Bioenerg. 9, 1-62.

25. Westerhoff, H. V. and Van Dam, K. (1980) Recl. Trav. Chim. Pays-Bas 99, 329-333.
26. Walz, D. (1979) Biochim. Biophys. Acta 505, 279-353.
27. Stucki, J. W. (1980) Eur. J. Biochem. 109, 257-267, 269-283.
28. Essig, A. and Caplan, S. R. (1981) Proc. Nat. Acad. Sci. U.S.A. 78, 1647-1651.
29. Rothschild, K. J., Ellias, S. A., Essig, A. and Stanley, H. E. (1980) Biophys. J. 30, 209-230.
30. Arata, H. and Nishimura, M. (1980) Biophys. J. 32, 791-806.
31. Koshland, D. E. (1960) Adv. Enzymol. 22, 45-97.
32. Kramers, H. A. (1940) Physica 7, 284-304.
33. Gavish, B. (1980) Phys. Rev. Lett. 44, 1160-1163.
34. Einstein, A. (1905) Ann. Physik 17, 549.
35. Mitchell, P. (1981) in Biomedical and Clinical Aspects of Coenzyme Q, (K. Folkers and Y. Yamamura, eds.) Vol. 3, Elsevier/North-Holland, Amsterdam, in press.
36. Reed, L. J. and Cox, D. J. (1966) Ann. Rev. Biochem. 35, 57-84.
37. Koppenol, W. H., Margoliash, E. and Mitchell, P. (1981) Abstr. M-C-5, VII Internat. Biophys. Congr. and III Pan-Am. Biochem. Congr., Mexico City, Mexico, Aug.23-28, 1981.
38. Mitchell, P. (1970) Membr. Ion Transp. 1, 192-256.
39. Gavish, B. and Werber, M. M. (1979) Biochemistry 18, 1269-1275.
40. Beece, D., Eisenstein, L., Frauenfelder, H., Good, D., Marden, M. C., Reinisch, L., Reynolds, A. H., Sorensen, L. B. and Yue, K. T. (1980) Biochemistry 19, 5147-5157.
41. Catterall, W. A. and Pedersen, P. L. (1974) Biochem. Soc. Spec. Publ. 4, 63-88.
42. Mitchell, P. (1981) in Mitochondria and Microsomes, (C. P. Lee, et al. eds.) pp. 427-457, Addison-Wesley, Boston, Mass.
43. Skou, J. C. (1957) Biochim. Biophys. Acta 23, 394-401.
44. Skou, J. C. and Norby, J. C. (1979) Na,K-ATPase: Structure and Kinetics, Academic Press, London.
45. Mukohata, Y. and Packer, L., eds. (1979) Cation Flux Across Biomembranes, Academic Press, New York.
46. Grisham, C. M. and Mildvan, A. S. (1974) J. Biol. Chem. 249, 3187-3197.
47. Grisham, C. M., Gupta, R. K., Barnett, R. E. and Mildvan, A. S. (1974) J. Biol. Chem. 249, 6738-6744.
48. Grisham, C. M. and Hutton, W. C. (1978) Biochem. Biophys. Res. Commun. 81, 1406-1411.
49. O'Connor, S. E. and Grisham, C. M. (1979) Biochemistry 18, 2315-2323.